William's
Words in *Science*

Written by Dr William Hirst

Edited by Sally Hirst

Illustrations by Jean Vincent

ISBN 978 0 9555207 0 9

All the diagrams, and more, are to be found at **www.smallwords.co.uk** and are free for use by educational establishments.

Illustrations by Jean Vincent (jean@victoria-sponge.com)

Printed at the Burlington Press, Foxton CB2 6SW (www.burlingtonpress.co.uk)

INTRODUCTION

Science has its own language, which is certainly related to English, but can be very confusing. For example, what do the words a *medium*, a *normal*, and a *moment* mean to you? If they immediately describe a material, a line at right angles and a turning force, respectively, then you know the language of science; but if you ask "a medium *what*?" then this dictionary is for you. Similarly, how many of these can you answer?

1. What is measured in bars?
2. Is hard water the same as ice?
3. What colour is lime water?
4. Do cells multiply when they divide?
5. How many two-word phrases that start or end in *plant* can you write down?
6. When was the diameter of the Earth first measured?
7. The chemical symbol for sulphur is S, and for silicon is Si, so why is Na the symbol for sodium and Ag the symbol for silver?
8. Which famous scientist was offered the post of President of Israel?
9. Another famous scientist was knighted for turning the Royal Mint into a profitable venture – who was he?
10. What is the main food of a crabeater seal?

(You can find the answers at the bottom of The Last Word, at the end of this book)

The Dictionary has been constructed for easy use: all two-word phrases appear as entries under each word (*eg* the definition of *hard water* will appear under both *hard* and *water*); variants of spellings are given, and reference is given to other words that sound the same, but are spelled differently (homophones).

Words and meanings are best learned by using the language; if you visit our website at www.smallwords.co.uk, you will find lots of word games (crosswords, wordsearches, cloze exercises, and Scidoku, which is a scientific-word version of sudoku) together with all the diagrams from this book and some additional cut-outs. All of them are freely downloadable. Any further ideas for using words should be forwarded to *william@smallwords.co.uk* and, if added, you will be given both acknowledgement and a free Dictionary.

I must give a huge vote of thanks to the several people who continually provided ideas about presentation; the typesetting of the main dictionary and collation of the whole work were brilliantly carried out by Lisa Kirkham (<Lisakirkham@ntlworld.com>), the other sections were typeset by Carolyn Griffiths (<textype@waitrose.com>) and the cover and all the diagrams were drawn by Jean Vincent (<info@victoria-sponge.com>).

The one person without whom this dictionary would never have been started is the Editor – my wife, who used her wisdom, knowledge and patience to ensure that each explanation is clear, concise and precise. I hope you enjoy using 'William's *Words in Science*'

A GUIDE FOR USING THIS DICTIONARY

The English language is precise, elegant and beautiful – however, the present usage reflects a troubled past. Words have been imported from Anglo-Saxon, Arabic, French, Greek, Hindi, Latin and Nordic – which leads to complexities of spellings caused by each word following the 'rules' of its origin, *eg* why should it be one len*s* yet many sperm? I have therefore included guidance as to the variations in spelling and to the formation of any plural that does not follow the simple rule of adding an "s" to the singular.

The three letters in each circle show the initial three letters of the first entry and the final entry on that page.

MAIN ENTRY WORDS

The entry words are printed in blue and are arranged in alphabetical order, ignoring any spaces, hyphens or dashes.

Each entry starts with a single key word; a blue solidus (/) indicates that alternative spellings are acceptable either in the British system (UK) or the American system (USA). Guidance is given in round brackets to words that sound the same, but are spelt differently, and have different meanings (*homophones*). The order of the meanings is adjective or adverb; nouns; verbs.

The key word is followed, in alphabetical order by phrases that start with that word, then by phrases that end with the key word; each phrase is separated by a vertical black line (|).

The entries for many chemicals are followed by the chemical formula [in square brackets]; these formulae are also gathered together at the start of the dictionary.

The names of scientists that have a biography in the Dictionary are printed in red and also feature in the time-line of the Really Useful Information at the start of the book.

PREFIXES AND SUFFIXES

Syllables followed by a dash are those that are used at the start of a word (a *prefix*) or at the end of a word (a *suffix*) in order to change the meaning *eg* pre– (*Latin* before) or –cide (*Latin* to kill)

Prefixes that are used with units are followed by three dots *eg* centi.../c... (*Latin* hundred).

All the prefixes and suffixes are gathered on page 15 of the Really Useful Information at the front of this Dictionary.

MICROPOEDIA

The micropoedia at the end, is a brief overview of fifty of the important concepts in Science; words in blue will be found as entries in the Dictionary – these overviews indicate that an explanation will make sense only if the reader understands the meaning of words in Science. Scientists whose work contributed significantly in that field are listed alongside each entry.

REALLY USEFUL INFORMATION

The next 18 pages, those with a red stripe down the edge,
are filled with information that you may need to use
but can not always remember.

%	per hundred / per cent	Da ..	deca (10^1)	IVF	*in vitro* fertilisation
A	amps	dB	decibel	J	joule
a ..	atto (10^{-18}) ..	dc	direct current	K	kelvin
ab	antibodies	DCPIP	2,6 dichloro-phenol-indo-phenol	k ..	kilo (10^3) ..
ac	alternating current			KE	kinetic energy
AI	artifical insemination	DDT	dichloro-diphenyl-trichloro-ethane	kg	kilogram
AIDS	acquired immuo-deficiency syndrome	DNA	deoxyribonucleic acid	kJ	kilojoule
am	ante-meridian, before mid-day	E ..	eta (10^{18}) ..	km	kilometer (USA) / kilometre (UK)
amu	atomic mass units	e^-	electron	kph	kilometres per hour
(aq)	aqueous, dissolved in water	eg	(*exempli gratia*) for example	kW	kilowatt
				kWh	kilowatt hour
B	bel	f	frequency	l	liter (USA) / litre (UK)
BNF	British Nutrition Foundation	f ..	femto (10^{-15}) ..	(l)	liquid
bp / b.pt	boiling point	fp / f.pt	freezing point	LDR	light-dependent resistor
BSE	bovine spongiform encephalopathy	G ..	giga (10^9) ..	LED	light-emitting diode
		g	acceleration due to gravity	LPG / lpg	liquified petroleum gas
C	coulomb	g	gramme	LSD	lysergic acid diethylamide
c	speed of light in a vacuum	(g)	gas	M ..	mega (10^6) ..
c ..	centi (10^{-2}) ..	GMO	genetically modified organism	m	metre
cal	calorie	GPS	global positioning system	m ..	milli (10^{-3}) ..
cc	centimetre cube/ cubic centimetre	h / hr	hour	m^2	metre squared
cd	compact disc	Hb	haemoglobin	mA	milli-amp
CFC	chloro-fluoro-carbons	HEP	hydro-electric power	MAFF	Ministry of Agriculture, Food & Fisheries
cm	centimetre	HIV	human immuno-deficiency virus	mg	milligram
cm^3	centimetre cubed	Hz	hertz	ml	milliliter (USA) / millilitre (UK)
CRO	cathode ray oscilloscope	I	current		
D ..	deca (10^1) ..	ICT	information communication technology	mm	millimeter (USA) / millimetre (UK)
d ..	deci (10^{-1}) ..	ie	(*id est*) that is	MMR	measles, mumps, rubella vaccine
Da	dalton	IR / ir	infra-red		

abbreviations

mp/m.pt	melting point	pm	post-meridian, after mid-day	T . .	tera (10^{12}) . .
mph	miles per hour			t	time
mps	metres per second	PMT	pre-menstrual tension	t	tonne (1000 kg)
Mr Grens	move, respire, grow, reproduce, excrete, nutrition, sense	pom	prescription only medicine	TB	tuberculosis
MRSA	methicillin-resistant *Staphylococcus aureus*	ppb	parts per billion	TIR	total internal reflection
		ppm	parts per million	TNT	tri-nitro-toluene
Mrs Gref	move, respire, sense grow, reproduce, excrete, feed	PTO	please turn over (the page)	TV	television
N	newton	PVC	poly vinyl chloride	TVP	textured vegetable protein
N	north	R	resistance	u	starting speed
n . .	nano (10^{-9}) . .	r	radius of a circle	UI	universal indicator
n^0	neutron	ram	relative atomic mass/ formula mass	URL	unique resource location
NASA	National Aeronautics & Space Administration	RBC / rbc	red blood cells	UV / uv	ultra-violet
NB	(*nota bene*) note well	rda	recommended daily allowance	V	volts
Nm	newton metre	RGB / rgb	red, green, blue	v	speed / velocity
nm	nanometre	rt	room temperature	W	watts
NPK	nitrogen, phosphorus, potassium fertiliser	s	distance	WBC / wbc	white blood cells
°C	degrees centigrade	s / sec	second	WHO	World Health Organisation
°F	degrees fahrenheit	(s)	solid	Y . .	yotta (10^{24}) . .
OHP	overhead projector	SARS	severe acute respiratory syndrome	y . .	yocto (10^{-24}) . .
OHT	overhead transparency	sec / s	second	Z . .	zetta (10^{24}) . .
otc	over the counter medicine	SETI	search for extra-terrestrial intelligence	z . .	zepto (10^{-24}) . .
P . .	peta (10^{12}) . .	SI units	Système International d'Unités	α	alpha
p . .	pico (10^{-12}) . .			β	beta
p^+	proton	SIDOT	speed is distance over time	γ	gamma
Pa	pascal			Δ / ∂	delta
pd	potential difference (voltage)	std	sexually transmitted disease	μ	mu, micro (10^{-6}) . .
PE	potential energy	stp	standard temperature and pressure (0°C, 760 mm mercury)	π	pi, 3.14159
PET	poly-ethene tetra-phthalate			Ω	ohms (resistance)

abbreviations

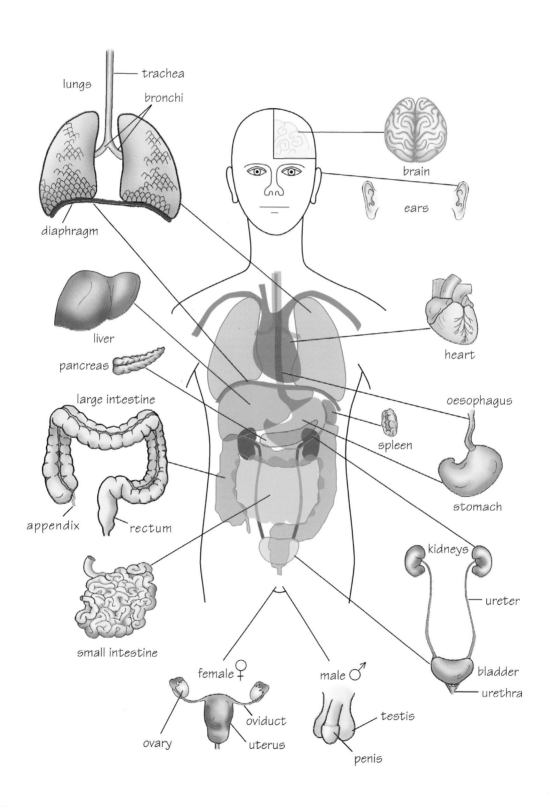

lungs — trachea
bronchi
diaphragm

brain
ears

liver
pancreas
large intestine
appendix — rectum
small intestine

heart
oesophagus
spleen
stomach

kidneys
ureter
bladder
urethra

female ♀
ovary — oviduct — uterus

male ♂
testis — penis

body organs

Classification

all life → kingdom → phylum → class → order → family → genus → species

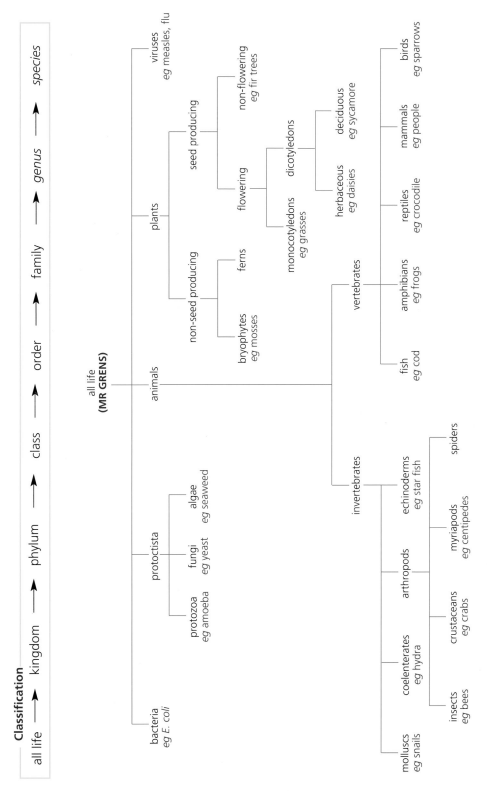

all life
(MR GRENS)

bacteria
eg E. coli

protoctista
- **protozoa** *eg amoeba*
- **fungi** *eg yeast*
- **algae** *eg seaweed*

animals
- **invertebrates**
  - **molluscs** *eg snails*
  - **coelenterates** *eg hydra*
  - **arthropods**
    - **insects** *eg bees*
    - **crustaceans** *eg crabs*
    - **myriapods** *eg centipedes*
    - **spiders**
  - **echinoderms** *eg star fish*
- **vertebrates**
  - **fish** *eg cod*
  - **amphibians** *eg frogs*
  - **reptiles** *eg crocodile*
  - **mammals** *eg people*
  - **birds** *eg sparrows*

plants
- **non-seed producing**
  - **bryophytes** *eg mosses*
  - **ferns**
- **seed producing**
  - **flowering**
    - **monocotyledons** *eg grasses*
    - **dicotyledons**
      - **herbaceous** *eg daisies*
      - **deciduous** *eg sycamore*
  - **non-flowering** *eg fir trees*

viruses
eg measles, flu

classification

9

Ag	(*argentum*) silver, proton number 47	$CH_2(CH_2OH)_2$	glycerol
$AgNO_3$	silver nitrate	$(CHOHCOOH)_2$	tartaric acid
Al	aluminium / aluminum, proton number 13	C_6H_5OH	phenol / carbolic acid
Al_2O_3	aluminium oxide	C_5H_7COOH	sorbic acid
Ar	argon, proton number 18	$C_6H_{12}O_6$	glucose
As	arsenic, proton number 33	C_6H_5COOH	benzoic acid
Au	(*aurium*) gold, proton number 79	$C_{17}H_{35}COOH$	stearic acid
Ba	barium, proton number 56	Cl	chlorine, proton number 17
$BaSO_4$	barium sulphate / barium sulfate	Cl^-	chloride ion
Br	bromine, proton number 35	ClO_3^-	chlorate ion
Br^-	bromide ion	CO	carbon monoxide
C	carbon, proton number 6	Co	cobalt, proton number 27
Ca	calcium, proton number 20	CO_2	carbon dioxide
$CaCl_2$	calcium chloride	$CO_3^=$	carbonate ion
$CaCO_3$	marble	$CoCl_2$	cobalt chloride
$CaCO_3$	calcium carbonate / chalk / limestone / marble	Cs	caesium / cesium, proton number 55
CaO	calcium oxide / quicklime / lime	Cu	(*cuprous*) copper, proton number 29
$Ca(OH)_2$	calcium hydroxide / slaked lime	$Cu(NO_3)_2$	copper nitrate
$CaPO_4$	calcium phosphate	$CuCO_3$	copper carbonate
$CaSiO_3$	calcium silicate	CuO	copper oxide
$CaSO_4$	calcium sulfate / calcium sulphate / gypsum / plaster of Paris	$CuSO_4$	copper sulfate / copper sulphate
		F	fluorine, proton number 9
CH_4	methane	F^-	fluoride ion
CH_3OH	methanol	Fe	(*ferrous*) iron, proton number 26
CHCl:CHCl	vinyl chloride / dichloro-ethene	FeS	iron sulfide / iron sulphide
CCl_2	trichloroethene	$FeSO_4$	iron sulfate / iron sulphate
C_2H_2	acetylene	H	hydrogen, proton number 1
C_2H_4	ethene	H_2	hydrogen gas
C_2H_6	ethane	HCHO	formaldehyde
C_3H_8	propane	HCl	hydrochloric acid
C_4H_{10}	butane	HCOOH	formic acid / methanoic acid
CH_3COO^-	ethanoate ion	H_2CO_3	carbonic acid
CH_3COOH	acetic acid / ethanoic acid	H_2O	water
C_2H_5OH	ethanol	H_2O_2	hydrogen peroxide
$(CH_3)_2CO$	propanone / acetone	H_3PO_4	phosphoric acid

chemical formulae

H_2S	hydrogen sulfide / hydrogen sulphide	NH_4Cl	ammonium chloride
H_2SO_4	sulfuric acid / sulphuric acid	NH_4NO_3	ammonium nitrate
He	helium, proton number 2	NH_4OH	ammonia solution / ammonium hydroxide
Hg	(*hydro argentum*) mercury, proton number 80	$[NH_4]_2SO_4$	ammonium sulfate / ammonium sulphate
I	iodine, proton number 53	Ni	nickel, proton number 28
I^-	iodide ion	NO_2	nitrogen dioxide
K	(*kalium*) potassium, proton number 19	NO_3^-	nitrate ion
KBr	potassium bromide	O	oxygen, proton number 8
KCl	potassium chloride	O_2	oxygen gas
$KClO_3$	potassium chlorate	O_3	ozone
KF	potassium fluoride	$O^=$	oxide ion
KI	potassium iodide	OH^-	hydroxide ion
$KMnO_4$	potassium manganate (VII) / potassium permanganate	P	phosphorus, proton number 15
KNO_3	nitre / potassium nitrate / saltpetre	Pb	(*plumbous*) lead, proton number 82
KOH	potassium hydroxide / caustic potash	$Pb(NO_3)_2$	lead nitrate
Kr	krypton, proton number 36	$PO_4^=$	phosphate ion
Mg	magnesium, proton number 12	P_2O_5	phosphorus pentoxide
$MgCO_3$	magnesium carbonate	Rb	rubidium, proton number 37
MgO	magnesium oxide	S	sulfur/sulphur, proton number 16
MnO_2	manganese (IV) oxide	$S^=$	sulfide ion / sulphide ion
N	nitrogen, proton number 7	Si	silicon, proton number 14
N_2	nitrogen gas	SiO_2	silicon dioxide
Na	(*natrium*) sodium, proton number 11	$SiO_3^=$	silicate ion
Na_2CO_3	sodium carbonate / washing soda	Sn	(*stannous*) tin, proton number 50
Na_2O	sodium oxide	SO_2	sulfur dioxide / sulphur dioxide
Na_2SO_4	sodium sulfate / sodium sulphate	SO_3	sulfur trioxide / sulphur trioxide
NaCl	salt / sodium chloride	$SO_4^=$	sulfate ion / sulphate ion
$NaHCO_3$	sodium hydrogen carbonate / baking soda / bicarbonate of soda / sodium bicarbonate	$S_2O_3^=$	thiosulfate ion / thiosulphate ion
		Ti	titanium, proton number 81
NaOH	sodium hydroxide / caustic soda	TiO_2	titanium dioxide
Ne	neon, proton number 10	U	uranium, proton number 92
$(NH_2)_2CO$	urea	W	tungsten / wolfram, proton number 74
NH_3	ammonia	Zn	zinc, proton number 30
NH_4^+	ammonium ion	ZnO	zinc oxide
		$ZnSO_4$	zinc sulfate / zinc sulphate

chemical formulae

Cycles

The cycles involving carbon, water, nitrogen and rocks are usually treated separately, but they do interact, *eg* the water cycle includes transpiration and respiration by organisms that are growing, dying and decaying and so are part of the carbon and nitrogen cycles; the growth of plants and movement of animals need carbon, water and nitrogen, then cause biological weathering of rocks.

Carbon cycle

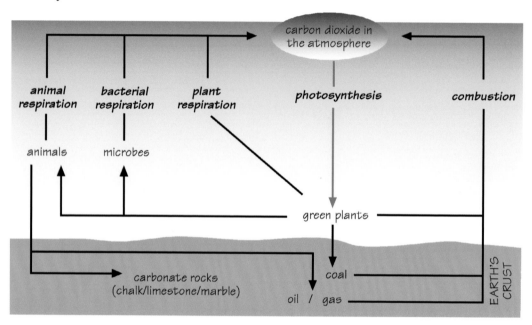

Nitrogen cycle

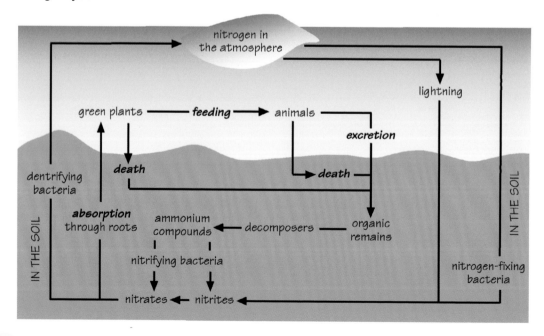

carbon cycle / nitrogen cycle

Rock cycle

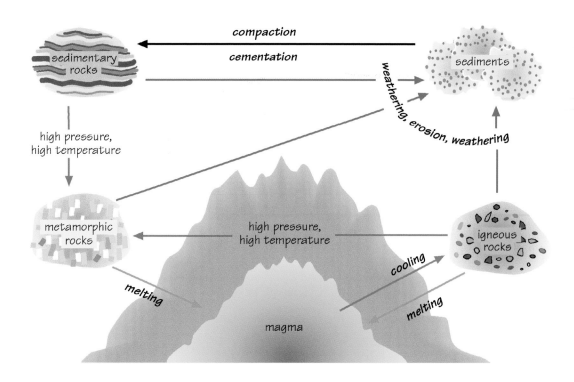

Water cycle

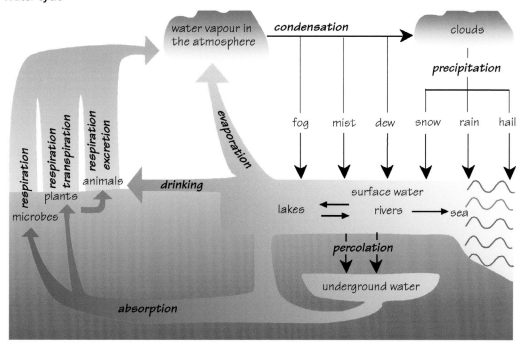

rock cycle / water cycle

air	hair / hare	caries	carries	fare	fair	hour	our
allowed	aloud	carpal	carpel	farther	father	humerus	humorous
aloud	allowed	carpel	carpal	father	farther	humorous	humerus
ant	aunt	carries	caries	filings	fillings	ill	hill
arm	harm	carrot	carat	fillings	filings	ion	iron
ate	eight	caught	court	fir	fur	iron	ion
aunt	ant	cell	sell	flaw	floor	it	hit
aural	oral	cereal	serial	flea	flee	knead	need
band	banned	cheap	cheep	flee	flea	knew	new
banned	band	cheep	cheap	flew	flu / flue	knot	not
bare	bear	chews	choose	floor	flaw	know	no
be	bee	choose	chews	flour	flower	knows	nose
beach	beech	chord	cord	flower	flour	lair	layer
bean	been	chute	shoot	flu	flew / flue	laps	lapse
bear	bare	coarse	course	flue	flew / flu	lapse	laps
beat	beet	coffin	coughing	for	four / fore	larva	lava
bee	be	coma	comma	fore	for / four	lava	larva
beech	beach	comma	coma	fort	fought	law	lore
been	bean	complement	compliment	forth	fourth	layer	lair
beet	beat	compliment	complement	fought	fort	leach	leech
bellow	below	conker	conquer	foul	fowl	leak	leek
below	bellow	conquer	conker	four	for / fore	leech	leach
bite	byte	cord	chord	fourth	forth	leek	leak
blew	blue	coughing	coffin	fowl	foul	lessen	lesson
blue	blew	course	coarse	fur	fir	lesson	lessen
boar	bore	court	caught	furry	fury	lightening	lighting
board	bored	currant	current	fury	furry	lightning	lightening
boggy	bogie / bogy	current	currant	gnaw	nor	links	lynx
bogie	bogy / boggy	days	daze	grater	greater	look	luck
bogy	bogie / boggy	daze	days	greater	grater	loose	lose
bolder	boulder	dear	deer	guessed	guest	lore	law
book	buck	deer	dear	guest	guessed	lose	loose
bore	boar	desert	dessert	hair	air / hare	luck	look
bored	board	dessert	desert	hangar	hanger	lumbar	lumber
born	borne	dew	due	hanger	hangar	lumber	lumbar
borne	born	die	dye	hare	air / hair	lynx	links
boulder	bolder	died	dyed	harm	arm	made	maid
boy	buoy	discus	discuss	hart	heart	maid	made
brake	break	discuss	discus	heal	heel / eel	mail	male
bread	bred	doe	dough	hear	here	main	mane
break	brake	does	dose	heard	herd	maize	maze
bred	bread	dose	does	hearing	ear-ring	male	mail
brewed	brood	dough	doe	heart	hart	mane	main
brood	brewed	due	dew	heat	eat	mat	matt
buck	book	dye	die	hedge	edge	matt	mat
buoy	boy	dyed	died	heel	heal / eel	maw	more
buy	by	ear-ring	hearing	herd	heard	maze	maize
by	buy	eat	heat	here	hear	meat	meet
byte	bite	edge	hedge	hill	ill	meet	meat
caning	canning	eel	heal / heel	hit	it	meter	metre
canning	caning	eight	ate	hole	whole	metre	meter
carat	carrot	fair	fare	home	ohm	micrometer	micrometre

homophones

micrometre	micrometer	pour	paw / pore	sell	cell	timbre	timbre
might	mite	pours	paws / pores / pause	sent	scent	time	thyme
mind	mined	practice	practise	serial	cereal	to	too / two
mined	mind	practise	practice	sever	severe	ton	tonne
miner	minor	pray	prey	severe	sever	tonne	ton
minor	miner	prey	pray	shoot	chute	too	to / two
missed	mist	principal	principle	shore	sure	torque	talk
mist	missed	principle	principal	sight	site	tri .	try
mite	might	pulls	pulse	silicon	silicone	try	tri .
more	maw	pulse	pulls	silicone	silicon	turn	tern
muscle	mussel	pus	puss	site	sight	two	to / too
mussel	muscle	puss	pus	smelled	smelt	vain	vane / vein
need	knead	radical	radicle	smelt	smelled	vane	vain / vein
net	nett	radicle	radical	some	sum	vein	vain / vane
nett	net	rain	reign / rein	sore	saw	waist	waste
new	knew	raise	rays	source	sauce	wait	weight
newton meter	newton metre	rapt	wrapped	stairs	stares	war	wore
newton metre	newton meter	raw	roar	stake	steak	ware	wear / where
no	know	rays	raise	stalk	stork	warn	worn
nor	gnaw	read	red	stares	stairs	waste	waist
nose	knows	read	reed	stationary	stationery	watt	what
not	knot	red	read	stationery	stationary	way	whey / weigh
ohm	home	reed	read	steak	stake	weak	week
or	ore	reign	rain / rein	steal	steel	weakened	weekend
oral	aural	rein	rain / reign	steel	steal	weakly	weekly
ore	or	right	write / rite / wright	stork	stalk	wear	ware / where
our	hour	rite	right / write / wright	sum	some	weather	whether
overeating	overheating	road	rode	sure	shore	week	weak
overheating	overeating	roar	raw	tail	tale	weekend	weakened
pail	pale	rode	road	tale	tail	weekly	weakly
pain	pane	roe	row	talk	torque	weigh	way / whey
pair	pear	role	roll	tare	tear	weight	wait
pale	pail	roll	role	taught	taut	what	watt
pane	pain	root	rout / route	taut	taught	where	ware / wear
passed	past	rout	root / route	team	teem	whether	weather
past	passed	route	root / rout	tear	tare	whey	way / weigh
pause	paws / pores / pours	row	roe	tears	tiers	which	witch
paw	pore / pour	sac	sack	teem	team	whine	wine
paws	pause / pores / pours	sack	sac	tern	turn	whither	wither
peace	piece	sail	sale	their	there	whole	hole
pear	pair	sale	sail	there	their	wind	wined
peer	pier	sauce	source	threw	through	wine	whine
piece	peace	saw	sore	throne	thrown	wined	wind
pier	peer	scared	scarred	through	threw	witch	which
place	plaice	scarred	scared	thrown	throne	wither	whither
plaice	place	scene	seen	thyme	time	wore	war
plain	plane	scent	sent	tic	tick	worn	warn
plane	plain	sea	see	tick	tic	wrapped	rapt
planing	planning	seam	seem	tide	tied	wright	right / rite / write
planning	planing	see	sea	tied	tide	write	right / rite / wright
pore	paw / pour	seem	seam	tiers	tears	yoke	yolk
pores	paws / pours / pause	seen	scene	timber	timbre	yolk	yoke

proton number	name	symbol	freezing point (°C)	boiling point (°C)	density (g / cm³)	date discovered	discovered by whom
1	hydrogen	H	−259	−252	0.000 089	1783	Lavoisier
2	helium	He	−272	−269	0.000178	1895	Ramsay
3	lithium	Li	180	1342	0.53	1817	Arfvedson
6	carbon	C	3730	4830	2.25 (graphite) / 3.51 (diamond)	ancient times	
7	nitrogen	N	−210	−196	0.000625	1772	Rutherford
8	oxygen	O	−218	−183	0.00072	1774	Priestley
9	fluorine	F	−223	−188	0.0017	1886	Moissan
10	neon	Ne	−249	−246	0.0009	1989	Ramsay
11	sodium	Na	98	883	0.97	1807	Davy
12	magnesium	Mg	649	1107	1.74	1808	Davy
13	aluminium	Al	660	2467	2.7	1825	Oersted
14	silicon	Si	1410	2355	2.33	1824	Berzelius
15	phosphorus	P	44	280	1.8 (white) / 2.3 (red)	1669	Brand
16	sulphur	S	113	445	2.1	ancient times	
17	chlorine	Cl	−102	−35	0.0030	1810	Davy
18	argon	Ar	−189	−186	0.0017	1894	Ramsay
19	potassium	K	64	759	0.86	1807	Davy
20	calcium	Ca	839	1490	1.54	1808	Davy
24	chromium	Cr	1857	2672	7.20	1797	Vauquelin
25	manganese	Mn	1220	1962	7.43	1774	Gahn
26	iron	Fe	1530	3000	7.86	ancient times	
27	cobalt	Co	1495	2870	8.9	1742	Brandt
28	nickel	Ni	1450	2732	8.9	1751	Cronstedt
29	copper	Cu	1083	2567	8.92	ancient times	
30	zinc	Zn	420	907	7.14	1500	Marggraf
33	arsenic	As	613	613	5.73	ancient times	
35	bromine	Br	−7	59	3.12	1826	Balard
36	krypton	Kr	−157	−152	0.0037	1896	Ramsay
47	silver	Ag	961	2212	10.49	ancient times	
50	tin	Sn	232	2270	7.28	ancient times	
53	iodine	I	114	184	4.9	1811	Courtois
55	caesium	Cs	29	669	1.88	1860	Bunsen
56	barium	Ba	724	1870	3.51	1808	Davy
74	tungsten	W	3410	5660	20.0	1783	de Elhuyar
78	platinum	Pt	1772	3827	21.5	1735	de Ulloa
79	gold	Au	1060	2970	19.3	ancient times	
80	mercury	Hg	−39	357	13.6	ancient times	
82	lead	Pb	328	1740	11.34	ancient times	
86	radon	Rn	−71	−62	0.010	1910	Ramsay
92	uranium	U	1132	3818	19.0	1789	Klaproth

discovery dates

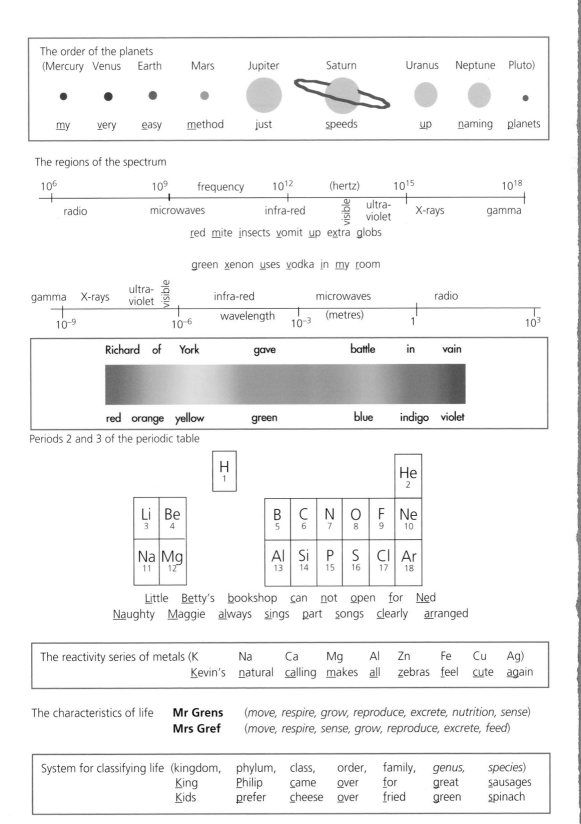

The order of the planets
(Mercury Venus Earth Mars Jupiter Saturn Uranus Neptune Pluto)

my   very   easy   method   just   speeds   up   naming   planets

The regions of the spectrum

10^6 10^9 frequency 10^{12} (hertz) 10^{15} 10^{18}

radio   microwaves   infra-red   visible   ultra-violet   X-rays   gamma

red mite insects vomit up extra globs

green xenon uses vodka in my room

gamma   X-rays   ultra-violet   visible   infra-red   microwaves   radio

10^{-9} 10^{-6} wavelength 10^{-3} (metres)   1 10^3

Richard   of   York   gave   battle   in   vain

red   orange   yellow   green   blue   indigo   violet

Periods 2 and 3 of the periodic table

H 1							He 2
Li 3	Be 4		B 5	C 6	N 7	O 8	F 9	Ne 10
Na 11	Mg 12		Al 13	Si 14	P 15	S 16	Cl 17	Ar 18

Little   Betty's   bookshop   can   not   open   for   Ned
Naughty   Maggie   always   sings   part   songs   clearly   arranged

The reactivity series of metals (K   Na   Ca   Mg   Al   Zn   Fe   Cu   Ag)
Kevin's   natural   calling   makes   all   zebras   feel   cute   again

The characteristics of life   **Mr Grens**   (move, respire, grow, reproduce, excrete, nutrition, sense)
Mrs Gref   (move, respire, sense, grow, reproduce, excrete, feed)

System for classifying life (kingdom,   phylum,   class,   order,   family,   *genus*,   *species*)
King   Philip   came   over   for   great   sausages
Kids   prefer   cheese   over   fried   green   spinach

Mnemonics (short phrases to help you to remember a number of related items)   17

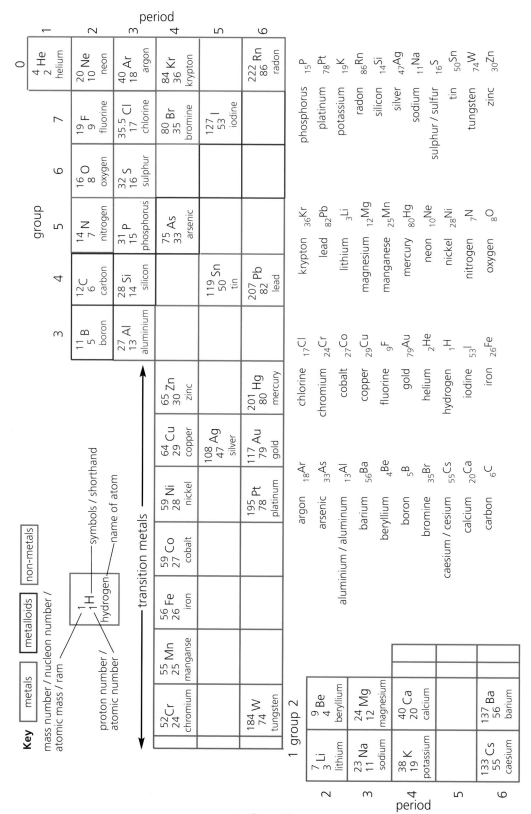

periodic table

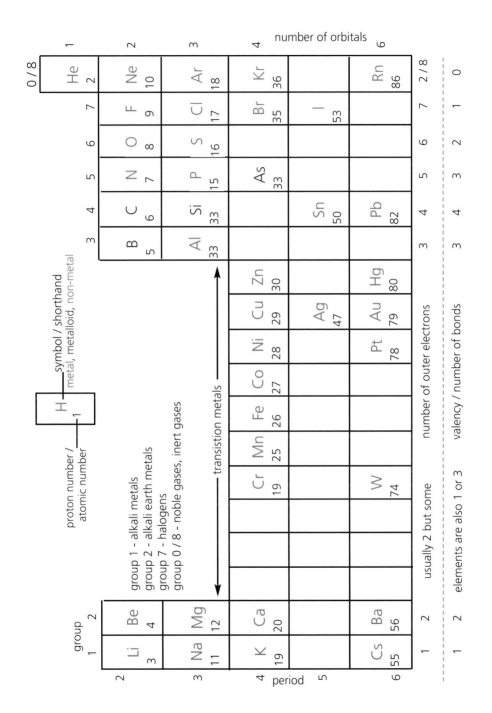

periodic table

a- / an-	not, without (Gk)	graph- / -graph	to write (Gk), drawn	osteo-	a bone (Gk)
amphi-	both (Gk)	haema-	blood (Gk)	ov-	egg (L)
ante-	before (L)	heli- / helio-	the Sun (Gk)	peri-	around (Gk), about
anti-	against (Gk)	hemi-	half (Gk)	photo-	light (Gk)
arthro-	a joint (Gk)	herb-	grass (L)	-phyll	a leaf (Gk)
atmo-	vapour (Gk)	hetero-	other (Gk)	-pod	foot (Gk)
auto-	self (Gk)	histo-	web, tissue (Gk)	poly-	many (Gk)
bi-	double (L) two	homo-	same (Gk)	post-	late (L)
bio-	life (Gk)	hydro-	water (Gk)	pre-	before (L)
carn-	flesh (L)	hyper-	above, beyond (L & Gk)	proto-	first (Gk)
cent-	a hundred (L)	hypo-	under, below (Gk)	pseudo-	false (Gk)
centri- / -centri	around a spike (Gk)	im-	not (L)	quad-	four (L)
chlor-	green (Gk)	in-	not (L)	re-	again (L)
chrom-	colour (Gk)	inter-	between (L)	sapr-	rotten (Gk)
-cide	to kill (L)	intra-	within (L)	-scope	a watcher (Gk)
co-	with, together (L)	iso-	equal (Gk), the same number of parts	semi-	half (L)
contra-	against (L)			sol-	Sun (L)
cyto-	a hollow (Gk) cells	-lite	rock (Gk)	-sperm	to sow (L & Gk)
de-	out, away (L)	kilo-	a thousand (Gk)	stereo-	solid (Gk)
deca-	ten (Gk)	litho-	stone (Gk)	sub-	under (L)
deci-	ten (L)	macro-	long (Gk), large	super-	over, above (L)
derm-	skin (Gk)	mal-	badly (L)	syn-	with (Gk)
di-	double (Gk), two	mega	great (Gk)	tele-	far off (Gk), at a distance
dis-	two(L), to remove	meta-	between, among (Gk)		
eco-	house (Gk)	-meter	measure (Gk)	tera-	monster (Gk)
ecto-	outside (Gk)	micro-	small (Gk), tiny, a millionth part	terra-	Earth (L)
endo-	within (Gk), inside			tetra-	four (Gk)
equa- / equi-	make even (L)	mill-	thousand (L)	therm-	heat (Gk)
exo-	outside (Gk)	mono-	one (Gk)	trans-	across (L)
extra-	beyond (L)	morph- / -morph	form (Gk)	tri-	three (L & Gk)
ferri- / ferro-	iron (L)	mort-	death (L)	troph-	to nourish, to feed (Gk)
fore-	in front (A-S)	multi-	many (L)		
gastro-	the stomach (Gk)	nano-	dwarf (Gk)	ultra-	beyond (L)
-geny	from (L), production	neuro-	a nerve (Gk)	uni-	one (L)
geo-	the Earth (Gk)	noct-	night (L)	-vore	to eat (L)
giga	giant (L)	non-	not (L)	xeno-	foreign (Gk)
glyco-	sweet (Gk)	omni-	all (L)	zoo-	animal (Gk)

prefixes & suffixes

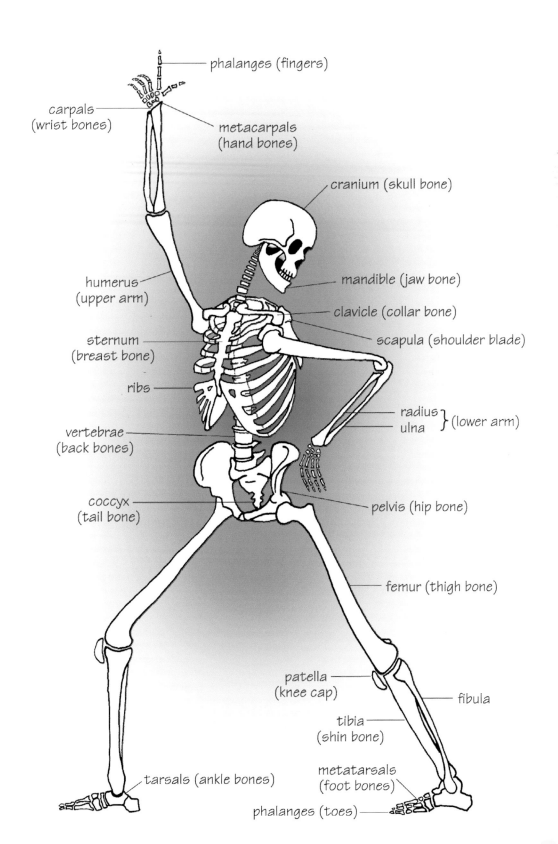

phalanges (fingers)

carpals
(wrist bones)

metacarpals
(hand bones)

cranium (skull bone)

humerus
(upper arm)

mandible (jaw bone)

clavicle (collar bone)

sternum
(breast bone)

scapula (shoulder blade)

ribs

radius
ulna } (lower arm)

vertebrae
(back bones)

coccyx
(tail bone)

pelvis (hip bone)

femur (thigh bone)

patella
(knee cap)

fibula

tibia
(shin bone)

tarsals (ankle bones)

metatarsals
(foot bones)

phalanges (toes)

human skeleton

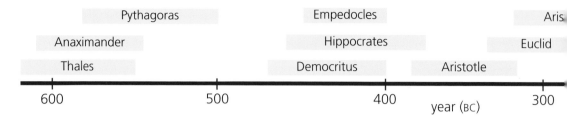

There were very few scientists in Western Europe during the sixteen hundred years that separated Eratosthenes from Leonardo da Vinci

Columella   1st century AD   Hero   20–70

Ptolemy   90–170   Galen   130–201

Science continued to be studied in the Far East and Persia – much of our knowledge of science and maths derives from the writings of these Arabic scholars

Al'Khwarizmi   780–850

Avicenna   980–1037

Ibn-al-Nafis   1126–1198

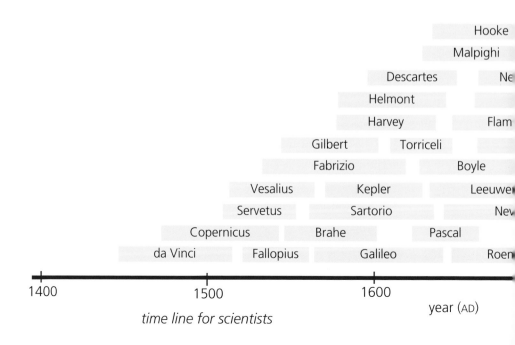

time line for scientists

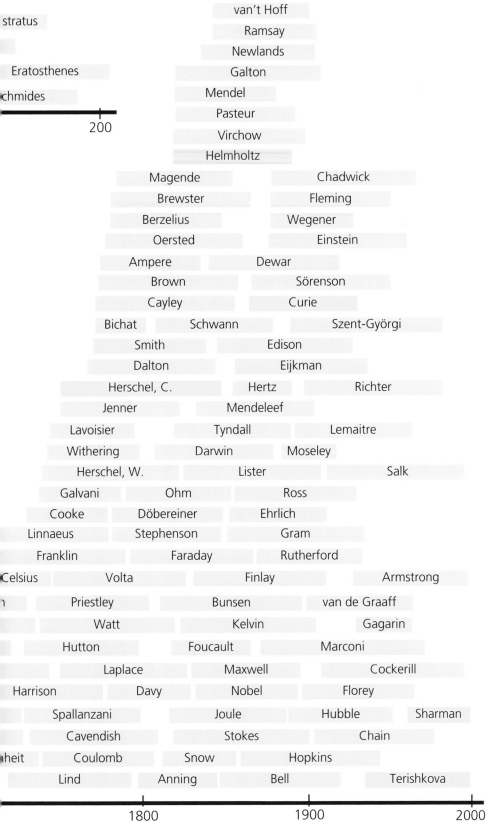

stratus

Eratosthenes

chmides

200

van't Hoff
Ramsay
Newlands
Galton
Mendel
Pasteur
Virchow
Helmholtz

Magende	Chadwick
Brewster	Fleming
Berzelius	Wegener
Oersted	Einstein
Ampere	Dewar
Brown	Sörenson
Cayley	Curie
Bichat Schwann	Szent-Györgi
Smith	Edison
Dalton	Eijkman
Herschel, C. Hertz	Richter
Jenner	Mendeleef
Lavoisier Tyndall	Lemaitre
Withering Darwin	Moseley
Herschel, W. Lister	Salk
Galvani Ohm	Ross
Cooke Döbereiner	Ehrlich
Linnaeus Stephenson	Gram
Franklin Faraday	Rutherford

Celsius   Volta   Finlay   Armstrong

Priestley   Bunsen   van de Graaff

Watt   Kelvin   Gagarin

Hutton   Foucault   Marconi

Laplace   Maxwell   Cockerill

Harrison   Davy   Nobel   Florey

Spallanzani   Joule   Hubble   Sharman

Cavendish   Stokes   Chain

heit   Coulomb   Snow   Hopkins

Lind   Anning   Bell   Terishkova

1800   1900   2000

time line for scientists

23

A / amp / ampère the unit of current, one amp is the flow of one coulomb in one second

a- / an- (*Greek* not–, without–)

a.../ atto... prefix for one million, million, millionth of a unit, 10^{-18}

ab [antibody] a chemical circulating in the blood that destroys foreign cells or chemicals

abbreviation a short form of a longer word

abdomen the section of a living body that contains the organs for the absorption of food; the human abdomen is between the chest and the pelvis

ability the skill or power to cause a change | hearing ability the skill to hear sound of a given frequency and intensity

abiotic factor a part that causes a change or influences an environment that does not involve life, *eg* amount of rain

abortion ending a pregnancy by removing a foetus that is not yet able to survive in the outside world

above greater, higher than

abrade to wear away, to rub down

abrasion the wearing away of a rock caused by movement

abrasive wearing away of a surface, a material that is able to scratch a surface | non-abrasive material that will not scratch a surface

absence the lack, something missing

absolute perfect, without comparing to others | absolute temperature a measure of how fast the particles are moving based on the behaviour of gases, a temperature scale measured in kelvins | absolute zero the temperature at which particles, including electrons, have no movement

absorb to take in fluid, *eg* living organisms absorb nutrients, light is absorbed by opaque material | absorb light to take in any light so that none is reflected | absorb nutrients to transfer small molecules through the wall of the intestine into the blood, to take small molecules from the soil into the root | re-absorb to take back into the starting place without any obvious change

absorbance a measure of how well light is transmitted by a material

absorbed taken in

absorbent able to take in fluid | absorbent material a substance, usually solid, that is able to soak up lots of a fluid

absorbing taking in | absorbing nutrients taking from the environment into the cell the small molecules that are essential for cell growth

absorption the act of taking in | absorption of heat material being heated leads either to a change of state or to an increase of temperature | water absorption taking water into a material, *eg* porous rock taking in water

abstract in the mind; a short summary of an article; to remove

abundance the number of living organisms that there is in a particular area, abundance does not mean that there is always lots of something (*see* abundant) | natural abundance the amount or population of something that occurs without the intervention of human beings

abundant lots of | abundant growth lots of plants

abuse to hurt, to injure, to mis-use | solvent abuse smelling the vapour from a liquid in order to cause a change in the activity of the brain

abusing drugs taking chemicals that cause changes to the brain in quantities that will cause long-term damage

ac [alternating current] – the electrons move backwards and then forwards

accelerate to increase speed

accelerating increasing speed

acceleration the rate of change of velocity (measured in metres / seconds squared, metres / second / second, m/s^2)

$$\text{acceleration } (m/s^2) = \frac{\text{change of velocity } (m/s)}{\text{time } (sec)}$$

| acceleration due to gravity the change of speed caused by the attraction of a nearby large body | centripetal acceleration the change of speed, directed towards the centre of a circle, caused by an object moving in a circular path | initial acceleration the rate of change of velocity near the start of the experiment

acceptable satisfactory or reasonable in that situation

accepted theory an idea that has been tested and found to explain lots of observations

access the method of approach; to open a file | continuous access able to meet at any time

accident an event that has happened without planning, often leading to damage | road accident a crash involving at least one vehicle that was moving on the highway

accommodation the ability of the eye to change focus so that objects near and far can be seen clearly

according agreeing, basing further discussion on

account an essay or description of an event; to provide a description of an event

accumulate to gather together, to increase | accumulate evidence collect the observations that support an idea

accumulation the gathering of substances into one place | bio-accumulation the increasing concentration of stable chemicals that occurs in moving from producer to prey then to predator

accuracy a measure of how near your measurements are to the accepted values, an estimate of error | **adequate accuracy** the measurements are acceptable for that experiment with that equipment | **relative accuracy** a comparison of the size of the error to the size of measurement

accurate reliable, repeatable, without error | **accurate clocks** instruments for measuring time that do not change their speed | **accurate measurements** being very close to the accepted value | **accurate method** a technique that is capable of giving results that are reliable and repeatable | **accurate observations** description containing sufficient details that another person could recognise the same change or object | **more accurate** results that are reliable and repeatable

accurately with as little error as possible

acetate a transparent sheet that can be written on with pen and used on an overhead projector | **acetate ion** [CH_3COO^-] ethanoate ion

acetic acid [CH_3COOH] vinegar, ethanoic acid

acetone [$(CH_3)_2CO$] propanone, an inflammable liquid that is a good solvent

acetylene [C_2H_2] a gas that reacts with lots of oxygen to give very high temperatures

ache hurting, throbbing; to feel hurt | **tooth ache** a pain in the tooth

achieve to succeed in reaching a target

acid a chemical which has a pH below 7, the word acid means sour | **"acid"** the illegal drug that causes hallucinations, LSD | **acid conditions** the reaction is taking place at a pH below 7 | **acid fumes** a vapour containing particles of a strong acid | **acid oxide** a compound containing two types of atom, one of which must be oxygen, that dissolves in water to give a pH below 7 | **acid rain** the falling rain has a pH below 7 caused by the water absorbing the oxides of nitrogen, sulphur and phosphorus from the air | **acid soil** earth that has a pH below 7 that could be caused by acid rain or by decay of dead plants producing peat, some plants prefer to grow in acid soil | **acetic acid** [CH_3COOH] vinegar, ethanoic acid | **amino acids** the building blocks of proteins | **ascorbic acid** the proper name for vitamin C | **battery acid** the sulphuric acid that is used in the type of battery (lead–acid battery) used in a car | **bench acid** the types and concentrations of acid that would be expected to be available at the laboratory bench | **benzoic acid** [C_6H_5COOH] a weak acid that forms white crystals | **carbolic acid** [C_6H_5OH] phenol, the original antiseptic | **carbonic acid** [H_2CO_3] a weak acid that is produced by adding carbon dioxide to water

under pressure, the acid in fizzy drinks (the fizz is carbon dioxide) | **citric acid** gives citrus fruits, such as oranges and lemons, their sour taste | **common acids** the acids that would be expected to be in most laboratories or in many shops | **concentrated acid** lots of acid particles in a small volume – tends to be corrosive and poisonous | **deoxyribonucleic acid** DNA, the molecule in the chromosome to which genes are encoded | **dilute acid** not many acid particles in a given volume of liquid | **ethanoic acid** [CH_3COOH] acetic acid, better known as vinegar | **fatty acids** chemicals that contain a -COOH group, the chemicals produced by breakdown of fats | **folic acid** one of the vitamin B group of chemicals that is found in liver and green vegetables and is important for the absorption of iron | **formic acid** [$HCOOH$] methanoic acid, the irritant injected by ants and nettles | **household acids** any acid, such as citric acid or vinegar, that is available at supermarkets | **hydrochloric acid** [HCl] a strong acid that is commonly used in the laboratory to produce chlorides | **laboratory acids** the acids (including hydrochloric acid, nitric acid, sulphuric acid) that are used in most laboratories | **lactic acid** a weak acid, that is found in sour milk | **malic acid** a sour-tasting chemical that is found in unripe fruit, especially apples | **methanoic acid** [$HCOOH$] formic acid, the irritant that is in the sting of ants and nettles | **mineral acids** any acid that does not contain carbon, the common laboratory acids | **nitric acid** [HNO_3] a strong acid that is found in most laboratories and produces nitrates | **nucleic acids** the very long molecules found in the nucleus that contain the genetic instructions | **phosphoric acid** [H_3PO_4] the strong acid produced when phosphorus pentoxide dissolves in water | **sorbic acid** [C_5H_7COOH] an organic acid that is used as a food preservative because it inhibits the growth of microbes, but can be used by animal cells | **stearic acid** the acid found in soap | **stomach acid** the hydrochloric acid that is found in the stomach | **strong acid** chemical that produce a solution with a pH below 3 even when dilute, eg hydrochloric acid | **sulfuric acid / sulphuric acid** [H_2SO_4] a laboratory acid that is used to produce sulfates / sulphates | **tartaric acid** [$(CHOHCOOH)_2$] an acid found in many fruits, especially grapes | **weak acid** a liquid with a pH that is near to, but below, pH 7, eg a concentrated solution of citric acid has a pH of 5 **"acid"** the illegal drug that causes hallucinations, LSD

acidic is similar to the word acid, meaning below pH 7 | **acidic conditions** where the liquid or gas has a pH below 7 | acidic gas a vapour that will produce a pH below 7 when dissolved in water | acidic lake an area of fresh water that has a pH below 5 and so is unsuitable for many fish or plants | acidic liquid a solution with a pH below 7 | acidic oxides are compounds of non-metals, such as sulphur or nitrogen, with oxygen that dissolve in water to give a pH below 7 | acidic rain is falling water with a pH below 7 | acidic solution a liquid with a pH below 7 | strongly acidic the pH of the liquid is below 3 | weakly acidic the chemical has a pH near to 7 when dissolved in water

acidity amount of acid, an estimate of the pH | reducing acidity adding a base so the pH increases towards pH 7

acids chemicals that dissolve in water to produce a pH below 7 and so will turn litmus to red. The common acids found in the laboratory are sulphuric acid [H_2SO_4], hydrochloric acid [HCl] and nitric acid [HNO_3], acids often found in the home include citric acid (in lemons), ethanoic acid (vinegar) and lactic acid (sour milk)

acorn the fruit of the oak that contains the seed

acoustics the study of sound, the quality of sound in a room

acquire to obtain, to gain

across over, connecting

act a performance; to do, to appear | Clean Air Act (1955) legislation resulting from the thick fogs seen in 1952, that banned the use of fuels that produced smoke

acting pushing | acting downwards pushing towards the ground

action a force trying to cause a change, which is opposed by the reaction | antibody action the chemical change that occurs when an antibody meets a foreign particle | capillary action movement of liquid through a very thin tube | involuntary action muscle movement that is not under your conscious control | pumping action movement of a muscle, such as the heart, that causes a liquid to flow | reflex action an automatic response, over which you have no control, to a stimulus | voluntary action using your mind to control the movement of your muscles

active able to carry out an activity or action | active volcanoes cracks in the Earth's crust through which magma is flowing | fully active working at maximum speed | radio-active the nuclei of an element are unstable and break down to produce radiation and new elements

activities (plural of activity) actions, responses | practical activities actions requiring performance

of experiments | range of activities many different types of experiments or investigations

activity (plural is activities) [not to be confused with reactivity] agility, amount of movement; the speed with which something occurs | activity clock a circular diagram showing movement, light or temperature over a 24 hour period | activity series the reactivity series, the metals put in the order of their speed of reaction with water, acid or oxygen | activity of yeast an estimate as to how fast the yeast are growing by measuring the production of carbon dioxide | animal activity movement of animals | antibody activity an estimate of how fast is the reaction of an anti-body with a chemical in the body | bacterial activity a microbe is growing, dividing and pro-ducing chemicals | cell activity a cell is growing, dividing and producing chemicals | cyclic activity events or changes that occur in a regular and repeated manner | geological activity move-ment of the crust of the Earth | group activity where several people co-operate to complete an experiment | hazardous activity actions that could lead to damage unless care is taken and skill is used | human activity people carrying out actions that could change the habitat | mental activity thinking | physical activity doing something that uses lots of muscles and is tiring | plant activity the chemical changes that occur in the cells of a plant | practical activity a piece of work that needs people to move around and to manipulate equipment | simple activity an experiment that requires very little action by the observer | volcanic activity the number and intensity of volcanoes that are exploding | yeast activity the rate at which yeast produces alcohol and carbon dioxide

acts causes a change, does something

acute sensitive, sharp, fine | acute angle an angle less than 90° | acute hearing able to react to sounds that are very low intensity | acute vision able to see fine details

adapt to change so as to become suitable for the current conditions

adapted changed in order to be better able to carry out a job or for an organism to survive | specially adapted changed to meet a unique need

adaption a change to the basic structure | appropriate adaptions changes in an organism that suits the surroundings | daily adaption changes in behaviour so as to make best use of the change of conditions that occurs over 24 hours | relevant adaptions changes in structure or behaviour that can be shown to be related to a specific need | **yearly adaption** the changes that take place in an organism each year in order to survive the different conditions that prevail in different seasons

adaptive characteristics changes to important features, *eg* length of hair or shape of beak, that allow the organism to survive better

add (not had which is a past part of to have) to sum, to take on extra items

addict / drug addict a person who is dependent on a chemical, usually an illegal substance, that could cause damage

addicted not able to give up or stop taking

addiction a dependence, a great need for a substance

addictive a substance that you can not give up – you need to have more | **addictive drugs / addictive substance** chemicals that cause a change in the chemistry of the brain and which are constantly needed

adding summing numbers, putting in more

addition the process of summing numbers, another | **in addition** furthermore

additional you need to keep on working in order to get more of something | **additional data** more information is needed | **additional evidence** more facts / data are needed | **additional experiments** you have to carry out more practical work | **additional information** more facts or figures need to be found | **additional tests** more experiments need to be carried out | **additional work** more experiments are needed

additive a chemical that is added in small quantities in order to bring about a change | **food additive** a chemical that is added to foods in order to improve the flavour, the shelf-life or the appearance

adequate enough, sufficient | **adequate accuracy** the results are close enough to the actual values as to be sufficient for that purpose | **adequate amount** the quantity is sufficient for that measurement or series of experiment | **adequate diet** your food contains enough nutrients and energy | **adequate precision** the data are accurate and repeatable, the instrument or meter that is being used will produce measurements that are accurate enough to be useful | **adequate sample size** there are sufficient numbers | **adequate size** diagrams are big enough to be clear and useful

adhesion sticking together of two different materials

adhesive a chemical that is able to bond to other materials so that they can not be separated

adjacent next to | **adjacent particles** small pieces of matter that are next to each other

adjust to change

adjustable able to be changed so as to give a good fit

administer to give, to ensure a drug gets into the body

administration the act of introducing a drug into the body | **oral administration** giving a drug by mouth, *eg* as a tablet or a liquid

adolescence a stage in the growth of an organism between immature young and the mature adult

adrenal gland a small group of cells that is found next to each kidney and secretes the hormone adrenaline

adrenalin / adrenaline the hormone produced by the adrenal gland that prepares the body for fight or flight, ephiderine

adult mature and so is able to reproduce sexually | **adult features** items that are characteristic of the mature animal

adulthood the events and reactions that occur while a person is capable of reproducing

advances moving forward, adding new ideas and knowledge | **medical advances** using new knowledge and results to improve the care of patients | **scientific advances** using new understanding and ideas to make and test further theories

advantages benefits

adventitious accidental, found in unusual places

advertisements public notices or displays, especially trying to get you to buy a product

advertising claims assertions made by manufacturers in order to improve sales

advice a recommendation | **dietary advice** details about the type and amount of food

advise to offer help, to inform

advisory leaflet a sheet of paper that recommends a course of action

aeon (UK & USA) / **eon** (USA) a time interval of 1000 million years

aerate to bubble air through a liquid

aeration blowing lots of air into a liquid | **aeration tank** the large container used in a sewage plant in order to provide air for the microbes

aerobic exercise repetitive movement so that the muscles have insufficient oxygen and start to produce lactic acid

aerobic respiration cells using oxygen to release energy from sugar (glucose) or fat, usually producing carbon dioxide and water

oxygen + sugar = carbon dioxide + water

aerobically a chemical reaction in a cell that requires oxygen

aerodynamic a shape, usually pointed and with gentle curves, that allows the object to minimise the air resistance.

aerogenerator wind turbine

aeroplane (UK) / **airplane** (US) transport that lifts off the ground using the movement of air over the wings

aerosol tiny droplets of liquid in the air | aerosol can a cylinder that is partially filled with liquid that is under pressure so that pressing on the top releases a mist of liquid

affect to act on or to influence (different from effect which is to cause a change) | temperature affects changes that occur only when the temperature changes, *eg* food can be stored for longer in a freezer

affected (not effected which means caused by) changed by

aforestation planting young trees in an area that had previously had all the natural forest chopped down

after later, behind, in the manner of

afterbirth the placenta, which is delivered after the birth of the child

aftercare the supervision and services that are provided after an operation

afterwards following a particular event

Ag silver (*Latin*, argentum), proton number 47, a precious metal

against in opposition, opposing, in contact with

agar a chemical extracted from seaweed that is used to make agar gel for growing microbes | agar gel / agar jelly the extract of | agar-agar (a seaweed) suspended in water | agar plates a layer of agar gel inside a sterile petri dish that is used for growing bacteria and fungi

age the number of days or years that something has existed, or a particular span of time; to change over time | ages long periods of time | age groups the division of information into sets that are relevant to people of a specified age | Bronze Age the time between the Stone Age (ended 3000 BC to 1500 BC depending on geographical region) and the Iron Age (from about 500 BC) | Dark Ages / Middle Ages the years between the collapse of the Roman Empire in the fifth century and the Renaissance in the fifteenth century, Arab scientists, *eg* Ibn-al-Nafis were important in maintaining Greek knowledge and making new discoveries | geological ages periods of time that are characterised by specific environmental conditions, especially temperature | Ice Age one of the several periods when the Earth was sufficiently cold that ice covered most of the surface, the last Ice Age ended about 10,000 years ago | Iron Age the last of the Ages of prehistory (the others are Stone Age and Bronze Age) which started in the Middle East over

3000 years ago | old age the time of life towards the end of a natural life-span | Stone Age the earliest Age of man, before the discovery of bronze, ended between 3000 BC and 1500 BC depending on the geographical region

ageing (UK) / **aging** (USA) the changes of process that occur in cells as they get older

agent a chemical that causes a change | causative agent the substance that brought about the change | drying agent a desiccant, a chemical that removes water vapour from the air | infectious agent a small organism that is able to live inside another organism, usually causing some feeling of ill-health | oxidising agent a chemical that will readily react to give away oxygen to another substance | reducing agent a chemical that removes oxygen from another substance

ages long periods of time | Dark Ages / Middle Ages the years between the collapse of the Roman Empire in the fifth century and the Renaissance in the fifteenth century, Arab scientists, *eg* Ibn-al-Nafis were important in maintaining Greek knowledge and making new discoveries | geological ages periods of time that are characterised by specific environmental conditions, especially temperature

aggregate a mixture of rock particles of many different sizes; to form a collection

agile active, alert, able to change direction rapidly

aging (USA) / **ageing** (UK) the changes of process that occur in cells as they get older

agitate to shake briskly, to disturb

agree to arrange, to match, to concur

agricultural concerned with raising crops for profit | agricultural land an area that is used for growing crops or raising animals for later sale at a profit | agricultural method the techniques, chemicals and schedule that are followed for the large-scale production of food

agriculture growing fruit and vegetables on a large scale

agro-chemicals the fertilisers, pesticides and antibiotics that are used to increase the yield of a crop

agro-chemistry the study of the chemicals and chemical processes that are associated with the growing of crops

AI [artificial insemination] placing sperm into a vagina, but not by intercourse, [artificial intelligence] a measure of the ability of a machine to make judgements about unfamiliar situations

aid an item that gives help; to give help | buoyancy aid equipment to help an object or person to float | hearing aid equipment to help a person to hear more clearly

AIDS [acquired immune deficiency syndrome] a disease caused by a virus (HIV) that usually leads to death

air (not hair which is a furry covering, nor hare which is an animal) the mixture of gases that is found in the atmosphere around us, the proportions of the gases that are found in air are approximately 78% nitrogen, 20% oxygen, 0.04% carbon dioxide, 1% other gases and variable amounts of water vapour | air-borne carried by the breeze | air bubbles small pockets of air that are found in a liquid | air currents large masses of air that are moving in one direction, carrying dust and molecules from place to place | air freshener a solid or liquid that gradually turns to vapour that will mask any unpleasant smells | air hole the gap near the base of a bunsen burner that allows entry of air to mix with the gas | air-in-glass thermometer a tube, sealed at one end and with a drop of liquid sealing the other end, the air in the tube changes volume as the temperature changes | air mass a large volume of the atmosphere with its own temperature and pressure | air particles the molecules that are found in the atmosphere | air passages the tubes through which air flows on its way to the lungs | airplane (USA) / aeroplane (UK) transport that is lifted off the ground using the movement of air over the wings | air pollution gases and fine solid particles that are found moving in air and may damage the environment | airport an area of hard ground that is used for landing and take-off of aeroplanes | air pressure the pressure (force per unit area) that is caused either by the weight of the atmosphere or by an enclosed volume of air | air pump equipment that is used for moving air either to increase or to lower the air pressure | air quality how much of specified pollutants are in the atmosphere | air resistance the force, caused by the particles of air, that try to slow down a moving body | air sacs (alveoli) the tiny structures in the lungs that allow gas exchange to take place | airship large craft, made from balloons filled with hydrogen or helium, that float in air and can be guided by engines | air space the gap between particles in a porous rock, the gap between cells in a leaf, the hollow at the end of a hen's egg | air stream the continual movement of large volumes of air in one direction for long periods of time | air temperature how hot is the surrounding atmosphere | air thermometer an instrument for measuring the temperature using the expansion of air with increasing temperature | air track an long, hollow bar with lots of small holes that allows almost friction-free movement | airways the tubes connecting the alveoli (air sacs) to the nose and mouth | cushion of air a layer of air is used to float an object above the ground | damp air the atmosphere is almost saturated with water vapour, so condensation may occur at cooler areas | dissolved air the gases, usually found in air, that have dissolved in a liquid | dry air the atmosphere is almost free of any moisture | exhaled air the gases that are breathed out and contain large amounts (up to 4%) of carbon dioxide | fixed air the name given in the eighteenth century to the gas (carbon dioxide) produced by fermentation | fresh air air of the Earth's atmosphere that does not contain pollutants or additives | gases in air the gases that are found in air, approximately 78% nitrogen, 20% oxygen, 0.04% carbon dioxide, 1% other gases and variable amounts of water vapour | hot air air that has temperature higher than the surrounding air and so rises to form convection currents | inhaled air the air that is taken into the lungs during breathing | layers of air areas of trapped air | liquid air a mixture of oxygen and nitrogen at approximately −200°C | moving air wind or draughts that cause movement of lots of air particles | normal air the air that is usually to be found away from human habitation | pockets of air many small amounts of trapped air | separation of air cooling air so that the different pure compounds can be isolated into different containers | trapped air any air that is in a particular spot and is unable to escape so preventing loss of heat by convection | vital air an early name for the gas that became known as oxygen

air-borne carried by the wind | air-borne diseases illnesses that are transmitted between people by breathing or are carried by the wind

airplane (USA) **/ aeroplane** (UK) transport that is lifted off the ground using the movement of air over the wings

airport an area of hard ground that is used for landing and take-off of aeroplanes

Al aluminium (UK) / aluminum (USA), proton number 13, a metal with low density that is used for making overhead power cables

alarm a fright, a shock; to startle | alarm bell an electrical device that clangs out a warning of danger | emergency alarm a switch that can be pushed in order to show that you need help immediately, a loud, distinctive sound that indicates that a crisis has occurred | personal alarm small equipment that can be easily triggered to give a loud noise if you are attacked |

smoke alarm equipment that detects when smoke is present then sounds a warning

alarming frightening, causing a sudden panic

albedo an estimate of the proportion of light that a solar object will reflect

albumen / albumin any protein that is soluble in water

alchemist (an Arab word meaning the Greek or the Greek knowledge) any scientist before the seventeenth century

alchemy the study of science up until about five hundred years ago, especially the search to turn lead into gold

alcohol [C_2H_5OH] ethanol, a chemical produced by yeast growing in a sugar solution without oxygen, a liquid that is drunk socially and may cause loss of motor control | alcohols a set of organic chemicals that always have an -OH group | alcohol burner a small heat source that burns alcohol | alcohol consumption a measure of how much alcohol has been drunk | alcohol content how much alcohol there is in a given volume of liquid, may be given as % or as proof | alcohol education telling people about the uses, benefits and drawbacks of drinking alcohol | alcohol emulsion test for fats – mix the food with pure alcohol, filter and add water to the clear liquid, formation of cloudiness indicates fats are present | alcohol extract mixing the substance with ethanol so that any lipids will dissolve | alcohol poisoning the symptoms produced by drinking so much alcohol that the liver is no longer able to work properly | alcohol thermometer / alcohol-in-glass thermometer a glass tube, often with a bulb or reservoir, that contains alcohol, coloured dye is added to make the liquid more easily visible | blood alcohol the concentration of ethanol in the blood | cetyl alcohol a chemical that spreads very easily so is used to coat the surface of reservoirs to prevent evaporation of the water | effects of alcohol the increased confidence and the lack of co-ordination resulting from alcohol causing changes in the brain | units of alcohol a measure of how much alcohol is in a specified volume of different alcoholic drinks

alcoholic a drink or food containing a large amount of alcohol, a person who needs to drink alcohol

alert awake; a warning; to give a signal

alga (plural is algae) seaweed

algae (plural of alga) organisms similar to plants, so are capable of photosynthesis, with a size range from single cell to giant seaweeds | filamentous green algae long, thin (like a filament) organisms that use chlorophyll for photosynthesis | green algae a set of organisms, some single-celled and some multi-cellular, that are considered to be part of the kingdom protista, although they carry out photosynthesis using chlorophyll

algal bloom a sudden dramatic increase in the number of algae which could prevent growth of other organisms

algebraic variable a letter that is used in an equation in order to represent a value that can change

alien foreign, not native

alight burning; to land after a jump

align to bring objects into a straight line

alignment arrangement into lines | alignment of grains how the tiny particles of a rock are arranged in the larger rock | crystal alignment arrangement of molecules within a crystal

alike similar, the same

alimentary canal the digestive system, the gut, the tube inside you, where food is broken down and the nutrients are absorbed, that starts with the mouth and ends with the anus

alive showing most of the characteristics of life (MR GRENS or MRS GREF)

alkali (plural is alkalis) a chemical that dissolves in water to produce a solution with pH above 7 and so turns litmus blue, usually the oxide of metal | dilute alkali a solution of the oxides of metals (pH above 7) which do not contain many particles of the oxide | strong alkali having a pH above 10 | weak alkali a chemical that dissolves in water to give a pH above 7 but not greater than 10

alkali earth metals group 2 in the periodic table' metals (conduct electricity) that produce oxides that are either weakly alkaline or insoluble in water, other compounds of the metals, *eg* carbonates, are found as ores in the soil

alkali metals group 1 in the periodic table, metals (conduct electricity) that react with oxygen or water to produce oxides which dissolve in water to give solutions that are strongly alkaline so the pH is above 11

alkaline above pH 7 | alkaline pyrogallate / alkaline pyrogallol a solution that is used to absorb oxygen | alkaline soil earth that has a pH above 7 when mixed with water | alkaline solution liquid with a pH above 7 | strongly alkaline having a pH above 10 | weakly alkaline having a pH that is above 7 and below 10

alkalinity a liquid that has a pH above 7 | reducing alkalinity adding a chemical to a liquid so that the pH is lowered towards pH 7

alkalis (plural of alkali) solutions that are above pH 7

alkane a hydrocarbon in which all the carbon atoms are connected by single bonds

alkene a hydrocarbon in which there is a double bond between one pair of carbon atoms and all other bonding is by single bonds

Al'Khwarizmi (Mohammed Ibn Musa 780–850) was a brilliant mathematician who must have travelled widely because he combined the theories of the Greeks with the numerical system of India then introduced a symbol for zero – the result was the counting system that we use today.

all every

alleles the different forms that can occupy a particular gene position | dominant allele the instruction that is always used | harmful allele the instruction encoded at that gene position in the DNA is likely to lead to ill health or the early death of that organism | recessive allele the form of the gene that is not expressed unless the alleles from both parents are recessive

allergen a chemical that causes inflammation of the skin or difficulty in breathing

allergic likely to react to a specific chemical or food | allergic reaction when a person is exposed to an allergen there is a chemical change in the body that may cause difficulty with breathing and may lead to shock

allergies (plural of allergy) over reaction of the immune system producing rashes or breathing difficulties

allergy (plural is allergies) reaction of an animal, to a chemical that has little affect on the majority of that species causing an inflammation or breathing difficulties | nut allergy the reaction of some people to nuts – in a severe case, being in the same room as a nut, such as an almond or a peanut, may cause the trachea to inflame and the person to be unable to breathe

alleviate to remove, to lessen

alligator a reptile, similar to a crocodile, that is found mainly in North America

allotment an area of land, used by a householder, to produce food for their own consumption

allow to be able to happen, to permit

allowance a share, an acceptance | recommended daily allowance amount of vitamin or mineral that is thought to be essential for good health

allowed (not aloud which is loudly) approved, permitted, approved

alloy a mixture of metals. Steel is an alloy made mainly of iron, an alloy made by dissolving metals in mercury is an amalgam.

along forward, on the same line

aloud (not allowed which is permitted) with a loud voice, audible, able to be heard

alpha / α the first letter of the Greek alphabet

alpha particles / alpha radiation helium nuclei [$_2^4$He^{++}] which have been given out by breakdown of an atomic nucleus

Alps high mountains near the borders of France, Italy and Switzerland

alsatian / alsation type of dog that is similar to a wolf, also called a German shepherd dog

alter to change

alternate on opposite sides, repeating pattern in pairs to change regularly from one to another | alternate layers two types of sheet in the sequence sheet 1: sheet 2: sheet 1: sheet 2: ...

alternating current (ac) movement of charge, usually electrons in a wire, that moves in one direction then in the other direction; mains electricity is 240 volts delivered at 50 hertz alternating current in the UK and at 110 volts 60 hertz alternating current in the USA

alternative a second or different way of doing things | alternative energy methods for obtaining work done that does not depend on burning fossil fuels | alternative energy resources places where energy can be found that do not depend on burning fossil fuels, eg kinetic energy sources such as winds, tides or hydro-electric power, geothermal energy or solar power | alternative explanation a different description of reasons, another theory | alternative method a second means of carrying out the work | alternative model a different description or idea | alternative source another place from which the resource can be obtained | alternative technique a different means of finding out something | alternative technology using renewable resources to use and to transform energy on a large scale | cheaper alternatives should give similar results and accuracy but at less cost

alternatively putting forward a second option

alters changes

although even though (connecting two opposing ideas)

altitude height above sea level | altitude sickness the symptoms of headache, disorientation and nausea produced by moving from close to sea level to several thousand feet above sea level in a short time | high altitude a large vertical distance above the Earth's surface

alum [$K_2SO_4.Al_2(SO_4)_3$] potassium aluminium sulphate, crystals produced by evaporation of a solution containing aluminium sulphate and potassium sulphate

aluminium (UK) / **aluminum** (USA) (Al, proton number 13, melting point 660°C) a metal with low density so it is often used for overhead power lines, a very reactive metal that easily forms a layer of inert aluminium oxide | **aluminium bar** a piece of aluminium with a square cross-section | **aluminium can** a cylinder for storing drinks | **aluminium foil** very thin sheet of aluminium that can easily be wrapped around objects | **aluminium oxide** [Al_2O_3] the chemical produced by oxygen (usually from air) reacting aluminium, alumina is aluminium oxide found underground as bauxite

aluminum (USA) / **aluminium** (UK) (Al, proton number 13, melting point 660°C) a metal with low density so it is often used for overhead power lines, a very reactive metal that easily forms a layer of inert aluminum oxide | **aluminum bar** a piece of aluminum with a square cross-section | **aluminum can** a cylinder for storing drinks | **aluminum foil** very thin sheet of aluminum that can easily be wrapped around objects | **aluminum oxide** [Al_2O_3] the chemical produced by oxygen (usually from air) reacting aluminum, alumina is aluminum oxide found underground as bauxite

alveolar duct the tiny tube connecting each air sac to the bronchiole

alveoli (plural of alveolus) the tiny air sacs that are at the ends of the airways in the lungs, their purpose is to allow exchange of gases (oxygen goes into the red blood cells, carbon dioxide diffuses out of the blood)

alveolus (plural is alveoli) an air sac or space in the lungs where the blood can collect oxygen and get rid of carbon dioxide

am [ante-meridian] the time before noon, morning

amalgam an alloy in which metals are dissolved in mercury

amazing fantastic, unforgettable, unique, unexpected, surprising, awesome

ambush a predator is waiting patiently for the prey; to set a trap

amend to change in a small way

amino acids a set of about 20 chemicals that are the building blocks for proteins. Proteins are very large molecules that need to be digested, or broken down, to the amino acids for absorption

ammeter an instrument used for measuring the electric current, ammeters are always in series with the component | **digital ammeter** an instrument for measuring current in which the output is in the form of numbers

ammonia [NH_3] a gas with a very pungent smell (makes you choke – contributes to the smell of urine in babies' nappies) that is the raw material for fertilisers and explosives | **ammonia production** the large-scale manufacture of ammonia from nitrogen and hydrogen using the Haber process | **ammonia solution** ammonia dissolved in water, ammonium hydroxide solution

ammonium / **ammonium ion** [NH_4^+] the charged particle produced when ammonia [NH_3] forms salts | **ammonium chloride** [NH_4Cl] a white crystalline material used in dry cells, a chemical that appears to sublime because heating causes breakdown to produce ammonia and hydrogen chloride that then easily recombine | **ammonium hydroxide** [NH_4OH] the chemical produced by dissolving ammonia in water | **ammonium ion** the charged particle of NH_4^+ | **ammonium nitrate** [NH_4NO_3] an important source of nitrogen in fertiliser, but has the disadvantage of being very soluble and so is washed out by the rain | **ammonium solution** ammonia gas dissolved in water | **ammonium sulfate** (USA) / **ammonium sulphate** (UK) [$(NH_4)_2\,SO_4$] a fertiliser used as a source of nitrogen. but it will dissolve more slowly than ammonium nitrate

amnion the membrane surrounding the foetus that is developing inside a uterus

amniotic fluid the liquid in which the foetus floats and which provide protection | **amniotic sac** the layers which are produced by the uterus during pregnancy

amoeba (UK & USA) / **ameba** (USA) a single cell organism that is found in ponds, a protozoon

among / **amongst** surrounded by, hidden, part of a crowd, part of a group

amorphous without a definite shape, shapeless

amount quantity | **adequate amount** sufficient, enough | **considerable amount** large quantity | **inadequate amount** not enough for the purpose | **sufficient amount** a quantity that is adequate for that purpose | **total amount** adding together all the different forms and states of that material | **trace amount** such small quantity that the actual weight is difficult to measure

amp / **ampère** / **A** the unit of electrical current, one amp is the flow of one coulomb of charge in one second

Ampère (Andre Marie 1775–1836) combined a passion for reading with a photographic memory and extraordinary abilities at mathematics and languages – fortunate as he was largely self-taught. His personal life was marred by disasters – his father was executed in 1793, his wife died in childbirth ten years later and his second marriage was miserable (the words '*happy at last*' are written on his gravestone!). He made many discoveries in physics, psychology and chemistry, but it was not until he was 45 that he started his most famous work – that on electricity. Oersted had shown that an electric current produces a magnetic field but Ampère showed the importance of size and direction of current and invented the right-hand grip rule, the solenoid and the meter for measuring the size of a current.

amphetamine (also called speed or benzedrine) a drug that increases alertness and self-confidence but is followed by depression and tiredness

amphi- (*Greek* both-)

amphibian an animal with a backbone (a vertebrate) that reproduces under water, but has lungs and may live on land

amplification making bigger, making sounds louder, increasing the number of molecules | amplification apparatus / amplification equipment the assembly of components that make the effect larger, apparatus for increasing the amplitude of a signal

amplifies makes louder, becomes larger

amplify to make a sound louder, to increase the number of molecules or cells

amplifying making bigger, making louder | amplifying force increasing the effort applied to the load compared to the force that you applied, *eg* in a lever or a car jack

amplitude the height of a wave above the mean or resting level, half the difference between the peak and the trough of a wave

amu [atomic mass unit] the mass of one proton, 1.6×10^{-27} kilogram

amylase the enzyme in saliva that increases the speed at which starch is broken down to give sugar

an- / a- (*Greek* not-, without-)

anaemia (UK) / **anemia** (USA) blood which is without sufficient iron so there is a lack of haemoglobin to carry the oxygen | sickle cell anaemia a disease in which the red blood cells have the shape of a half-moon, and are less-effective at carrying oxygen compared to the normal (circular) cells

anaerobic respiration release of energy by a living cell in the absence of oxygen

anaesthetic (UK) / **anesthetic** (USA) a chemical that is given intentionally to render a patient unable to feel pain | general anaesthetic a chemical that causes the patient to lose consciousness and so to be unable to feel pain | local anaesthetic a chemical that is applied so as to remove all feeling from that area

anagram a re-arrangement of all the letters from a word or a sentence to produce a new word or sentence

analgesic a drug that removes pain

analog (USA) /**analogue** (UK) using a pointer and a dial (as compared to digital with its use of numbers) | analog equipment apparatus in which the control or the output can take any value, *eg* use a dial and needle | analog input the signal that enters the equipment is able to vary continuously | analog meter a dial showing the output by moving a needle over a scale | analog output the signal from the equipment can take any value | analog scale a line divided into equal sections that can be used to help measurement

analogies (plural of analogy) using comparisons between different ideas in order to highlight similarities between them

analogue (UK) /**analog** (USA) using a pointer and a dial (as compared to digital with its use of numbers) | analogue equipment apparatus in which the control or the output can take any value, *eg* us a dial and needle | analogue input the signal that enters the equipment is able to vary continuously | analogue meter a dial showing the output by moving a needle over a scale | analogue output the signal from the equipment can take any value | analogue scale a line divided into equal sections that can be used to help measurement

analogy (plural is analogies) comparison between two different ideas in order to highlight similarities between them

analyse (UK) / **analyze** (USA) to take apart, figuratively or actually, in order to find why and how something works | analyse data to look at the information in order to find patterns or support for an idea

analysis the process of taking something apart or analysing | DNA analysis using enzymes and chemical methods to cut the genetic material into pieces that can be separated and characterised

analyze (USA) / **analyse** (UK) to take apart, figuratively or actually, in order to find why and how something works | analyze data to look at the information in order to find patterns or support for an idea

anatomical model a diagram or an inanimate (usually plastic) representation of a human body in order to show where all the various organs are to be found

Anaximander (610–546 BC) was an astronomer ahead of his time. Anaximander was fortunate to be born in Miletus – the home town of Thales. He realised the horizon was curved and so proposed that the Earth was a cylinder hanging in space.

ancestor a great, great…. great grandparent

anchor a hook for holding the position of a floating object; to hold in position

anchoring holding fast to a solid object

ancient very, very old | ancient Greeks the people who lived in the land of the Eastern Mediterranean in the five centuries before Christ | ancient times a period that was many centuries past

AND gate electronic component that will only work if both inputs are positive or have a voltage

anechoic without any echoes, so there is no reflection of sound | anechoic chamber a room that is lined with sound-absorbent material, very important in recording studios

anemia (USA) / **anaemia** (UK) blood which is without sufficient iron so there is a lack of haemoglobin to carry the oxygen | sickle cell anemia a disease in which the red blood cells have the shape of a half-moon, and are less-effective at carrying oxygen compared to the normal (circular) cells

anemometer instrument used for measuring wind speed

anemone a perennial flower | sea anemone a group of cylindrical marine animals that anchor one end of the body to a rock and have a mouth at the other end

aneroid without air | aneroid barometer an instrument for measuring air pressure that uses a container from which air has been removed

anesthetic (USA) / **anaesthetic** (UK) a chemical that is given intentionally to render a patient un-able to feel pain | general anesthetic a chemical that causes the patient to lose consciousness and so to be unable to feel pain | local anesthetic a chemical that is applied so as to remove all feeling from that area

angina a disease of the heart

angiosperm a flowering plant

angle a direction, a measure of separation for two lines that meet; to move in a different direction | angle of incidence the angle between the incoming ray and the normal (a line at right angles to the surface) | angle of reflection the angle between the normal and the ray after reflection from a surface | angle of refraction the angle between the normal and the ray that continues moving into a transparent material | acute angle an angle of less than 90° | critical angle refraction will occur below this angle (measured from the line at right angles [90°] to the surface) and internal reflection will occur above this value | right angle 90° | measure angles to use a protractor to find the size of an angle accurately

angular fragments pieces that have broken off and have sharp edges | angular measurements measuring angles between two lines or planes

anhydrite a sedimentary rock of calcium sulphate powder

anhydrous without water

animal living organism made from lots of cells and able to move, animals are characterised by being made from cells that have a nucleus but no cell wall | animal activity behaviour and movement of animals, especially concerning sex and looking for food | animal cells cells that have a nucleus but no cell wall | animal dispersal spreading of seeds by using animals, some fruits are eaten and the seeds excreted later, others catch on the fur or feather of the animal | animals' food supply the amount of the special food that a particular animal eats in order to obtain nutrients | animal kingdom one of the five divisions, or kingdoms, of living organisms | animal material some part of the animal that is to be looked at in more detail | animal plankton microscopic sea creatures that drift in the oceans | animal population the number of a given type of animal in a given area | animal protein the type of protein (a long chain of amino acids) that is found principally, or only, in animals | animal species a particular type of animal, the animal kingdom is divided into seven different genus and each is then further divided into species | animal waste the chemicals that an animal excretes or egests after all the nutrients have been absorbed from the food | aquatic animals animals that live principally in water, eg fish, frogs | common animals animals that are easily found in that habitat or locality | domestic animal animals that are intentionally found in a house, eg dogs, cats | extinct animals animals that used to exist, but are no longer found on Earth | farm animal livestock, animals that are likely to be sold for meat, eg cows, sheep | free-swimming animals creatures that are able to move themselves through the water | grass-eating animals herbivores, animals that obtain most nutrients from grass, eg cows, sheep, rabbits | grazing animals herbivores that eat plants con-tinuously | individual animal specifying a par-ticular animal in a locality or herd | invertebrate animals animals that do not have a backbone, these include the jelly fish and octopus, as well as all insects | land animals animals that live all their lives on the land | large animals con-sumers that are easily seen by people | marine animals consumers or animals that live in the sea | pedigree animals the parents, grandparents and going back many generations can all be named | predatory animals animals that live by killing and eating other animals | small animals animals that are less than 10 centimetres long and so are difficult to see | soil animals consumers that obtain nutrients from the organic matter in the earth, eg earthworms, insects | type of animal an organism showing the characteristics of that group | typical animal an organism that shows many of the features that are expected of most animals | wild animals animals that are able to survive in the outdoors but would cause a mess if brought into a house

animate alive; to give the characteristics of life | inanimate without life, not showing any signs of being alive

animated moving | animated sequence a series of diagrams that seem to show movement when viewed rapidly in the specified order

animations scenes that appear to move because several drawings are shown in rapid sequence

anion a negatively charged particle, produced by an atom gaining electrons

ankle the joint that allows the foot to move easily | ankle bones tarsals, the many small bones that are found between the lower leg and the foot

annelid / annelid worms a phylum of invertebrates, tubular animals with bodies divided into distinct segments

Anning (Mary 1799–847) was born and lived her entire life at Lyme Regis in Dorset, first helping her father to collect and sell fossils then running the business herself. Her first major find was the complete skeleton of an Ichthyosaur (a reptile similar to a dolphin), at age 11. She went on to find a vast number of new fossils which formed the foundation of many major collections.

annotate to add labels and pointers to a picture so you end up with | annotated diagrams which make more sense than just a bare picture

annotating adding small notes and labels to a diagram

annotation a note or label that helps explain a diagram

annual every year | annual growth new material that an organism adds each year | annual movement a migration, the journeys that some animals undertake each year in order to get the best chance of finding food and shelter | annual production the amount of material or crop that is made each year

anode the conducting rod with a positive charge that dips into an electrolyte or conducting liquid

anodise (UK) / **anodize** (USA) to use a metal, often aluminium, as the anode of electrolysis circuit so the metal is coated with an even layer of metal oxide

anomalies (plural of anomaly) unexpected results, pieces of information that do not fit the general pattern

anomalous out of place, does not fit a pattern | anomalous results data that do not fit the general pattern or trend

anomaly (plural is anomalies) a piece of information that does not fit the general pattern

anorexia total loss of appetite

another one more, a new example

answer a reply, an explanation; to reply | numerical answers the results are measured using a scale, quantitative

ant (not aunt which is a female relative) a social insect that forms large colonies with a single queen

antacid a chemical (usually magnesium oxide) that is taken in order to reduce the concentration of hydrochloric acid in the stomach

antagonistic muscles / antagonistic pairs pairs of muscles that are on opposite sides of a joint so one can pull (contract) while the other relaxes, eg biceps and triceps

Antarctic / Antarctica the South Polar continent – a land of 15 million square kilometres covered with an average of 1500 metres of ice

ante- (Latin before-) (not anti- which is against-)

antelope a mammal, similar to a goat, that is found in Africa

ante-meridian am, before noon, in the morning

antenatal before birth

antenna (plural is antennae) a wire for collecting radio signals, one of the sense organs protruding from the head of insects

antennae (plural of antenna) the sense organs that extend on filaments from the head of insects

anther male part of a flower that produces the pollen

anthrax a highly infectious disease that will not only kill sheep and cows, but can also be transmitted to humans

anti- (Greek against-) (not ante- which is before)

antibiotic a chemical, usually produced by a fungus, that kills bacteria (but has no affect on other living things such as viruses or fungi) | antibiotic disc small circles of filter paper containing a drop of antibiotic that can be used on an agar plate to test the effectiveness of an antibiotic | antibiotic resistance bacteria can evolve, or change, so they are no longer affected by antibiotics | wide-spectrum antibiotic chemicals that are able to kill a wide range of unrelated bacteria

antibodies (plural of antibody) proteins (long chemicals made from amino acids) that are found in the blood and help to neutralise attacks by bacteria and viruses

antibody (plural is antibodies) a protein in the blood that help to neutralise invasion by bacteria and viruses | antibody action the way in which some proteins in the blood will help to prevent infection | antibody activity the rate with which the antibodies, or specific anti-microbe proteins, can stop an infection | antibody level the concentration of a particular type of antibody in the blood (there are thousands of different antibodies) | antibody-producing cells specialised cells in animals that manufacture antibodies in response to an antigen, usually part of the infecting microbe

anti-bump granules / anti-bumping granules fragments of pot, glass or wood that allow many small bubbles to form in a boiling liquid

anticline an upfold in rock layers

anti-clockwise in the opposite direction to that which the hands of a normal clock would move | anti-clockwise moment a turning force applied in the opposite direction as the clock hands move

anticyclone outward movement of air from a region of high pressure

antifreeze a chemical, usually glycol [(CH$_2$OH)$_2$], that is added to water which both lowers the freezing point of the water to as low as −20°C and means that the mixture forms a creamy mush before becoming solid

antigen any substance that causes an animal to produce an immune response | foreign antigen the chemical causing the immune response is from a cell that is not normally found in that animal

anti-microbial / anti-microbial compound a chemical that prevents the growth of microbes such as fungi (anti-fungal compounds), viruses (antiviral compounds) or bacteria (antibiotic compounds)

anti-oxidant a chemical that slows down the rate of reaction between oxygen and some chemicals

antiperspirant a chemical that prevents a person from sweating (perspiring)

antiseptic a chemical that kills any living organisms, iodine solution is used on grazes as an antiseptic

anti-toxin a chemical that removes a poison from the blood by combining with the molecule

antiviral / antiviral drug a chemical or organism that destroys viruses

ants small social insects that live in large colonies

anus the opening at the bottom end of the digestive (alimentary) canal through which faeces are excreted

anvil the middle of the three small bones (ossicles) that join the ear drum to the cochlea

anxious afraid, fearful, nervous

aorta the major artery, or blood vessel, leaving the heart

apart separate in time or place, not being included | further apart the distance is greater | pull apart use force to separate two pieces

Apatosaurus also known as Brontosaurus, a giant dinosaur that lived in shallow water eating vegetation

aperture opening

aphids greenflies, insects that feed on the liquid in leaves, and are sometimes found in ant colonies

Apollo / Apollo program the series of NASA missions that was intended to put a man on the Moon by the end of the 1960s. Apollo 11, commanded by Armstrong, landed on the Moon on 20 July 1969 and the last mission (Apollo 17) left the Moon in December 1972

apparatus equipment | amplification apparatus the assembly of components that make the effect larger, apparatus for increasing the amplitude of a signal | appropriate apparatus equipment that is correct for the results expected of that experiment | distillation apparatus the equipment that is used to separate a mixture of liquids into pure components | electrical apparatus equipment that transform electrical energy into other forms of energy | heating apparatus equipment that can be used to heat a material | micro-projection apparatus equipment that can take the image from a microscope and project it onto a screen

apparent amount that is seen or measured | apparent depth the distance that a point seems to be when observed from the surface | apparent distance the separation of two objects as seen by the eye | apparent movement measuring the change in position relative to a landmark

appear to come into view, to resemble

appearance a description of what something looks like, *eg* colour, transparency

appendix a blind passage (like the finger of a glove) at the junction of the small intestine and the large intestine, extra writing at the end of a book

appetite a need for food, a desire to eat

apple a fruit in which the seeds are in the core | apple core the centre of an apple | ripe apple the fruit is ready to eat | unripe apples apples that are not ready for eating

appliance equipment | electrical appliance a piece of equipment that uses electricity as the energy source | everyday appliances machines that are found in most households, *eg* washing machine, television | heating appliance equipment that is used for increasing temperature |

household appliance equipment that is sold in shops for use in the home, and uses electricity as the power source

application usage, effort | application rate the amount of chemical that is applied to each square metre of surface | practical application using the scientific knowledge to make a task easier in everyday life

applied direction that a force pushes; practical works; to have pasted some chemical onto a surface, to have asked for a job, to have worked hard | applied force the measured push that is given

apply to ask for a job, to work hard, to cover a surface with a liquid

appraise to assess | appraise text to look at what is written in order to find the few simple ideas

appreciate to admire, to value, to acknowledge a value

approach the idea behind the method; to move nearer | appropriate approach method of trying to find out information | common approach similar method for solving a problem | different approaches two or more methods for solving the same problem | effective approach a method that solves the problem at a very small cost | possible approach a method of investigation that could answer the question | practical approach how the problem can be solved using the equipment that is available | proposed approach the way of investigating, a method that could work | suitable approach a method that could work, but may not be the quickest, cheapest or safest

appropriate suitable to the purpose or work that is being done | appropriate adaptions changes in an organism that suit the surroundings | appropriate apparatus equipment that is correct for the results expected of that experiment | appropriate approach method suitable for trying to find out particular information | appropriate conclusions outcomes that match the information available | appropriate curve the shape or the drawing of the line of best fit | appropriate equipment apparatus or hardware that is correct for the type and accuracy of an experiment | appropriate evidence the clues and pointers that are correct for that experiment and conclusion | appropriate form may refer to a suitable type of table (a form) or to the general presentation | appropriate format general appearance and sequencing of the writing | appropriate graph the variables, axes and range are correct for that experiment | appropriate indications correct or suitable pointers and

information | appropriate information data that is sufficiently accurate and of wide enough range for that purpose | appropriate language use of suitable words and grammar that can be understood by the listener or reader | appropriate measurements lengths, weights and volumes that give important information for that experiment | appropriate method a procedure that is simple and safe, which gives the information that is required | appropriate number suitable number of measurements with the resources available | appropriate observations using instruments and senses so as to notice the changes, or lack of change, that could be important | appropriate places suitable positions | appropriate precision recording the answers with regard to the accuracy of the method and the metres used | appropriate presentation method of showing the data that keeps everything simple but with sufficient detail | appropriate procedures using methods that are safe and that give results to a suitable accuracy | appropriate proportions correct ratio of each of the materials in a mixture | appropriate quantity using an amount that is safe and sufficient, but not so much as to make the method dangerous or too expensive | appropriate questions ask questions that can be answered with the knowledge, time and equipment that is available | appropriate range allows widest number of measurements with the resources and time available | appropriate resources use chemicals, texts, computers that are suitable to help solve a problem | appropriate sample a suitable number from random parts of the whole population | appropriate samples take the items from places and times that are acceptable for that experiment | appropriate sample size take the correct number of measurements | appropriate scales a starting point and range of the axes of a graph that are suitable for that data | appropriate scientific language correct use the specialised words of science in the right place | appropriate sequence correct order | appropriate size right size for the job, eg diagrams need to be large enough to show all the detail, but not too large for the book | appropriate strategy a series of experiments that will allow a particular problem to be solved simply and accurately | appropriate tables columns of data that have the correct titles and units | appropriate technique suitable method | appropriate terminology use of words and equations that can be understood by the audience | appropriate terms correct words | appropriate thermometer use the thermometer that is correct for that task, *eg* use a clinical thermometer to measure body temperature | **appropriate time-scale** allow sufficient time for the experiment to be completed, without wasting time, to ensure that the time axis on a graph covers the same time interval as was measured in the experiment | **appropriate units** use measurements which are suitable for that experiment and the measuring equipment available | **appropriate variables** decide which are the important things that can be changed and which things can not be changed or are likely to be unimportant | **appropriate vocabulary** use words, equations and terms that the audience should be able to understand

approximately nearly, almost

approximation a figure close to the estimated value, but not exact

(aq) (aqueous) dissolved in water

aquatic living in or near fresh water (not salty nor sea water – that is called marine) | **aquatic animals / aquatic creatures** animals that live in fresh water, *eg* ponds | **aquatic habitat** the conditions (*eg* temperature, moisture, pH) near or in fresh water | **aquatic plants** plants (organisms that can carry out photosynthesis) that live in, or very close to, water

aqueous solution a mixture of any substance dissolved in water

aquifer an underground lake of water absorbed into rock

Ar argon, proton number 18, an inert gas

arable land ground that is suitable for growing crops or food

arachnid / arachnida spiders, invertebrate animals that has a body in two sections and has four pairs of legs

arbitrary random, without pattern | **arbitrary scale** there is no valid scientific reason why the scale should have the fixed points or range that are being used

arc a part of a circle, a continuous spark between two electrodes; to move in a curve

arch (plural is arches) a bend, a curve, a vault, a feature in fingerprints; to bend above a feature, to join by soaring in a semi-circle | **simple arch** the ridges of fingerprints form a bridge-like structure

Archimedes (born in Syracuse, around 287 BC, died 212 BC) was a member of the royal family in Sicily and is considered to be one of the three great princes of science (the others are Newton and Gauss) because of the vast number of new ideas that he produced. He developed the use of pulleys and screws and worked out methods for calculating the area and volumes of cones and spheres. Archimedes is remembered for jumping out of his bath then running through the streets shouting *eureka (I have found the answer)* when he realised that he could find the amount of gold in a crown by measuring the volume of displaced water. He helped build weapons to destroy the Roman fleet in 215 BC, but he was killed when they eventually invaded the city.

Arctic concerned with the area within about 10° of the North Pole | **Arctic conditions** the type of climate, very cold and windy, associated with the North Pole in winter

area the extent of a surface | **areas of science** the different parts of science such as biology or chemistry | **circular area** the surface has the shape of a circle | **coniferous area** a region in which cone-bearing trees form the majority of the vegetation | **cross-sectional area** the area that is exposed when an object is cut | **deciduous area** a region in which the trees are mainly broad-leafed and the leaves fall in autumn | **suburban area** the place where people live near the edges of the town | **surface area** extent of a bounding wall or membrane | **volcanic area** the places on the Earth where volcanoes are likely to erupt

Arfvedson (Johann August 1792–1841) was educated at Upsalla and completed two degrees, in law and minerals, by 1812. Arfvedson worked with Berzelius and discovered lithium, in 1817, while analysing mineral rocks. He toured Europe for a few years then spent the rest of his life using his business contacts to become more wealthy.

argon (Ar, proton number 18, boiling point −186°C) an inert gas found as almost 1% of the atmosphere, often used to provide a protective atmosphere when welding aluminium

argue to discuss, to debate, to put forward a point of view, to persuade

argument a discussion, a disagreement, the part of a mathematical formula that can vary | **reasoned argument** an explanation that is based on observation but uses logical connections

arid dry, very dry | **arid land** desert, a dry area, a region that has received no rain for many years

arise to get up, to follow as a consequence

arising a consequence or importance based on new evidence

Aristarchus (of Samos 320–250 BC) proposed that the Earth moves around the Sun and the stars must be vastly more distant than the Sun He attempted to measure the size of the Moon and the distance from the Earth to the Moon. His ideas were developed nearly 2000 years later by Copernicus and Kepler

Aristotle (384–322 BC) was the son of the court physician in Athens where he spent his early career, he moved to northern Greece as tutor to Alexander the Great then, just before his fiftieth birthday, he returned to Athens to establish a school at the Lyceum. Aristotle believed in using the ideas of others and arriving at a conclusion by reasoning alone with almost no experimental support. He dominated scientific thinking in the Western world for 2000 years, possibly because 50 of his books survived and were translated into both Latin and Arabic, Ibn Al-Nafis was an enthusiastic supporter of Aristotle in the eleventh century. Harvey, in 1616, after careful dissection and minute observation, proposed that the heart pumped blood around the body, thus disproving Aristotle's assertion that the heart was the command centre of the body with the brain cooling the blood. Aristotle knew the Earth was a sphere from the shadow cast on the Moon during an eclipse, but the idea of a universe with the Earth at the centre survived, and indirectly was the cause of Galileo's house arrest in 1622. Aristotle presented the ideas of Empedocles on elements which then became the accepted and unquestioning truth until Boyle published *The Sceptical Chymist* in 1661. Four years later, Newton disproved the idea that a body needs a constant force in order to remain moving.

arm (not harm which is to cause damage) the limb of the upper body, made from three bones, the humerus, in the upper arm, and the radius and ulna, in the lower arm | arm pit the concave area of skin between arm and the upper body | arm-span the distance between finger tips when the arms are stretched out, almost the same distance as your height | human arm emphasising a structure in which there is an upper arm bone, a joint then a pair of lower arm bones | lever arm any length of rod or a beam that is used to move something up and down | lower arm the part of the arm between the elbow and the wrist, contains the radius and ulna | side-arm a small tube leading from the neck of a flask or the side of a boiling tube | upper arm (humerus) the bone between the shoulder joint and the elbow
armature / iron armature a piece of iron that is attracted to an electromagnet

armor (USA) / **armour** (UK) protective plates worn on the outside of the body

Armstrong (Neil Alden 1930–) had a passion for flying and obtained his license before he could drive. He flew as a fighter pilot then became a civilian test pilot (flying new, untried aeroplanes at the limit of their performance) before starting to train as an astronaut in 1962. Armstrong commanded *Gemini 8* in 1966 and, three years later, he became the first person to step on to the Moon, he was watched by 500 million people!

army an organised set of people who are trained, ready, willing and able to fight an enemy
aroma the scent, a pleasant smell
around approximately, nearly
arrange to put in a specific order, to agree a meeting
arranged placed into order
arrangement the form in which the parts are organised | arrangement of particles the pattern formed by tiny particles in a solid | electronic arrangement the distribution of electrons in the orbitals around the nucleus, the number of electrons in each shell | parallel arrangement two tasks or operations occurring at the same time
array an arrangement of several items
arrive to reach
arrows are used to show direction
in chemical reactions
reactant → product
in energy changes
starting energy → desired energy
→ waste energy
in food chains
producer → consumer → predator
| force arrows arrows that show the direction and size of a force
arsenic (As, proton number 33, melting point 613°C) a grey substance that sometimes behaves like a metal (the chemical used as rat poison and beloved by writers of murder novels is arsenic (III) oxide)
artefacts (UK) / **artifacts** (USA) made by people, a false observation caused by the method of preparation
arteries (plural of artery) the thick walled tubes that take blood away from the heart
arteriole a tiny artery
arteriosclerosis blocking of the arteries so blood circulation is more difficult
artery (plural is arteries) a thick wall blood vessel (tube) that takes blood away from the heart (not all arteries carry oxygenated blood, but they all have thick walls) | coronary artery the vessel that takes the blood to the muscles of the heart |

pulmonary artery the main blood vessel carrying blood from the heart to the lungs | renal artery the vessel that takes blood to the kidneys

artesian well a vertical tube connecting an underground lake of water to the surface

arthritic having pains in the joints between bones making movement difficult

arthritis changes to the joints, the synovial fluid or the cartilage at the ends of the bones so that movement is painful and restricted

arthro- (*Greek* a joint-)

arthropod an animal with jointed legs, includes spiders, insects and millipedes

article an object, an item in a newspaper

articulate able to bend, to express feelings clearly

artifact / artefact an object made by people, a false observation caused by the method used

artificial made by humans, not found naturally, man-made | artificial element an atom that is not found in Nature, an atom with a proton number greater than 92 (the proton number of uranium) | artificial heart a small pump that is intended to be placed in the chest so as to re-place the real heart | artificial heart-valve a con-struction of plastic and metal that replaces one of the valves in the heart | artificial immunity causing the body to produce antibodies by in-jection with part of a microbe so the person can resist infection by that microbe | artificial insemination (AI) to collect sperm from the male, store, and then use tubes to place the sperm into a female | artificial limbs arms or legs, made from metal, plastic or wood, that replace a limb that has been badly damaged or removed | artificial respiration to breathe air from your lungs and mouth into the lungs of someone who can not breathe for themselves | artificial satellite an object sent into space that orbits around the Earth or another planet | artificial selection choosing to breed only from animals or plants that have the characteristics that you think are desirable | artificial ventilation blowing air into a room so as to make sure that there is no increase in the concentration of dangerous gases

As arsenic, proton number 33

asbestos a variety of fibrous minerals, mainly derived from magnesium silicates, that are heat-insulators and are resistant to high temperatures

ascidian belonging to a group of molluscs that have a type of backbone for part of their lives

ascorbic acid vitamin C, a chemical that the body can not make, but that is essential to prevent scurvy

aseptic without allowing microbes in | aseptic technique method of working in which no microbes are allowed in to the work area

asexual without the use of sex, reproducing without a partner | asexual method / asexual reproduction division of a cell or an organism into two new, smaller offspring without the need for a partner, the new organisms are identical to the parent

ash a type of tree that drops its leaves in winter, the material left after a fire, material ejected by a volcano | ash tree the leaves are small and arranged in rows along a stem | volcanic ash particles that are small enough to be thrown into the air by a volcanic eruption and then fall to earth as a covering material

asleep resting, unaware of the surroundings

aspects sides or interpretations | environmental aspects changes that a particular situation could cause to the habitat and food webs

aspirin (acetyl salicylic acid) a pain-killing drug that is found naturally in the bark of willow

assemble to put ideas, mechanical bits or infor-mation together so as to give one simple object | assemble data to gather the information and measurements into a simple table | re-assemble to put back together again

assess to measure, but usually with some amount of uncertainty involved | assess risks to look at a situation and decide where dangers occur and what is the possibility of an accident | critically assess to look at every small part of the idea or workings

assessment a test, a judgement of progress | risk assessment deciding the level of danger, thinking about the probability that a accident will occur and what would be the consequences of such an accident

assign to give a particular name, number or group to some object

assimilate to put a series of facts or objects into a larger picture

assimilation incorporation of food chemicals into the cell

associate to form a group, to bring together

associated supported by, given help | associated muscles the contracting tissues (muscles) that are needed to allow a specified function, *eg* muscles move food in the gut | associated organs the groups of tissues that are needed to allow a task to be completed

association a group, a linking

assume to take for granted, to give a value without definite evidence

assuming taking for granted without questioning

assumptions taking information or previous

knowledge for granted and not discussing or measuring any further

astable circuit an electronic circuit that switches regularly between two states of resistance and current

asteroids bits of rock that move around the Sun between the orbits of Mars and Jupiter, ranging in size from a speck of dust up to a thousand kilometres diameter (called *Ceres*), | asteroid belt the whole collection of millions of bits of rock that are in orbit between Mars and Jupiter

asthma a difficulty with breathing caused by a decrease in the diameter of the air passages

astrology trying to predict the future from the position of the planets and stars

astronauts people who travel into space (Russians call them cosmonauts)

astronomer a person who studies objects and observations that arrive from beyond the atmosphere

astronomical concerned with the stars, extremely large | astronomical unit the average distance from the Earth to the Sun, 150 million kilometres

astronomy the study of the objects that are beyond the atmosphere, *eg* stars, planets

astro-physicist a person who studies the formation and evolution of stars

astro-physics the study of the changes that occur to stars and the atoms when they are in the massive gravitational force of a star

-ate a suffix used to show that oxygen is part of a molecule, *eg* sulphate [=SO_4], nitrate [-NO_3], carbonate [=CO_3]

ate (not eight which is a number) eaten

athlete a competitor in a race | athlete's foot a fungus that grows under the skin around the toe area of the foot and causes a rash and itchiness | disabled athlete a competitor who does not have full control of all their joints and muscles

atmo- (*Greek* vapour-)

atmosphere the layer of gas that surrounds any planet, often refers to the 20 kilometres deep layer of air that surrounds the Earth

atmospheric concerned with the air around us, especially using the pressure of air | atmospheric equilibrium the composition of the air does not seem to change because the removal of carbon dioxide and water by plants is balanced by the output of these two chemicals by respiration | atmospheric gases the gases that are found in high concentration in the air around a specified planet | atmospheric pollution chemicals that get into the air in sufficient quantity that the properties of the air are changed | atmospheric pressure the force per metre square (pressure) that is caused by that 20 kilometres deep layer of

air pushing down on to you and on to everything around you

atoll an island made of coral

atom the smallest stable particle into which an element can be divided | neighboring atoms (USA) / neighbouring atoms (UK) the atoms that are close to the specified point | nitrogen atom emphasising that the object is the atom with proton number 7, not nitrogen gas [N_2] | number of atoms how many atoms have a specific property, *eg* how many are found in a certain volume or take part in a reaction | radio-active atom an atom with an unstable nucleus | stable atom an atom in which the nucleus is stable so the proton number will not change and radio-activity is not produced | type of atom a fundamental particle with a particular set of properties

atomic something to do with the atom, especially the nucleus of the atom | atomic bomb a nuclear bomb, a large cylinder containing sufficient uranium so as to produce a very large explosion | atomic clock a very accurate method for measuring time that depends on the breakdown of caesium nuclei | atomic energy the heat and light that is released when the nuclei of atoms change the number of protons or neutrons | atomic mass the mass of that atom, also called relative atomic mass or ram, equal to the number of neutrons and protons in the atom, mass number | atomic mass unit (amu) the mass of a proton or a neutron, 1.6×10^{-27} kg, one dalton | atomic nucleus the tiny object at the centre of the atom, made from protons and neutrons and so has all the mass of the atom | atomic number proton number, the number of protons in the atom, this number is specific for each atom, the periodic table is all the atoms in order of atomic number | atomic particle any of the neutrons, protons or electrons in the atom | subatomic smaller than an atom

at rest remaining in one position, not moving

atria (plural of atrium) the two chambers at the top of the heart

atrium (plural is atria) an entrance room, one of the chambers of the heart

attach to join

attack an illness; to fight, to hit, to damage intentionally | heart attack a sudden change to the control of the heart so that the pumping of blood either stops or becomes ineffective

attacker an animal that starts a fight with another animal

attempt an effort; to try, to make an effort | record attempts to write down or film the details of an experiment, to try to break a record

attitude a person's mental view of the world, the orientation of a moving object

atto.../ a... prefix for one million, million, millionth of a unit, 10^{-18}

attract to pull towards each other, opposite charges (+ and – or positive and negative) will attract, opposite poles of a magnet (north and south) will attract

attracted pulled towards each other

attracting pulling towards each other

attraction a force pulling things towards each other, could be caused by charge, magnetic poles or gravity | forces of attraction anything that causes two bodies to move towards each other | gravitational attraction two bodies are attracted to each other because each has mass, the greater the mass then the greater is the force of gravitational attraction | magnetic attraction the force that cause a magnet to be attracted to iron, nickel, cobalt or the opposite pole of another magnet

attractive force causes two or more objects to become closer

atypical different from most others

Au gold (*Latin*, aurium), proton number 79, a precious metal

auburn golden-brown

audible able to be heard | audible range the range of frequencies, from lowest to highest, that a person or animal is able to hear

audience the people watching a performance or receiving a message

audio sound or hearing | audio nerve / auditory nerve the pathway joining the sensitive parts of the cochlea to the brain | audio tape magnetic tape that is used for recording sound

auditory nerve / audio nerve the nerve that carries messages from the ear to the brain

aunt (not ant which is a social insect), a female relative, the sister of one of your parents

aural (not oral which is the mouth) by sound, hearing

auricles the atria, the top chambers of the heart

Australia a continent, a large mass of land that was isolated from the other land masses by the Pacific Ocean and so the animals and plants are often unique to that country

author a person who writes for the public

auto- (*Greek* self-)

autoclave a high pressure cooking pot so is able to heat water to 120°C before the water boils, used for sterilising agar media and old petri dishes so that all the bacteria are killed

automatic responding without human help

automatically without thought, a reflex action

autumn the period of time, between summer and winter, when trees produce fruit then lose their leaves and the days are becoming shorter

availability how much can be obtained, growth of the numbers and size of organisms may depend on the availability of food, water or oxygen | availability of food whether nutrients are present in a form that the animal can eat | oxygen availability how much oxygen is present that can be used | water availability how much water is present in a usable form

available present and able to be used | available evidence the information that can be interpreted or used

avalanche a sudden flow of large volumes of rocks, snow or ice down a mountain

average near the middle, add the value of each item then divide by the number of items | average speed total distance travelled divided by total amount of time from start to finish

aviation concerned with flying, aeroplanes | aviation fuel the hydrocarbon that is burned in the jets of aeroplanes

Avicenna (Ibn Sina 980–1037) was born in Kazakhstan, becoming a physician and philosophical guide to the Sultan of Persia. He wrote over 200 books, including comments on Aristotle, discussions of science and religion, and a medical text that quoted much work from Galen and Hippocrates, and became standard of teaching for five centuries.

avoid to take steps so as not to meet something

awake not asleep, able to think and react consciously, alert

aware knowing about

away removed | worn away becoming thin through use over a long period

awful terrible, not pleasant

axes (plural of axis) the two lines, one going up and the other across, that are used when drawing graphs. The axes should be labelled with what is being measured and the units that are used

axis (plural is axes) a line defining one side of a graph, a line around which something can turn | axis of rotation / axis of spin the imaginary line around which a body spins

axle a shaft or circular bar around which a wheel rotates

b / bar a unit of pressure

B / bel the unit of sound, although the decibel (dB) is more commonly used

babies (plural of baby) children from birth to about 2 years old

baby (plural is babies) human from birth to 2 years old | babyhood the period of time when a young animal or human is totally dependent on the parents | baby teeth the temporary teeth that start to become visible at a few weeks old and drop out about six years later | newborn baby a human child that is less than a week old | premature baby a child born after a period of pregnancy (gestation) that was less than 35 weeks | test-tube baby the child that is born after fertilisation of the ovum by sperm has occurred in a small dish, the fertilised egg implanted into the uterus and pregnancy continued as normal | unborn baby the foetus, the offspring within the uterus

babyhood the period of time when a young human is totally dependent on the parents

bacilli (plural of bacillus) rod-shaped bacteria

bacillus (plural is bacilli) a bacterium in the shape of a rod, many have a flagellum | tuberculi bacillus the bacterium that causes tuberculosis (*Mycobacterium tuberculosis* causes TB in the lungs)

back-bone the spine, a set of bones that not only supports the body and protects the spinal cord but is also flexible, made up of bones called vertebrae

background radiation the radio-activity that is all around you as a result of radiation from the stars (including the Sun) and radio-activity in some rocks, especially granite

backwards in reverse order, opposite direction to forwards, retreating

bacon the meat of a pig that has been preserved by treatment with smoke or salt

bacteria (plural of bacterium) single-cell organisms (microbes) that are able to grow and reproduce, but do not have a nucleus | bacteria-killing able to kill microbes, anti-biotic | cyanobacteria blue-green algae, a group of organisms that are similar to bacteria and are among the oldest organisms known, may cause algal blooms or eutrophication | denitrifying bacteria microbes that convert nitrates to nitrogen gas | growing bacteria to increase the number of bacteria by putting the microbes either into a liquid or onto a plate so as to encourage cell division | lactic acid bacteria microbes, often found in milk, that produce lactic acid as a waste product | nitrifying bacteria microbes that convert ammonium compounds to nitrates | nitrogen-fixing bacteria microbes that can convert nitrogen gas from the atmosphere into ammonium compounds | photosynthetic bacteria microbes that are capable of converting sunlight into sugars | putrefying bacteria microbes that breakdown cells | specific bacteria growing a single strain of microbe or stating the actual strain | useful bacteria microbes that can be grown in order to produce products such as yoghurt and cheese from milk, or beer and wine from sugars

bacterial caused by a bacterium | bacterial activity a microbe is growing, dividing and producing chemicals | bacterial cells the cells have cytoplasm, a cell membrane and a chromosome, but do not have a nucleus | bacterial growth an increase in the number of that type of microbe

bacterium (plural is bacteria) a single-cell organism without a nucleus | *Salmonella bacterium* a type of microbe that causes food poisoning

bad not good, unfit for eating | bad breath an unpleasant smell produced by bacteria in the mouth and apparent when breathing out

bag a sack, a purse | carrier bag a cheap sack with handles that is made from paper or polythene | membranous bag a thin sack | mesh bag a sack made from string, cotton or twine which can hold large items but has lots of holes | sleeping bag a sack made from insulating layers that should keep you warm when sleeping in a tent or the open air | tea bag a porous paper sac that retains the tea leaves, but allows the water to pass in and out

bake to heat to a high temperature without burning

bakery (plural is bakeries) a place where cooking with flour, milk and eggs takes place

baking cooking food, especially mixtures of flour and butter in an oven | baking powder a mixture of sodium carbonate and tartaric acid that releases carbon dioxide when dissolved in water | baking soda [$NaHCO_3$] sodium hydrogen carbonate

balance apparatus for measuring the weight of a substance, to adjust the distribution of weight so an item remains vertical or horizontal; to bring to equal on each side | balance formula the law of moments

(moment = force x distance to pivot)

sum of clockwise moments = sum of anti-clockwise moments

| balance of gases the total amount of carbon dioxide released by respiration is used in photo-synthesis so that the amounts of oxygen and carbon dioxide remains constant | beam balance

a method for weighing in which a known weight at one end of beam is balanced by the unknown weight at the other end | chemical balance a type of weighing scale suitable for accurate measurements of small amounts | counter balance (often used to prevent cranes tipping over) a weight that is put on one end of the lever so as to balance a weight that is being lifted at the other end | digital balance a weighing machine that uses an electronic component to measure the weight and produces an output that is in the form of numbers | electronic balance equipment for weighing material in which addition of the weight causes a change in some electrical property | newton balance a spring which is calibrated in newtons and is used for measuring weight | spring balance equipment for weighing that uses a spring that obeys Hooke's law *ie* the extension is proportional to force applied | top pan balance equipment which has a plate on which the unknown weight is placed

balanced two things are happening in opposite directions so you do not actually see any change | balanced diet the amount of food ingested is just sufficient to provide all the energy and vitamins needed so there is no loss or gain of body weight and the body is healthy | balanced equation the number of atoms at the start of the reaction is identical to the number and type of atoms at the end, although the atoms will have formed new molecules | balanced forces two equal forces are trying to change the direction or speed of an object but the two forces are in opposite directions and so cancel out | balanced moments the torque, moment or turning force (= force x distance to pivot) in the clockwise direction is exactly matched by torque or turning force in the anticlockwise direction | balanced symbol equation each reactant and product is given its correct chemical shorthand then the number of molecules adjusted until the number of each type of atom is identical at the start and the end of the reaction

balancing the act of matching two sides, making two forces equal | balancing equations changing the number of molecules on each side so that the number of atoms at the start of the reaction is identical in type and number to the atoms in the products

Balard (Antoine-Jérôme 1802–1876) spent the first half of his life in Montpellier before moving to Paris in 1842. He isolated bromine, the Greek word for 'stink', in 1825 while analysing the chemicals in sea water.

bald without features, without hair | bald tire (USA) / bald tyre (UK) the raised treads in the rubber surface have been worn smooth

ball a sphere | ball-and-ring / ball in a ring a method for showing expansion using a ball that will fit through the ring when both are cold but heating the ball causes expansion so the hot ball can not pass through the ring | ball-and-socket joint a part of the skeleton where the end of a long bone forms a ball that fits into the socket of another bone so that movement can occur in three dimensions | ball-and-spoke model method for showing the structure of a molecule – the balls represent the atoms and the spokes are the bonds joining the atoms | ball bearing one of several small spheres that separate two moving surfaces and reduce friction | eye ball the sphere that is one complete eye of a mammal | polystyrene ball a sphere made from expanded polystyrene so the ball has a low density and is an electrical insulator | tennis ball a pressurised rubber sphere used in tennis

ballast heavy weights added to increase stability | ballast tank the cylinders on the side of a submarine that can be partially filled with water so the submarine remains at a particular depth

balloon a sphere, sac or sausage made from elastic material that will increase in size if the pressure inside is greater than the pressure outside; to increase rapidly in size | balloon ride travelling in the gondola of a helium or a hot-air balloon | helium balloon a sealed sac is filled with helium, which has low density (0.18 g / l) and so floats in air (density of 1.4 g / l) | hot-air balloon the sac is open at the lower end, heat is applied causing the air in the sac to expand and so the density decreases and the balloon floats | hydrogen balloon a gas-proof sack that is filled with hydrogen (a gas that is less dense than air) so as to give uplift in air | weather balloon a balloon that carries measuring instruments to a great height, then bursts! (The instruments are recovered by parachute)

band (not banned which means prevented) a loop of material, a ring, a pop music group | band of rock a stratum, a distinct layer of a particular type of rock | elastic band / rubber band a loop of material that is stretched by a force then returns to its original shape when the force is removed | rock band a layer of rock that differs from adjacent strata in colour or texture, a group of musicians that play loud music

bandage a long, flat strip of material that can be used to protect a wound or to prevent movement of a limb; to wrap with a long, thin strip of material

bang a sudden loud sound of short duration; to hit with a force that is large enough to cause a change of shape | Big Bang the explosion at the start of the universe

bank a collection of items, the area next to a river; to put into a collection | bottle bank a collection point for discarded glass objects that can then be recycled | river bank the area of flat land just above the river level

banned (not band which means a ring or a group) prevented, prohibited, forbidden

bar a rectangular block, an obstruction, the unit of measurement for the pressure of the atmosphere, meteorologists prefer to use the millibar (mb) | bar chart a graph in which the size of the rectangles represent values | bar code a series of parallel stripes giving information about the product | bar fire an electrical heater in which a wire is wound around a porcelain rod that is placed at the centre of a semi-circular reflective metal plate | bar graph / bar line-graph a graph in which the height of each bar reflects the value of the dependent variable | bar magnet a magnet with a rectangular shape | aluminium bar (UK) / aluminum bar (USA) a piece of aluminium with a square cross-section | handle bars the length of metal that has a hand grip on each end | isobar a line on a map joining points of equal pressure | metal bar a long block of metal, could be round or square, made from metal | millibar a thousandth part of a bar, used as the common unit when measuring atmospheric pressure, which averages 1013.25 millibar at sea level | sand bar a ridge of sand, that may be above water at high tide, but there is always sea water between the ridge and the land | steel bar a rod or beam made from steel

barbecue a method for cooking food, usually outdoors, using the heat from burning wood or charcoal; to cook over an open fire

barbiturates a group of over fifty drugs that are made from barbituric acid (discovered on St Barbara's day in 1863) that cause sleep, but are addictive

bare (not bear which is a large mammal) uncovered, naked | bare hands without using any equipment, not wearing gloves | bare metal metal (conductor of electricity) without any paint or grease on the surface

barely only just, almost missed

barite / barytes the form of barium sulphate [$BaSO_4$] that is found as a mineral

barium (Ba, proton number 56, melting point 725°C) a reactive alkali earth metal, group 2 element | barium meal a liquid containing barium sulphate that is swallowed and provides a medium that strongly absorbs X-rays as the meal passes through the gut | barium sulfate / barium sulphate [$BaSO_4$] an insoluble compound of barium that is opaque to X-rays

bark the hard outer covering of a tree, the sound of dog; to make a sound like a dog

barley a cereal crop

barnacle a marine creature with a hard shell that attaches itself tightly to a rock, a ship or even a whale's body and feeds by filtering the water

barometer an instrument for measuring air pressure (bars) caused by the weight of the atmosphere, useful in predicting weather and measuring altitude | aneroid barometer measures by following the change in size of a box from which air has been removed | mercury barometer uses the height of mercury in an inverted tube to measure air pressure

barrage a wall, a barrier | tidal barrage the wall that is built across a bay so the changing height of tide forces water to pass through the dynamos

barrel a tub, a cask, a container, the chimney of a bunsen burner, a cylindrical container with a lid, the cylinder through which a bullet travels in a gun | barrel of oil the standard unit (equal to 159 litres) used to measure crude oil

barrier anything that prevents movement | natural barriers geographical features, such as mountains or sea, that prevent organisms from moving | tidal barrier a wall across the bay that prevents free movement of the sea | waterproof barrier a wall or layer that prevents the entry or exit of water

barrow / wheelbarrow a container with one wheel and a pair of handles

barytes / barite the form of barium sulphate [$BaSO_4$] that is found as a mineral

basalt igneous rock with very fine grains, lava

base oxide or hydroxide of a metal, a base will neutralise an acid, a zero line for a measurement, the bottom of something, eg pan or bunsen burner | baseline the starting point, the norm | base metal a cheap metal, usually unattractive, that could be covered with gold or silver | base sequence the exact order the building blocks (the bases adenine, cytosine, guanine and thymine) are found in a strand of DNA | base units the agreed values of measurement from which all other measurements are derived | complementary bases the pairs of nucleotide, or building blocks, that are able to join together – adenine always links to thymine, cytosine always links to guanine | database a collection of facts, observations and measurements concerning some item or events | metal base a small sheet of heavy metal that is used to give a stable foot; chemically, emphasising that a metal oxide is basic and will neutralise an acid | pan base / saucepan base the metal at the bottom of the pan through which heat is conducted

baseline the point from which all other measurements are taken, the measurement that is made before any stimulus is applied | baseline temperature the stable temperature before the experiment started

basic able to neutralise an acid, fundamental | basic facts simple but important observations that need to be agreed before ideas can be discussed | basic oxide a chemical made from a metal bonded to oxygen, that is able to react with acids to produce a pH of 7 (neutral) | basic structure the arrangement that is common to all members of the family or group | basic unit a building block, the simple parts hat join to produce a complex structure | basic units agreed measurements for length (metre), mass (kilogram) and time (second)

basically simplifying an idea to give the essential parts, the fundamental requirements

basin a bowl | evaporating basin a glass dish, approximately 5 centimetres diameter, that is used for turning liquid water rapidly into a vapour

basis the reason for something happening, a foundation

basket a rigid container with handles so that ii can be easily lifted

bat a flying mammal, similar in size to a mouse, that hunts insects at night using echo location

batch the amount produced at one time, a set

bath a container that is large enough for a whole object, or person, to be immersed in the liquid | bath salts powder or crystals that are a mixture of scents and soaps for use while bathing | ice bath a container containing ice floating in water that is used to ensure that samples remain at 0°C | swimming baths a building containing both a large pool of clean (treated) water, in which to immerse and exercise, and the facilities for changing

bathroom an enclosed area where a person can excrete or clean themselves in private | bathroom scales a balance for measuring your weight

bathylith a block of igneous rock produced by the magma slowly cooling underground

batteries (plural of battery) more than one battery

battery (plural is batteries) a means for converting chemical energy into electrical energy, should be two or more electrical cells joined in series, but often is used for a single electrical cell | battery acid the sulphuric acid that is used in the type of battery (lead–acid battery) used in a car |

battery charger a piece of apparatus that is plugged into the mains 240 volts supply and is used to cause a chemical change in a battery | battery holder an insulated pack in which electrical cells can be held and connected to-gether | battery-operated power is supplied from a battery | car battery the series of six lead–acid cells that are joined in parallel and produce 12 volts for use in a car | flat battery a structure that would be expected to provide a voltage, but does not because the chemicals have all changed | lead–acid battery several lead–acid cells joined in series in a single container | nickel–cadmium battery / NiCad battery a rechargeable cell that contains nickel and cadmium | rechargeable battery a series of electrical cells that provide a current in one direction, but can be recharged by passing a current in the opposite direction | reserve battery a cup with a top that can be filled with sea water and will then provide a high current for a short time during an emergency

bauxite the ore of aluminium, mainly aluminium oxide

BCG [Bacillus Calmette-Guérin] the weakened form the tuberculosis bacterium that is used in a vaccine | BCG jab an injection that will cause the body to produce antibodies to tuberculosis

be (not bee which is a flying insect) to exist, to happen

beach (not beech which is a tree) large area of sand at the junction of land and sea | blue flag beach an area of sea that has been tested for microbes and found to be safe for swimming

bead a drop, a sphere | bead of oil a drop of oil that is used to show the height in a tube

beak the bill, the horny part of a bird's head that projects outwards | beak shape a characteristic feature of birds that reflects the diet of that bird

beaker a cylindrical cup, made from glass or plastic that is used for mixing chemicals | glass beaker the cylinder is made from glass and so can be heated safely | plastic beaker the cup is made from plastic and so can be used for mixing chemicals, but should not be heated

beam a wide ray, a bar | beam balance weighing scales in which a length of metal (the beam) with a pan at each end is balanced on a pivot | beam bridge a crossing made from a single length of hard material | beam of light the visible light, joining a light source to an object, caused by dust particles scattering the light | electron beam a ray of electrons, millions of negatively charged particles moving in a continual stream | I-beam a structural steel joist that has an I or H shape when cut across | incident beam the light that is moving towards a boundary and will be reflected or refracted | laser beam light of a single frequency in which all the peaks and troughs of the wave are in step | light beam what you see when light is being reflected by dust particles | reflected beam light after it has bounced off a polished surface | refracted beam light that has changed direction at a boundary

bean (not been which indicates the past) a type of seed similar to a pea | garden beans the variety of beans that can be grown in ground near the house | soy bean / soya bean the edible seed of a plant that has been cultivated for centuries in Asia and is now used as a source of meat-free protein

bear (not bare which is uncovered) a large mammal with a shaggy coat and strong claws; to carry | polar bear an animal that is adapted to Arctic conditions with a white, insulating coat and hairs on the undersides of the paws

bearing carrying, a direction | ball bearing one of several small spheres that separate two moving surfaces and reduce friction | seed-bearing producing seeds | spore-bearing an organism that can reproduce by spreading spores | wheel bearing the low-friction surface (ball-bearing, needle-bearing or white metal) between the axle and the wheel that rotates

beast an animal, a carnivore | micro-beast general term for any creature that is difficult to see without the aid of a magnifying glass or a microscope

beat (not beet which is a plant) a musical rhythm, the sound of the heart; to hit hard, to win | heart beat the thumping sound that is the result of the rhythmic contraction and relaxation of the heart

beating hitting | tree beating hitting the branches of a tree so as to dislodge the small forms of life

beautiful pleasing to the eye

because a word joining an event to a reason

Becher (Johann Joachim1635–1682) a German chemist, physicist and adventurer. From age13, he had to support his mother and brothers while studying at night. He started publishing books at 19, and became a teacher of doctors in 1666. Three years later, he was involved in establishing a new country between the Amazon and the Orinoco. Subsequently, he proposed a vast canal across Europe. His ideas of combustion led to Stahl's theory of phlogiston.

Becquerel (Antoine Henri1852–1908) succeeded his father and grandfather as Professor of Physics in Paris. Partly by chance, but following several years of related experiments, he showed that uranium could cause a change to a photographic film without using light. His investigations into uranium and the mysterious rays led to an understanding of radio-activity.

bed an area to grow plants, usually large scale, a place to sleep | bed rock a impermeable layer of rock | capillary bed the network of tiny, single cell blood vessels (capillaries) that bring blood close to cells in tissues and organs | filter bed layers of rock and sand through which dirty water is drained so that clean water emerges from the bottom of the bed | flower bed an area of ground in which flowers are being grown intentionally | fluidised bed (UK) / fluidized bed (USA) a layer of powder behaves like a liquid when a continuous stream of air is blown through the base | reed bed an area of the river or lake that is covered in tall plants with underwater roots | river bed the layer of material at the bottom of a river | seabed the landscape that is at the bottom of the sea

bedding thin layers in rock, the sheets and blankets used for comfort at night | current bedding some sedimentary layers are at angles to the direction of the main stratum

bee (not be which is a verb) a flying hairy insect that visits flowers, in order to gather nectar, and accidentally transfers pollen from one flower to another | bee hive shelf a short, cylindrical pot with a semi-circular entrance in one side | bee sting the defence used by bees – they use a thin probe to inject an acid that is irritating to the skin

beech (not beach which is an area of sand) a type of tree | copper beech a tree in which the chemical essential for photosynthesis is purple coloured xanthophyll

beef meat from a cow | beef cattle cows that have been selected for their ability to provide meat for eating

bee hive shelf a short, cylindrical pot with a semi-circular entrance in one side

been (not bean which is a type of seed) in the past

beer a drink containing alcohol made by allowing yeast to react with an extract of fermented barley

beet (not beat which is to hit) a type of plant | beetroot a swollen root that can either be eaten or used to produce a chemical that will change colour with pH | sugar beet a plant with a large swollen root form which sugar can be extracted

beetle Coleoptera, a large order of insects with hard wing-cases

beetroot a swollen root that can be either eaten or used to produce a chemical that will change colour with pH

before earlier, previously

began started, initiated

begin to start

begun started

behave to act in a specific way

behavior (USA) / **behaviour** (UK) the way in which something (or somebody) acts | magnetic behavior / magnetic behaviour the response that a material has to a magnetic field

bel / B the unit of sound, although the decibel (dB) is more commonly used

belief a faith, a thought | cultural belief an idea or standard of behaviour that is held by the majority of the people in that area | religious beliefs ideas that are held by faith rather than being proven by experiment

Bell (Alexander Graham 1847–1922) opened a school for teaching the teachers of deaf pupils in 1872 in the USA (he had left his native Scotland in 1870, following the death of two of his brothers from tuberculosis) and started to look for a way to make artificial speech – he realised that turning speech into electricity and then the electricity into speech could be used to send messages over long distances – the first message was from the room, where he had spilt acid on himself, to his assistant in the next room. This invention led to the founding of the Bell Telephone Company and AT & T, which are still going strong, and an explosion in the number of people who had telephones. He went on to develop a boat that held the water-speed record for nearly fifty years, flat disc records (improving Edison's cylindrical recordings), and a kite that could carry a man. He helped start the *National Geographic* and *Science* magazines

bell equipment that makes a sound that demands attention | bell jar large glass vessel in the shape of a straight sided bell | alarm bell an electrical device that clangs out a warning of danger | door bell a bell inside the house with the switch on the outside | electric bell pushing the button completes the circuit which causes the striker to move, a movement that also breaks the circuit so the striker returns to its rest position, completing the circuit

bell jar large glass vessel in the shape of a straight sided bell | bell-jar demonstration shows particles are needed for sound to move, (a clock or bell is put inside a bell jar, the bottom sealed with a plate and air is removed – the sound will get

less as the number of air particles is reduced) | bell-jar model equipment demonstrating how air enters the lungs, (a balloon is put inside a bell jar, the bottom sealed with a flexible sheet that can be moved up and down, like a diaphragm, causing the balloons to change shape)

bellow (not below which is lower) to shout loudly | bellows a box with flexible sides that is used to blow air into a furnace

belly the soft part of the body that contains the digestive organs

below (not bellow which is to shout) lower

belt long, flat, flexible material that is used to produce a circle | asteroid belt the whole collection of millions of bits of rock that are in orbit between Mars and Jupiter | conveyor belt a loop of material that is moved by rollers and is used for transport of heavy goods in straight lines | Kuiper belt a vast belt of particles, in the size range of dust to planets, that extends beyond the orbit of Neptune

bench a table, a work surface | bench acids the dilute solutions of acids that are often stored on the working bench | bench lamp a small bulb in a holder that can be used to light specific areas, especially useful with microscopes

bend to change the shape of a sheet or block

bending moving through an angle, changing shape | bending force a push or pull that causes an object to change shape without moving position

bends changes of shape, an painful illness of scuba divers, caused by nitrogen bubbles forming at the joints, that occurs upon too rapid ascent from deep water

bendy able to change shape when a large turning force is applied

Benedict's solution turns from blue to red (with intermediate colours of yellow and green) when heated with sugars

beneficial advantageous, helping you

benefits advantage or improvement

benign harmless, friendly | benign tumor (USA) / benign tumour (UK) a growth of cells that should not cause any major problems

bent changing direction, not straight

benzoic acid [C_6H_5COOH] a weak acid that forms white crystals, the sodium salt is used as a preservative

berries small fruit, containing a fertilised egg as the seed, produced by some trees | colored berries (USA) / coloured berries (UK) are fruit produced by many plants and become brightly coloured when ripe so as to attract the birds that eat them

Berzelius (Baron Jons Jacob 1779–1848) an orphan who graduated in medicine at 23 and then studied chemistry, becoming a professor five years later. He measured the atomic masses of all the 28 known elements and so could correct the errors of Dalton, he introduced the modern symbols for chemistry (in Sweden, potassium is called kalium and sodium is natrium hence their symbols of K and Na), discovered three new elements and developed many branches of chemistry. One important wedding present, at the age of 56 to a bride of 24, was that the King of Sweden made him a baron.

best the highest, the most appropriate | best fit with least error so most points lie near to the curve | best-fit curve/ best-fit line / line of best fit a line, that may be straight or curved and usually goes in one direction, that passes mini-mises the differences between the line and the actual measurements

beta / β the second letter of the Greek alphabet | beta radiation a stream of electrons (e⁻) from the nuclei of some atoms

bi- (*Latin* two-)

bias showing favouritism to one side

biased having an opinion, leaning in one direction, not objective

bicarbonate / bicarbonate ion [$HCO_3^=$] hydrogen carbonate, an ion that is always found attached to metals, produces carbon dioxide when heated or acid is added | bicarbonate indicator a liquid that turns from red to yellow when carbon dioxide is present | bicarbonate of soda [$NaHCO_3$] sodium hydrogen carbonate, | sodium bicarbonate / sodium hydrogen carbonate [$NaHCO_3$] baking soda, used with tartaric acid to produce baking powder

biceps a muscles, joining the inside of the lower arm to the shoulder, that is used for raising the lower arm

Bichat (Marie-Francois Xavier 1771–1802) followed his father into medicine and taught medicine from 1797. He distrusted examinations using microscopes, but was able to describe 21 different tissues found in the organs of the body. He suggested that an illness usually affects a specific tissue in an organ.

biconcave a plate the dishes inwards at each side

bicuspid valve the structure between the atrium and ventricle on the left side of the heart that prevents blood flowing backwards

bicycle two wheels suspended from a frame with pedals for increasing speed | bicycle pump a piston in a cylinder that is used to put air into cycle tyres | bicycle tire (USA) / bicycle tyre (UK) an inflated rubber tube that provides grip and a smoother ride

biennial every two years, a two year cycle

big large, grand | Big Bang the explosion at the start of the universe

biggest largest

bike shortened form of bicycle; to travel on a bicycle

bile a liquid that is produced by the liver then stored in the gall bladder, which acts like washing up liquid to dissolve fats in digestion | bile duct the tube connecting the gall bladder to the small intestine

bill a beak, the amount paid for goods or services | electricity bill the account sent by the Distribution Companies asking you to pay for the electrical energy that you have used

billion a unit of measurement that is 1000 million in the USA and 1 million million in the UK

bimetal strip / bimetallic strip two thin lengths of metal that are joined together, each metal will expand by a different amount when heated and so the pair are forced to bend

bin a box, a small container for waste

binary involving two | binary code the use of 1 and 0 to produce instructions, used by all computers | binary compound a chemical made from only two types of atom | binary fission something breaks into two parts, a living cell could divide to give two daughter cells or an atomic nucleus could split into two parts, usually releasing radioactivity and heat energy | binary information data that is produced as a string of 0s or of 1s | binary key identifying a particular object by asking questions that have one of two possible answers, ie yes or no | binary numbers counting that uses two numbers, computers use 1 and 0 only

bindweed a herbaceous plant that has a long, trailing stem

binocular vision using two eyes so as to obtain an estimate of distance and size

binoculars a pair of parallel telescopes arranged so that both eyes can be used to examine a distant object

bio- (*Greek* concerned with life)

bio-accumulation increasing concentration of a chemical in a series of organisms going up the food chain

bio-chemistry the study of the chemicals and reactions that occur in the living cell

bio-degradable will be broken down by microbes | bio-degradable waste unwanted material that can be broken down by weather, water or microbes | non-biodegradable not able to be broken down by any creature and so will last a very long time

bio-degrade to break down using living organisms, often microbes

bio-diversity a measure of how many different types of organisms there are in a particular area

bio-fuel anything that grows and can be used to give light and heat by burning

bio-gas the fuel gas produced by breakdown of biological material, usually methane [CH_4]

bio-hazard damage or death may occur if these living organisms are allowed to escape

biological of life | biological catalyst an enzyme, a protein that can speed up a reaction | biological detergent a surfactant, or soap, that contain enzymes that will break proteins into soluble fragments | biological investigation an experiment to find about some part of an organism or an ecosystem | biological material bits taken from an organism | biological means changes that are brought about by living organisms | biological processes chemical reactions that occur in living organisms | biological studies looking at how living things interact between each other and within themselves | biological systems could be large scale, such as all the organisms in an area *ie* an ecosystem, or could refer to the organs within a living creature | biological washing powder contains enzymes (biological catalysts) that break down proteins and so dissolve stains | biological weathering breakdown of rocks caused by living things, *eg* plants opening cracks by growth of stem or root, animals wearing paths by walking | non-biological not produced by a living organism or not containing chemicals that have produced by an organism

biologist a person who studies anything to do with life

biology the study of life and how one organism depends on the environment and on other forms of life

bio-mass the total weight of the specified type of organism in a stated area | bio-mass energy the total amount of chemical energy on a stated mass of living organisms | plant-biomass the total weight of plants in that area | pyramid of bio-mass the mass of producers that is needed to support a smaller mass of primary consumer that supports a tiny mass of secondary consumer

bio-sphere the layer around the world that contains life

bio-technological / bio-technology using an understanding of the processes of life to make new materials, the biggest user of biotechnology is biologically active washing powders | bio-technological process a method that uses the cutting, manipulation and insertion of nucleic acids into a microbe

biotic factor the influence on the environment of microbes, animals or plants

biotite a mineral, similar to mica, that is found distributed in all types of rock

bioviewer looks like a microscope but is used to view film strips

birds warm-blooded vertebrate animals that lay eggs and are covered in feathers | bird droppings the excretion products of a bird's digestion that often will contain large amounts of phosphate | bird population the number of birds in a particular area at that time of year | birds of prey feathered animals that feed on other animals | bird sanctuary an area which has been changed so as to be safe and appealing for birds | native birds the winged creatures with feathers that are found in that area or were there before humans arrived | wild birds the species of birds that are native to that area

birth the process or time when the foetus, which is dependent on the mother, is ejected from the womb and enters the world as a baby capable of living | birth canal (vagina) the passage, usually called the vagina, through which the foetus leaves the womb (uterus) and enters the world | birth control having intercourse, but taking steps to ensure that the sperm is not able to fertilise the ovum | birth rate the number of offspring born per thousand of population | birth-weight the weight of a baby when he / she is born | after-birth the placenta, which is delivered after the birth of the child | child-birth moving the foetus from dependence on the mother in the womb to an independent baby | premature birth the baby is born after a period of less than 35 weeks gestation | multiple births the mother delivers more than one offspring at the same time

bistable circuit a set of electronic components that is either on or off

bit a binary digit, a single 0 or 1 in computer code, a small part, a fragment | drill bit the rotating end that cuts into the material

bite (not byte which is eight binary digits) to break, or to grip, using your teeth | insect bite a tiny wound produced by an insect attacking the skin

bitter not sweet, one of the four taste senses, unpleasant

bitumen tar, black substance made from high molecular-weight hydrocarbons

biuret test is specific for proteins, blue biuret solution reacts with proteins to give a violet colour

Black (Joseph 1728–1799) was considered to be a Scottish physician, but was born in Bordeaux and educated in Belfast. His major work was carried out in Edinburgh and Glasgow. He emphasised the importance of making accurate measurements, especially of mass, and showed that *fixed air* (carbon dioxide) was made in fermentation and respiration. In 1763, he showed that heat was needed to change state, but that the temperature remained constant.

black absence of any colour | Black Death a disease (plague) caused by the bite from the fleas found on rat which killed vast numbers of the population of Europe in the 14th century | black hole an astronomical object that is so massive that passing light is attracted and captured | black light ultra-violet radiation, part of the spectrum that has a wavelength shorter than visible light | black surface not only will absorb any light or heat energy, but is also very good at radiating energy | matt black (UK & USA) / matte black (USA) a surface that is dull and will not reflect any light

blackberry (plural is blackberries) a fruit produced by a biennial bush, the extract from the fruit can be used as a pH indicator

blackbird an omnivorous bird that inhabits scrubs and woodland

Black Death a disease (plague) caused by the bite from the fleas found on rat which killed vast numbers of the population of Europe in the 14th century

bladder any bag-like structure in biology, especially the sac protected by the pelvis which collects and stores urine | gall bladder a small sac, underneath the liver, for storing bile

blade a sharp edge | blade of grass a long, thin leaf of grass | shoulder blade (scapula) a flat bone strengthening the shoulder joint

blanket a thick covering; to cover with a thick layer | electric blanket a layer of wires that is sealed between two sheets and can be heated by passing a current | fire blanket a flame-resistant sheet that can be wrapped around a burning object so as to smother the flames by preventing movement of oxygen

blast a sudden high wind; to blow violently | blast furnace manufacturing process for the extraction of iron using a vast tower which is kept at high temperature by vast amounts air being blown in at high speed

blasting blowing hard | sand blasting removing a surface layer by aiming a jet of fast air containing sand crystals

blaze a line of white hair among the dark-coloured hair; to burn fiercely

bleach a chemical, often containing chlorine, that turns a coloured object to white, and is used to kill microbes

bleeding losing blood | menstrual bleeding the monthly loss of blood from women of child-bearing age

blend a mix with specific ingredients and proportions; to mix together thoroughly

blew (not blue which is a colour) past of blow

blight a disease of plants caused by a fungus; to ruin | potato blight a fungus that attacks potatoes, often the first signs are seen when it is already too late to save the crop

blind unable to see; a cover for a window; to damage eyes so they can not see | blind spot the area at the back of the eye where the optic nerve makes a hole in the cornea so there are no light receptor cells and you are blind in this spot | color blind (USA) / colour blind (UK) a person who is able to see, but can not recognise some colours, the common form is the inability to distinguish red from green

blindfold a strip of material that covers the eyes so the person is unable to see

blindness inability to see | night blindness having difficulty in distinguishing black and white at low light intensities, often cured by eating carrots (for vitamin A)

blister a swelling caused by liquid under the skin; to produce a swelling

blistering producing swellings on a surface

block solid object, usually transparent, which is often in the form of a prism, a semi-circular lens or a rectangle to stop | block graph a bar chart | brake block heat-resistant material that is pressed against a rotating wheel in order to slow the motion | building block rectangular shapes that are used in constructing buildings | circular block any material that is like most coins – a thick circle | cylindrical block a shape that is circular in cross-section, but the diameter is less than the height | glass block any solid made from glass | metal block a solid made from metal | Perspex block a solid shape made from Perspex™ | rectangular block cuboid – like six rectangles joined together at right angles | semi-circular block a flat piece of material has been cut into a half circle | transparent block any solid through which light is able to shine | triangular block a prism - a triangle has been cut out of a thick sheet of material | wooden block any regular shaped object that is made from wood

blocked stopped, movement is prevented | blocked oviduct something is preventing the ovum from moving down the fallopian tube / oviduct to the womb

blond / blonde having hair that is light in colour

blood the mixture of plasma, cells and molecules that carries oxygen, nutrients and waste chemicals around the body | blood alcohol the concentration of ethanol in the blood | blood-borne carried in the blood | blood capillaries tiny blood vessels or tubes | blood cells are of two types – red or white. The red blood cells (rbc) look like discs and do not have a nucleus, their function is to carry the oxygen which is attached to haemoglobin inside the cell. White blood cells ingest, or eat, any microbes that are found in the blood | blood circulation the continual movement of the blood around the body, pumped by the heart | blood clot the solid plug formed either at the skin to stop bleeding or within a blood vessel | blood corpuscle a red blood cell | blood donor a person who voluntarily gives some of their blood, usually 500 cm³, to be used for medical purposes | blood flow movement of blood around the body and through the organs | blood group classifying the blood according to three different proteins, each of which may be present (shown by A, B or Rh [rhesus]) or absent (shown by an O) | blood plasma the liquid part of blood complete with all dissolved chemicals | blood poisoning a disease that is often fatal caused by bacteria releasing toxins into the blood stream | blood pressure pumping of the heart produces a force or pressure that pushes the blood around the body | bloodstream / blood stream all the liquid in the blood vessels | blood supply how effectively the blood, with its oxygen and nutrients, reaches each cell | blood system the heart, veins, capillaries and arteries in the body | blood transfusion using blood donated by one person to supplement the circulation of another | blood type the human blood has been analysed to see if any of the antigen markers A,B or rhesus are present as giving the wrong type of blood to a patient can be fatal | blood vessels tubes (arteries and veins) containing blood | blood volume the total amount of blood in the body | de-oxygenated blood blood leaving the tissues that has most of the oxygen removed | filtering blood passing blood through a special matrix so as to separate the blood cells from the plasma | flow of blood the movement of blood through the vessels | loss of blood the bleeding that allows blood to leave the body | oxygenated blood blood leaving the lungs is saturated with oxygen, in the form of brilliantly red oxy-haemoglobin | type of blood the classification of human blood depending on the presence, or absence, of three proteins called A, B and rhesus

blood-stream the flow of blood around the body | fetal blood-stream (USA) / foetal blood-stream (UK) the blood that flows around the foetus, to the placenta, where chemical exchange occurs, and then back to the foetus

bloom a growth of yeast on fruit, a flower; to start to flower | algal bloom a sudden dramatic increase in the number of algae which could prevent growth of other organisms

blotting paper paper that is highly absorbent

blow the movement caused by the wind; to force air in one direction by rapidly deflating your lungs

blown inflated, melted | blown bulb an electric lamp in which the filament has broken | blown fuse the fuse wire has melted because the current was too high | wind-blown spread to other areas by the movement of air

blubber an insulating layer of fat found in whales and seals

blue (not blew which is the past of blow) one of the colours (the others are red and green) to which the eye is sensitive | blue-flag beach an area near the sea that has been tested for microbes and none have been found so the sea is safe for swimming | blue flame the flame produced when there is lots of oxygen, the hole at the base of the bunsen burner is fully open, so combustion is complete | blue ink a solution of dye in water that can be used for writing | Blue Planet Earth, because reflection of light from the oceans makes the planet appear blue | blue wire the colour of the plastic coat that shows the wire goes to the neutral connection of a mains plug | bromothymol blue an indicator that is yellow below pH 7, and blue above pH 7

bluish the colour seems to be blue, but other colours are mixed in

blunt not a sharp edge, unable to cut

blur not in focus; a rapid motion; to lose the details of a sharp image

blurred out of focus, not a sharp image | blurred vision the image that is formed on the retina is not in sharp focus

BNF [British Nutrition Foundation] an organisation that supports research into food and eating habits

boar (not bore which is to make a hole) a wild pig

board (not bored that means can not find anything to do) a plank | quiz board a sheet with questions and answers randomly arranged on one side but correctly connected by electrical wires on the hidden side | skate board two pairs of wheels joined by a plank on which a person may stand and push themselves along

boat a ship with one deck

bobsleigh a platform on runners that is intended for high speeds on ice

bodies (plural of body) objects, things | heavenly bodies anything that can be seen in the sky at night, the stars, planets, comets and asteroids that are in space

body (plural is bodies) any object the whole animal or the part remaining after removing the arms and legs, a mass of water | body defences methods for keeping microbes out of the body, these include the skin and linings of the gut and lungs, white blood cells and antibodies | body hair the fine hair that is found all over the skin | body heat the energy produced, usually by the muscles, that keeps the human body temperature at 37°C | body mass the mass of the animal | body organs any of the visible structures inside the body | body shape a description of size, length, width or streamlining of a body | body size how big is the animal after removing arms and legs | body systems organs inside the animal | body temperature how hot is the inside of the body | dead body recognisable remains of an organism that was recently alive | human body the arrangement of tissues, bones, muscles and organs in human beings | larger body the bigger of two objects | lower body the part of the human body below the waist | segmented body the hard shell of an external skeleton is in several parts or segments | slimy body the outside of the organism is slippery | upper body the part of the human body above the waist

bog land that is saturated with water, a marsh | peat bog an area of ground that is waterlogged with some water-plants and small islands of grass

boggy (not bogie / bogy which is a truck) ground covered with water so that the soil is soggy and marshy

bogie / bogy (not boggy which is marshy) a truck with four wheels

boil to change rapidly from liquid to gas at a constant temperature

boiled heated in water at 100°C | boiled egg a hen's egg has been heated in boiling water so the contents have turned solid because the proteins have changed irreversibly | boiled peas are used to show that heating will destroy enzymes and so respiration can not occur | boiled water the water has been boiled so as to get rid of all the dissolved air

boiler a container, usually sealed except for one or two tubes, in which a liquid is heated

boiling rapidly changing from liquid to gas at a fixed temperature | boiling point the temperature at which bubbles of gas appear inside the liquid, the boiling point of water is 100°C | boiling temperature the temperature of the liquid measured when boiling | boiling tube a glass cylinder, sealed at one end, with a shape suitable for safe heating of liquids | boiling water water at a temperature of 100°C

boiling point the temperature at which bubbles of gas appear inside the liquid, the boiling point of water is 100°C | fixed boiling point the temperature at which a liquid turns to gas and is unchanging for that liquid

bolder (not boulder which is a rock) with more confidence

bolt a large screw with parallel edges, a flash of lightning

bomb a lump of molten rock, an explosive device | atomic bomb / nuclear bomb a large cylinder containing sufficient uranium so as to produce a very large explosion, an explosive device where the heat energy arises from the loss of mass that occurs in some nuclear reactions | stink bomb a container of two chemicals that release hydrogen sulphide when mixed

bombard to attack violently, to use many weapons

bond / chemical bond the method by which atoms attach to each other; to join one atom to other atoms | bond energy the amount of energy required to make or break the bond between two specified atoms for one mole of material | covalent bond the atoms share electrons to get a full outer shell | ionic bond electrons are lost or gained, to produce ions, then ions with opposite charges will attract each other

bonded joined together

bone hard structure that provides support, the human body contains over 200 bones | bone cells the tiny living structures that make up the soft marrow inside the bone and which produce the blood cells | bone marrow the inside part of the bone where blood cells are produced | bone marrow transplant to take some bone marrow from a donor and inject into the bone of a recipient so as to make sure that the right numbers and type of blood cells are produced | ankle bones (tarsals) the many small bones that are found between the lower leg and the foot | back bone (vertebrae) the spine, a set of bones that not only supports the body and protects the spinal cord, but is also flexible | breast bone (sternum) the bone joining the left ribs to the right ribs | collar bone (clavicle) a bone joining the top of the ribs to the shoulder |

ear bones (ossicles) three tiny bones in each ear (hammer, anvil and stirrup) that transmit sound from the ear drum to the cochlea | foot bones (metatarsals) the long bones in the feet | funny bone the nerve on the outside part of the elbow | hand bones (metacarpals) the long bones in the hand | healthy bones the bones are rigid and able to withstand bending and hitting, and the bone marrow will produce a sufficient number of blood cells | lower jawbone / jawbone (mandible) the bone that move up and down in the joint at the bottom of the skull | shin bone (tibia) the thick bone joining the knee to the ankle | spine bone backbone, vertebrae | stirrup bone (stapes) the smallest of the ossicles in the middle ear | thigh bone (femur) the biggest bone in the body, connects the pelvis to the knee | wrist bones (carpals) the many small bones in the area between the arm and the hand

bonfire a large, outdoor fire either for a celebration or to burn garden waste

book (not buck which is a male deer or hare) a written work, a number of pages joined together | data books printed collections of information that could be useful, but is difficult to remember or find out | reference book printed literature that is an authority on the subject

booklet a book with few pages, often for instructions | identification booklet a small book that allows many similar, but distinct, species to be identified

boom a loud sound with low frequency | sonic boom the loud bang that occurs when an aeroplane breaks through the sound barrier

boost a sudden increase; to give a sudden increase

booster causing an increase | booster injection a second injection of a weakened form of a microbe that causes a disease in order to increase the number of antibodies in the blood | booster stage used by rockets going into space in order to get extra speed

bore (not boar which is a wild pig) to drill a hole

bored (not board, which is a plank) can not find anything to do

born (not borne which is carrying) given birth | new-born an offspring that is so young that the age is measured in days

borne (not born which is birth) carried, transmitted | air-borne carried by the breeze | blood-borne carried in the blood | food-borne diseases, such as food poisoning, that are transmitted in food | water-borne carried by rivers or streams

borosilicate glass a type of glass that can be heated to high temperatures

boss / clamp boss (plural is bosses) block of metal with screw fittings that holds the rod of the clamp fingers to the upright rod

botanical gardens areas in which plants are studied, propagated and raised

botany the study of plants

both two together, a pair

bottle a jar, a container with a stopper | bottle bank a collection point for discarded glass objects that can then be recycled | dropping bottle a container with a small hole in the stopper which allows loss of one drop of liquid at a time | PET bottle a container, with a screw lid, made from the polymer called PET (Poly Ethene Tetra phthalate) | plastic bottle any closable vessel made from plastic

bottled in a sealed, glass container with a narrow neck | bottled water taking water from a specified area or spring, then sealing into bottles for worldwide distribution

bottling preserving material by transferring to sterile containers that are then sealed

bottom the lowest point

boulder (not bolder which means more confident) a rock which is too big to carry | boulder clay a layer containing rocks of all sizes mixed together

bounce to hit a surface and be reflected

bouncing being reflected from one surface to another and another and… , hitting the floor and rising again followed by a fall and another rise

bound glued, joined, stuck | tightly bound strongly joined

boundaries (plural of boundary) lines which mark the furthest extent or the edge where two materials meet

boundary (plural is boundaries) a line where two areas meet | sharp boundary a sudden change, an obvious border

bovine caused by a cow, associated with cattle

bow a long, curved strip of wood with the ends connected by string that is used to send arrows speeding towards a target, a way of tying a ribbon; to bend at the waist

bowel the intestines | large bowel the large intestine where water is absorbed | small bowel the small intestine where food is digested and the nutrients absorbed

bowl a hollow, open-topped vessel for holding liquid

box a container with rectangular sides | enclosed box the container has a lid that can seal the box | fuse box a container in which the weakest links in the electrical circuits are all lined up | light-proof box a container with solid walls that will not allow any light to enter | ray box the housing for a lamp into which plates can be positioned, leaving small slits through which beams of light can shine | shoe box a disposable carton in which shoes are stored while awaiting sale | voicebox larynx, the top part of the windpipe that is used for producing sound

boy (not buoy which is a marine signal) a young man, a male person who is not sexually mature

Boyle (Robert 1627–1691) the youngest of 14 children, Boyle had a good ability at languages and studied maths as a distraction during a childhood illness. He toured Europe from 1638 until the death of his father, in 1644, caused him to return home to the family estate in Dorset. He tested Galileo's idea, that all objects fall with the same speed in a vacuum, using a pump made by Hooke. He showed that if you change the pressure of a gas then the volume will change so that the product (pressure x volume) always remains constant. In his book, *The Sceptical Chymist*, published in 1661, Boyle proposed an element is a simple body and that compounds were combinations of elements – both ideas are accepted today.

boys young men, immature males
bp / b.pt. [boiling point] the temperature above which the liquid form can not exist
Br bromine, proton number 35, a halogen
bracelet an ornamental band worn around the wrist or arm
bracken ferns, an ancient type of plant

Brahe (Tycho 1546–1601) famous for losing his nose in a duel over a mathematical argument when he was 19! He did make himself another nose, out of silver – so how did he smell? Brahe is probably the greatest astronomical observer before the invention of the telescope (made by Galileo in 1610), he used his remarkable powers to good effect when he built an observatory on the island of Hven which he was given by the King of Denmark so that he could measure the positions of over 700 stars with great accuracy. In 1596, he was asked to leave Hven so he moved to Prague where he was given a castle, where he employed Kepler as his assistant.

Braille (Louis 1809–1852) born near Paris, he was blinded in an accident when he was 3 years old. He attended, then taught, at a school for blind children. His invention, of using a pattern of raised dots on paper so that blind people could feel each letter, was derided at first but subsequently found success with the army as the officers were able read instructions in the dark without using lights.

braille a method of writing, using a block of six dots that are raised in particular patterns to show each letter
brain the control structure of an animal | brain damage changes have been inflicted on the brain, possibly caused by chemicals, mechanical injury or genetics, so the brain no longer functions properly | human brain the complicated set of ten thousand million nerve cells that controls all our actions and is protected by the skull
brake (not break which means to split) a method of slowing down; to use friction to stop, turning the kinetic energy into heat | brake blocks / brake pads / brake shoes the pieces of material that are heat resistant but have lots of friction that are pushed onto a rotating wheel in order to slow it down | brake cylinder pressure in the brake fluid causes the piston to move outwards, causing friction on a rotating surface | brake pedal the lever that is pressed by a foot in order to slow the movement of a car | disc brake (UK & USA) / disk brake (USA) equipment for slowing cars which consists of a disc, to which a braking force can be applied, on the same axle as a wheel | drum brakes a method for stopping a car in which brake-shoes are pushed against the inside surface of rotating drums | hydraulic brakes the force is transmitted from the pedal to the brake drums and shoes through the fluid in a pipe
braking slowing down | braking distance the length travelled by a vehicle between the brakes being applied and the vehicle stopping
branch (plural is branches) a limb that divides from the trunk of a tree, a side line; to divide
branches (plural of branch) where something divides, *eg* branches in a tree, the branches that form as the bronchi and bronchioles become smaller in the lungs | electrical branches the different parts of a parallel circuit

Brand (Hennig died 1692) was born in Hamburg. His attempt at trying to obtain gold from vast volumes of urine led to the production of a wax-like solid that glowed in the dark – Brand had isolated accidentally discovered a new element that was named phosphorus.

brand the manufacturer, the name of the maker

Brandt (George 1694–1768) helped his father in his pharmacy in Sweden, trained as a medical practitioner in the Netherlands, worked in France then, in 1730, returned to Sweden to run the Royal Mint. In 1742, he isolated cobalt and showed that it was a magnetic metal that easily formed an alloy with iron.

brass a mixture of copper and zinc that is yellowish in colour | brass instrument musical instrument mad from a tube of brass, *eg* trumpet, trombone

bread (not bred which is reproduced) a food made by cooking dough of flour and water, which may have had yeast added | bread dough made by mixing bread with yeast and water then leaving to rise as bubbles of carbon dioxide are produced – useful system for measuring the effects of temperature on the activity of yeast | bread making allowing a dough of flour, yeast and water to rise, and then baking in an oven | crispbread a type of biscuit made from flour, cereal and water, but without eggs or butter

break (not brake which is to reduce speed) to split into smaller parts || breakdown the splitting into smaller parts | break down to stop working because something has gone wrong, to turn large molecules into smaller molecules by breaking bonds | break off to stop an activity, to remove a portion | break through a method that helps solve many problems; to make a discovery, to reach the other side of a barrier | break up to disconnect, to separate white light into many colours, to disperse | fire break a gap in the forest to prevent fire from spreading | thermal break material that is inserted between the two sides of a window frame so as to prevent heat being conducted through the frame

breakdown the splitting into smaller parts | chemical breakdown using enzymes or heat to split complex chemicals into smaller molecules | mechanical breakdown using teeth to chop material into smaller pieces | protein breakdown to break the bonds, or links, between some of the amino acids to give smaller molecules

breakfast the first meal of the day when you break your overnight fast | breakfast cereal seeds of grasses that have been treated or processed so they able to be eaten without further cooking

breaking dividing into pieces | breaking bar experiment demonstrates expansion by heating a bar, clamping the ends then waiting for the bar to contract as it cools, and eventually it breaks

breaks splits, divides | breaks down stops working

breast front part of an animal, specially near the ribs, the mammary gland that provides milk for the offspring | breast bone the sternum which is the bone to which the ribs are joined at the front of the chest | breast feeding a baby obtains nutrients and antibodies by taking the milk from the mothers mammary glands (breasts) | breast milk the liquid produced by the mammary glands that is a perfect nutrient for a human baby

breath (not breathe which means to move air in or out) the amount of air taken in or given out | breath test estimating the amount of alcohol in the blood by measuring the amount in a breath | bad breath an unpleasant smell produced by bacteria in the mouth and apparent when breathing out | human breath the air that is expelled from the lungs of a person

breathalyser equipment used by police for the rapid identification of people who are likely to have a high concentration of alcohol in the blood stream

breathe (not breath which is a single gasp) to take air into the lungs and push the air back out again, to ventilate | breathe in to take air into the lungs by increasing the volume of the chest cavity | breathe out to blow air out of the lungs

breathing taking air into the lungs and pushing the air back out in a regular fashion | breathing rate the number of breaths taken each minute | breathing tubes the several tubes (trachea, bronchi and bronchioles) that connect the outside world to the air sacs of the lungs

bred (not bread which is made from flour) produced by mating, often refers to a particular type of organism | cross-bred the offspring of two different varieties of an organism | pure bred a single strain, an animal with known parents and grandparents

breed a specific type of organism to reproduce | rare breed a type of animal of which there are only a few left

breeder the person in charge of specifying the potential male and female parents the animal which is providing one of the gametes | mouth breeder a fish that protects its young in its mouth | plant breeder a person who specialises in reproducing and growing plants

breeding reproducing | breeding program (USA) / breeding programme (UK) achieving some specific characteristics in an organism by choosing the parents and then deciding which offspring should be used as new parents | cross-breeding ensuring that the two gametes are from organisms of the same species but very different families | selective breeding choosing the parents so as to try to give the best characteristics to the offspring

brew to use fermentation with yeast, to produce a solution containing alcohol

brewed (not brood which is a family) made beer by leaving yeast to react with malted barley

brewer the skilful person who takes hops, barley and yeast and produces beer

brewery where beer is produced by leaving yeast to react with hops and barley (fermentation)

Brewster (Sir David 1781–1868) trained as a church minister, but turned to studying light and those odd effects that you see whenever you carry out experiments involving refraction or reflection. His lasting invention is that childhood joy – the kaleidoscope. He helped to found the British Association for the Advancement of Science in 1831

brick a building block, usually made of clay with six rectangular sides | brick red the colour that is found for most building bricks

bridge a structure joining two parts separated by a gap; to provide a structure that will allow transport across a gap | beam bridge a crossing made from a single length of hard material | drawbridge a large plate that allows traffic to cross a ditch or moat, but which can be raised so as to prevent entry of unwanted people | road bridge a structure that supports a road over an obstacle such as a river or a valley

bright producing or reflecting lots of light | bright flash a source of light that has a high intensity for a brief period of time

brighter producing or reflecting more light than another

brightest the one object in a group that produces or reflects the most light

brightly clearly, highly visible

brightness the intensity of the light, the amount of light energy passing through 1 m² of surface | brightness control the variable resistor that changes the intensity of an image

brim the edge of a cup, the top of a beaker

brine a solution of salt (sodium chloride) in water | brine lake a pond of water containing a concentration of salt that is so high that crystals may form | brine shrimp a delicate, microscopic animal that lives in salty water, the eggs can be stored dry and remain viable for long periods

bristles short stiff hairs

British Heart Foundation (BHF) a charity group that carries out research into methods for reducing the number of deaths due to heart disease

British Nutrition Foundation (BNF) a group that seeks to find out which is the best diet for a healthy and long life

brittle likely to be easily broken by a slight amount of bending

broad wide, diverse | broad bean a member of the pea family so nitrogen-fixing bacteria grow in legumes on the roots | broad-leaved plant a flowering plant that has flat leaves

broaden to increase the width, to bring in more information

broader wider, more diverse

broad-leaved plant a flowering plant that has flat leaves

broken no longer working, in pieces | broken down unable to work, damaged, turned into smaller pieces | broken off damaged, destroyed, removed by force | broken tablet the pill has been split into smaller pieces

bromide / bromide ion [Br⁻] any salt made of a metal bonded to bromine | potassium bromide [KBr] a white crystalline chemical similar to common salt

bromine (Br, proton number 35) a halogen; [Br₂] a brown liquid, melting point −7°C, boiling point 59°C

bromothymol blue an indicator that is yellow below pH 7, and blue above pH 7

bronchi / bronchii (plural of bronchus) the large tubes that are formed when the windpipe branches into the lungs

bronchioles small air passages that connect the major air tubes (bronchi) to the air sacs (alveoli)

bronchitis any difficulty with breathing as a result of damage to the bronchi

broncho- (Latin windpipe) concerned with breathing | broncho-constrictor a chemical that causes the tubes to the lungs (bronchi) to become narrower | broncho-dilation opening of the air passages in the lungs | broncho-dilator a chemical that causes the tubes to the lungs (bronchi) to become wider

bronchus (plural is bronchi) one of the tubes at the base of the trachea

bronze an alloy of copper with tin to which lead or zinc could also be added | Bronze Age the time between the Stone Age (ended 3000 BC to 1500 BC depending on geographical region) and the Iron Age (from about 500 BC)

brood (not brewed which is making beer) the offspring of one set of parents, especially those born at the same time

broth a thin soup, a chemical solution containing nutrients needed for the growth of microbes | nutrient broth a liquid containing all the nutrients needed for the growth of microbes

brothers boys who have the same parents

brought carried, lead, borne

brow the top | eye brow the line of hairs above the eye in mammals

Brown (Robert 1773–1858) was born in Montrose, studied medicine at Aberdeen and Edinburgh then joined an expedition to Australia where he collected several thousand plant species over five years and then spent another five years trying to classify them. His two famous discoveries occurred close together in mid-life. He observed the random movement of tiny particles such as pollen that is now called 'Brownian motion' and is the direct evidence for the existence of molecules. Four years later, he named the nucleus (from the Latin for a little nut)

brown / brownish the colour produced by mixing yellow and red paints | brown limestone the metamorphic form of chalk that contains lots of iron and so is coloured rusty | brown wire the colour of the plastic coat that shows the wire goes to the live connection of a mains plug

brownish/ brown the colour produced by mixing red and yellow pigments then adding a small amount of black

Brownian motion random motion of large particles, such as smoke or pollen, caused by random movement of air or water molecules

brush a rod or block of wood with hair attached to one edge; to push gently using a brush | paint brush an instrument, made by attaching fibres to a stick, that is used to apply liquids to a solid surface

bryophyte a plant that does not possess a true root and has no xylem nor phloem tissue, *eg* moss, liverwort

BSE [bovine spongiform encephalopathy] mad cow disease, a slowly progressive wasting of the brain caused by a virus-like organism

bubble a sphere; to introduce a stream of gas into a liquid

bubbled a gas has been passed through a liquid, a liquid has produced a gas

bubbles spheres of gas inside a liquid or solid | air bubbles small amount of air, as gas bubbles, in a liquid | collect bubbles to guide the rising bubbles into a container | gas bubbles visible volumes, usually small, of a gas in a liquid

bubbling a liquid is producing visible bubbles of gas

bubonic plague a disease, caused by a bacterium in the gut of rat fleas, leading to localised swellings (buboes), fever and death. The disease spreads rapidly through a population, the biggest epidemics were the Black Death (1437–1451) and the Great Plague of 1665 which led to Newton returning home and making all sorts of wonderful discoveries

buck (not book which is a collection of pages) a male deer, a male hare

bucket a drum-shaped container with handles used for moving liquids, a pail

bud the method by which some microbes, such as yeast, reproduce by growing a small branch

which falls off producing offspring, the first sign of a leaf on the branch of a tree; to reproduce by forming a small shoot that drops off | cotton bud a wad of cotton wool on the end of a small plastic stick | scale bud a plate-like growth that will develop into a shoot or root | taste bud the cells on the surface of the tongue that will respond to different flavours | terminal bud the structure at the end of a twig that will become a leaf

budding reproducing by forming small growths that fall off and develop independently

bug a microbe, a problem in a computer programme

buggy (plural is buggies) a small vehicle | snow buggy a small vehicle that will slide across snow or ice, and may be powered by an engine or by the wind

build to construct; to put together

building a structure that people can enter, increasing in size | building blocks any units that are used to make a larger structure, *eg* amino acids are the building blocks for proteins | building materials any substance that can be used to improve the structure of a building | building stone rocks that have properties making them suitable for use in buildings | model building putting a structure together that will reflect the properties of the real item and hopefully allow predictions of behaviour

bulb an electrical lamp, which is a very hot, the underground part of some plants, the container for liquid at the bottom of a thermometer | bulb holder the plastic collar containing electrical contacts into which a bulb is placed | blown bulb an electric lamp in which the filament has broken | light bulb a lamp, a filament of metal, in a sealed envelope of glass, that is electrically heated to white heat | onion bulb a vegetable of the allium family, all of which have a pungent smell | pearl bulb a filament lamp in which the glass envelope has a pale grey powder on the inside | spot-light bulb a high intensity lamp in which the half of the bulb envelope that is nearest to the connector is covered with reflective material | torch bulb the lamp that is powered by a battery

bulge a swelling, a growth under the surface; to get bigger in one spot

bulk large scale

bull a male cattle (female cattle are cows)

Bulldog™ clip a spring-powered clasp that is used for holding papers together

bulldozer a powerful vehicle that moves on tracks and has a massive vertical blade at the front

bumper a protective bar, a buffer, a fender

bum
↓
but

bundle a set that is bound together | vascular bundles the structures for moving fluid in plants, groups of xylem and phloem

bung a cylindrical piece of rubber that is used to block a tube; to block | rubber bung a slightly flexible stopper for a bottle

Bunsen (Robert Wilhelm 1811–1899) studied chemistry at Gottingen, Paris, Berlin and Vienna before settling at Heidelberg in 1852, he always said that he was too busy to marry. Although he was superb at carrying out experiments, Bunsen chose to study a group of chemicals that have such a repulsive and persistent odour that he was banned from many houses. These chemicals are also explosive and Bunsen lost the sight of one eye in an accident. He discovered two new elements, improved the methods for isolating several others and studied gases from many, smelly sources. Although he devised many new pieces of laboratory equipment, the bunsen burner was not one of them, the credit for this invention must go to his technician, Peter Desdega, using an idea from Faraday.

bunsen burner equipment that is used to burn gas in a controlled manner. The collar can be turned so that the size of the air hole changes: a hot, blue flame is produced when the air hole is fully open then the colour becomes cooler, more yellow and produces lots of carbon as the air hole is reduced in size

buoy (not boy which is a young man) a highly visible float that is anchored to the sea bed to give warning of a maritime hazard

buoyancy an upwards force that allows objects to float, the size of the force is the same as the volume of water displaced by the object | buoyancy aid equipment to help an object or person to float | neutral buoyancy the object remains suspended at a constant depth of fluid, neither rising nor falling

buoyant the ability of an object to float in water

burdock a plant with flower heads that have prickles

buret (USA) / **burette** (UK) a long cylinder with calibrated volumes down the side and a tap at the bottom so that the volume of liquid used can be controlled and accurately measured

burglar a person who enters a house or vehicle and takes items without permission of the owner

burial the act of placing a dead body under ground and covering with soil

buried hidden, not visible, underground

burn a damage to the area of skin caused by extreme temperatures; to react with oxygen

releasing heat energy | cold burn damage to the skin caused by touching something that is very cold | sun burn damage to the skin caused by exposure to too much of the Sun's heat

burned / burnt damaged or destroyed by fire

burner equipment used to produce a controlled flame | alcohol burner / spirit burner a small stove that uses a wick dipped into a container of alcohol | bunsen burner equipment that is used to burn gas with a air hole that can be changed in size

burning chemical reaction, usually occurring at temperatures that could damage your skin, in which there is an exothermic reaction between some chemical and oxygen | burning candle the wax in the wick evaporates and burns to produce heat and light | burning fuel most fuels are the remains of living material, *eg* plants, wood or fat, that react with oxygen with the intention of producing heat or light | burning glass a magnifying glass that is used to focus the heat radiation from the Sun in order to heat some material (very useful before the invention of the bunsen burner) | burning materials any substances that react with oxygen to release heat energy | burning sensation feeling as though your skin is on fire

burns damage caused by exposing the skin to a temperature that is too high and causes permanent chemical change | burns graft covering the area damaged by high temperature with a piece of skin from elsewhere in the body

burnt / burned damaged or destroyed by fire

burrow a series of tunnel dug by animals for protection; to dig tunnels

burrowing making tunnels in the soil

burst to break, to spilt

bursting splitting apart

bury to hide underground

bush a woody plant with branches starting close to the ground | holly bush a small evergreen tree with leaves that are very spiky and which produces red berries near the start of winter | rose bush a small tree, up to 2 metres tall, that usually has thorns and produces bright flowers

butane [C_4H_{10}] a hydrocarbon that is used as a convenient fuel because it will turn to liquid under slight pressure

butte an isolated hill with a flat top

butter a mixture that gradually turns from a hard solid at 0°C to a liquid at 40°C, prepared by stirring milk

butterfly (plural is butterflies) a flying insect that is active during the day | cabbage white butterfly a large butterfly, found in Europe, North Africa and North America, also called as the large white

buy (not by which means next to) to purchase, to pay for

buzzer / electrical buzzer electrical equipment for producing a sound of fixed frequency

by (not buy which means to pay for) next to, at, near | **divided by** the material that prevents the separate objects from meeting | **sell by** the date by which the shop should have sold the goods

byte (not bite which is to crush with teeth) the standard word length of eight bits (1 s and 0 s) that is used in computers

buy

byt

C carbon, proton number 6, an element that will conduct electricity but produces an acidic oxide

C / coulomb the unit of charge

c the speed of light in a vacuum, 300,000 kilometres per second

c... / centi... (*Latin* a hundred) prefix for a hundred

°C temperature in degrees centigrade or degrees Celsius

Ca calcium, proton number 20, an alkaline earth metal

cabbage a plant grown for the leaves to be eaten before the flower develops | cabbage water the solution that results when cabbage is cooked in hot water | cabbage white butterfly a large butterfly, found in Europe, North Africa and North America, also known as the large white | red cabbage a vegetable of the *Brassica* or cabbage family, the colour can be extracted in water and will turn red in acid and green in alkali

cable a wire, or a collection of wires, each of which is covered in an insulating material to join items together electrically | cable grip the part of a plug that holds tight to the covering of the wires | electric cable a length of conducting material made from many thin strands of copper or aluminium wire forming a thick spiral | overhead cables / overhead power cables the thick aluminium wires that carry low-current / high-voltage electricity from generating station to the local neighbourhood | steel cable many strands of wire that are wound around each other to give a long structure that is strong under tension | transmission cable the very thick wires that are used for conducting high-voltage electricity around the country

cacti (plural of cactus) a large family of plants that are specially adapted to life in arid conditions, *eg* in the desert; the stem can swell so the plant can store water, the surface area is low and thorns prevent animals from eating the cacti

cactus (plural is cacti) a plant from the Americas that is adapted to arid climates

caesium (UK) / **cesium** (USA) (Cs, proton number 55, melting point 29°C) an alkali metal, a group 1 element that is so reactive that caesium is rarely kept in school laboratories

caffeine a stimulant that is found in cola, tea and coffee | caffeine sensitive a person who shows a strong and immediate reaction when they ingest a drink containing caffeine | decaffeinated having had the caffeine removed

cage an enclosure, a box made from metal bars; to put into a sealed area | gauze cage an enclosure for small animals made from metal with lots of holes | rib cage the cylindrical structure, formed by the spine and sternum being attached to each end of the ribs, which protects major organs such as heart and lungs

cake mix / cake mixture a powder to which egg and milk are added and then cooked to produce an edible cake

cal [calorie] an old unit of energy, one calorie of energy is needed to heat 1 gram of water by 1°C

calamine / calamine lotion a suspension of iron (III) oxide and either zinc oxide or zinc carbonate, that is used to soothe inflamed skin

calcite a crystal form of calcium carbonate [$CaCO_3$]

calcium (Ca, proton number 20, melting point 839°C) a group 2 metal, an alkaline earth element | calcium carbonate [$CaCO_3$] the major chemical in chalk, marble and limestone | calcium chloride [$CaCl_2$] is very attractive to moisture so calcium chloride is often used to keep items dry | calcium hydroxide [$Ca(OH)_2$] produced by dissolving calcium oxide in water and is then known as lime water – the chemical reacts with carbon dioxide to give a white precipitate of calcium carbonate | calcium nitrate [$Ca(NO_3)_2$] the soluble salt of calcium that is produced when calcium oxide reacts with nitric acid | calcium oxide [CaO] lime, which is used to neutralise acidity in soil, and which gives out a brilliant white light (limelight) at high temperature | calcium phosphate [$CaPO_4$] a mineral that is important in providing strength to teeth and bones | calcium silicate [$CaSiO_3$] a salt that forms very large chains and sheets, that is found in many types of rock, eg asbestos, mica, talc | calcium sulfate (USA) / calcium sulphate (UK) [$CaSO_4$] a white powder, also called gypsum or plaster of Paris, that is mixed with water and sets hard when it dries

calculate to work out, especially using numbers

calculation working out the result mathematically

calculator equipment for executing arithmetic tasks

calendar a plan of dates and times | calendar month one of the 12 divisions of the year that is decided on a social (rather than any observational) basis, 28–31 days

calf (plural is calves) the young of a cow or a whale

calibrate to mark a scale so that other people can repeat an experiment

callipers measuring instrument made by joining two strips of material at one end | fat callipers equipment for measuring the thickness of fat layer in the skin

calm not troubled, little movement | calm weather there are few clouds, only a little wind and no waves

Calorie a thousand calories, a kilocalorie, the energy required to raise the temperature of 1 kilogram of water by 1°C

calorie an old unit of energy (equal to 4.2 joules), the amount of heat needed to change the temperature of 1 gram of water by 1°C | kilocalorie a thousand calories

calorimeter equipment used to measure the energy value of a chemical by using the heat from burning the chemical to heat some water

calves (plural of calf) the offspring of cattle or whales

camels animals that are superbly adapted to living in desert conditions, eg their feet have a large surface area so as not to sink into sand, its colour makes the animal difficult to spot against the sand, and all the fat is stored in the hump

camera an instrument for putting an image on to a screen, most modern cameras will have some method for retaining a permanent record of the image | camera obscura a mirror, on a tower, reflected the image of the outside scene on to a table in a darkened room | digital camera a recording device that stores the picture as a series of numbers | infra-red camera is used to take pictures using the heat that is being given off by an object | pinhole camera a light-tight box with a pin hole at one end and an opaque screen at the other | speed camera a device that measures the speed of a car then, if the speed limit is being exceeded, will take a picture for identification of the number plate | video camera equipment for making permanent records of moving images

camouflage colour and structure that makes something blend into the background and so is difficult to detect (useful if you are trying not to be seen, eg by a predator)

campaign a series of activities aimed at a common goal to undertake several activities over time, all with a single purpose

camping stove a portable heater for cooking small quantities of food

can a container, or closed cylinder, made from metal and sealed; able to do | cannot / can not impossible | can opener equipment for opening a sealed cylinder safely | aerosol can a cylinder that is partially filled with liquid that is under pressure so that pressing on the top releases a mist of liquid | aluminium can a cylinder for storing drinks | collapsing can a demonstration experiment that shows the presence of air pressure | drinks can the hollow cylinder of metal, sealed at both ends, that is used for storage, transport and sale of drinks | eureka can cylinder with a spout close to the top that is used for measuring the volume of funny shaped solids |

metal can a storage box made from metal, usually with a lid | oil can a container for transporting lubricating oil, a small container, with nozzle and trigger, that allows controlled application of oil | steel can a closed cylinder made from steel that is used for storing food and drink | tin can a sealed cylinder, made from iron coated with tin to prevent rust, for storing food

Canadian pond weed (Elodea) a small perennial fresh water plant that has submerged leaves

canal Italian word for a tube which is used all over the body eg ear canal, birth canal, a man-made channel for control of water flow | alimentary canal the digestive system, the gut, the tube inside you that starts with the mouth and ends with the anus where food is broken down and the nutrients absorbed | birth canal the passage, usually called the vagina, through which the foetus leaves the womb (uterus) and enters the world | ear canal the tube from the outside world that ends with the ear drum | Panama Canal the waterway connecting the Atlantic Ocean to the Pacific Ocean that is a mixture of canal and lakes and was completed in 1914 | semi-circular canals the three tubes in each ear that are responsible for sensing the position and movement of the head | spiral canal the cochlea, a tube that has been turned around a cone

cancel to delete, to remove, to call off

cancer uncontrolled cell growth, a tumour | cancer cells the cells that have lost regulation and grow out of control | lung cancer an uncontrolled growth of cells in the lungs | skin cancer uncontrolled growth of groups of skin cells, often caused by exposure to ultra-violet light

cancerous cells cells that grow out of control and may spread through the body

candle a porous wick is surrounded by layers of solid wax that melt in the heat of the flame, an old-fashioned method of providing light and some heat | burning candle the wax in the wick evaporates and burns to produce heat and light | wax candle a wick inside a column of wax

cane the tall stem of a plant such as bamboo or raspberry, a walking stick (USA); to hit with a thin piece of wood | sugar cane a plant with a very tall stem, similar to bamboo, which contains a sugar solution

canine related to dogs or meat eaters | canine teeth teeth that are adapted for penetrating and then gripping flesh: mammals often have four canine teeth - one at each corner of the mouth

caning (not canning which is preserving food) hitting another person with a long stick as a punishment

cannabis (ganja / hemp) a plant the leaves of which are smoked to provide a relaxing effect – an illegal drug

canning (not caning which is to hit a person) a method of preserving food by enclosing the food in a sealed container that is sterile

cannot / can not impossible, not achievable

canopy (plural is canopies) a covering | tree canopy the branches and leaves of a tree that form a layer above the ground

canyon a deep gorge, a ravine formed by erosion | Grand Canyon an enormous gorge (gorge 350 kilometres long, up to 25 kilometres wide and sometimes as deep as 2 kilometres) in Arizona that was the result of erosion by the Colorado River | submarine canyon a deep gorge, with steep sides, opening the ground below an ocean

cap a hat, a top piece; to prevent upwards movement | cap rock a hard, impermeable layer that prevents upward movement of fluids such as gas or oil | ice caps / polar ice caps the very cold areas of a planet that are furthest from the equator | knee cap (patella) a circular bone that covers the front of the knee joint and prevents the lower leg from bending forwards

capable to have the knowledge and expertise that is needed for that task

capacitor a component that is able to store small amounts of charge

capacity maximum volume | chest capacity either the total volume of the lungs or the volume of gas that can be moved in and out of the lungs | heat capacity/thermal capacity the amount of energy that is needed to increase the temperature of an object, often heat capacity will be specified for a 1 gram of material changing by 1°C | vital capacity the maximum volume of air that can breathed out after taking a very deep breath

Cape Canaveral / Cape Kennedy the site of the Kennedy Space Centre was established in 1961 and was known as Cape Kennedy between 1963 and 1973

capillaries (plural of capillary) thin tubes especially blood vessels with walls only one cell thick

capillary (plural is capillaries) a thin tube, especially the single cell blood vessels | capillary action pulling of water through a thin gap, important because the movement can be in any direction including upwards | capillary bed all the tiny blood vessels in a particular organ | capillary network the millions of tiny tubes that allow blood to reach individual cells | capillary tube a small glass tube with a thin wall and a fine hollow centre | capillary vessels tubes, made by rolling single cells that allow blood to get very near to the other cells of the body | capillary wall the very thin, single layer of cells that comprise the walls of a capillary, the smallest vessels in the blood circulatory system | blood capillary a very thin blood vessel | skin capillary a very thin blood vessel in the skin that can be opened or closed so as to control loss of heat

capsicum sweet pepper

capsule a box, a small container that is easily broken or dissolved, the part of a movable joint that encloses the synovial fluid, a dry case for seeds | space capsule the container, that is just large enough for the astronauts in their space suits, in which early astronauts travelled as far as the Moon and were returned to Earth

caption a simple statement that aims to explain the importance of an illustration

capture to gain control , to acquire, to record | capture hypothesis the idea that the Moon was a large rock in space that was attracted by the Earth's gravity

car vehicle with wheels that is used to transport people or animals | car battery the series of six lead–acid cells that are joined in parallel and produce 12 volts for use in a car | car exhaust emissions the gases that are produced by burning petrol or diesel fuel in an internal combustion engine | car headlights the main lamps that are used for lighting the road at night | car jack machinery to lift a car that can be used at a roadside | car park an area for leaving cars | car radiator the black-painted tubes through which hot water from the engine is passed in order to lose heat | car tires (USA) / car tyres (UK) air-filled rubber tubes around the outside of the wheels which provide grip on the road and also increase the comfort of the ride | toy cars small, wheeled vehicles

caramel a sticky brown solid produced by heating sugar solution

carat (not carrot which is a root vegetable) a weight (about 0.2 grams) for measuring precious stones, a measure of the proportion of gold in an alloy

carbohydrase / carbohydrase enzyme a chemical that increases the speed with which large carbo-hydrate molecules are turned to sugar

carbohydrates chemicals made from carbon, hydrogen and oxygen in which the ratio of hydrogen to oxygen is 2:1, the same as in water [H_2O] eg sugars, glucose, starch, cellulose

carbolic acid [C_6H_5OH] phenol, the original antiseptic

carbon (C, proton number 12, melting point 3730°C) an unusual element in that graphite, one of the two forms of carbon, will conduct electricity and so is a metal, but the oxide of carbon (carbon dioxide) is an acid in water and therefore carbon should be a non-metal. The explanation is that putting the atoms into the periodic table, carbon with a proton number of 12 is on the boundary between metals and non-metals. Carbon has two forms; diamond, which is a giant structure producing a hard, transparent material, and graphite, which is a black solid that easily forms a powder | carbon cycle the movement of carbon atoms between carbon dioxide in the atmosphere, which is incorporated into the molecules in plants, using photosynthesis; the plants are eaten by animals and respiration releases carbon dioxide back into the atmosphere. A vast store of carbon is the fossil fuels, coal and oil, which means the amount of carbon dioxide in the atmosphere is about 0.04%, burning these fuels releases the carbon back into the cycle so the level of carbon dioxide will increase | carbon dioxide [CO_2] colourless, odourless gas that is essential for photosynthesis and released in respiration, was known as *fixed air* but is now called greenhouse gas, turns directly to a solid at −79°C | carbon dioxide concentration amount of carbon dioxide in each litre of air, humans breathe in air that is approximately 0.04% carbon dioxide and breathe out 4% carbon dioxide | carbon fiber (USA) / carbon fibre (UK) a filament of pure carbon that is very strong and flexible | carbon monoxide [CO] a poisonous gas that binds to the haemoglobin in the red blood cell so the blood can no longer carry oxygen

carbonate / carbonate ion [$CO_3^=$] a group of atoms that is often found together in a fixed ratio, but can not be isolated | carbonate-containing rocks pieces of the Earth's surface that contain carbonate attached to a metal such as calcium or magnesium | carbonate content the amount or concentration of a metal carbonate in a rock | carbonate indicator a dye that turns from yellow to red if carbonate is present in the solution | carbonate-rich a rock or liquid containing a high concentration of a carbonate | carbonate rocks rocks that are made mainly from a metal carbonate, *eg* chalk is calcium carbonate | carbonated water water which has had carbon dioxide gas added, often under pressure | calcium carbonate [$CaCO_3$] the major chemical in chalk, marble and limestone | copper carbonate [$CuCO_3$] a green material that is easily broken down by heat to give a black powder of copper oxide | magnesium carbonate [$MgCO_3$] the form in which magnesium occurs in many ores such as dolomite | metal carbonate a

compound that is a metal bonded to a carbonate ion [$CO_3^=$] | sodium carbonate [Na_2CO_3] washing soda | sodium hydrogen carbonate / sodium bicarbonate ($NaHCO_3$) baking soda, mixed with tartaric acid to produce baking powder

carbonated water water which has had carbon dioxide gas added, often under pressure

carbonic acid [H_2CO_3] a weak acid (pH 5.5) produced by dissolving carbon dioxide in water

carboniferous rock material formed between 360 million and 290 million years ago when the carbon dioxide concentration was high and plants grew rapid and high

carcinogen chemical that is likely to cause cancer, *ie* the uncontrolled growth of cells

card stiff paper, paper with a density above 120 grams per square metre, equipment for a computer that contains several components | information card a small sheet that contains specific information, often concerning safety | key-fact card a piece of paper that contains the major ideas concerning a subject or object | sound card computing equipment that decodes bits into sound

cardboard a thick paper with a density above 200 grams per square metre | cardboard tube a circular tunnel made from thick paper

cardiogram / cardiograph the line that is drawn when the potential difference between two parts of the chest is measured, a graph that indicates the functioning of the heart

cardiovascular anything to do with the heart (cardio) and the blood vessels or tubes (vascular tissue) | cardiovascular function how well the heart and the blood vessels are carrying out their job of pumping blood around the body | cardiovascular system the whole set of arteries, veins, capillaries and the heart itself

care to be concerned, to work safely | hair care using soaps and liquids intended to keep hair clean, shiny and free from nits | skin care using ointments that will ensure a healthy skin

careful exact, thorough | careful observations accurate examination with painstaking recording

carefully precisely, safely, accurately

caries (nor carries which is moving) tooth decay

carn- (*Latin* flesh) to do with meat

carnivores life forms (usually animals but can be plants) that feed mainly by eating animals | top carnivore the predator that eats lower consumers, but is rarely eaten by anything else

carnivorous living mainly on meat | carnivorous plant a plant, so capable of photosynthesis, that will also trap and digest insects

carpal (not carpel which is the female part of a flower) wrist bone | metacarpal the bones in the hand joining wrist to fingers

carpel (not carpal which is a wrist bone) female sex organs in a flower

carpet a thick covering for a floor; to cover completely

carriage a vehicle with four wheels, the glider that moves on an air track

carried transported, moved, brought, drifted

carrier an organism that has a set of genes for a particular condition, but the genes are not used – they are recessive | carrier bag a cheap sack with handles that is made from paper or polythene

carries (not caries which is tooth decay) lifts and moves

carrot (not carat which is a weight or proportion) a root vegetable that is orange because of the carotene pigment, this coloured molecule is very easily turned into vitamin A

carry to move | carry out to perform, to do something

cartesian co-ordinates using ordered pairs of data in order to produce a graph (named after Descartes)

cartilage strong, white, rubbery mixture of cells and fibres at the end of each bone that provides a friction-free surface between bones at a joint | cartilage cells the cells that are found in cartilage and produce fibres

carton a cardboard box | fruit carton a box made from paper, used for storing fruit juice

cartoon a simple drawing, a representation

cartridge a cylindrical case, a small cylinder containing gunpowder | cartridge fuse the replaceable fuse that fits into a plug, two metal plates connected by a fuse wire surrounded by a glass cylinder

carving a figure or representation made by cutting material away, producing artwork by removing material, cutting into slices

case / case study concentrating on analysing one example in order to illustrate many points | egg case the hard container is large enough to protect an egg and to allow development of the immature insect | extreme case the rare outcome that results from the inputs being unusually high or low | film case an opaque cylinder that is used for storing photographic film | plastic case a flexible but strong container made from a plastic | range of cases several examples of a similar investigations with different approaches, equipment and measurements | staircase a set of horizontal planks or steps that connect two floors at different heights

casing the outer shell, often protective or decorative

casserite / cassiterite an ore of zinc

Cassini (Giovanni Domenco 1625–1712) an Italian who built an observatory on the top of a church tower then was invited to Paris. He became Director of the Paris Observatory, then used the new instruments to discover several moons of Saturn.

Cassini-Huygens spacecraft a two-part space probe that was launched in 1997 and reached Saturn in 2004, Cassini continues to orbit Saturn, sending back data and information, but Huygens was deliberately crashed into Titan in January 2005

cast a mould, an empty vessel into which a liquid is poured and allowed to set, a throw; to throw | cast iron the type of iron that flows from a blast furnace, the iron contains 4% carbon and is brittle

caster sugar / castor sugar very small crystals of sugar

castor-oil the liquid obtained from crushing the seeds of an evergreen tree

cat a carnivorous mammal that has been domesticated for over 4000 years | catflap a swing-door that is sufficiently large to allow a cat to pass through | wild cat a cat that lives in the wild, surviving without any help from humans

catalog (USA) / catalogue (UK & USA) a book illustrating the items to be sold, a list of items eg stars, with details to produce a book containing items and details

catalyst a chemical that speeds up a reaction but remains chemically unchanged at the end | biological catalyst an enzyme, a protein that can speed up a reaction

catalytic causing a vast increase in the rate of a chemical reaction | catalytic converter a mesh coated with expensive metals (so as to increase surface area at minimum cost) increases the speed at which carbon monoxide is oxidised to carbon dioxide, and nitrogen oxide is reduced to nitrogen gas in the emissions from a car engine | catalytic cracking heating large hydrocarbon molecules with a catalyst so as to produce smaller, more useful, hydrocarbons

catch (plural is catches) a mechanism for keeping a door open or closed; to observe at a particular time, to stop the movement of a speeding ball, to be infected with a microbe | door catch a mechanism for ensuring that the door will remain closed | magnetic catch a magnet and a piece of steel – one is on a door or flap and the other is on the surroundings, so the door is kept closed but can be easily opened

categories (plural of category) group of objects with common features | categories of drugs chemicals that can affect the body (drugs) that are separated into groups with common features

categorise (UK) / **categorize** (USA) to put objects into groups

category (plural is categories) a set, a group with common characteristics

caterpillar larva with body in rings or segments and legs which turns into a butterfly | caterpillar track a continuous loop of rectangular plates that are jointed together and that reduce the pressure of the vehicle on the land

catflap a swing-door that is sufficiently large to allow a cat to pass through

cathode a metal in an electrolyte (fluid that conducts electricity) that has a negative charge | cathode ray oscilloscope / CRO equipment with a small screen that shows a spot moving in response to the electrical signals that are put into the instrument

cation charged particle formed by an atom losing electrons

cats carnivorous mammals that range in size from 2 kilogram to 200 kilogram

cattle farm animals that provide milk and meat | cattle food the plants and crops that are suitable for feeding to cows | beef cattle cows that have been selected for their ability to provide meat for eating | dairy cattle cows that have been bred to produce lots of milk

caught (not court which is for law) to be infected, to be captured

causal due to, the reason | causal organism the creature that brings about the effect

causality having proof that a change in one property or item will affect another substance

causative agent the substance that brought about the change

cause the reason for something happening, the person or thing causing the change; to bring about a change | chemical cause a permanent change brought about by using chemicals | environmental cause the changes produced by a combination of temperature, rain and wind | inherited cause the reason for the change is to be found in the genes | physical cause a change that may be reversible and is caused by differences in temperature or by movement | specific cause the single reason that brought about the incident

caustic corrosive, damaging to skin | caustic potash [KOH] potassium hydroxide, a very strong alkali that can remove skin fron bodies | caustic soda [NaOH] sodium hydroxide, a very strong

alkali that can remove paint from doors | caustic substance any chemical that irritates the skin or causes paint to peel

cave a hole in the ground caused by chemical weathering | cave system an underground set of caverns and vaults that are inter-connected by passages | limestone caves holes underground produced by the rain water removing parts of the limestone

Cavendish (Lord Henry 1731–1810) was wealthy (the grandson of the 2nd Duke of Devonshire, so very English although he was born in France), healthy (he lived to be nearly 80), but perhaps not wise – he was described as *the richest of the learned and the most learned of the rich.* Lord Cavendish lived and worked alone, avoided any conversation with women and spoke only to a few friends (orders to servants were always left as notes), but he was generous with money – his large library was free to be used by anybody. As with many scientists, Cavendish worked in many areas; in chemistry, he studied fixed air (CO_2), inflammable air (H_2) and showed that water could not be an element. He started work in physics by estimating the mass of the Earth and then investigating the electromagnetic effect of a current and the ideas of charge. He was honoured, not by the usual means of having a unit named after him, but by giving his name to a major physics centre in Cambridge, UK.

cavity a hole or a gap | cavity foam insulation placing foam in the gap between the inner and outer brick works of a wall in order to reduce heat loss | cavity slide a microscope slide that has a concave dimple | cavity wall the normal method of house building using two walls, one inside the other, with a gap in between so as to reduce heat loss | cavity wall insulation introducing some material into the cavity of a cavity wall so as to reduce heat loss | chest cavity the space between the ribs and the diaphragm that contains the heart and lungs | pulp cavity the space inside the dentine of the tooth that contains the pulp, the nerves and the blood vessels

Cayley (George 1771–1857) born on the Yorkshire coast, Cayley was an inventor who was interested in transport, especially the new railway system, and the usage of land, two areas that came together when he invented the use of caterpillar tracks. He flew his first glider in 1808 and, at the age of 82, managed to produce a glider that could carry a human – the first heavier-than-air flying machine.

cc [cubic centimetre, centimetre cubed] a measure of volume that is the same as the millilitre

cd / cd-rom / CD-ROM compact disc – read-only memory, a device on which data is stored that can be retrieved but not changed

cease to stop

ceiling (not sealing which is closing) the top surface inside a room

celery sticks the shoots of the celery plant, can be used to show the xylem

cell (not sell which is to exchange goods for money) the tiny building block of life (named by Hooke), two pieces of different metals separated by an liquid that can conduct electricity, one box in a spread sheet | **cell activity** the chemical changes that occur in a cell | **cell cycle** the changes that a cell undergoes from being first produced, through growth to when the cell divides asexually | **cell division** reproduction of a cell, the nucleus produces an exact copy then the cell breaks into two, each half having a nucleus | **cell function** the job that a cell has to carry out so there are many specialised cells with shapes specific to their job | **cell malfunction** when something goes wrong with the instruction set in the nucleus so the cell can not work properly and either dies or undergoes uncontrolled division | **cell membrane** the thin lipid layer on the outside of the cell that controls the type and amount of chemicals that will be allowed into the cell and which chemicals should be ejected from the cell | **cell nucleus** the tiny structure inside the cell (organelle) that contains the DNA which controls everything that a cell has to do (named by Brown) | **cell sap** a sugar solution that is found inside the vacuole of a plant cell | **cell size** a typical cell has a diameter of about 10 micrometres (0.01 millimetres), but the range is from about 1 micrometres up to 2 metres for the nerve cell | **cell structure** what can be seen inside the cell and how the different parts are connected together | **cell-surface membrane** more often called the cell membrane, separates the cytoplasm from the outside world | **cell theory** the idea that all living organisms are made from tiny units called cells | **cell type** the characteristics that are seen when the cell is examined | **cell wall** a rigid structure that is found on the outside of some bacteria and of every plant and fungus cell | **animal cells** cells that have a nucleus but no cell wall | **antibody-producing cells** specialised cells in animals that manufacture antibodies in response to an antigen | **blood cells** any of the types of cell that are found in blood | **bone cells** the tiny living structures that make up the soft marrow of the bone and which

produce the blood cells | **cancer cells / cancerous cells** the cells that have lost regulation and grow out of control | **cartilage cells** the cells that are found in cartilage and produce fibres | **cheek cells** the cells found on the inside of the cheek that are easily removed by gentle scraping | **chemical cell** two different metals, separated by an electrolyte will produce a voltage | **ciliated cells / ciliated epithelial cells** cells that have one surface covered in tiny hairs | **cone cells** light sensitive cells in the eye that respond to one of the three primary colours (red, blue, green) | **damaged cells** some part of the cell has been broken so the cell can no longer function fully | **daughter cells** new cells, identical to the parent, produced by asexual reproduction | **dividing cells** the cells are reproducing asexually | **dry cell** an electric power source (cell) in which the electrolyte is in a jelly so the cell can be turned upside down without all the contents spilling out | **egg cells** female reproductive cell, or gamete, that is very large and immobile because it is full of nutrients | **electric cell / electrochemical cell** two different metals separated by an electrolyte will produce a potential difference | **electrolysis cell / electrolytic cell** equipment allowing an electric current to be passed through a liquid | **epithelial cells** the cells, which look like tiles, that are found in the outermost part of skin or an organ lining | **fat cells** cells that are used for storing fat, may form a layer below the skin or produce bundles of cells in the body | **female cell** any cell from a female, in humans this means that the sex chromosomes will be XX | **female reproductive cells / female sex cells** ova, eggs, the gamete that can not move | **fertilised cell (UK) / fertilized cell (USA)** the zygote, the nucleus of the male gamete has fused with the nucleus of the female egg | **fuel cell** an object that reacts fuel with oxygen at room temperature producing electrical energy | **galvanic cell** two different metals separated by a fluid that will allow charge to move and so produces an electric current | **germ cell** a non-specialised cell that is produced during the early stages of embryo development | **gland cells** the cells that produce a secretion such as hormones or enzymes | **goblet cells** lining cells that produce a liquid | **guard cells** pairs of cells that control the opening of the stomata of leaves | **lead-acid cell** an accumulator, a cell made from plates of lead in sulphuric acid that can be changed chemically by an electric current | **leaf cells** the individual growing units that are found in the leaf | **light-sensitive cell** any cell that responds rapidly and specifically to light |

lining cells the cells that are found on the inside of tubes, canals or ducts in the body | lithium cell an electrical cell in which lithium is one metal | liver cell any cell from the liver that removes chemicals that could be dangerous to the body and breaks down old red blood cells | living cells cells, the basic units of life, that show the ability to grow and reproduce | male cell any cell that contains the chromosomes that are associated with male characteristics in humans, this means XY | male sex cell the sex cell, containing half the usual number of chromosomes, that will move to meet the female sex cell | milk cells the cells in the mammary glands that produce the milk | model cells to make a drawing or a structure that shows the position of the different organelles within the cell | mucous-producing cells / mucus-producing cells the epithelial cells, lining tubes such as the trachea or the intestine, that produce mucus | muscle cell the individual cells that are found within a muscle, these cells can only contract or relax | nerve cells the many types of cell that detect a change, carry messages to or from the brain or cause changes to other cells | new cells the offspring, by asexual reproduction, that have identical genes to the parent but may appear or react in a different way | nickel–cadmium cell / NiCad cell a rechargeable electrical cell that contains nickel and cadmium | palisade cell a type of cell that is tall and thin, and is found in leaves of plants | parent cell the cell that started a line of cells with features of special interest | parts of a cell the several structures that form special areas within a cell, *eg* the nucleus | photo-cells thin layers of material that produce a potential difference when exposed to light | pigment-producing cells the layer of the skin that is made from cells that produce melanin, a coloured chemical that protects against dangerous ultra-violet light | plant cells the building block of all plants, characterised by having a cell wall composed of cellulose, a very few plant cells will have chloroplasts | pollen cell the male sex cells of a plant | protective cells the tough layer of cells that protect the underlying cells | receptor cells / receptors cells that are able to detect a specific stimulus and respond by sending a message to the brain | rechargeable cell an electrical cell that provides a current in one direction and can be recharged by passing a current through it in the opposite direction | red blood cells / red cells the circular cells in the blood that contain haemoglobin and so are able to transport oxygen | reproductive cells the special cells, or gametes, that are used in sexual reproduction and contain half the usual number of chromosomes | reserve cell a cup with a top that can be filled with sea water and will then provide a high current for a short time during an emergency | respiring cells the cells are chemically changing sugars so as to release carbon dioxide, other chemicals and energy | rod cells are found in the retina, at the back of the eye, and are very sensitive to light, but give no information about colour | root hair cells the long cells with thin membranes through which the root absorbs the water | sex cells gametes, the cells used in fertilisation, special cells that have half the usual number of chromosomes | single-celled organism a creature that is made from one cell | skin cells the flattened cells that from a protective layer around vertebrate animals | smell cells the sensory cells in the nose of an animal or the antenna of an insect that are able to detect specific scents, odours and chemicals | solar cells devices that convert sunlight directly into electricity | specialised cells (UK) / specialized cells (USA) the building blocks of life have become modified so that each can carry out a particular function or job | specific cells particular cells, parts of tissue with distinctive properties | sperm cell a single male gamete | spongy cells the cells near the bottom of a leaf that are separated by gaps so gases can diffuse through the layer | stem cells the cells from an embryo, which have not yet become specialised | stinging cells specialised cells that have either static barbs or small harpoons in order to deliver an unpleasant chemical beneath the skin of a consumer | type of cell the building block of life with particular characteristics | typical cell a cell that shows all the important features | unspecialised cells stem cells, cells that have no special function, but can develop into specialised cells | voltaic cell an electrical cell | white blood cells / white cells the blood cells that are able to engulf and destroy microbes, so causing their own death

'cello a stringed instrument that is played with a bow and produces sound of low pitch

cellular arising from the cell | cellular fusion two reproductive cells (gametes) join together to form a new offspring | cellular structure the arrangement of the smaller parts with a cell | multicellular made from many cells

cellulose a polymer of glucose that provides the rigid structure in the cell walls of plants | cellulose paste a suspension, produced by boiling cellulose, that can be used as a glue

Celsius (Anders 1701–1744) an astronomer who was born, educated and became professor at Uppsala in Sweden. In 1742, he suggested that a temperature scale should be used in which water boils at 0°C and water freezes at 100°C (no – it is not a typing error – this was what Celsius proposed), an idea that was reversed five years later.

Celsius scale a scale for measuring temperature, developed by the Swedish astronomer Celsius in the 1740, with fixed temperatures at 100°C and 0°C so is also called a centigrade (100 degrees) scale | degrees Celsius the temperature measured using the Celsius scale

cement a powder made by heating limestone and clay at high temperature, the material that holds teeth into the gums; to glue together

cementation the process leading to sedimentary rocks sticking together

cementing joining together, gluing

cemetery (plural is cemeteries) an area for burying dead people

cent- (*Latin* a hundred-)

center (USA) / **centre** (UK) middle | center of gravity / center of mass the one point through which all the mass of an object seems to be concentrated, the point at which an object will be balanced | control center one area that tells others what to do, usually refers to the cell nucleus | fitness center a building containing equipment that will measure variables such as heart rate and weight then provide exercise that will improve your heart rate and blood pressure | garden center a business that sells anything that could help you to grow plants | leisure center an area or building that provides lots of facilities for physical activities such as squash or football | nature center an area, often indoors, that interprets and gives meaning, to the signs, history and life in the immediate area | rare breed center a zoo or farm that deliberately breeds and uses animals that were found on farms but are not compatible with today's conditions

centi... /c... (*Latin* hundred) prefix for a hundredth part

centigrade scale a measure of temperature, invented by Celsius with fixed points at 100°C (boiling point of water) and 0°C (freezing point of water)

centimeter [USA] / **centimetre** [UK] / **cm** a hundredth part of a metre | centimetre cube / cubic centimetre (cc, cm³) a unit of volume that is almost the same as the millilitre

centipede a carnivorous arthropod with many segments, each segment has a pair of legs

central in the middle, pivotal | central nervous system (CNS) the nerve cells in the spinal cord and the brain

centre (UK) / **center** (USA) middle | centre of gravity / centre of mass the one point through which all the mass of an object seems to be concentrated, the point at which an object will be balanced | control centre one area that tells others what to do, usually refers to the cell nucleus | fitness centre a building containing equipment that will measure variables such as heart rate and weight then provide exercise that will improve your heart rate and blood pressure | garden centre a business that sells anything that could help you grow plants | leisure centre an area or building that provides lots of facilities for physical activities such as squash or football | nature centre an area, often indoors, that interprets and gives meaning, to the signs, history and life in the immediate area | rare breed centre a zoo or farm that deliberately breeds and uses animals that were found on farms but are not suitable for today's conditions

centri- / -centri (*Greek* around a point) | geocentric a satellite in orbit around the Earth | heliocentric the idea that the Sun is at the centre of the Solar System

centrifugation spinning material at very high speed so as to sediment fine particles, cells or cell components

centrifuge a machine for spinning objects at high speed – useful for separating the different cells from blood

centripetal acceleration the change of speed, directed towards the centre of a circle, caused by an object moving in a circular path

centuries (plural of century) several hundred years

century (plural is centuries) one hundred years

ceramic an object made from a hard-baked clay | ceramic magnet a permanent magnet made from fine iron filings baked in a clay | ceramic material a hard brittle substance often made from clay

cereal (not serial which is one after another) grass that has been developed so that the seeds are large enough to eat or to provide flour | cereal crop the grasses that are grown in large quantities for the grain they produce | breakfast cereal seeds of grasses that have been treated or processed so they are able to be eaten without further cooking

cerebellum the back part of the brain that processes signals received from the senses

cerebrum the main part of the brain

ceremony a formality, a ritual, a series of scripted actions

cervix where the vagina (birth canal) meets the uterus (womb)

cesium (USA) / **caesium** (UK) (Cs, proton number 55, melting point 29°C) an alkali metal, a group 1 element that is so reactive that cesium is rarely kept in school laboratories

cesspit a pond or reservoir for storing excretion products such as urine and faeces

cetyl alcohol a chemical that spreads very easily so is used to coat the surface of reservoirs to prevent evaporation of the water

cfc / CFC [chloro-fluoro-carbons, chloro-fluoro-hydrocarbons] chemicals that used to be in spray tins and refrigerators but they also destroy the ozone layer and so removing from our atmosphere part of the protection

Chadwick (Sir James 1891–1974) did research with Rutherford in Manchester, then rather unfortunately moved to Berlin just before the First World War. He returned to work with Rutherford, in Cambridge, UK. He used alpha radiation to prove that the atom has a tiny nucleus, and eventually, to show that the nucleus must possess neutrons.

chaffinch a small bird found in most parts of Europe and Asia, which migrates south in winter

Chain (Sir Ernst Boris 1906–1979) born in Germany, but honoured by a British knighthood and giving his name to a major laboratory in London. You have Chain to thank every time you are given antibiotics by a medic because he isolated penicillin from the murky mixture of a growing fungus. He shared the Nobel Prize for chemistry in 1945 with Florey and Fleming.

chain a flexible length made by one ring linking a neighbour, which links onto the next ring and so on, a series of related statements; to form a set of links | **chain reaction** a continually increasing change as one breakdown causes several more changes, each of which then causes more breakdowns | **energy chain** the energy changers involved and the route taken by energy moving from source to final usage | **food chain** a line or sequence of organisms that starts with a producer and finishes with the top consumer | **polypeptide chain** a string of amino acids

chairs furniture, with backs and legs for comfortable sitting

chalk [$CaCO_3$] calcium carbonate, a sedimentary rock, the remains of shellfish | **chalk dust** powder produced by breaking pieces of chalk

challenge a difficult task; to invite a response

challenging questions producing problems to which there are no easy answers

chamber a room, a compartment | **anechoic chamber** a room that is lined with sound-absorbent material so there are no echoes | **choice chamber** a box, usually with a transparent lid, in which several habitats can be built, then arthropods allowed to roam freely to find the one that is most suitable | **magma chamber** an underground reservoir of liquid rock that is less than 10 kilometres below the surface

chance by accident, the probability, unplanned

change the variation, the difference; to make different | **change color** (USA) / **change colour** (UK) to start with one colour, something happens and a new colour is produced | **change ideas** to start with one thought as to how something happened, but new evidence means that a rethink is required | **change over** a sudden transformation of one object or colour into another, distinct object or colour | **change (of) speed (acceleration)** either increase or decrease the rate at which distance is being covered | **change (of) state** reversible physical change involving the states of solid, liquid or gas | **change (of) temperature** make the temperature higher or lower | **chemical change** a permanent difference in which the starting materials are turned into new products | **climate change** a difference in the so the type of vegetation and suitability for animal life changes | **color change** (USA) / **colour change** (UK) when an object starts with one colour which changes to a different colour under particular conditions | **daily changes** differences that occur each day *eg* in temperature, wind conditions, rain or light | **emotional changes** difference in reaction to events | **energy change** converting one form of energy into another | **environmental changes** differences in an area brought about by changing some conditions | **everyday changes** differences that are expected to occur *eg* amount of light or heat | **geological changes** differences in the structure of the Earth over a very long time | **irreversible change** a permanent difference, a chemical reaction in which products are formed that will never re-form the reactants | **lifestyle changes** a new pattern of work, play, exercise and feeding | **measurable change** a difference that is sufficiently large that it can be quantified | **model changes** to make a structure that will react in a similar way to the real world | **observable change** a difference that is able to be seen | **periodic changes** differences that occur at regular intervals, usually in response to an external stimulus | **permanent change** the reaction that produced the new materials can not be reversed | **physical change** a difference that occurs without any change in the chemicals, *eg* freezing of water, the differences that occur in visible features such as weight, tone of voice or amount of hair | **population change** the difference in the numbers of a species in an area between surveys taken at different times | **pressure change** the pressure is different at other points or times, leading to effects such as winds | **record change** to write down the differences that were observed | **relative changes** qualitative description as to which item is more affected by an event | **reversible change** a difference that can be taken back to the starting point *eg* water can be frozen to ice and then thawed to give the original water | **seasonal changes** differences in appearance, growth or temperature that always occur at a known time of the year | **social change** a difference that has occurred | **sudden change** an abrupt shift | **temperature change** a variation in how hot or cold is the substance to the way that people live, work, interact or travel | **useful change** a difference that make the work easier | **visible change** a difference that can be seen | **yearly changes** the cycle of differences that occur in growth, colour, size or activity each year

changers items that bring about a change | **energy changers** transducers, components that convert energy from one form to another

changes the differences that are brought about

changing the stages during which a substance is being transformed from one set of features to a different set of characteristics

channel a tube, a passage; to force a flow into one direction | **irrigation channel** a small canal for directing water to specific areas, *eg* for growing crops

char to damage material by burning slightly

characterise (UK) / **characterize** (USA) to state or define the special features

characteristic some observable feature that is always found in that particular type of organism | **characteristic feature** the one important item or behaviour that is always associated with that organism | **characteristics of life** the important features that all forms of life should show, MR GRENS, MRS GREF (excretion, growth, movement, feeding or nutrition, reproduction, respiration, sensing the surroundings) | **characteristic temperature** the temperature at which an obvious change occurs for that material, *eg* water freezes at 0°C | **adaptive characteristics** changes to important features *eg* shape of beak, that allow

the organism to survive | **chemical characteristic** the way in which a particular material will react with other chemicals, especially some reaction that is typical of a class | **common characteristics** similar features seen on the different organisms | **compare characteristics** to observe and emphasise features that are similar and those that are different | **desirable characteristics** features that are important in improving the chances of survival and reproduction | **different characteristics** features that are easily observed and look or behave in dissimilar ways | **dominant characteristic** the feature that is always seen when the cells has at least one of the dominant alleles for that trait | **human characteristic** features and behaviours that are associated with people | **inherited characteristics** any feature that is caused by the instructions in the nucleus of your cell, *ie* the genes | **key characteristics** features or behaviours that are important or will define that organism | **particular characteristics** unique features especially those adapted for survival, special marks | **plant characteristics** the features that either distinguish plants from other kingdoms of life or allow different plants to be recognised | **recessive characteristic** a feature that is coded in the genes but is not expressed if the gene for a dominant characteristic is present | **select characteristics** to choose the features that are important and use a breeding programme to ensure that all the offspring have that feature | **sex characteristics / sexual characteristics** the features that are always associated with gender | **suggest characteristics** decide the features that can be used for producing a key or are useful for survival | **useful characteristics** features that will help the organism to survive

charcoal wood that has been heated in the absence of air that can be used as a fuel

charge property responsible for the effects seen with electricity, electrons have a negative charge are easily moved, protons have a positive charge and rarely move, ions are atoms that have gained or lost electrons | **electric charge / electrical charge** the property that causes electrons to repel each other and for protons to attract electrons | **electrostatic charge / static charge** the electrons are added or removed to an insulator and so remain without moving | **flow of charge** is an electric current and may be movement of electrons or of ions | **like charges** there is an identical type of charge on each areas | **negative charge** one of a pair of things called charge, conventionally the electron is given the negative charge and the proton has a positive charge |

opposite charges one charge is positive and the other is negative | positive charge the property that makes a proton attractive to an electron, the state that results when electrons are removed from a neutral substance | standing charge the fixed amount charged by gas, electricity and telephone companies for providing a service | static charge / electrostatic charge the electrons are added or removed to an insulator and so remain without moving

charged having that electrical characteristic called charge | charged particle a molecule, or a grain of dust, that has either a negative or positive charge

charger / battery charger apparatus that is plugged into the mains 240 volts supply and is used to cause a chemical change in a battery

Charles (Jacques Alexandre 1746–1823) was a clerk in the French civil service when, in 1783, he accompanied his brother on the very first ascent in a hydrogen balloon. He proposed a law that the volume of a gas depended on the temperature that eventually led to the idea of absolute zero (0 kelvin).

Charon the moon that appears to be orbiting Pluto

charring heating sufficiently to cause damage, but at a temperature that is too low for fire to occur

chart a graph, a diagram showing information, a map; to draw a graph | bar chart a diagram showing discontinuous variables as a series of columns | color chart (USA) / colour chart (UK) a card that shows the different colours produced when the pH of universal indicator is changed | flip chart a large block of paper on an easel | flow chart a picture to show the movement of energy, chemicals or information, but without any details of the processes involved | growth chart a table, graph or line that shows the height that is achieved or expected for boys and girls at different ages | height / weight chart a graph or table showing the expected weight for a person of that height, age and gender | pH chart a card showing the colours that an indicator will produce at each pH | pie chart a way of showing data in which a circle is divided into segments – just like a pie | tally chart a table in which each event is given a stroke, tick or tally

chase to run after in order to capture

cheap (not cheep which is bird talk) not expensive

cheaper costing less money | cheaper alternatives another method or approach that should give similar answers, but at less cost

cheek the outside portion of the mouth, an inappropriate reply | cheek cells the cells found on the inside of the cheek that are easily removed by gentle scraping

cheep (not cheap which is low in price) a cry of a young bird; to produce a small sound

cheese a solid produced by adding specific bacteria to milk | cheese factory place for large-scale production of cheese

chemical any substance, but usually containing only one type of molecule | chemical balance type of weighing scale suitable for accurate measurements of small amounts | chemical bond a joining force between atoms | chemical breakdown using enzymes or heat to split complex chemicals into smaller molecules | chemical causes an irreversible reaction between chemicals causes the change eg formation of caves by chemical weathering | chemical cell (commonly called a battery) two different metals, separated by an electrolyte (a fluid containing ions) will produce a potential difference or voltage | chemical change permanent conversion of one substance into new materials | chemical characteristic the way in which a particular material will react with other chemicals, especially some reaction that is typical of a class eg alkali metals react violently with water | chemical composition which molecules and how much of each substance are present in a mixture | chemical compound emphasising that a substance has a known number of atoms bonded together | chemical digestion the breakdown of food by enzymes to produce nutrients that can be absorbed | chemical energy the ability to do work that changes when a chemical takes part in a reaction | chemical equation on the left-hand side shows the chemicals at the start of the reaction and on the right-hand side shows the substances that are formed, the molecules may be shown as words or as chemical shorthand | chemical formula the type and number of all the atoms in a molecule eg water is H_2O, meaning two atoms of hydrogen (H) bonded to one atom of oxygen (O) | chemical heater a method for producing heat by mixing two chemicals together, often the mixing will occur in a sealed tube | chemical means permanent changes that are brought about by rearranging the atoms | chemical messengers hormones, molecules produced by a few cells in one part of the body that circulate in the blood and cause widespread, long-term changes | chemical name official name for a substance that has been known for a long time by another title eg the chemical name for chalk is calcium carbonate | chemical plant a factory for the large-scale production of chemicals |

chemical precipitation production of a powder from a solution by adding another chemical | chemical processes any reaction involving changes of substance, especially when describing the fine detail of the chemical reactions that occur in living organisms | chemical propellant the rocket fuel that is burned in order to provide thrust | chemical property an irreversible reaction in which a substance will take part if the appropriate chemicals are added | chemical protection the use of a sacrificial, reactive metal eg magnesium or zinc, to prevent rusting of iron | chemical reaction the change from starting materials to new products | chemical reagent another name for a substance that takes part in a reaction, especially the chemicals that are found in every laboratory | chemical shorthand a representation of a molecule showing the symbol and number of each atom | chemical symbol abbreviation for each atom | chemical tests methods (that should be simple, rapid, specific and safe) that are used to decide which molecules are present | chemical weathering destructive changes to the structure of rocks or buildings caused by the chemicals that are dissolved in water | agro-chemicals the fertilisers, pesticides and antibiotics that are used to increase crop yield | colored chemicals (USA) / coloured chemicals (UK) pure substances that show a colour other than white | common chemicals the chemicals that are likely to be found in any laboratory, pharmacist or chemistry set | flavoring chemicals (USA) / flavouring chemicals (UK) substances that are added to foods in order to improve or enhance the taste | hazardous chemical a substance that could cause damage, either to property or to a person, if not stored, transported and handled correctly | household chemicals any chemical that could be bought at the local supermarket | insoluble chemical material that will not dissolve in the specified liquid | light-sensitive chemical a substance that undergoes a permanent change when exposed to light eg silver nitrate changes to silver | poisonous chemical a substance that will cause death if they get into the body by ingestion or inhalation | pure chemical the material is made from one type of molecule | waste chemicals substances that are produced as part of a process but are not useful, especially the poisonous chemicals that need to be excreted from the body

chemically a reaction has led to the formation of products with properties that differ from those of the reactants | chemically combined the atoms are bonded together so the properties have

changed and the atoms are difficult to separate | react chemically to start with one set of chemicals and end with another set

chemist a person who studies permanent changes caused by chemical reactions, a pharmacist

chemistry the study of permanent changes | agrochemistry the study of the chemicals and chemical processes that are associated with the growing of crops | biochemistry the study of the chemicals and reactions that occur in the living cell | electrochemistry the study of permanent changes that are either caused by electricity eg electrolysis, or produce electricity, eg an electric cell | environmental chemistry the study of reactions that could change the conditions of an area | food chemistry the study of the chemicals that humans eat, including the storage, preparation and digestion of such chemicals | petro-chemistry the study of the changes involved when producing and using oils and hydrocarbons

chemotherapy the use of chemicals to bring about a change in the body, the use of specific chemicals that will kill cancer cells, but leave well-behaved cells alone

cherry tomatoes tomatoes that are very small and sweet when ripe

chest front part of the body between neck and gut or inside the rib cage | chest capacity either the total volume of the lungs or the volume of gas that can be moved in and out of the lungs | chest cavity the space between the ribs and the diaphragm that contains the heart and lungs | chest volume the amount of air that is needed to fill the lungs | chest wall the ribs and membrane surrounding the lungs

chew to break down food by crunching in the mouth

chewed-up the material has been broken into pieces and formed into a moist ball

chewing using the teeth and adding saliva so as to cause mechanical breakdown of food

chews (not choose which is to decide) moves food around the mouth and then uses the teeth to crunch large bits

chick / chicken a young hen

chickenpox an infectious disease, that is uncomfortable but not fatal, caused by a virus

chilblains hot, swollen patches of itchy skin on the hands and feet caused by cold and wet

child (plural is children) a human who is too young to be sexually mature

child-birth moving the foetus from dependence on the mother in the womb to an independent baby

childhood the behaviour and treatment of young people who are to walk and talk but are not sexually mature | childhood diseases illnesses, caused by viruses, that are non-fatal but usually occur in most children, examples include chickenpox, mumps and rubella

child-proof a simple lock prevents entry by a child, but allows access by an adult | child-proof container a box for pills that a child should not be able to open

children (plural of child) young people who are able to walk but need help in order to survive

chilled cooled to a low temperature | chilled food meals that have been prepared then frozen rapidly

chimney a tube for removing the products of combustion, the tube part of a bunsen burner

china pottery, dishes for food and vessels for drinking made from fired clay

chippings rocks, between 1 centimetre and 5 centimetres across, with sharp edges

chips pieces of silicon containing many integrated circuits, potatoes cooked in hot oil | polystyrene chips random shapes of polystyrene foam with sizes up to 3 centimetres | silicon chips a slice of silicon on which has been etched millions of electronic components

chisel a tool with a sharp edge to remove small parts of wood or stone; to remove small parts intentionally

chitin a large molecule, made from many sugar molecules joined together, that is main part of the cell wall of fungi

Chlamydomonas a single cell organism that is able to move freely and to carry out photo-synthesis

chlor- (*Greek* green)

chlorate (V) / chlorate (V) ion [ClO_3^-] a charged particle | potassium chlorate [$KClO_3$] weed killer

chloride [Cl^-] the charged particle (ion) produced by chlorine gaining an electron | chloride salts chemical made from a metal bonded to chlorine atoms, chloride salts produce a white precipitate with silver nitrate | ammonium chloride [NH_4Cl] a white crystalline material used in dry cells, a chemical that appears to sublime because heating causes breakdown to produce ammonia and hydrogen chloride, which then easily recombine | calcium chloride [$CaCl_2$] is very attractive to moisture so calcium chloride is often used to keep items dry | cobalt chloride [$CoCl_2$] a chemical that is pink in water, but turns blue when dried | magnesium chloride [$MgCl_2$] the salt formed by magnesium reacting with hydrochloric acid | metal chloride a compound made from a metal bonded to chlorine | potassium chloride [KCl] a white crystalline solid similar to sodium chloride and which is used to replace common salt in

some diets | sodium chloride [$NaCl$] salt, common salt, table salt

chlorination adding sufficient chlorine to water so that the microbes are killed but the water is drinkable

chlorine (Cl, proton number 17) a halogen; [Cl_2] a deadly green gas, boiling point −102°C | chlorine solution is made by dissolving chlorine in water and can be used as a sterilising and bleaching agent

chloro-fluoro-carbons (CFCs) chemicals that were used in refrigerators until found to cause damage to the ozone layer

chlorophyl (USA) / **chlorophyll** (UK & USA) the green molecule found in plants that converts light energy into chemical energy by the process of photosynthesis

chloroplast the small bag, or organelle, that contains chlorophyll in green plants

choice chambers boxes, usually with transparent lids, in which several habitats can be built then arthropods are allowed to roam freely to find the one that is most suitable

cholera a disease, which is usually fatal, caused by infection with a bacterium, with nasty symptoms such as losing 20 litres of water a day in diarrhoea | cholera poison the chemical that causes the symptoms of cholera and is produced by the cholera microbe

cholesterol a chemical found in blood that is essential for good health, but too much can cause blockage of blood vessels

choose (not chews which is crunching food) to decide, to make a decision between several options

choosing deciding, selecting

chopped cut, sliced

chord (not cord which is string) a straight line joining the ends of an arc, a pleasant mixture of musical notes played together

chordates animals that during development have special column of cells down the back – these turn into the spine in vertebrate animals

chorus a group of organisms singing together; to speak as a group | dawn chorus the loud singing of birds that occurs just as the Sun is starting to provide light

Christmas tree lights a string of electrical lamps that are put around a tree so as to provide decoration

chrom- (*Greek* colour)

chromaloy a mixture of metals including a large proportion of chromium

chromatogram the picture that is produced when substances are separated using chromatography showing the position of each component

chromatography the standard method for separating different molecules in order to find which chemicals are present in a mixture. The test material is placed as a spot near the end of a piece of chromatography paper, liquid is allowed to move slowly through the paper and the different molecules move at different rates | chromatography paper the special paper, with very fine fibres, that is used to separate the components in chromatography | circular chromatography solvent is dropped onto the sample spot so the separated components are seen as concentric rings | linear chromatography a method for analysing the components in a mixture, the solvent flows through the sample spot and the components appear as a line of ovals

chromium (Cr, proton number 24, melting point 1857°C) an unreactive metal that is used as a shiny coating on a cheap metal, discovered independently by Klaproth and Vauquelin in 1798.

chromosomes structures that control the cell, each chromosome is a long strand of DNA surrounded by proteins, the human cell contains 46 chromosomes | identical chromosomes the sequence of DNA and of the genes are the same in two or more chromosomes | sex chromosomes the two chromosomes that are associated with gender, XX is a female and XY is a male | X chromosome one of the two sex chromosomes, every human cell has at least one X chromosome | Y chromosome the small chromosome, shaped like a letter Y, that is possessed by every man but not by any woman

chronological in time or date order

chronology the study of time and the events that occur in a particular sequence

chronometer a very accurate watch, essential for accurate navigation (see Harrison)

chrysalis the case in which a pupa eg a caterpillar, completes the change into an insect

churn to mix thoroughly

chute (not shoot which is a stem; to fire) a tube down which objects or people can travel

-cide (Latin to kill) | insecticide a chemical that kills insects | pesticide a chemical that kills organisms that are pests

cigarette a tube of paper surrounding dried tobacco leaves that is burned and produces nicotine together with lots of damaging gases, which humans inhale | cigarette lighter equipment designed for easy transport and producing an instant flame | cigarette smoke the poisonous, smelly suspension produced by incomplete combustion of cigarettes

cilia hair-like projections that are capable of bending in a regular manner and so move along bits of phlegm (in the trachea) or an ovum (in the oviduct)

ciliary muscle the tiny muscles that control the size of the lens in the eye so the image is focused onto the retina

ciliated cells / ciliated epithelial cells specialised cells that have one surface covered in cilia – the hair-like structures that are capable of bending – so they can protect the trachea and move the ovum through the oviduct

circle all points on the line are a constant distance from the centre | semi-circle a circle cut into half by a line through the centre point

circuit a complete path for an electric current, one lap of a track | circuit breaker safety feature in an electrical circuit, a switch moves if the current (and therefore the magnetic field strength) is too high, the switch is easily reset after the fault has been cleared | circuit component any bit of the circuit eg lamps, motors | circuit diagram a simple method of showing how the parts of the circuit are arranged with all connecting wires shown as vertical or horizontal lines, and each component using a symbol | circuit symbols simple pictures that represent each component in a circuit (some symbols are shown on the inside front cover) | astable circuit an electronic circuit that switches regularly between two states of resistance and current | bistable circuit a set of electronic components that is either on or off | complete circuit an unbroken loop that starts with an electrical power source then goes through components, joined by connecting wires, and returns to the power source | control circuit an electrical set up that will turn components on and off | electric circuit/ electrical circuit the path taken by the charge from the source, such as a cell or power pack, through wires and components then back to the source | ignition circuit the cables and components that cause the engine plug to produce a spark | incomplete circuit there is a gap in one of the connecting wires so no current will flow | integrated circuit all the components that are needed for that circuit are on one piece of material, usually silicone | mains circuit the arrangement of wires, switches, lamps and sockets that are found in a house | micro-circuit a collection of many thousands of electrical components that are made into a tiny package | open circuit there is a break in the circuit so no current flows | parallel circuit has pairs of junctions so the current can flow in more than one branch | protection circuit a part of the circuit that can be ignored in normal use, but which opens the main circuit, therefore preventing any flow of current, if the current becomes too high | ring circuit the way that cables are arranged through the house in the distribution of the mains electricity, the wires within the cable start at the distribution box, are laid around the house and then returned to the starting point | series circuit the components occur one after another | short circuit a wire accidentally connects two parts of the circuit that should be separated, leading to a high current and increased amount of heat | torch circuit the switch, connectors and battery that are needed to make the bulb light in a torch

circular precise meaning is something that moves at a constant distance from a centre point, but circular is often used to mean that you start at one point, do something then return to the same point by a different route | circular area the surface has the shape of a circle | circular block a solid material, such as glass or Perspex™, that looks like a thick coin because it is a circle in one dimension and rectangular in the other two | circular chromatography solvent is dropped onto the sample spot so the separated components are seen as concentric rings | circular field pattern / circular magnetic field the shape of the magnetic field that surrounds a single wire, the lines of magnetic force form circles around the wire with their centres in the wire | circular motion moving at a constant speed around the circumference, or outside, of a circle | circular orbits the shape of the tracks that planets follow in their movement around the Sun or the paths taken by satellites as they move around the Earth

circulate to go from a point, move around, then return by a different route to the same point, *eg* blood circulates in the body from the heart to the cells and back again

circulating hormones chemical messengers that are produced in a few cells in one part of the body and move, in the blood, to all other parts of the body

circulation the flowing, the circling | circulation problems difficulty with getting nutrients to the cells or removing the waste because the blood does not flow correctly | circulation system all the vessels and pumps that move the blood around the body | blood circulation the continual movement of the blood around the body, pumped by the heart

circulatory system all the vessels and pumps that move the blood around the body

circumference the length of the outside line of a circle

circumstances occasions, a set of parameters

circus travelling entertainment that shows the skill and fun of people, a series of small experiments that are fun, but also develop skills

cirrhosis a disease of the liver

cirrus thin clouds at high altitude made from ice particles

citrate the salt produced when citric acid is neutralised

citric acid gives citrus fruit, such as lemons or oranges, their characteristic sour taste

citrus fruit fruit with a thick skin that contains citric acid, *eg* lemon, lime, orange, grapefruit

city location area where lots of people (and cats, dogs, mice and rats) live closely together

Cl chlorine, proton number 17, a halogen

Cl_2 chlorine gas, a green coloured gas that is highly poisonous and will bleach anything that is damp

cladding layers of insulation that provide no strength

claim to tell, to demand | advertising claims assertions made by manufacturers in order to improve sales | manufacturers' claims the information provided by the company that produced the goods

clamp solid structure, usually metal but can be wood, that is used like scaffolding in order to hold apparatus in place; to hold in place firmly | clamp boss block of metal with screw fittings that holds the rod of the clamp fingers to the upright rod | clamp fingers the parts of a clamp that are like two fingers that can be closed to hold apparatus | clamp stand the base and upright rod of the clamp equipment, the whole set of equipment used to make a clamp stand (base, upright rod, boss and fingers)

clamped held rigid, a solid fixing that can be removed if needed

clarify to make clear, especially ideas and assumptions | clarify ideas to explain observations in a very simple manner, with no ifs or buts

class (plural is classes) several items that are characterised by a common feature or behaviour, a division of a phylum that is a group of related orders | class investigation the set of young people divide the work between them and then pool results at the end | class set enough equipment for each group in the class

classes (plural of class) sets, groups

classification putting items with common features into sets or groups | classification system a method for putting objects into groups on the basis of observable features | scientific classification dividing objects into sets based on observable features

classify to put into groups based on common properties or features | re-classify to move an article from one category to another

clavicle (collar bone) connects the ribs to the shoulder

clawed having hooks or talons on the feet; having been attacked with talons

claws hard toes on the ends of feet or hands that allow the animal to rip or break other items or animals | sharp claws talons, the toes can rip and grip

clay soil particles with a diameter less than 0.004 millimetres | boulder clay a layer containing rocks of all sizes | fired clay the hard pot that results from leaving clay at high temperatures

clean sufficiently pure for the purpose | Clean Air Act (1955) prevented further use of smoky fuels | clean fuel a chemical the reacts with oxygen, releasing heat, but the products do not pollute the environment, hydrogen is a clean fuel that burns to produce water | clean water water that is suitable for drinking

cleaner less dirty, material for removing dirt | dry cleaners a company that removes dirt and stains from clothes without using water | toilet cleaner a chemical that removes the sludge and bacteria that grow on the inside of a toilet | vacuum cleaner household equipment in which a motor reduces the air pressure in a cylinder so allowing collection of dust and dirt by suction

cleaning removing dirt, making pure | cleaning materials substances that help remove dirt, *eg* by abrasion, using solvents | dry cleaning removing dirt from clothes using a solvent other than water

clear able to see through, obvious, transparent | clear cut distinct, obvious, unequivocal, no room for doubt | clear drawings diagrams showing important aspects | clear liquid a fluid that lets light through | clear pattern obvious relationship | clear plastic a polymer that allows all colours to pass through without scattering | clear water water that has no colour and is transparent

clearance a removal, a cleaning | forest clearance the cutting down of trees so the land can be used for some other purpose

clearer seen more easily

clearing removing a blockage, becoming less misty; an area of grass within a forest

cleavage a split, cell division of the fertilised egg

clergyman a person who is knowledgeable about religious matters and is authorised to carry out weddings, funerals and other ceremonies

click a sudden, short sound

cliffs high vertical drops from land to sea, favoured by many birds for safe nesting places | cliff face the vertical part of a landscape

climate long-term conditions, especially temperature, wind and rainfall | climate change a difference in the so the type of vegetation and suitability for animal life changes | climate control / control of climate trying to make sure that the long-term weather conditions are suitable for the purpose that is intended | micro-climate the range of temperature, amount of moisture or light and wind that is found in a very small area, such as under a log | warmer climate having a higher average temperature for every month

climatic stress long-term changes in weather have meant that organisms, such as animals or plants, find survival more difficult

climb a steep walk; to use hands, feet and rope to go up a cliff face, to ascend

climbers people who enjoy ascending mountains and hanging from rocks

climbing plants plants with very thin stems and so need support from other plants in order to reach light

cling to hold tight | cling film sheets containing a plastic that melts at about 35°C so the plastic is melted by hand heat, moulded to a shape that is retained when cool

clinging holding tight, grasping

clinical very clean, concerned with medical treatment, detached viewpoint | clinical thermometer an instrument for measuring temperature that shows the highest temperature reached, so the temperature inside the body can be measured | clinical trial the stages involved in developing a drug

Clinistix™ thin rectangles that have chemicals on the surface that will change colour depending on the concentration of a solute such as sugar

clip a small part to cut off a small piece | Bulldog™ clip a spring-powered clasp that is used for holding papers together | crocodile clip a spring-loaded metal grip with edges that look like teeth | paper clip a piece of plastic or metal that can be used for the temporary holding of sheets of paper | video clip a short film, often part of a longer section

cloche a small polythene tunnel that is used to protect seedlings

clock instrument for measuring time, to measure a time period | accurate clock an instrument that will keep time without any variation | activity clock a circular diagram showing movement, light or temperature over a 24-hour period | atomic clock a very accurate method for measuring time that depends on the breakdown of caesium nuclei | stop-clock an instrument that can be set to zero then used to measure an interval accurately

clockwise following the same direction as is expected for the hands of an analogue clock in which the top of the hand rotates to the right | clockwise moment a turning force that tries to push the lever in the same direction as the hands of a clock move | anti-clockwise the object is rotating with the part above the pivot moving to the left

clockwork using the energy stored in a circular spring that has been tensioned by winding

clog to block a passageway or tube

clone a replica, the offspring of an organism that all have identical genes and so have identical features; to reproduce an organism in such a way that the offspring have genes identical to the parent

cloning producing identical offspring by asexual reproduction

close near; to shut | close observation looking for all the tiny details | close together near to each other, separated by a small distance

closed sealed, pushed together

closely packed there is no room for any more

closest nearest

closet a small room, a cupboard | water closet the wc, the room containing the toilet, the loo

clot a solid block of blood, that should form only when there is a cut or a wound in order to prevent loss of blood; to form a solid with blood | blood clot the solid plug formed either at the skin to stop bleeding or within a blood vessel

cloth a sheet of material made from wool or cotton | cloth fiber (USA) / cloth fibre (UK) a part of one of the millions of thin strands of cotton or wool that cross over each other to produce a material | woollen cloth material made from the fibres that have been combed or cut from the coat of animals such as sheep, goats or rabbits

clothe to cover most of the surface

clothes garments that include trousers and dresses

clothing body coverings (usually of cloth) that keep you warm by preventing convection | reflective clothing coats and jackets that have highly reflective strips so they are very easily seen at night | safety clothing covering that provides added protection | thick clothing covering that contains many layers or is filled with in-sulation material

clouds condensation of water vapour at high altitude, may lead to rain | cloud seeding spraying a chemical into clouds in order to encourage the falling of rain | cumulus clouds clouds that extend vertically and may be white, fluffy and dispersed or the threatening solidity of cumulo-nimbus clouds | Oort cloud a vast volume of millions of particles, in the size range of dust to planets, that extends to about 1 light-year beyond the orbit of Neptune | stratus cloud the lowest layer of clouds, up to about 500 metres above ground level

cloudy there is sufficient cloud to obscure the Sun

clove of garlic / garlic clove a sub-division of a bulb of the *Allium* which is used in cooking

clover a flowering plant that has nitrogen-fixing bacteria growing on the roots

clues pointers, supporting evidence, indicators

clump a cluster, a small gathering; to join many small pieces together in a random shape

clumsy awkward, likely to cause accidents

cm [centimetre (UK) centimeter (USA)] a hundredth part of a metre (UK) / meter (USA)

cm³ [centimetre cubed (UK) centimeter cubed (USA)] a unit of volume, almost a millilitre (UK) / milliliter (USA)

Cnidaria one of the divisions (phyla) of the animal kingdom, contains simple multicellular marine animals such as anemones and jelly fish

CNS (central nervous system) the nerve cells in the spinal cord and the brain

Co cobalt, proton number 27, a magnetic metal

co- (*Latin* with, together)

coagulation clotting, curdling

coal a fossil fuel that started as giant ferns growing in an atmosphere rich in carbon dioxide millions of years ago, the plants died, were covered in sand and soil then cooked at great depth, under vast pressure for a very long time so you are left mainly with the carbon bits | coal gas the fuel that is produced when coal is heated strongly in the absence of air (leaving coke behind) | coal layers a thickness of coal in the rock | coal mining digging coal out of the ground | coal seams layers of coal that can be cut out profitably | coal tar the dark liquid produced by heating coal then condensing the vapour

coalesced blended, merged

coarse (not course which is a path nor cause which is to bring about) large size, rough, uneven | coarse focus moving the objective lens relatively large distances, so as to approach a sharp image | coarse mesh a net in which the gaps are large

coast the land close to the sea; to continue to move forward | coast-line where the land meets the sea

coastal close to the sea, the area of sea shore affected by the closeness of the sea | coastal environment the conditions of temperature, wind, movement that are found near the boundary of land with the salt sea

coat a covering that often prevents entry of material; to cover with a layer of material | furry coat an insulating covering of thick hair | plastic coat a protective layer of a polymer or a rubber | protein coat / virus coat the outer layer of a virus that surrounds the DNA in the centre | seed coat the thin outer layer of a mature seed | summer coat the fur that some animals develop in summer that is less dense and darker coloured than their winter coat | winter coat a fur that is deeper, warmer and lighter coloured than the summer coat

coating applying a liquid as a single layer, covering completely, a single layer of liquid | plastic coating a protective layer of a polymer or a rubber

cob the cylindrical part of a maize, or Indian corn, plant on which the seeds are found, a stocky horse | corn-cob the fibrous spike of maize around which the seeds of corn are arranged

cobalt (Co, proton number 27, melting point 1495°C) a transition metal that can be attracted by a magnet | cobalt chloride [CoCl$_2$] a chemical that is pink in water, but turns blue when dried | cobalt chloride paper is made by dipping filter paper into cobalt chloride solution and drying carefully, indicates the presence of water as cobalt chloride paper is sky blue when very dry, but turns to pale pink (almost white) if there is water vapour present

cocaine a white powder, extracted from the coca shrub of South America that stimulates the brain, but is an addictive and illegal drug

cocci (plural of coccus) ball shaped bacteria

coccus (plural is cocci) a bacterium with the shape of a sphere

coccyx a triangular mass of bone at the lowest part of the spine formed from fusing of several vertebrae

cochineal (E120) a red colour obtained by crushing the cochineal beetle, and is used as a food colouring

cochlea the snail like structure in the ear that turns the sound vibrations into the nerve messages that are sent to the brain

Cockerill (Sir Christopher 1910–1999) worked on radio and radar before constructing the first hovercraft using parts from a vacuum cleaner in 1950 – commercial development took a further decade because no one was prepared to put money into a revolutionary form of transport. Cockerill believed that he had put more money into development costs than were ever recovered in royalties.

coconut the fruit of a coconut palm, which is able to float between islands and then germinate on landing

cocoon a protective case in which a larva changes into the mature insect

cod a sea-water fish eaten by people

code a system for communicating information | binary code uses only 0s and 1s | genetic code the arrangement of atoms in the DNA that ensures the correct proteins are made at the right time | Highway Code guidance for the safe use of public roads, or 'highways'

coelenterate an aquatic carnivore that has a soft body and a single opening that is used both for the food to enter and to excrete waste material

coffee a drink containing the extract of roasted beans

coffin (not coughing which is a sudden deep exhaling) a box in which the dead are buried

coherent all in step, making sense | coherent text writing that develops arguments in a logical way

coil a spring, a solenoid, a series of loops made from the same length of rope or wire; to turn a length of wire around into several identical circles with a common centre | contraceptive coil a small circle of material that is inserted into the womb to try to prevent conception | solenoid coil a long, thin coil of wire surrounding a movable iron core | straight coil a solenoid, a wire is wrapped many times around an object so the length is greater than the diameter

coins money made from metal (and usually covered with bacteria when in common use) | copper coins low values currency that are made from copper mixed with other metals | nickel coins metal currency containing nickel, coins that are not worth a lot of money

coke abbreviation for the addictive and illegal drug called cocaine; short for the drink Coca Cola

cold low temperature, a disease caused by a virus that causes you to feel ill and your nose to produce lots of mucus (be runny) | cold-blooded animals with a body temperature that is always similar to their surroundings | cold burn damage to the skin caused by touching something that is very cold | cold conditions temperature around you is lower than is comfortable | cold cure a medicine that relieves the symptoms of a cold | cold day the temperature is sufficiently cold that a coat is needed for comfort | cold flame there is not enough oxygen (the hole in the bunsen burner is closed) so there is less heat | cold front the mass of moving air is at a lower temperature than the volume of static air often leading to rain | cold place an area where the temperature is such that lots of clothing is needed to stay comfortable | cold sore an eruption or 'sore' on the lips caused by *herpes* virus | cold surface an area that is feels to be at a temperature below the surroundings | cold virus the microbe that causes a person to feel ill with a cold | cold water water that is at a temperature much lower than that of the body (but above 0°C) | cold weather the temperature outside is much too low for comfort | ice cold any temperature below 0°C | resistance to cold able to survive at temperatures well below the freezing point of water

colder at a lower temperature

collaborate to work together

collaboration people in a group who are working with each other, on a common project, with the same goals

collaborative / collaboratively achieved by working together | work collaboratively to carry out experiments as a group and agreeing roles for each person

collapse to fall down

collapsing can a demonstration experiment that shows the presence of air pressure. Water is heated in vessel, such as a 5 litre oil can, the can is sealed then allowed to cool – the can eventually bends because of atmospheric pressure

collar the circle of metal at the base of a bunsen burner that can be so as to change the amount of air reaching the flame

collar bone clavicle, connects the shoulder to the top centre of the ribs

collate to bring together in a neat form | collate data to collect all the information available | collate ideas to bring the different thoughts together so as to end with a single theory

collect to gather similar items together | collect bubbles to guide the rising bubbles into a container | collect data gather measurements on a specific subject | collect evidence gather the information that will allow a particular question to be answered | collect gases gather the molecules of a named gas, usually by letting the gas push out (displace) a liquid | collect information gather observations and measurements

collected gathered, brought to one place

collecting gas using tubes to direct the gas, which would otherwise disperse into the air, into a collection flask

collection lots of items, with features in common, gathered into one place | data collection the recording of the information that will be analysed later

collector a gatherer, a person who gathers | solar collector equipment for concentrating the energy from the Sun that falls over a wide area into a small area

collide to hit (two rapidly moving items come together), to come together accidentally

collision two or more objects coming together and possible causing damage | collision hypothesis the speculation that the Moon resulted from a large body hitting the Earth | collision theory kinetic theory, the idea that particles must collide with sufficient energy for a chemical reaction to occur

colloid tiny spheres of material are suspended in a fluid so the mixture is stable, but is not a solution

colon the large intestine, part of the gut

colonies (plural of colony) (not colonise which is to form an isolated group) groups of specified organisms, each group living together

colonise (UK) / **colonize** (USA) (not colonies which is several isolated groups) to leave the major collection of individuals and form a self-sufficient group elsewhere

colony (plural is colonies) a group of specified organisms living together | bacterial colony a group of microbes found as a spot on an agar plate | space colony where people are living together in space (hypothetical at present)

color (USA) / **colour** (UK) a characteristic that objects show because the light they reflect has different wavelengths that cause different chemical reactions in the eye | color blind a person who is able to see, but can not recognise some colors, the common form is the inabilty to distinguish red from green | color change when an object starts with one color which changes to a different color under particular conditions, often used in tests such as litmus for pH, Benedict's solution for sugar or iodine for starch | color chart a card that shows the different colors that are produced when the pH of universal indicator is changed | color fast able to be washed without losing color | color filter material that will transmit a limited range of colors or wavelengths | color of rock a feature that is used to identify different types of rock and where they came from | color vision the ability to see different colors, human eyes are usually sensitive to red, green and blue (RGB), all other colors are made by mixing these three primary colors | change color to start with one color, something happens and a new color is produced | different colors each object or organism has a specific color | eye color the color of the iris, around the pupil, in the eye | flame color the frequencies of light produced by burning fuel, depends on the amount of oxygen reaching the flame, adding metal salts produces characteristic colors, *eg* copper salts are green in a flame, sodium gives a yellow flame | flower color the color of the petals that should attract insects and so may be in the ultra-violet | hair color the color of the hair on the head | primary colors the three frequencies of light to which the eye is sensitive *ie* red, green, blue (RGB) | secondary colors the effects produced when any pair of primary colors are mixed, cyan, magenta and yellow (CMY) | skin color the color of the skin, characteristic of the race, but may be modified by exposure to sunlight

colored (USA) / **coloured** (UK) a description of the light that an object reflects | colored berries are fruit produced by many plants and become brightly colored when ripe so as to attract the birds that eat them | colored chemicals pure substances that show a color other than white | colored crystals structures with regular and shiny sides that have a particular color, *eg* copper sulphate crystals are a beautiful bright blue color | colored dyes chemicals that dissolve in water and can be used to change the color of cloth or paper | colored filters glass or gelatine plates that let through the stated color of light | colored lamps / colored lights objects that give out light of a particular color, rather than the whole visible spectrum | colored lighting use of colored lights to give a particular effect because the appearance of an object depends on the light that is shining on it | colored object any structure that reflects one or more colors but is not white (which reflects all colours) | colored salt a compound between a transition metal and a non-metal that is not white or colorless | colored substance material, usually a solid, that has a discernible color | colored water water that has had a chemical added so as to change the color | colored wires the outer covering of the flex (metal conductor inside and insulating cover) is colored – this is useful for identification when you have lots of wires, but does not affect the electrical properties of the conductor

coloring (USA) / **colouring** (UK) adding one or more colors to a white material | food coloring mixtures that have bright colors and are used to make food look more attractive

colorless (USA) / **colourless** (UK) all wavelengths are transmitted equally and so has no visible color

colostrum the protein-rich liquid that is produced by the mammary glands or breasts for a new-born baby | colostrum rich milk that also contains many of the chemicals found in colostrum

colour (UK) / **color** (USA) a characteristic that objects show because the light they reflect has different wavelengths and these different wavelengths cause different chemical reactions in the eye | colour blind a person who is able to see, but can not recognise some colours, the common form is the inabilty to distinguish red from green | colour change when an object starts with one colour which changes to a different colour under particular conditions, often used in tests such as litmus for pH, Benedict's solution for sugar or iodine for starch | colour chart a card that shows the different colours that are produced when the pH of universal indicator is changed | colour fast able to be washed without losing colour | colour filter material that will transmit a limited range of colours or wavelengths | colour of rock a feature that is used to identify different types of rock and where they came from | colour vision the ability to see different colours, human eyes are usually sensitive to red, green and blue (RGB), all other colours are made by mixing these three primary colours | change colour to start with one colour, something happens and a new colour is produced | different colours each object or organism has a specific colour | eye colour the colour of the iris, around the pupil, in the eye | flame colour the frequencies of light produced by burning fuel, depends on the amount of oxygen reaching the flame, adding metal salts produces characteristic colours *eg* copper salts are green in a flame, and sodium burns yellow | flower colour the colour of the petals that should attract insects and so may be in the ultra-violet range | hair colour the colour of the hair on the head, may be affected by environment or hereditary | primary colours the three frequencies of light to which the eye is sensitive *ie* red, green, blue (RGB) | secondary colours the effects produced when any pair of primary colours are mixed, cyan, magenta and yellow (CMY) | skin colour the colour of the skin, characteristic of the race, but may be modified by exposure to sunlight

coloured (UK) / **colored** (USA) a description of the light that an object reflects | coloured berries are fruit produced by many plants and become brightly coloured when ripe so as to attract the birds that eat them | coloured chemicals pure substances that show a colour other than white | coloured crystals structures with regular and shiny sides that have a particular colour, *eg* copper sulphate crystals are a beautiful bright blue colour | coloured dyes chemicals that dissolve in water and can be used to change the colour of cloth or paper | coloured filters glass or gelatine plates that let through the stated colour of light | coloured lamps / coloured lights objects that give out light of a particular colour rather than the whole visible spectrum |

coloured lighting use of coloured lights to give a particular effect because the appearance of an object depends on the light that is shining on it | coloured object any structure that reflects one or more colours, but is not white (which reflects all colours) | coloured salt a compound between a transition metal and a non-metal that is not white or colourless | coloured substance material, usually a solid, that has a discernible color | coloured water water that has had a chemical added so as to change the colour | coloured wires the outer covering of the flex (metal conductor inside and insulating cover) is coloured – this is useful for identification when you have lots of wires, but does not affect the electrical properties of the conductor

colouring (UK) / coloring (USA) adding one or more colours to a white material | food colouring harmless mixtures that have bright colours and make food look more attractive

colourless (UK) / colorless (USA) all wavelengths are transmitted equally and so has no visible colour

Columella (Lucius Junius 1st century AD) was born in Cadiz, in Spain, and published a collection of twelve books that provided a comprehensive guide to best practice in agriculture and horticulture. The books contained advice on conserving and moving water, growing and caring for trees, vines and farm animals and details of the duties of the farm manager.

column a cylinder in which the length is much greater than the diameter, data arranged in a vertical line | fractionating column a tower that is used to improve the separation given by distillation | spinal column the set of vertebrae that produces a backbone that is both flexible and protects the nerves | vertical column an upright cylinder, a group in the periodic table

columnar appearing like shafts

coma (not comma which is a punctuation mark) continuing to breathe, but not showing any voluntary response to stimuli, deeply unconscious

comb a flat plate with teeth that is used for untangling hair or fibres, the upright skin on the head of some hens; to search in detail, to straighten using a comb

combination when two or more events or objects occur at the same time and same place

combine to join together | combine data taking information from more than one source | combine ideas bringing together several people's thoughts so as to reach a single conclusion | combine results collecting the data from several

different groups or experiments | chemically combine the atoms bond together so the properties have changed and the atoms are difficult to separate | recombine to cause to be reconnected

combining power valency, number of bonds for that atom

combustion burning – a chemical reacts with oxygen releasing heat and light energy, so producing a high temperature. The common combustion reaction is between a fuel and oxygen producing carbon dioxide and water | combustion reaction any chemical change in which burning occurs | combustion spoon a small spoon at right angles and on the end of a long rod. The spoon allows small quantities of chemicals to be burned safely in a jar of oxygen | combustion tube a tube made from heat-proof glass in which a small amount of material can be heated and then burned | complete combustion burning with lots of oxygen so no smoke or carbon monoxide is produced | incomplete combustion the amount of oxygen is not sufficient to allow the fuel to burn completely, so smoke and carbon monoxide also form

comets bodies made from rock and ice (dirty snowballs on a very large scale!) that are found in space. The orbit of a comet is not only a very long oval, with the Sun near one end and the other end near the orbits of the outer planets, but is also out of the solar plane

comma (not coma which is an unconscious state) a mark in writing that indicates a pause

commencing starting, beginning

comment a short sentence, an utterance, an opinion

commercial used to try and make a profit, as a business | commercial greenhouse very large glass-covered building that may be kept warm, and with more than expected amount of carbon dioxide, so as to increase the rate of growth and the size of the crop

common usual, normal, found in many places, having similar properties | common acids the acids that would be expected in most laboratories | common animals animals that are easily found in that habitat or locality | common approach similar method for solving a problem | common characteristics features that are seen on the different organisms | common chemicals the chemicals that are likely to be found in any laboratory, pharmacist or chemistry set | common compounds chemicals that are found, or are prepared, in most laboratories | common elements atoms that are found in great amounts and in many locations | common features share similar characteristics | common fuels chemicals that are often used for burning in order to produce heat | common gases / common gasses gases, such as those found in air and hydrogen, that are easily prepared in the laboratory | common hazards potential dangers that are found in many places | common materials substances that are easily obtained | common mixtures gases, powders and liquids that are often found, or are needed, together | common name the name, description or title that is used in everyday speech | common objects items that would be expected to be easily obtained in your town | common pattern behaviour that is found either repeatedly in one type of situation or in different materials undergoing the same reaction | common properties the characteristics that are the same in the different objects | common salt sodium chloride, table salt | common situations events that are expected to occur frequently | common sounds sounds with which you are expected to be familiar | common structure arrangement, often referring to atoms or to cells, which shows a pattern that is repeated in many places | common temperatures temperatures, such as the boiling point of water, with which you are expected to be familiar

commonly usually, often follows another event

communally working together towards a common aim

communicate to tell something to someone, to interact

communication a message, passing on information | communications satellite a piece of ironware that is in a geostationary orbit (takes 24 hours per orbit) and is used for receiving and transmitting radio signals

communities (plural of community) the organisms living together

community (plural is communities) the many different organisms within a specified area | living community emphasising that the many different producers, consumers and decomposers that are dependent on each other will be constantly changing | pond community the number and type of organisms that are living in a pond | soil community the many types of creatures and microbes that live together, and on each other, in the earth

compact close together, an agreement; to push together | compact disc a data-storage medium using the surface of a silver disc in which are tracks of binary digits

compacted pushed together | compacted grains small rocks that have been pushed together

compacting forcing together under the weight of the material that is above

compaction getting smaller in volume, because the air spaces are getting less

comparative / comparative information similar data has been obtained by a different method or from other sources

compare to examine differences and similarities | compare characteristics to observe and emphasise features that are similar and those that are different | compare distributions to look at the number and types of organisms in different environments | compare methods to find the advantages and disadvantages of different methods for obtaining similar results | compare results to look at the reliability and accuracy of data obtained from similar experiments

comparison an examination for similarities and differences | fair comparison looking in an objective way at similarities and differences between observations that are related but not identical | make comparisons to find details that are similar and items that are different

compartment a room within a ship or a train, a pocket in a piece of furniture

compass (plural is compasses) a pair of legs (joined at one end) that is used for drawing a circle, a small magnet that is free to revolve and so ends up pointing to the poles of the Earth | compass needle a lightweight piece of steel, iron, nickel or cobalt that has been magnetised and is free to rotate | magnetic compass a freely rotating magnet that lines up along a line from north to south | plotting compass a small magnetic compass that can be used to mark the lines of force or the field around a magnet

compensate to make allowance for

compete to fight, to enter a contest, to attempt to be the best

competition occurs when there are too many organisms for the resources available so the winner gets food, shelter and a mate and the loser could get nothing – and sometimes dies

competitor another animal or plant that is trying to use the same limited resource

compilation a gathering of information, a collection

compile to bring together and then sort out into neat, usable bundles

complement (not compliment which is praise) material that adds a substantial amount, a protein that is part of the immune system

complementary fitting together | complementary bases the pairs of nucleotide, or building blocks, that are able to join together – adenine always links to thymine, cytosine always links to guanine

complete entire; to finish | complete circuit an unbroken loop that starts with an electrical power source then goes through components, joined by connecting wires, and returns to the power source | complete combustion burning with lots of oxygen so no smoke or carbon monoxide is produced | complete silence no noise at all

completely totally | react completely to use up all of one of the reactants in a chemical reaction

complex many sided, with lots of different paths and connections | complex food webs many different predators eat several different prey and each prey could be eaten by several of the predators | complex interactions the web of cause-and-effect that occurs when several members of a group are affected by the others and cause the other members to change | complex mixtures a solution or a powder that contains many different chemicals | complex organism the life form is made from many different organs and tissues, each of which has a particular function and a specialised form | complex processes any change that has many parts, such as time, temperature, concentration of different chemicals, and the many parts all have an affect on each other | complex structures entities or buildings that have many parts that interact with each other

complexity an estimate of how many interactions are involved

complicated lots of different parts that act on each other so that understanding is difficult

complication a change that causes many difficulties

compliment (not complement which is to add) an expression of praise; to congratulate

component item that is part of something larger, could be an electrical component or could be an ingredient that is put into a chemical reaction | component list a table showing all the equipment and parts that will be used | circuit component any bit of the circuit eg lamps, motors | dietary component one part of what you eat | electrical component any item that uses electrical energy in order to do something useful, such as producing heat or light | food components the different types of plants and animals that go into a meal | smoking components the chemicals that are produced when a cigarette is burned

composed made from

composite a material that can be seen to be made from more than one constituent, eg concrete, plywood, fibre glass | composite flower the head

of the flower comprises many tiny flowers packed closely together eg a daisy

composition the chemicals (molecules or atoms) and the amount of each that is found in a substance | chemical composition which molecules and how much of each substance are present in a mixture | definite composition / fixed composition the individual components are always found in a particular proportion | mineral composition the amount of a specific metal compound that is found mixed in with the sand and soil in an ore | variable compostion / varying composition the amount of each component is not fixed and may change

compost dead plants that have been left to rot | compost heap a mixture of dead plants and waste material that is able to be broken down by microbes then returned to the soil

compound always contains more than one of some important working part, a chemical containing more than one type of atom, but the number of each atom is in a definite ratio to all the other atoms, and each atom is bonded to one or more other atoms | compound eye the visual organs of insects that have many tiny eyes in one large structure | compound microscope an instrument that has more than one lens and is used to magnify tiny objects | compound variable a measurement that will change depending on two or more other variables, eg pressure, which affects the speed of a gas reaction, depends on force and area | antimicrobial compound chemicals that can be used to kill bacteria | binary compound a chemical made from only two types of atom | chemical compound a substance that has a known number of atoms strongly bonded together | common compounds chemicals, such as salt or vinegar, that are likely to be found in most homes | ionic compound chemicals produced by the atoms forming ions so they are crystals when solid and able to conduct electricity when fluid | metal compound a chemical containing a metal bonded to other atoms | new compounds chemicals that were not previously available | nitrogen compound a chemical that contains nitrogen atoms bonded to other atoms | pure compound the material contains only one type of chemical and so should have a fixed melting point | useful compounds chemicals that are easily changed into other materials

comprehension understanding

compress to push tightly together

compressed pushed together, reduced in size by a force | compressed gas pressure is applied to a gas so that the volume decreases as the particles are pushed together | compressed spring push the ends of the spring towards each other so the length decreases

compressible able to be pushed together like the coils of a spring or the molecules in a gas

compression the length or volume has been reduced because a force is being applied

comprise made up of

computer equipment for carrying out complex instructions automatically

concave bending inwards | concave lens a circular piece of glass that is thinner at the centre than at the edges

conceive an ovum is fertilised by a sperm, eventually producing a baby

concentrate the residue after evaporation; to remove water without affecting the amount of solute

concentrated lots of particles in a small volume of another liquid | concentrated acid lots of acid particles, usually in a small volume of water | concentrated solution any liquid containing lots of particles dissolved in a small volume of water | concentrated source a resource in which there is a large amount of usable energy | concentrated sulphuric acid a very corrosive liquid, a solution containing lots of particles of sulphuric acid [H_2SO_4] in a small volume of water

concentration the number or mass of a compound in a stated volume of liquid, often given as grams per 100 cm^3 or as moles per litre | carbon dioxide concentration the amount of carbon dioxide [CO_2] in each litre of air, important in deciding the rate at which you breathe and the speed that plants will grow | hormone concentration the amount of a specified chemical messenger that is in each litre of blood | maximum concentration the largest amount of chemical that you can dissolve in a solvent at the temperatures, the highest amount that can be tolerated | optimum concentration the best amount to be used in that volume for a specific purpose | oxygen concentration the mass of oxygen in each litre of air | sugar concentration the mass of sugar in each litre of blood or urine

concept an idea | concept diagram / concept map relevant observations are written down then joined by lines on which are written the connecting ideas

conception the act or time when the nuclei of the sperm and ovum fuse

conclude to reach a decision; to end

conclusions ideas that are supported by the evidence | appropriate conclusions outcomes that match the information available | draw a conclusion to use the evidence to provide a simple explanation | evaluate conclusions decide if the data are sufficiently accurate to support that conclusion, to see if your ideas are supported by other information | firm conclusion the observations are reliable and fit the theory very closely | practical conclusions an outcome that has some working application or use | reliable conclusions the ideas produced are based on reliable data and do not conflict with other information | scientific conclusion the theory is based on logical analysis of experimental information, which allows predictions to be made | state conclusions to tell others the meaning and importance of your investigation | support conclusions the summary is based on the measurements | test conclusions look at the predictions produced by your ideas then carry out further experiments | valid conclusion all the information supports your idea | validity of conclusions the agreement between the conclusion from your experiment and what is usually found or expected in similar experiments

Concorde the first (and only) passenger aircraft that was capable of flying at twice the speed of sound, built by Britain and France and in service from 1976 to 2005

concrete mixture of cement, sand and stones that is strong under compression

condensation gas turning into a liquid, usually because the temperature is low | condensation point the temperature at which the gas turns into liquid, the temperature below which the liquid is able to exist at the same time as the gas

condense to turn from vapour to liquid or solid on cooling

condenser apparatus that cools a gas so as to produce a liquid | Liebig condenser the tube through which the vapour passes is surrounded by a larger tube through which water flows

condensing turning from a gas into either a liquid or a solid | condensing vapor (USA) / condensing vapour (UK) reducing the temperature so a gas becomes saturated and turns into a liquid

conditions the limitations of variables such as temperature, pressure, concentration that are being used in the experiment | acid conditions / acidic conditions the solution has a pH below 7 | Arctic conditions the temperature is below −20°C and the wind is blowing | cold conditions temperature around you is lower than is comfortable | controlled conditions the conditions in the environment (noise level, temperature, humidity, light intensity) are kept at known levels |

cooler conditions the temperature in the new area is much lower than in the previous place | damp conditions the soil has water close to the soil particles and the air contains moisture | desert conditions clear skies mean that the days are hot, and possibly windy, while the nights are very cold | dry conditions an environment that contains very little moisture | environmental conditions the values for moisture, light intensity, wind and temperature in that area | freezing conditions the temperature is below 0°C so water is turning to ice | heart condition a disease of the heart leading to a loss of the effectiveness with which the blood is pumped around the body | lighting conditions the intensity and frequency (colour) of visible light | past conditions the situation of food, temperature and water that existed some time ago | unhygienic conditions fat and bits of food waste are left lying around, allowing microbes to grow, and encouraging the presence of rodents, insects and microbes | warm conditions the temperature is slightly too high to be comfortable | weather conditions what has been happening to the wind, rain and temperature over the past days and into the near future

condom tube shaped piece of rubber that fits over the penis and prevents sperm entering the vagina

conduct behaviour; to direct, to let through | conduct electricity movement of electrons through a metal, movement of ions through an electrolyte | conduct heat movement of heat (vibration of the outer electrons) from a place with a high temperature to other places

conducted moved, shown a direction

conducting wire metal cables covered in insulating plastic that are intended to connect components without heating

conduction movement of heat or electricity through a solid (usually metal) | conduction of electricity movement of the outer electrons in one direction, pushed by the potential difference | conduction of heat / heat conduction movement, from hot to cold, of the vibration of the outer electrons

conductivity a measure of how easily electricity or heat will pass through the material | electrical conductivity a measure of how easily a charge will pass through a wire, reciprocal the resistance per metre of wire | thermal conductivity a measure of how quickly the two ends of a rod will reach the same temperature

conductor a substance that will allow the movement of heat or electricity | current-carrying conductor a wire connected into a complete circuit so that charge is flowing through the metal | electrical conductor a metal object that is used to connect parts of a circuit | good conductor a metal, a substance that will allow heat or electricity to move with little resistance | heat conductor solid material that allows heat to move rapidly | lightning conductor a method for protecting buildings that was said to be invented by Franklin, a thick copper bar has a spike at the top, to attract the lightning, and the other end is buried in the ground | non-metallic conductor a type of material that will allow electricity to flow, but is not a metal | poor conductor allows a small amount of heat or electrical charge to flow | semi-conductor material that will allow a current to flow under certain circumstances | thermal conductor allows heat to flow easily

cone a seed-bearing structure produced by some trees, a three-dimensional structure with a circular base and straight sides that meet at a point, the shape formed by eruption of magma from a volcano | cones / cone cells light-sensitive cells in the eye that respond to one of the three primary colours (red, green, blue; RGB) | cone-producing a large group of trees that produce their seeds in cones | volcanic cone the tall hill with a circular base that results from the emergence and cooling of the magma

confidence a measure of how certain you are

confident certain, sure

confine to restrict, to prevent free movement

confirm to check, to prove to be true

confirmation proof

conflict a struggle or a battle

conflicting evidence one set of observations leads to one explanation, but another piece of evidence leads to a second, contrasting, conclusion

confusion uncertainty, lacking in logic, information is conflicting and the conclusion is not clear

conglomerate bits of rock, larger than 2 millimetres diameter, set in a cement of silt or hard clay

conical flask glassware that is in the shape of a cone with a short neck | side-arm conical flask a conical flask (sloping side, flat base) with a small tube leading from the neck

conifer any of a group of trees that produce seeds on the surface of cones and are evergreen

coniferous area a region in which cone-bearing trees form the majority of the vegetation

conjunctiva a tough, transparent layer protecting the front of the eye

conjunctivitis an infection of the conjunctiva by bacteria – irritating and itchy!

cond
↓
conj

conker (not conquer which is to overcome) the shiny brown fruit of the chestnut tree

connect to join together, to link

connecting joining together | connecting wire piece of metal that joins components of an electric circuit, usually a flexible metal surrounded by a coloured, insulating plastic coat

connection a joint, a junction, a link | connection points the spots or positions that allow joinings to be made easily | parallel connections two or more attachments that allow independent movement along each branch

connector a terminal, the end that joins onto the equipment

conquer (not conker which is a chestnut) to overcome, to be victorious

consent to give permission, to agree, to allow to happen | informed consent giving permission after all the advantages and drawbacks have been explained

consequences results, often unpleasant | overall consequences the final or significant outcome

conservation staying the same, resisting change | conservation of energy the total amount of energy at the start of the process or reaction must be identical to the amount at the end | conservation of mass mass can never be created nor destroyed, so the total mass at the start and finish of a reaction must be identical | conservation organisation (UK) / conservation organization (USA) a group of people who try to ensure that a particular part of the environment remains unchanged | energy conservation using as little energy as possible, increasing the amount of insulation so less energy is lost | fuel conservation using as little fuel as possible so the fuel takes longer to run out

conserve to keep, to preserve

conserved preserved, steps have been taken that will prevent further decay

conserving preventing further decay, resisting change | energy conserving changes that have taken place so that less energy is needed in order to achieve the same effect

consider to think about | consider critically to think about all the things that could have gone wrong or could have led to false results | consider evidence to look at the observations and try to reach a conclusion | reconsider to think again

considerable large, significant | considerable amount large quantity | considerable variation large differences between repeat measurements

consideration giving regard to others, thinking things through

considered thought through carefully | considered viewpoint providing an analysis that takes account of all the evidence and prejudices

consistent the same every time or following a simple curve

console the control centre; to comfort

consolidate to bring together into one package

constant without stopping, unchanging, a number that always takes a particular value | constant force a push, pull or twist that stays the same | constant height the distance from a specified level does not change | constant mass the weight does not change, despite repeating the heating or the drying | constant speed the rate at which a given distance is covered remains constant | constant temperature the temperature does not change, in particular, a pure substance will change state at a constant temperature | near-constant almost unchanging

constantly without interruption, without a break

constellation a group of stars that seems to form a pattern when seen from the Earth

constipation difficulty in passing faeces out through the anus

constituent component | constituent elements the atoms that are in a particular substance | food constituent what chemicals were either used in preparing the food or are found in the food as it is been eaten

constrict to cause a tube or passage to become narrower

constriction the portion of a tube that is narrower than the rest

constrictor a chemical that causes a tube, duct or canal to become narrower in internal diameter | broncho-constrictor a chemical that causes the tubes to the lungs (bronchi) to become narrower | vaso-constrictor a chemical that causes some blood vessels to become narrower

construct to build | construct an equation to decide which chemicals need to be on each side of the equation and then try to balance the equation | construct graphs to take the data and turn into a graph with labelled axes

construction a building, the putting together of all the components in a structure | construction line a very fine line that helps to construct a drawing, although it will not be visible in the final diagram

consume to eat

consumer an organism that obtains nutrients by eating other living things | primary consumer the animal that eats the plant or producer | secondary consumer the animal that eats the primary consumer | tertiary consumer eats the secondary consumer | top consumer the animal at the top of the pyramid of biomass

consumption eating, a lung disease similar to tuberculosis | alcohol consumption how much beer or spirits has been drunk | energy consumption how much energy is being used to carry out particular tasks | fuel consumption / petrol consumption the volume of petrol, or diesel, that a car uses in order to travel 100 kilometres

contact a meeting, a junction between two electrical components; to get in touch with | contact friction the force caused by two surfaces being in contact and moving at different speeds | human contact people touching or interacting | in contact communicating, touching | switch contact the piece of metal that actually completes the circuit when the switch is closed

contagious / contagious disease an illness where the causative microbe is spread by touching an infected person

contain to keep within a boundary

container a vessel, box or jar for holding a liquid | child-proof container a box for pills that a child should not be able to open | pressurised container the pressure (force per unit area) inside the can is greater than the force outside | sealed container the vessel will not allow any material to get in or out

containing having something within

contaminate to make unsuitable for use because another chemical has become mixed in

contaminated containing impurities in addition to the substance that you think is there | contaminated water chemicals have been added to the water so the water is no longer suitable for drinking

contamination unintentional mixing of one substance with another material, usually by accident or laziness

contemporary current, at the same time | contemporary description an account that was written at the same time as the event was occurring | contemporary examples using ideas, information and thoughts that were available at the time of the event

content satisfied, what is contained within a container | contents a list of headings from a book, the bits inside, *eg* the contents of a cell | alcohol content the volume of alcohol in a liquid mixture | carbonate content the amount or concentration of a metal carbonate in a rock | energy content the amount of energy that is released when the food or fuel reacts with oxygen | mineral content the amount of a metal

compound in the ore | nutritional content the amount of nutrients such as vitamins, energy or minerals that is in the food | organic content the amount of chemicals that have been produced by animals or plants | organise content (UK) / organize content (USA) to put the information or data into an order based on a simple idea | tar content the amount of nasty black tar that is produced when the cigarette is burned | vitamin content the weight of a named vitamin in the food

context a description of the events before and surrounding the change that may have affected the experiment | environmental context discussing the number and behaviour of organisms in particular conditions | every-day context events in the normal life of most people | familiar contexts situations that could have occurred many times to most people | industrial context where large-scale production is involved | novel context a new or different scene

continent one of the large divisions of the Earth's land (Africa, Antarctic, Asia, Australia, Americas and Europe) and the Arctic ice cap

continental concerned with one of the large land masses | continental drift the idea that the continents, and smaller bits of land, are slowly moving around each other. Wegener produced the idea in 1912 to explain why the outlines of the west coast of Africa and the east coast of South America fit together so well | continental shelf / continental slope the underwater area extending from the land to the sudden drop of the deep oceans

continual unbroken, very frequent, incessant

continued started again after a short break, to carry on

continuing carrying on, extending

continuous connected without interruption, unbroken, without stopping | continuous access able to meet at any time | continuous process a manufacturing method in which the machines never stop – the raw material is fed into one end and the product emerges at the other, *eg* fractional distillation of oil | continuous scale a line which means that measurements are not restricted to a few numbers, but may take any value | continuous supply something is always available | continuous text strings of words that are written as complete sentences that follow on from each other | continuous variable a measurement that can take any value | continuous variation differences that can take any value, *eg* height or weight, compared to discontinuous variation, *eg* gender

cons

↓

cont

continuously repeatedly

cont **contra-** (*Latin* against)

contraception preventing conception, *ie* preventing the fertilisation of the ovum

conv **contraceptive** a method by which intercourse can take place, but fusion of sperm and ovum is prevented | contraceptive coil a small loop of plastic or copper that is inserted into the wall of the uterus and prevents pregnancy | contraceptive pill a tablet, containing female hormones, that is taken daily and prevents pregnancy

contract an agreement, a legal document; to become shorter, to catch a disease

contraction a shortening, especially of a muscle, the change in shape of the uterus at child birth | rhythmical contractions shortening and relaxation of a muscle at regular intervals | thermal contraction an object becoming smaller because the temperature has become lower

contradictions opposites

contrary opposite opinion or idea

contrast opposite and so stands out easily; to compare

contrasting habitats comparing two areas that have very different environments and so sustain different forms of life

contribute to provide, to give

contribution a donation, a gift

control the experiment that is carried out in order to see if the conditions themselves cause a change, the component that defines the amount of power; to rule or to tell what to do | control center (USA) / control centre (UK) one area that tells others what to do, usually refers to the cell nucleus | control circuit an electrical set up that will turn components on and off | control (of) climate trying to make sure that the long-term weather conditions are suitable for the purpose that is intended | control experiment is where nothing is changed so you can see if changing some variable does have an effect | control key variables make sure that the important items, that could cause your results to vary, are kept constant | control system the sensors, network of wires, the processing unit and the other components that allow automatic control of an event | control technology the hardware, from simple switches to complete computer systems, that allows you to decide the value of each important variable | control (of) variables making sure that items that could change are either measured or kept constant | birth control preventing the sperm from meeting the ovum | brightness control the variable resistor that changes the intensity of an image | climate

control able to adjust the temperature and humidity | disease control preventing the spread of an illness | focus control the method for changing the distance between object and lens in a microscope, so the image is sharp, and details can be seen | motor control / muscle control the ability to guide your muscles smoothly and with precision | pest control reducing the number of unwanted animals such as rats or microbes | remote control a box that allows control of an object that is not attached, controlling the actions of an item with which you are not in direct contact | smoke control taking steps to reduce the amount of carbon particles that are produced | volume control the knob that is moved in order to change the loudness of the sound | voluntary control deciding an action then carrying out the change, especially in deciding which muscles to use

controlled kept within boundaries | controlled conditions / controlled environment anything that could affect the growth of a plant or animal (*eg* water availability, temperature, light intensity) is kept at a particular value | controlled investigation carrying out experiments where one variable at a time is changed and a control experiment is always available | controlled movement using your brain and nerves to cause a movement in a particular direction at a known speed and strength

controlling giving instructions, keeping constant, directing | controlling variables ensuring that the important factors are either unchanging or measured

controversial likely to cause an argument, a basis for disagreement

convection upward movement of a hot fluid or the downward movement of a cold fluid | convection current circular movement of a fluid as the hot fluid rises and cold fluid falls

convenient suitable, close by, easy to use

convention a way of doing, an agreement, a gathering of people to try to reach an agreement

conventional accepted as working rules by the professionals | conventional current the direction of the current that is shown on circuit diagrams, this direction is opposite to that taken by the electrons | conventional symbols diagrams that are used as simple ways of showing a particular item, such symbols are used in maths (you all know what + and − mean), science, electricity and maps

converge to come together

converging moving towards a single point | converging lens a piece of transparent material that causes the light rays to meet at a point

converse *vice versa*, in the opposite order; to talk together

conversion change from one form to another

convert change from one form or measurement to another form or measurement

converter equipment for bringing about change | catalytic converter a mesh coated with expensive metals (so as to increase surface area at minimum cost) increases the speed at which carbon monoxide is oxidised to carbon dioxide and nitrogen oxide is reduced to nitrogen gas in the emissions from a car engine

convex bulging outwards | convex lens a converging lens, a circular piece of glass which bulges out

conveyer / conveyor a mechanism for the automatic movement of material from one place to another | conveyor belt a loop of material that is moved by rollers and is used for transport of heavy goods in straight lines

Cook (Sir James 1728–1779) joined the Royal Navy in 1755 and was given his own command at age 19! He studied the depths of the seas and the movement of currents then was sent to Tahiti in 1768 to observe the transit of Venus, he then explored around New Zealand and Australia. He returned to the southern hemisphere in 1772 – 1775 and, by following Lind's advice to provide citrus fruits, he lost only one sailor to scurvy. He was made Fellow of the Royal Society in 1776

cooker an oven, a stove | pressure cooker a closed vessel with a safety valve so that food can be cooked at up to 120°C | solar cooker an inverted umbrella made of aluminium foil that reflects and focused the Sun's heat onto a kettle

cooking changing food, by heat, to make it more easily digested | cooking oil an extract produced by crushing some plant storage organs that is suitable for frying food | cooking smells the odours and scents produced when food is being heated | cooking time the period needed to turn raw food into a form that is enjoyable to eat | cooking utensils the pots, pans, woks, knives and spatulas that are essential for the cooking to take place safely

cool when the temperature is lower than is comfortable, but is above the freezing point of water; to lose heat, to lower the temperature

cooled the temperature has been reduced

cooler less hot; equipment for reducing the temperature | cooler conditions the temperature in

the new area is much lower than in the previous place | cooler fluid the liquid or gas is at a lower temperature | cooler particles grains that are at a lower temperature, molecules that are moving more slowly

cooling losing heat | cooling curve measure the temperature as a liquid is cooling then plot the results on a graph, a liquid which is a single chemical will show a horizontal line that marks the freezing point | cooling effect the decrease in the average world temperature that could be caused by acid rain | cooling magma molten rock that is turning solid either underground (intrusive) or above ground (extrusive) | cooling method the procedure or equipment that is used to remove the heat | cooling rate the slope of the cooling curve, the change of temperature each second | cooling tower the massive structures at power stations that turn steam back into water | cooling water the liquid that is used to reduce the temperature of a tube or container | rapid cooling the temperature changes rapidly, leading to small crystals or a structure similar to glass | rate of cooling the amount of energy lost each minute | slow cooling the temperature takes a long time to reduce and so any crystals tend to be large | speed of cooling the rate at which the temperature changes, the number of degrees Celsius lost each minute

co-operative working together

co-ordinate to direct others, to work together | co-ordinates pairs of points that show the position of a point exactly | cartesian co-ordinates using ordered pairs of data in order to produce a graph (named after Descartes)

cope to manage successfully despite drawbacks

Copernicus (Nicolaus 1473–1543) was a Polish cleric who did very little observational work, but looked at the data from everybody else and then revolutionised our thinking about the motions of stars and planets. He proposed that all the planets, including the Earth, were in orbit around the Sun and that other stars were a vast distance away – the book containing these ideas was banned by the Catholic Church until 1835.

copies (plural of copy) reproductions, exact replicas

copper (Cu, proton number 29, melting point 1083°C) a reddish coloured metal that is unreactive and a very good conductor and so is used in most electrical circuits | copper beech a tree that grows up to 20 metres tall and has leaves that are red in colour | copper beech leaves the leaves of the copper beech tree have that colour because the chemical used in photosynthesis is not chlorophyll (green stuff) but xanthophyll | copper carbonate [$CuCO_3$] a green material that is easily broken down by heat to give a black powder of copper oxide | copper coins low values currency that are made from copper mixed with other metals | copper mine a hole in the ground from which copper ore is obtained | copper nitrate [$Cu(NO_3)_2$] a salt prepared by heating copper oxide with nitric acid | copper oxide [CuO] a black powder that is produced by heating copper carbonate or burning copper | copper pipe a tube made from copper | copper powder fine particles of copper | copper roof thin sheets of copper are used as the material of the roof – starts off looking reddish, but rapidly turns a dull green colour | copper sulfate (USA) /copper sulphate (UK) [$CuSO_4$] a beautiful blue salt, that is found either as a solution or as crystals, produced when copper oxide or copper carbonate reacts with sulphuric acid, can be used to kill algae in water | copper wire the thin conductor is made from copper, often covered with a plastic insulator

copulate to perform sexual intercourse, to mate

copulation the act of depositing the sperm on the ova

copy (plural is copies) an identical offspring; to cause an identical item (exact replica) to be made | identical copy a second object that can not be distinguished from the original

coral the external skeleton of sea creatures that live in colonies and use tentacles to waft food into the opening that both receives food and excretes waste | coral reef structure formed by growth of many similar animals

cord (not chord which is in maths or music) twine, string, a rope | spinal cord the thousands of nerve cells, joining brain to muscle or sense cells, that are found as a bundle in the spine | umbilical cord the rope-like structure that joins the foetus to the placenta | vocal cords voice box, method for producing speech

core the centre | apple core the centre of an apple | Earth's core the metal sphere at the centre of the Earth | inner core a solid sphere of nickel and iron, approximately 2500 kilometres diameter, at the centre of the Earth | iron core a piece of iron that is placed down the centre of coil of wire to increase the magnetic strength | outer core a layer of molten nickel and iron near the centre of the Earth that extends from the base of the mantle, at 2900 kilometres to the inner core, at 5100 kilometres

cork stopper for a tube, the bark of a cork tree which is used for making stoppers (the first cells

to be drawn were pictures of cork cell drawn by Robert Hooke, of Hooke's law fame, in 1665)

corm an enlarged underground stem

corn a cereal, maize, a plant that produces edible seeds | corn-cob the fibrous spike of maize around which the seeds of corn are arranged | corn oil the liquid extracted by squashing the seeds of maize

cornea the transparent part at the front of the eye

corona the fiery ring seen around the Moon during an eclipse

coronary anything to do with the heart, death caused by the heart becoming non-functional | coronary artery the major blood vessel that takes blood containing oxygen to the muscles of the heart | coronary heart disease the heart is not working properly because there are problems with the blood vessels that transport nutrients to the heart

corpuscle a cell | blood corpuscle a red blood cell

correct accurate; to remove errors | correct sequence the instructions are in the right order

correction putting right, a mark showing the true value or meaning

correctly accurately, properly

correlate to relate two items or sets of data so that you know what will happen to one when you change the other

correlation two or more variables that change together so that knowing the value of one variable then the values of the others can be predicted

corresponding matching sets of data so that related pairs are produced

corrode to change the properties of a metal by reaction with the atmosphere

corroding changing from ductile and malleable metal to a powdery compound, *eg* iron changing to rust

corrosion change in properties of a metal caused by the metal reacting with another chemical, such as oxygen or an acid, so that a new material is produced that is more easily broken than the original metal | corrosion-resistant metal that has been treated with paint, grease or oil so as to separate the metal from the environment, or other metals have been added to produce an alloy | metal corrosion the reaction of a metal with air or water to give metal compounds so that the desirable properties, *eg* of strength and ability to bend, are lost

corrosive causes a solid surface to disintegrate, any chemical that causes a metal to lose its strength because the metal has taken part in a chemical reaction | corrosive substance a chemical that is able to cause the loss of desirable properties of another material

corrosiveness the ability of a fluid to change the metal into a material that is easily broken

corrugated the surface is deliberately wrinkled so as to give a wave-like structure in one plane

cortisol / cortisone a hormone secreted by the adrenal gland

corundum an extremely hard mineral composed of aluminium oxide [Al_2O_3]

cos lettuce a type of lettuce, a plant that is grown for the leaves to be eaten

cosmic concerned with the universe | cosmic rays any part of the electromagnetic spectrum that originates from outside the Solar System

cosmology the study of the cosmos or the stars and sky

cosmonauts the term used by Russians to describe those brave people who travel into space

cost the money, time and resources that will have to be paid in order to obtain a benefit to give a value; to provide a charge | cost-effective the large amounts of money used at the start are outweighed by the long-term profits and benefits | production costs the amount of money needed to make a specified amount of that substance or instrument | running costs the amount of money that is needed in order to sustain the specified activity

cottage a small house, usually built for labourers (but the 'cottages' on Rhode Island are magnificent holiday residences for the wealthy)

cotton a long fibre that is obtained from the bud of a cotton plant | cotton bud a wad of cotton wool on the end of a small plastic stick | cotton fiber (USA) / cotton fibre (UK) a single filament of cotton | cotton reel a cylinder with a hole drilled between the flat surfaces | cotton wool cotton that has been treated to produce separate fibres

cotton reel a cylinder with a hole drilled between the flat surfaces | cotton reel vehicle a moving cylinder made by holding an elastic band at one end of the hole and twisting a pencil at the other end

cough sudden pushing out of air from the lungs with the intention of removing some irritant material | cough mixture a liquid medicine that helps remove the cough | whooping cough (pertussis) a highly infectious disease of the lungs that usually has little effect in childhood, but can be very serious if caught as an adult

coughing (not coffin which is a box for the dead) using sharp changes in lung volume to remove material from the bronchi

could (not cud, which is chewed by cows) was able, has the ability

Coulomb (Charles Augustin de 1736–1806) was in the French Army until 1791, and later became part of Napoleon's Government. His early work concentrated on military engineering and this led to novel ideas of friction and development of a very sensitive balance that allowed him to measure the forces between electric charges. He was one of the Commissioners, others included Laplace and Lavoisier, that developed the metric system of measurement.

coulomb / C the unit of charge, 6 million, million, million (6×10^{18}) electrons have a total of 1 coulomb of charge, 1 amp is the movement of 1 coulomb in 1 second

count to add up, to find the number present | pollen count the number of pollen grains in one cubic metre of air | recount to tell a story | re-count to count again, to add up again | sperm count the number of sperm ejaculated in each cm^3 of semen

counted the number of objects has been measured

counter the opposite, a table top in a shop, a coin; to give the other side, to oppose | counter balance a weight providing a force in the opposite direction that should prevent movement or bending, often used with levers | counter weight / counterweight a weight providing a similar force in the opposite direction | Geiger counter equipment used to measure the amount of radio-activity

countered opposed, fought back

counting finding the number of relevant and related items

countries (plural of country) areas or regions, each having a Government, flag and currency | developed countries the countries where public money over the past two centuries has provided useful roads, hospitals, schools and libraries | developing countries non-industrial states that are trying to raise their standard of living | poorer countries areas of the world in which the majority of inhabitants have very little money

country (plural is countries) land with a Government, flag and currency, the land outside of towns and cities

countryside areas of land that are mainly plants, including crops and trees, mainly uninhabitied by humans

couple two, a pair; to join together | infertile couple two people who are unable to conceive a child by intercourse

course (not coarse which is rough) a path, a defined route | damp-proof course a rubber membrane that prevents any water from rising up the brickwork and through the walls of a house

court (not caught which is captured) a collection of people who uphold the law, people connected with Royalty

Courtois (Bernard 1777–1838) was the son of a saltpetre manufacturer in Dijon. He was apprenticed to a pharmacist and isolated pure morphine while serving in the army. He returned to Dijon, where, almost by accident, he isolated iodine. He was so lacking in confidence that he asked a famous scientist called Désormes to continue the research.

courtship a male and female animal making moves, calls, smells and displays to see if they are suitable partners

covalent / covalent bond atoms sharing pairs of electrons, producing a strong joint between them | covalent bonding the joining together of atoms by sharing pairs of electrons

cover a protective material; to place one item above another | cover slip a thin slice of glass that is used to cover the specimen on a microscope slide | glass cover a sheet of glass is used to protect the object from dust, dirt or prying fingers | manhole cover an iron lid that is level with the road but is easily removed for access to the underground pipes | protective cover a layer that is fitted in order to prevent damage | vegetation cover the amount of leaves that cast a shadow on the ground

covered surrounded by material, hidden

cow type of animal that is raised for meat or milk | milking cow dairy cattle, cattle that are selectively bred so as to give high yields of milk

Cr chromium, proton number 24, a shiny transition metal

crab a marine animal with a hard shell that walks side-ways on four pairs of legs | hermit crab a crab-like crustacean that has a soft body and so uses an empty snail shell as portable protection

crabeater seal a marine mammal that is found in the Southern hemisphere and lives mainly by feeding on krill (despite its name)

crack a sudden loud sound, a split or long opening in a solid; to break open

cracking braking, splintering | catalytic cracking heating large hydrocarbon molecules with a catalyst so as to produce smaller, more useful, hydrocarbons | freeze–thaw cracking the breaking of rocks by water seeping into cracks, freezing then thawing

craft a skill, a transport vessel; to make skilfully | hovercraft a vehicle, invented by Cockerell in 1955, that was lifted by a cushion of air so the bottom surface was a few millimetres above the ground and there was no friction | space craft a vessel designed either to move objects from the Earth's surface to beyond the atmosphere or to allow objects to be transported in space

cramp a prolonged, involuntary and painful contraction of a muscle; to restrict

cranberry (plural is cranberries) a small purple fruit produced by a perennial bush

crane a tall bird with long legs that lives in wet lands, a tall structure used for lifting a load; to stretch

cranium the skull

crash a violent collision, a sudden drop; to collide and cause damage | population crash a sudden drop in the numbers of a specified animal in a stated location

crate a large storage box

crater a depression in the ground, the centre of a volcano

creamery a building, kept very, very clean, where milk is turned into butter, cream and cheese

create to make something that did not exist previously

creative able to make novel items from familiar materials | creative thought taking known facts and providing new explanations

creatures organisms or living things | aquatic creatures animals that live in water | living creatures any consumer that shows many of the life processes (MR GRENS) | sea creatures animals that live in the oceans | small creatures animals that are less than 10 centimetres long

creep to crawl, to move silently and low

creeped / crept slithered silently, moved silently

crescent an arc, half of a circle | crescent moon the Moon appears as part of a circle just before and just after a new moon

cress a small plant that grows easily and rapidly on any damp support

crest the highest part of a wave, the top of a hill

crime an illegal act, an action that could harm an individual or the community

crises (plural of crisis) events that are critically important but unexpected and difficult to deal with

crisis (plural is crises) a turning point in a disease, an unexpected but very important event | energy crisis a time when there will not be sufficient coal or oil for everyone who wants the fuel

crisp brittle, hard but easily shattered | crispbread a type of biscuit made from flour, cereal and water, but without eggs or butter

criterion (plural is criteria) a standard, a test that must be passed

critical pointing out detail, vitally important | critical angle refraction will occur below this angle (measured from the line at right angles to the surface) and internal reflection will occur above this value

critically very importantly, crucially | critically assess to look for any point that may cause the theory to be wrong | consider critically to think about all the things that could have gone wrong or could have led to false results

criticise (UK) / **criticize** (USA) to give an opinion, to express disapproval, to disagree while giving reasons for the disagreement

CRO [cathode ray oscilloscope] looks like a small television, is used to show electrical changes

crockery the plates and dishes made from clay that are used at a meal, pottery dishes

crocodile a large amphibious carnivorous reptile that is covered in square scales | crocodile clips spring-loaded metal grips with edges that look like teeth

crop fruit and vegetables that have been planted deliberately so they can be picked and stored later, part of the throat of a bird; to cut, to harvest | crop fields large areas of land that are used for producing that type of food | crop pests insects and microbes that may destroy a crop | crop plants the types of plants that are grown for food | crop production growing a plant or vegetable for sale as food | crop rotation changing the type of plant that is grown in a field on a regular basis | crop yield the mass of a specified crop produced in one acre of land | cereal crop the grasses that are grown in large quantities for the grain they produce | disease-resistant crop the plants are not affected by a particular microbe | food crop plants that are grown for eating | fruit crop trees and bushes that are grown for their fruit

cropping cutting, harvesting | double cropping sowing seeds from a slow-growing plant and a fast-growing plant at the same time into the same ground then they can be harvested separately

cross (plural is crosses) angry; a shape made by two sticks at right angles; to pass over a boundary | cross-bred the offspring of two different varieties of an organism | cross-breeding ensuring that the two gametes are from organisms of the same species but very different families | cross-pollination pollen from one flower lands on the stigma of the flower of a different plant (as opposed to self-pollination where the same flower provides pollen and ovule) | cross-section the picture produced when an object is cut across without any of the internal parts changing shape

or position | cross-sectional area the amount of material that is revealed when an object is cut horizontally | crossword a word puzzle in which you have clues to discern each word and a pattern of boxes into which each letter must fit | mono-hybrid cross sexual reproduction in which one gene of the offspring is being studied

crouch to remain with the soles of the feet on the ground while trying to get the body as low as possible

crowd a large number of people in a small space; to push close together

crowded lots of people in a small space so movement is difficult

crown the top of the head, the part of a tooth that you are able to see, a very expensive circle of gold and precious stones

crucible small dish made from porcelain and so can be heated to high temperatures without damage | crucible lid the cover that goes over a crucible and prevents loss of chemicals

crude oil the dark sludge (the remains of fish that have been cooked for a few million years) that is a mixture of hydrocarbons that is pumped from underground

crumble to fall apart, to break down into a coarse powder

crumbling pieces of material are breaking off so the structure is falling down

crumpled scrunched up without breaking

crush a lot of people in a small space, a fruit drink; to break into smaller pieces especially by using high pressure

crushed broken into a powder | crushed tablet the pill has been mechanically ground to a powder | crushed yeast intense pressure has been used to break open the cell wall of the yeast | finely crushed pressure was used to turn an object into a powder

crust a thin, hard outer layer | Earth's crust the thin layer (up to 90 kilometres thick) that is the solid outer part of the Earth

Crustacea /crustaceans aquatic arthropods (jointed legs) with an external skeleton (exoskeleton) that has three distinct sections

cryolite sodium–aluminium fluoride [$3NaF.AlF_3$], heated above its melting point, this is used as the solvent for bauxite in the extraction of aluminium

crystal a shiny solid with a regular shape | crystal alignment the direction in which all the shiny structures point | crystal growth the increase in size of crystals if the solution is left for longer time | crystal size the average or maximum length of the crystal | crystal structure a description of the repeating pattern of ions in a solid |

colored crystals (USA) / coloured crystals (UK) structures with regular and shiny sides that have a particular colour | ice crystals the regular shaped objects that appear when water is frozen slowly | large crystals the big version of regular, shiny solids, usually easily seen and easy to handle | purple crystals tiny shiny objects that reflect violet light, solid potassium permanganate | salt crystals small regular solids of sodium chloride | small crystals structures produced from a solution that are less than 1 millimetre across

crystalline looking like a crystal with a regular shape and shiny surfaces | crystalline rock a rock containing many small crystals

crystallisation (UK) / crystallization (USA) the process of producing crystals from a solution by evaporating the water | water of crystallisation the definite amount of water that is found in a crystal, eg copper sulphate is always $CuSO_4.5H_2O$

crystallise (UK) / crystallize (USA) to produce regular, shiny solids of a solute from a saturated solution

crystallography studying the structure of crystals | X-ray crystallography producing a pattern by reflecting a beam of X-rays from a crystal, then using the position of the atoms to explain the pattern

Cu copper, proton number 29, a transition metal that is used in electrical wiring in the home

cube a solid made from six squares joined at the edges | centimeter cube (USA) / centimetre cube (UK) (cc, cm ^{3}) a unit of volume that is almost the same as the millilitre | ice cube water at a temperature below 0°C

cubic centimeter (USA) / cubic centimetre (UK) (cc) a unit of volume

cubit a unit of length, the distance from the elbow to the finger tip

cuboid a solid made from six rectangles joined at the edges

cuckoo a woodland bird that is found worldwide, abut half of the species lay their eggs in the nest of another bird

cucumber a long fruit, that is almost all water, covered with a green coat

cud (not could which is a possibility) the food that is stored in the first stomach of a cow and will be chewed again

cull to reduce the population by killing a certain number

culling the planned killing of a proportion of a population

cultivate to take care of the soil and plants so as to grow crops for food

cultural social, shared common knowledge |

cultural belief an idea or standard of behaviour that is held by the majority of the people in that area | cultural issues discussions that may arise from difference between the expectations and lifestyles of different groups of people

culture a liquid containing microbes, a way of life; to grow microbes on an agar plate

culturing plants growing plants with a great deal of knowledge and care

cumulo-nimbus clouds that have great height (up to 10 kilometres deep) and usually bring thunderstorms

cumulus / cumulus clouds clouds which extend vertically and may be white, fluffy and dispersed or the threatening solidity of cumulo-nimbus clouds

cup a mug, a cylindrical pottery, plastic or metal container with a volume of approximately 200 cm^3 | paper cup a drinking cylinder made from a waterproof paper | polystyrene cup a drinking vessel without a handle, made from a solid white foam so the heat is not conducted to the outside

cupboard a cabinet, a fixed box used for storage | fume cupboard a large box, with safety glass sides and a fan for extracting the air, in which experiments may be conducted that might produce toxic products

curd white solids produced when milk turns sour

cure a medicine or process that stops an illness; to cause an illness to disappear, to change a liquid glue or resin to a solid | cold cure a medicine that relieves the symptoms of a cold | possible cure a method that may restore an ill person to good health

Curie (Marie 1867–1934) was born into a relatively poor family, but became the first woman scientist of international distinction. Maria earned money to support both herself and her sister who was studying medicine in Paris. In 1891, Marie joined her sister in Paris and started studying physics, she was a hardworking perfectionist who graduated first in the order of merit. During 1894, she met the 36 year old Pierre Curie and they married the following year. Working in his laboratory, she discovered that both uranium and thorium are radioactive elements, but did not realise the dangers of radioactivity and hence took none of today's precautions – this means that her notebooks are still too radioactive to be handled! In 1898, she discovered polonium (she was Polish) and, starting with 10,000 kilogram of waste uranium ore, she isolated 0.1g of radium. She was jointly awarded, with her husband and Becquerel, the 1903 Nobel Prize in Physics. Three years later, on the death of her husband,

Marie was elected the first woman professor at the Sorbonne. In 1910, Marie was turned down for election to the Academy of Sciences in Paris and herself refused to accept a Lègion d'Honneur. In 1911, she was awarded the Nobel Prize in Chemistry for discovering two new elements.

curling bending, throwing stone discs across ice

currant (not current which is the flow of charge) dried grapes used in cooking

current (not currant which is a dried grape) present time, flow of charge measured in amps, movement of water in an ocean | current bedding the sedimentary layers that are at angles to the direction of the main stratum | current-carrying conductor a wire connected into a complete circuit so that charge is flowing through the metal | current detector equipment for finding wires in which electrons are flowing | current electricity the flow of charge | current flow emphasising that something (water or charge) is moving in a particular direction | current issues some recent experiment or trial over which there is discussion and disagreement | current rating the maximum flow of charge that a component can safely carry before too much heat is produced | current reading the measurement either at present or of the flow of charge | current values numbers that are measured either now or for the flow of charge | air currents the movement of air, vertically and horizontally, caused by differences in temperature | alternating current (ac) the electrons flow in one direction, then flow in the reverse direction – this occurs 50 times each second in mains electricity | convection current large-scale movement of a fluid caused by hot fluids rising and being replaced by cold fluids moving downwards | conventional current the direction of the current that is shown on circuit diagrams, this direction is opposite to that taken by the electrons | direct current (dc) the electrons flow in the same direction all the time | electric current / electrical current flow of charge, the movement of electrons in a wire or of ions in fluids | high current any current that is likely either to damage a person or cause a fire | induced current the flow of electrons (current) caused by moving a wire between the opposite poles of a magnet | thermal current convection current, the upward movement of a fluid caused by heating the lower regions | water current bulk movement of water in a general direction

curtain a sheet covering a door or a window hanging from near the ceiling to close to the ground

curvature the bend, a continual change of direction

curve a line (which may be straight or bend), usually a simple shape and drawn to show the relationship between points on a graph | appropriate curve the shape or the drawing of the line of best fit | best-fit curve the line that minimises the difference between the actual points and the curve | cooling curve a graph of temperature against time as the material loses energy | decay curve the graph showing the loss of activity of a radio-active source as time progresses | heating curve a graph of temperature against time as the material gains energy | smooth curve a line which is continuous and has no sharp changes of direction | solubility curve the graph depicting the maximum amount of a material that will dissolve at each temperature against the temperature (on the bottom axis)

cushion a bag containing material that can be compressed, a pillow, a pad for sitting upon; to provide a soft landing | cushion of air a layer of air is used to float an object above the ground

cut an opening in the skin; to break open using a sharp blade | cut down the organism fell over because the base had been chopped away, made smaller | cut-outs safety devices that open the circuit when the current becomes too high, outlines drawn on paper that are to be cut out and stuck together | clear-cut distinct, obvious | freshly cut the separation has occurred very recently

cuticle protective layer covering the upper side of leaves and preventing evaporation, dead skin around the base of fingernails | waterproof cuticle emphasising that the thin layer of cells at the top of the leaf is to prevent evaporation of water | waxy cuticle the lipid coating on the upper surface of some leaves that helps prevent evaporation of water

cutlery knives, forks and spoons that are used for eating food

cut-outs safety devices that open the circuit when the current becomes too high, outlines drawn on paper that are to be cut out and stuck together

cuttings / plant cuttings parts of a plant that are taken with the intention of raising a new plant | magazine cutting a paper on which is printed relevant and important information, that has been cut from a newspaper

cyan a deep blue colour produced by mixing yellow and green light

cyanobacteria blue-green algae, a group of organisms that are similar to bacteria and are among the oldest organisms known, may cause algal blooms or eutrophication

cycle going round in circles or repeating themselves, a form of transport with wheels; to push in a circle | cycle design the planning of the shape and the selection of materials so as to give a wheeled transport | bicycle two wheels suspended from a frame with pedals for increasing speed | carbon cycle carbon atoms are used by plants in photosynthesis then released back into the atmosphere when respiration occurs | cell cycle the changes that a cell undergoes from being first produced, through growth to when the cell divides asexually | design cycle the planning of the shape, the selection of materials and then redesigning and reselection to give a finished product | estrus cycle (USA) / oestrus cycle (UK) the changes that occur as an egg is being produced, may be the annual cycle in some animals or the monthly cycle in women | freeze–thaw cycle the freezing of wet material below 0°C then heating to melt the ice is repeated many times leading to a fragmenting of rock | life cycle the regular change from birth, through a juvenile to maturity and reproduction | lunar cycle the different appearances of the Moon from the crescent of a new moon through waxing and waning | menstrual cycle the changes that occur over the period of a month in the chemistry of a woman's body, starting with the menstrual bleeding | monocycle a transport vehicle with a single wheel | monthly cycle an event, or a series of events, that occurs every 28 days | nitrogen cycle nitrates in soil are used by plants to produce amino acids that are used by animals then returned to the soil by microbes | oestrus cycle (UK) / estrus cycle (USA) the changes that occur as an egg is being produced, may be the annual cycle in some animals or the monthly cycle in women | recycle to use an object again either for the same purpose or as a source of raw material | rock cycle the changes that occur in rock from the cooling of igneous rock through fragmentation, sedimentation and metamorphism to melting back into the magma |

saturation – drying cycle production of layers of sedimentary rock by material dissolving in water and the water evaporating so the dissolved material falls out of solution | water cycle evaporation of water from oceans is followed by condensation and precipitation as rain which flows through the land and back to the seas

cyclic activity a task or observation that occurs at regular intervals

cyclist a person who travels by pedalling a bicycle

cyclone circular movement of air centred on an area of low pressure | anticyclone outward movement of air from a region of high pressure

cylinder object that is a circle when viewed from one direction and a rectangle when viewed from the other two directions (like a coin) | brake cylinder pressure in the brake fluid causes the piston to move outwards, causing friction on a rotating surface | gas cylinder a strong, metal tube that is used for storing and transporting gas under high pressure | hot-water cylinder the circular tank in which heated water is stored | master cylinder the equipment in which the piston is pushed so that a braking force is transmitted through the brake fluid to the brake cylinders | measuring cylinder apparatus that is used for measuring volumes of liquid

cylindrical looking like a jar that is circular in cross-section | cylindrical block a shape that is circular in cross-section, but the diameter is less than the height

cyst a group of cells that has developed a thick wall in order to survive challenging conditions, a swelling within a tissue

cystic fibrosis a genetically determined disease that causes mucus to become thickened and therefore more difficult to move

cyto- (*Greek* a hollow) concerned with cells

cytoplasm the liquid inside the cell membrane in which occur all the chemical reactions of the cell

cytoplast any structure that is in the cytoplasm of a cell, an organelle

D... / da... / deca... (*Greek* ten) prefix for ten of a unit

d... / deci ... (*Latin* ten) prefix for a tenth part of a unit

Da / dalton mass of a proton, atomic mass unit, 1.66×10^{-27} kg

daily something that happens each day, or every 24 hours | daily adaption changes in behaviour so as to make best use of the change of conditions that occurs over 24 hours | daily changes differences that occur each day, *eg* in temperature, wind conditions, rain or light | daily life the habits, food and communications that most people experience | daily variation the change in growth, direction, sleepiness or colour caused by the changing amount of heat and light from the Sun

dairy (plural is dairies) the place where milk is obtained from cows and may be turned into other products | dairy cattle cows that have been bred to produce lots of milk | dairy produce / dairy products any food made from milk

daisy (plural is daisies) a small perennial plant with composite flowers that grows in grassland

dalmatian / dalmation a breed of dog that is white with lots of black or brown spots

Dalton (John 1766–1844) was born in Cumbria, then moved to the big city of Manchester where he remained as a teacher for fifty years – for all of that time, he also kept daily records of the weather, this interest in meteorology led to a study of gases and then onto the idea that elements consist of atoms that are small, indivisible and indestructible, and that compounds are made by joining elements – he measured the atomic mass of many of the elements.

dalton / Da unit for measuring atomic mass, a proton or a neutron has a mass of 1 dalton or 1.66×10^{-27} kg

dam a large wall preventing the flow of water, a mare with foal

damage the extent of breakage; to break, to stop working | brain damage changes have been inflicted on the brain, possibly caused by chemicals, mechanical injury or genetics, so the brain no longer functions properly | dust damage changes in cells caused by the tiny particles of dust | frost damage the breakages produced when the temperature is so low that water turns to ice | lung damage changes to the air sacs, making them less effective at exchanging gases, often caused by inhaling cigarette smoke | physical damage the material has changed shape or size so becoming less useful | specific damage the area of breakage, the type of injury

damaged not working properly | damaged cells the cells are not able to function properly | damaged hearing changes to the ear that may restrict the frequencies that can be heard or the intensity that is needed in order to hear | damaged joint the parts where the bones move over each other have changed so that movement is either restricted or painful

damp moist, small amounts of water are present | damp air the atmosphere is almost saturated with water vapour so condensation may occur at cooler areas | damp conditions the soil has water close to the soil particles and the air contains moisture | damp environment small amounts of water are always present with lots of condensation as the temperature is lowered slightly | damp-proof water is not able to penetrate | damp sand silicon dioxide (sand) mixed with enough water to stick the sand together, but not enough to cause drainage | damp washing clothing that has been soaked in water and not all the water has evaporated | rising damp moisture is rising up the walls of a building because of capillary action in the bricks and cement

damper more humid; equipment that slows the rate of movement

dampness an estimate of the amount of moisture

damp-proof water is not able to penetrate | damp-proof course a rubber membrane that prevents any water from rising up the brickwork and through the walls of a house

dance studio a room with a suspended wooden floor and mirrors covering all the walls

danger anything that could cause injury if not treated with skill, caution and thoughtfulness

dangerous could lead to damage if not carried out carefully | dangerous fumes vapours that will cause illness or death if breathed in

dangle to suspend, to hang loosely, to swing

Daphnia a microscopic water flea

dark lacking in light, not reflecting much light | Dark Ages the years between the collapse of the Roman Empire in the fifth century and the Renaissance in the fifteenth century, Arabic scientists *eg* Al'Khwarizmi, Avicenna and Ibn-al-Nafis were important during this thousand year period

darkened room a chamber in which the light intensity is just adequate for seeing outlines

darkens change that mean less light is reflected or transmitted

darker dimmer, absorbing more light

darkest the object in a group that absorbs most light

darkness absence of light, night time

dart a small arrow that is thrown by hand at a circular target; to move rapidly over short distances

Darwin (Charles Robert 1809–1882) found that studying was 'intolerably dull' despite trying careers in medicine and the church. He joined a naval survey ship, HMS Beagle as an unpaid naturalist for a five-year trip around the world, starting in 1831. He studied many animals and plants in great detail and found that the finches, tortoises and plants were similar but different on a group of islands called the Galapagos Islands. He published his *Journal* in 1839, but continued to think about development and changes that occurred in species. He published many of his ideas in 1858 to be followed a year later by *The Origin of Species by Natural Selection*, the ideas in this book are still being discussed today.

data (plural of datum) information, measurements | data base a collection of facts, observations and measurements concerning some item or events | data books printed collections of information that could be useful but is difficult to remember of find out | data collection the recording of the information that will be analysed later | data handling collection of information and standard methods for changing or presenting that information | data-logger an instrument for automatic collection and storage of measurements | data-logging equipment the instruments and computer that is used to collect, store and display measurements and graphs | data search looking through a collection of information in order to find the item that is of interest to you | data set the measurements that refer to the changes caused by a particular event | additional data more information | analyse data (UK) / analyze data (USA) to find out if the information allows a simple idea to be presented or supported | assemble data to collect the information from several experiments into one section | collect data gather measurements on a specific subject | combine data to use information from more than one source to support an idea | environmental data information concerning the surroundings and conditions in the habitat | evaluate data to see if the information reflects the question and to estimate the error on the observations | experimental data information that was collected by carrying out an experiment | first-hand data information that you have collected by direct

measurement | input data the information put into a computer; to put information into a computer | insufficient data there is not enough information or measurements to allow a conclusion to be drawn | interpret data to say what the information means and what can be predicted if the theory is correct | long-term data information that has been collected over a long period of time | manipulate data to change the information so that conclusions are more easily reached | monitoring data looking for trends and changes in information that is being produced continually | national data the information has been collected for the whole country | numerical data the information is a set of numbers | observed data changes that you have seen happen, measurements that were made | organise data (UK) / organize data (USA) to put similar information together, to put the information into a table with titles and units | patterns in data a simple relationship, model or series of changes that link one variable to another | performance data information concerning how well a task has been carried out | present data to show your information, in a neat form, to other people | process data to modify the data so as to make analysis easier | qualitative data the information gives a rank order of larger, hotter or faster | quantitative data the information is recorded as numbers | record data to write the information down or collect the information on a disc | reliable data information that appears to be accurate and repeatable | remote data information obtained by a sensor that is a long distance from the object being studied | represent data to show the information as a diagram or a cartoon figure | sample data the information obtained from a small number that should be identical to the whole | secondary data / second-hand data information that has been obtained from other people, information that you have been told or read about | speed data information concerning the rate at which an object is covering a distance | store data to put the information to one side for later use | sufficient data enough information | suitable data the information collected is appropriate to answer the question that was set | survey data the information obtained by examining an area of land | synthetic data information that has been prepared from theory | tabulate data put the information into a table format | temperature data information concerning how hot a object is at different places and times | type of data information with common properties |

use data to allow the information to support a claim | **valid data** information that is thought to be true and accurate

data collection the recording of the information that will be analysed later | **remote data collection** obtaining data using instruments that are a long way from the object being observed *eg* using satellites to look at the Earth

date a specific day in a month, the fruit of a palm tree | **date line** an imaginary line between the Poles and running through the Pacific Ocean | **menstruation date** the time at which menstrual bleeding first occurs | **ovulation date** the time at which the egg was released from the ovary

datum (plural is data) a piece of information

daughter cells the offspring that are produced by asexual reproduction of any cell

da Vinci (Leonardo 1452–1519) painter, sculptor, engineer, scientist, architect – name a subject and Da Vinci was the master. His drawings of the difference in muscles when moving, show that he must have (illegally) cut bodies open. His ideas for flying machines and parachutes were still being studied five hundred years on. Leonardo was born and worked mainly in Italy but was later employed, and given a pension, by the Kings of France

Davy (Sir Humphrey 1778–1829) started work as an apprentice pharmacist in Cornwall, but was given the task of investigating laughing gas (nitrous oxide) and was appointed to the Royal Institution in 1801 – an organisation that he turned into the centre for social and scientific meetings. He isolated sodium and potassium, by electrolysis, then moved on to chlorine and fluorine (all four are very dangerous elements). He did not like theories, but he was a superb presenter of science and was fortunate to employ Faraday as his assistant.

dawn the first rays of sunlight at the end of the night; to suddenly see a solution to a problem | **dawn chorus** the loud singing of birds that occurs just as the Sun is starting to provide light

day the time taken for the Earth to rotate completely on its own axis, the time when the Sun is above the horizon | **day length** the number of hours for which the Sun is providing light | **day light** the intensity at each frequency in the light provided by the Sun | **daytime** the period when the Sun is providing light | **cold day** the temperature is sufficiently cold that a coat is needed for comfort | **mid-day** noon, the time when the Sun is at its highest point | **planetary day** the length of time taken for that planet to

rotate once on its own axis | **present day** this decade, contemporary, modern | **working day** the interval between starting work and finishing work | **working days** the amount of time that is spent completing the job

daylight the intensity at each frequency in the light provided by the Sun | **daylight filter** transparent material that transmits different colours to different extent so the spectrum of a light bulb is similar to that of the Sun | **daylight hours** day time, the time during which the Sun is above the horizon

days (not daze which is being confused) a period of time in which the Sun has risen and set several times

daze (not days which is time) the brain is not fully awake, a state of confusion

dB [decibel] – the unit for measuring loudness of sound

dB(A) [decibel – audible] – a modified method of using decibels that takes account of the way the ear works

dc [direct current] the electrons flow in one direction only

DCPIP [2,6 dichloro-phenol-indol-phenol] is blue in solution, but becomes colourless if sufficient vitamin C is added

DDT [dichloro-diphenyl-trichloro-ethane] a long-lasting insecticide that accumulates in the predators of the food chain and may lead to their extinction

de- (*Latin* down, away)

dead no longer alive | **dead bodies** the organic remains of an organism that was once alive | **dead layer** the outermost layer of cells in the skin

Dead Sea a body of water at the border of Jordan and Israel that is the lowest point on land, the water has such a high concentration of dissolved salts (up to 370 grams per litre) that fish and most microbes are unable to survive

deaf unable to hear | **profoundly deaf** never had any ability to hear, totally insensitive to sound

deafness lost sensitivity to sound resulting in a loss of hearing | **inherited deafness** the cause of the lack of hearing is in the genetic instructions | **permanent deafness** the ability to hear will not be restored | **temporary deafness** a loss of hearing that will be restored as the body repairs the damage

deal to set out, to distribute

dear (not deer which is a mammal with four legs) expensive, precious

death the change from being alive to when the cells stop respiring | **death rate** the number of people dying per thousand of that population |

death toll the number of people who have died due to an event such as accident or a specified illness | Black Death an illness, carried by the insects that live on rats, which killed vast numbers of people in Europe in the 14th century

debate to present both sides of an argument, to put forward ideas and evidence in order to reach an agreement

debris broken parts, discarded waste material

deca... / da... / D... (Greek ten) prefix for ten of a unit

decaffeinated the stimulant caffeine has been removed

decant to pour out carefully so the liquid leaves the vessel but solid material remains behind

decay to fade away, often after being broken down | decay curve the graph showing the loss of activity of a radio-active source as time progresses | decay rate the speed with which something fades away | natural decay break-down caused by microbes or weathering | tooth decay caries, the breaking down of the inside of the tooth

deceased dead

decelerate to slow down, to lose speed

decelerating slowing down, losing speed

deceleration losing speed, the rate at which speed is being lost, negative acceleration

deci... / d... (Latin ten) prefix for one tenth of a unit

decibel / dB a tenth part of a bel, the unit for measuring the intensity of sound | decibel scale the agreed series of steps that allow the loudness of a sound to be compared by different people

decide to reach a conclusion

deciding considering the various factors, reaching a conclusion

deciduous / deciduous tree a woody plant in which all the leaves fall off at one time of year (Fall or autumn) and are replaced a few months later in the spring | deciduous area a region in which the trees are mainly broad-leafed and the leaves fall in autumn

decimal each digit is one of ten values

decision a course of action, the conclusion

deck a level platform, one storey of a boat

declaration an announcement, a public promise

decline to go down in number or strength, to refuse

decompose to break down

decomposer a microbe that breaks down excretion products or the body of a dead organism so that all the chemicals can change and then be absorbed

decomposition breaking down | decomposition reaction a chemical reaction involving one chemi-cal that changes to produce simpler substances |

thermal decomposition to use heat in order to break a chemical into two or more products

decorative / decorative features items that are added so as to make the object stand out more clearly

decrease a reduction; to get less, to reduce

deduce to use the available information to reach a conclusion

deep far below the surface | deep layers / deep strata thicknesses of rock that are far below the surface | deep space any part of the universe that is beyond the Solar System

deeper further, lower

deer (not dear which is precious) a four-legged mammal in which the male has antlers | deer park an area of woodland and grass that is safe and suitable for deer | fallow deer a hoofed mammal that is native to Mediterranean countries, the coat is gray in winter, turning pale brown with white spots in summer | red deer a hoofed mammal with horns that has a coat that turns from light brown in summer to dark brown in winter | roe deer the smallest of the deer (approximate height of 75 cm), lives near the edge of woodland

defeat the loss of a battle; to beat, to ruin

defence mechanisms / defence systems methods by which the body prevents microbes from invading and damaging the body, the first defence system is the skin, then the white blood cells and the antibodies try to digest any microbe that gets into the body | body defences methods for keeping microbes out of the body, these include the skin and the linings of the gut and lungs, as well as white blood cells and antibodies | natural defences items that do not need changing in order to prevent entry of an invading organism

defender a protector, an item that helps prevent damage | ear defenders covers for the ears that reduce the intensity of sound that reaches the ear drum

defibrillator equipment that is used to make the heart beat regularly

deficiency (plural is deficiencies) a shortfall, too little, lacking some essential item | deficiency disease illness (and death) caused by lack of chemicals such as minerals (lack of iron leads to anaemia) or vitamins (lack of vitamin A leads to night blindness, lack of vitamin C allows scurvy to develop) | deficiency symptoms showing the signs that a specific chemical is missing from the diet | mineral deficiency the amount of minerals, eg sodium, calcium, magnesium, phosphate, is too low | nutrient deficiency there is not sufficient of some nutrient in the food that is eaten | protein deficiency kwashiokor, the diet is either generally low in amino acids and proteins or missing specific amino acids

define to give meaning, to explain simply

defined specified, known, distinct

definite fixed, certain | definite composition the number and amount of each component is known and is fixed

definition giving the meaning, the separation of dots in a picture, the number of lines on a television

deflagrating spoon a rod with a heat shield near one end and a flat pad at the other that can be used for safely burning small amounts of material

deflate to lose air and so become smaller

deflect to push to one side, to prevent a collision

deforestation the removal of vast areas of trees and undergrowth

deform to push a structure out of shape

deformation to change a structure, without breaking, by applying a force | deformation of rocks / rock deformation bending of the rock layers

deformed visibly different from the expected shape

degenerate to break into pieces, to work less effectively, to lose structure

degeneration breaking down, working less effectively, loss of form

degradable able to be broken down into simpler parts | bio-degradable will be broken down by microbes | photo-degradable can be broken down by light

degrade to break down | biodegrade to break down using living organisms, often microbes

degree a unit of temperature, either Celsius or Fahrenheit, a proportion, a qualification | degrees Celsius the temperature measured using the Celsius scale | degree of precision how near is the measurement to the actual value

dehydrate to remove water

dehydration removing water

deionised water water that has had all the charged particles

delay a wait; to slow down progress | developmental delay some event has prevented change from one stage to another form

deliberately on purpose, with intent

delicate easily damaged, not robust | delicate organ a group of tissue that is easily prevented from working properly

delivery tube a long glass tube that connects the source of a gas, usually a flask or boiling tube, to the collecting point

delta / Δ / δ the fourth letter of the Greek alphabet, the triangular-shape produced by a river that has divided many times, a very small change | river delta a wide area of low lying land at the mouth of a river caused by precipitation of the silt as the river meets the sea

def ↓ ▼ den

demagnetise (UK) **/ demagnetize** (USA) to remove the magnetic properties from a permanent magnet

demand a request, a requirement; to ask | on demand provided when requested

demijohn a glass bottle with a narrow neck and a body capable of holding up to 5 litres

Democritus (of Abdera 470–400 BC) (the happy philosopher) proposed that the universe was made from atoms in a vacuum, that atoms are hard, invisibly small, eternal and always moving. His theory was not accepted for 2000 years.

demonstrate to show by example, to establish, to make a point

demonstrating showing the method

demonstration showing by experiment | bell jar demonstration using a bell jar from which air has been removed to show that light will travel through a vacuum, but sound will not | visual demonstration showing something that involves sight

dendrite a branch of a nerve cell that is able to send or receive a signal

denitrification conversion of nitrates to nitrogen gas

denitrifying bacteria the microbes in soil that convert nitrates to nitrogen gas

dense the density of the object (mass / volume) | less dense the density of one material is lower than that of the other material | more dense the mass per centimetre cubed is greater than the density of another item

denser each centimetre cubed has a greater mass | denser medium the material has a higher density, the material will not allow light to penetrate

densities (plural of density) the masses of each centimetre cube or each cubic metre

density (plural is densities) the mass of each cubic centimetre of a solid or a liquid, or of each cubic metre of a gas

$$\text{density (g/cm}^3) = \frac{\text{mass (g)}}{\text{volume (cm}^3)}$$

| relative density comparing the density of a substance with that of water at the same temperature (approximately 1 g / cm^3 at 20°C)

dent- (Latin tooth)

dented showing the effects of being struck with a hammer

dentine the soft material that takes up most of the volume inside the tooth

dentist a person who has a knowledge of teeth and is able to cure or to prevent dental problems

deny to state that a claim is untrue, to prevent

de-oxygenated the oxygen has been removed | de-oxygenated blood blood leaving the tissues and returning to the lungs, that has most of the oxygen removed

deoxyribonucleic acid / DNA the very, very long molecule in the form of a double helix in which the genes, or instructions for life, are encoded

depend to rely, or to be a consequence, of something else

dependent influenced, determined by something else | dependent variable the value of the dependent variable is determined by the value of the independent variable | functionally dependent the ability of one part to work properly is reliant on another part | psychologically dependent a person has developed that habit of carrying out certain actions and is unable to stop repeating the action

depending relying on a previous event

deplete to reduce to almost nothing

depleted used up, emptied

depletion getting less, reduction over time | ozone depletion the thinning of the layer of ozone high in the atmosphere, possibly caused by use of CFCs (chloro-fluoro-carbons) and leading to increased risk of skin cancer | progressive depletion the gradual and continuing loss of number of species and populations

deposit to drop

deposited dropped

deposition sedimentation, precipitation | deposition of rocks where any geological material falls down, often because either the river slows down or the glacier stops moving | dry deposition dropping smoke particles or sand that have been carried by the wind

depress to lower, to push down, to cause gloom

depressant a substance that reduces an activity | depressant drug a chemical that reduces the activity of nerves

depression an area of the atmosphere that has low pressure, an indent into a surface, an illness in which a person feels unwanted and unhappy

deprive to prevent from using

depth the distance from the surface of a liquid to a point in the liquid | apparent depth the distance that a point appears to be when viewed from the surface

derive / derive from to work out from previous knowledge | derived units measurements that

are not defined (fundamental units are decided by agreement) but must be calculated using formulae

derm- (*Greek* skin)

dermis the layer of skin cells that are alive and able to divide

DERV the fuel sold for a Diesel Engined Road Vehicle

desalination obtaining pure water by getting rid of the salt from sea water | desalination plant equipment or a building that is used to obtain fresh water from sea water

Descartes (René 1596–1650) a French man with a fortune, Descartes became a soldier in Bohemia and Hungary before settling in Holland. His main contributions are to the thinking parts of science (*I think therefore I am* was a starting point), whenever you draw a scatter graph or line graph then think of Descartes – they were his ideas. In 1649, he was persuaded to leave the relative warmth and comfort of Holland to tutor the headstrong Queen of Sweden, and he died shortly afterwards of a lung disease.

descend to go down

descent the act of going down

describe to represent using words | describe patterns to use words to tell what relationships you are able to find

description a statement of what you are able to see | contemporary description an account that was written at the same time as the event was occurring

desert (not dessert which is the last part of a meal) an area which has very low rainfall, the lack of clouds means hot days and cold nights | desert conditions an arid environment similar to what could be expected in a desert | desert plant a producer that is adapted to living in a hot region where rain rarely falls | Sahara Desert the largest desert in the world, covering most of North Africa

design a plan; to plan | design cycle the planning of the shape, the selection of materials and then redesigning and reselection to give a finished product | design an experiment to plan what is going to be done, with reasons for the choice of each material and method and an idea of weights and times | cycle design the planning of the shape and the selection of materials so as to give a wheeled transport | vehicle design a plan for an object with wheels

designate to indicate, to appoint

desirable something which you want or which could be helpful | desirable characteristics features that are important in improving the chances of survival and reproduction

desired wanted or required

dessert (not desert which is land without growth) the last part of a meal, usually sweet

destination the place at which you are hoping to arrive

destroy to break into pieces so it can no longer be used

destruction the breaking into useless pieces

detail a small section, part or observation that may not seem important but may turn out to be significant | fine detail emphasising that any change may be very, very small

detailed observations recording every tiny change

detect to find out, to react to a stimulus

detection the discovery of a substance

detective a person who tries to find the solution to a mystery using clues and observations

detector equipment that is sensitive to a particular stimulus | current detector equipment for finding wires in which electrons are flowing | odor detector (USA) / odour detector (UK) equipment that will respond to specific chemicals in the air | smoke detector equipment that sounds a loud alarm if carbon particles (smoke) are detected

deter to stop, to put off

detergent chemical, usually a long molecule with a charge at one end, that forms a structure that allows fats and oils to be suspended in water | biological detergent a surfactant, or soap, that contains enzymes that will break proteins into soluble fragments

deteriorate to become worse, to break down

deterioration getting worse

determine to find out

determined found out, concluded, unstoppable | environmentally determined some item, such as weight, that depends on the local conditions and not on the genetics of the organism

de Ulloa (Antonio 1716–1795) was born in Spain then went to Peru in 1735. Almost immediately, he isolated platinum but he continued working with geographical expeditions for another 10 years. He returned to Spain and wrote a book of his adventures. He returned to Peru in 1754 and, in 1766, became the first Spanish Governor of Louisiana.

devastate to destroy on a large scale

develop to improve | develop ideas to improve, to enlarge or to expand some theories

developed changed and modified an old idea so the new article is useful, grown to maturity | developed countries the countries where public money over the past two centuries has provided infrastructure, including useful roads, hospitals, schools and libraries

developing improving, getting bigger, growing mature | developing countries non-industrial states that are trying to raise their standard of living | developing fetus (USA) / developing foetus (UK) the embryo in the womb becoming larger and the specialised cells and organs form getting ready for birth

development the growth, the advancement | development pattern the route or plan that is followed when change occurs | development of the Earth / Earth's development changes in the structure of the Earth over periods of millions of years | embryo development the change in the structure and number of cells as the fertilised egg divides to produce a baby | external development the fertilised egg develops outside the body of the mother, eg the eggs of fish, frogs and birds | internal development the fertilised egg develops into an embryo then a foetus inside the mother and the offspring is born alive | medical developments changes in the surgery and drugs given caused by changes in scientific knowledge | pattern of development the series of changes that occur at specific times as an organism ages | prenatal development changes in the foetus, especially in the later stages of pregnancy | scientific developments changes in theories due to new observations | sustainable developments changes, especially in the areas of energy and food production, that should still be in use in a centuries time | technological development providing new devices or equipment by the application of science

developmental delay some event has prevented change from one stage to another form

device an instrument, a machine, a means | domestic device equipment that is used in the home | electrical device any equipment that uses electricity as the energy source | energy device any instrument or component that uses energy for some useful purpose | flotation device equipment that prevents other bodies from sinking | household device equipment that is sold by the shops in town for use in the house | industrial device equipment that is intended for large-scale or continuous use, often in a dirty and dusty environment | magnetic device equipment that uses a magnet force to hold on to a piece of iron | range of devices a variety of instruments using different methods to achieve the same result | relevant devices equipment that could be used for that task | useful device equipment that makes life more pleasant

devise to think of new methods

dew (not due which is expected) a thin layer of water formed during cold nights | dew pond a collection of stones in a depression that always remain cool so dew forms and the water can be collected

Dewar (Sir James 1842–1923) born in Edinburgh, Dewar started life studying the chemistry of cells. In 1877, he was elected professor at the Royal Institution (following in the steps of Davy and Faraday – do you watch the Royal Institution Christmas lectures?) and started work on liquid gases – a strange term that means he took gases and cooled them sufficiently to turn them into liquid, he therefore needed a storage jar and developed the Dewar vessel – more commonly known as a Thermos™, or vacuum, flask. He managed to turn most gases into a liquid and even produced solid hydrogen. Dewar also studied soap bubbles (up to 1 metre in diameter), the Sun's temperature, colours and the chemicals in coal. He has been described as 'the most quarrelsome man in science'!

Dewar flask / Dewar vessel an insulated flask, developed by Sir James Dewar (1842–1923), the jar has double walls with a vacuum between the two walls

di- (Greek two, double)

diabetes a disease in which there is not enough of the hormone insulin so the patient is unable to control the concentration of sugar in the blood

diabetic / diabetic person a person who is unable to control the level of blood-sugar automatically and so needs insulin to be injected

diagram a simple picture that shows the features and ideas that are important to that experiment | annotated diagram a drawing with labels added | circuit diagram using symbols to show the path that the current will take in the real components | concept diagram the main idea is at the centre joined by lines with explanations written on, to other ideas | draw a diagram to show the information or instructions as a picture | energy level diagram the total energy in the bonds of the reactants, the separated atoms and the bonds of the products are shown as horizontal lines | flow diagram a picture to show the movement of energy, chemicals or information but without any details of the processes involved | force diagram using arrows to show the size and direction of forces | frequency diagram bar chart, pie chart, a drawing showing how often an event occurs | genetic diagram a punnet square, a grid that shows the alleles for each pair

along the axes, then the boxes show the possible gentic combinations | kite diagram a method of data presentation used in ecology in which the distribution of plants along a line is shown as a curve above the y-axis and a mirror image of the distribution is shown below the y-axis | particle diagram a drawing that shows the tiny particles in a substance in order to emphasise their behaviour as a gas, liquid or solid | ray diagram a sketch showing the expected path of a light beam | Sankey diagram arrows that show the flow of energy through a system | scale diagram the picture is the same as the real object, but all lengths have been changed by the same ratio | sequence of diagrams a series of drawings | simple diagrams drawings that show only the essential parts | simplified diagram a drawing that shows the essential parts only | spider diagram the main idea is at the centre, joined by lines to possible variations and changes, each of these is joined to other variations | Venn diagram using overlapping circles to show how different items belong to different classes

diagrammatic form showing information by using sketches and drawings

diagrammatically using drawings

dialysis using a membrane to remove waste products (especially urea) from the blood – a job that should be done by the kidneys

diameter a line joining opposite sides of a circle and passing through the centre

diamond the hardest material found in Nature, made from millions of carbon atoms that are covalently bonded to each other | diamond tipped having a single diamond at the end of a pointer, having many small diamonds firmly bonded to the end of a probe

diaphragm a large, thin sheet, the muscle that separates the chest cavity from the abdomen and helps in breathing, a flexible disc that is inserted across the opening of the cervix to prevent conception, a method for controlling the aperture in a camera

diarrhea (USA) / **diarrhoea** (UK) runny, watery faeces or excreta, which may lead to dehydration

diatom one of millions of types of single-celled organism that possess chlorophyll and are found in most bodies of water. a molecule made from two atoms

diatomic containing two atoms | diatomic molecule a compound that is two atoms bonded together

dicotyledons a group of flowering plants whose seed produces a pair of leaves

dictionary a book of words in alphabetical order with the meaning of each word

die (not dye which is to colour) to stop living
died (not dyed which is to colour) no longer alive

Diesel (Rudolph 1858–1913) born in Paris of German parents, raised in London Diesel then graduated from Munich! He was employed to develop refrigerators but worked on an engine that used rapid compression of gas to produce temperatures in excess of 600°C. Diesel disappeared on his way to discuss engines with the British Admiralty.

diesel / Diesel oil a type of fuel, a hydrocarbon with 13–25 carbon atoms

diet the food or drink that an organism consumes; to reduce the amount of food | adequate diet the food is sufficient to prevent any signs of a deficiency disease but may not contain the recommended amount of all nutrients | balanced diet the amount of food ingested is just sufficient to provide all the energy and vitamins needed so there is no loss or gain of body weight and the body is healthy | healthy diet the food contains sufficient amounts of each nutrient for the activity of the person but no food is in excess amounts | human diet the types of food that are eaten by people | inadequate diet some nutrient, essential for healthy growth, is missing | inappropriate diet the amount or type of food was wrong for that person | low-calorie diet the food does not contain much energy in the form of carbohydrates and fats | special diet different from the normal human diet because the food needs to be prepared in a special manner, new chemicals need to be added or certain foods have to be avoided | unbalanced diet / unhealthy diet contains too much of one or more components, usually sugar or salt | varied diet there will be lots of different foods eaten over a period of weeks or months

dietary concerned with what you eat | dietary advice details about the type and amount of food | dietary component one part of what you eat | dietary disease an illness caused by not matching what you eat to what you need | dietary information advice as to the type and amount of foods that would best suit your lifestyle

differ not the same in the ways that are then stated; to disagree

difference features that are unlike each other | difference in temperature the change in temperature in going from one place or time to another | environmental differences comparing the changes caused by unlike conditions | identify differences compare objects and point out things that are not the same | inherited

differences characteristics that identify individuals and which are controlled genetically | key differences the features that allow different organisms to be distinguished | observable differences features that can be seen without detailed or internal examination | potential difference (pd) voltage, the force causing a current

$$\text{potential difference} = \text{current} \times \text{resistance}$$
$$\text{(volts)} \qquad \text{(amps)} \qquad \text{(ohms)}$$

| significant differences important distinctions, there is a meaningful difference between the numbers | temperature difference how much hotter one item is compared to a second item

different not the same | different approaches unlike ways, routes or methods for reaching the same goal | different characteristics features that are easily observed and look or behave in dissimilar ways | different colors (USA) / different colours (UK) each object or organism has a specific colour | different from comparing two items that share many features, but show some important differences | different functions the job that each part has is specific to that part and is unlike the job of the others | different habitats the place where organisms live have some features of temperature, wind or water that are not the same | different ideas contrasting opinions, alternative suggestions, various explanations | different individuals two or more organisms are selected and studied in detail | different materials the substances or fabrics that are used are unlike in some way | different methods the practical approach or experiments that can be carried out to reach a certain goal are not the same in one or more ways | different rates the speed with which a change occurs can be faster or slower | different soils the layers of rock particles in which something is growing are unlike in some features | different sources the information or data were obtained from two or more independent places | different ways using more than one route to achieve the same objective | different weights comparing the weights of two components

differential a mathematical operation to find the slope of a curve, equipment in motor vehicles that allows each wheel to move at a different speed

differently using methods that are not the same

difficult not easy, complicated, needs hard work

difficulty a problem | identify difficulties to point out the items that may cause problems

diffract to bend the edge of a wave at an opening

diffraction the spreading of a wave at the edges of an opening

diffuse spread around; to move away from an area of high concentration | diffuse reflectance / diffuse reflection scattering of light from a rough surface, although every part of the surface will follow the law of reflection

diffusion the movement of particles from a volume of high concentration to everywhere else around

digest to break down large food particles into small molecules that can be absorbed | semi-digested food that has been broken into smaller pieces but is not sufficiently small to be absorbed

digested broken down, large molecules have been turned into nutrients that can be absorbed | digested food the mash produced by the pummelling of the stomach, the hydrochloric acid and the many digestive enzymes

digestion breaking food down into small parts that can be absorbed | chemical digestion using enzymes to break food molecules into pieces that are small enough to be absorbed | physical digestion breaking food into smaller pieces by grinding or dissolving in water | principles of digestion the ideas that explain how the food that goes into the mouth is moved through the gut and is broken into small molecules that can be absorbed | products of digestion the new chemicals that are made when food is broken into smaller pieces

digestive enzymes the proteins that speed up the breakdown of food particles | digestive juices the liquid, especially in the stomach, which causes food to be broken down into small molecules | digestive system the organs and tissues that allow food to be taken in then broken down and absorbed into the blood | digestive tube the long passage, starting with the mouth and ending with the anus, where the breakdown of food occurs

digestor a container in which bacteria and fungi can break down waste material producing compost and biogas

digit a finger, a number

digital using numbers (as opposed to analogue which uses a dial) | digital ammeter an instrument for measuring current, which shows the measurements as figures | digital balance a weighing machine that uses an electronic component to measure the weight and produces an output that is in the form of numbers | digital camera a recording device that stores the picture as a series of numbers | digital display the output is shown as a series of numbers | digital equipment apparatus that uses numbers | digital information data, knowledge that is transmitted as a string of digits (binary is 0s and 1s, hexadecimal is from 0 to 16) | digital input the data arrive as a stream of numbers, often 0s and 1s only | digital meter an instrument in which the output is in numbers | digital output the signal is a stream of numbers, often the binary digits of 0 and 1

digitalis a drug, prepared from the leaves of a foxglove, that encourages that heart to beat regularly

dike / dyke a ditch, a moat, a low dam that protects land from flooding

dilate to open up, to become wider

dilation the widening of the bore in a tube, an increase in the size of the pupil of the eye | dilation of the pupils when the black centres of the eye become wider in dim conditions | broncho-dilation opening of the air passages in the lungs

dilator a chemical that causes a circle to increase in diameter | broncho-dilator a chemical that causes the tubes to the lungs (bronchi) to become wider | vaso-dilator a chemical that causes some blood vessels to become wider

dilute not many particles in a volume, not concentrated (note – dilute is not the same as weak – weak means near to pH 7) | dilute acids acids (pH below 7) which are dissolved in lots of water and so are safe to use | dilute alkalis solutions of the oxides of metals (pH above 7) which do not contain many particles of the oxide | dilute hydrochloric acid (HCl) the concentration of acid which is to be found in most laboratories | dilute solution any solid (solute) dissolved in a large volume of solvent

diluted water has been added so the overall concentration of solute is lower

dilution low concentration

dim / dim light the amount of light is sufficient to see black and white, but not enough that different colours are able to be distinguished

dimensions sizes, number of axes

diminished became smaller, less important

diminishing becoming smaller, getting less

dimmer less bright | dimmer switch a variable resistor that can be used to control the current and so change the brightness of a lamp

dimple slide a piece of glass, approximately 5 cm x 2 cm, which has a dip in the centre for examining microscopic creatures in water | dimple tile / dimple tray a rectangle of plastic or pottery, about 15 cm x 10 cm, that has a pattern of indentations or dimples for small scale reactions

dinner the main meal of the day

Dinorwic the site of a pumped-water storage scheme in Wales

dinosaurs a diverse group of animals, probably related to reptiles, that lived for various periods between 250 million years ago and 65 million years ago

diode an electronic component that will allow current to flow in one direction only, the diode acts as an open switch if the current tries flowing in the other direction | light-emitting diode (LED) an electronic component that will allow the current to flow in one direction only and will then give out light

diorite a dark-coloured igneous rock that turned solid near the bottom of the Earth's crust

. . . dioxide a chemical containing two atoms of oxygen linked to one or more different atoms | carbon dioxide [CO_2] the gas produced by respiration and burning that is essential for photosynthesis, the air is 0.04% carbon dioxide | nitrogen dioxide [NO_2] a brown gas, formed whenever any cell burns, that dissolves in water to produce nitric acid | silicon dioxide [SiO_2] forms the giant molecule that is seen as sand | sulfur dioxide / sulphur dioxide [SO_2] forms whenever any cell burns and falls as acid rain | titanium dioxide [TiO_2] a powder that can be spread to give brilliant white surfaces

dip a small drop; to fall to a lower level | magnetic dip the angle between the horizontal and the Earth's magnetic field

diphtheria infection of the throat, caused by a bacterium, which may be fatal

dipped became lower for a time, then returned to normal

direct straight line | direct current (dc) the flow of charge is in one direction only (as opposed to ac or alternating current, where the current changes direction periodically) | direct method using a technique that gives the required answer rather than an indirect technique where the answer is derived from the measurements

direction the line along which something is moving, the place towards which they are moving | direction-finding equipment a device for establishing the line along which you should be moving | opposite directions one object leaves a point, then another object leaves the same point along the same line but in the other direction | particular direction on a known angle of the magnetic compass | upward direction above, at greater height

directly straight away, by the most direct means

dirt contamination, materials that make an item look unpleasant

dirty not clean, contaminated, greasy

dis- (*Latin* to separate) in two parts

disability a restriction, an inability | physical disability a change to a joint or a bone that causes movements to be restricted

disabled not able to work fully | disabled athlete a competitor who does not have full control of all their joints and muscles

disadvantage an unfavourable factor

disagree to express the opposite opinion

disappear to vanish

disaster something has gone terribly wrong, often with lots of damage and many people injured or starving | natural disaster massive damage caused by an earthquake, torrential rain or high winds

disastrous threatening ruin, a calamity is likely

disc (UK & USA) / **disk** (USA) a vinyl record, a circle cut from a flat piece of material | disc brake equipment for slowing cars that consists of a disc, to which a braking force can be applied, on the same axle as a wheel | antibiotic discs small circles of paper that have been soaked in different drugs that are placed on agar plates on which bacteria are growing so as to test how effective is each drug | compact disc (cd) a data-storage medium using the surface of a silver disc in which are tracks of binary digits | floppy disc (UK & USA) / floppy disk (USA) a method of storing digital information, originally the discs were thin plastic and had to be kept in cardboard cases | slipped disc a common term to explain back pain, more properly should be said that a disc of cartilage between two vertebrae has become weakened

discard to throw out, to get rid of

discharge to remove the charge from an item

discoloration fading, staining, changing colour

disconnect to remove a cable at its joint with another item

discontinuous has breaks or is intermittent | discontinuous variation differences between individuals that can only take specific values *eg* eye colour or sex

discover to be the first to find something

discovered found | newly discovered found in the recent past

discovery (plural is discoveries) finding some new feature or idea

discrepancy a difference between what is ex-pected and what is actually found

discus (not discuss which is to talk) a circular object that is used in throwing contests

discuss (not discus which a disc to be thrown) to talk about the observations and what is known so as to arrive at an agreement, to present both sides of an argument

discussion a talk about a common idea from people with different viewpoints | discussion point talking in detail about one very specific aspect of the work

disease illness | disease control preventing the spread of an illness | disease prevention stopping an illness occurring in a particular part of the population eg by giving injections before the disease arrives | disease-resistant an organism that shows no signs of ill health when exposed to the microbe that would cause an illness to the rest of the population | air-borne diseases illnesses that are transmitted between people by breathing or are carried by the wind | childhood disease any illness that is common in children, but is often more serious if caught by an adult | contagious disease an illness where the causative microbe is spread by touching the infected person | coronary heart disease the heart is not working properly because there are problems with the blood vessels that transport nutrients to the heart | deficiency disease illness caused by a nutrient being missed from the diet, eg anaemia (lacking iron), night blindness (lacking vitamin A), scurvy (lacking vitamin C) | dietary disease an illness caused by some component in the diet, eg some people react to milk, others can not eat food containing flour | emerging diseases illnesses that have been seen only in recent years, eg AIDS, Ebola virus | fungal disease an illness that is caused by infection with a fungus | heart disease an illness that affects the ability of the heart to work effectively | hereditary disease an illness caused by a genetic defect | incidence of disease where, how often and when did an illness occur | infectious diseases an illness that can be caught by breathing the same air as an infected person | local diseases illnesses that are usually found in that area because of the environmental conditions | Minamata disease mercury poisoning | modern disease an illness that has been important only in the past few years | plant diseases disorders that affect growing plants, caused by infection with a virus or a fungus | resistance to disease / resistant to disease will not be affected by the microbe that in other animals or plants of the same species could cause symptoms or death | respiratory disease illness affecting the ability of the lungs to exchange gases | sexually transmitted diseases illnesses that are passed between people during sexual intercourse | specific disease the stated illness | tropical diseases illnesses that are usually seen in the hot, wet places that are within 20° of the equator | water-borne diseases illnesses that are transmitted through creatures that live in water, eg river blindness (a child dies every 8 seconds from water-borne diseases)

dish (plural is dishes) a plate | evaporating dish a glass bowl, approximately 5 centimetres diameter, that is used for turning liquid water rapidly into a vapour | petri dish pairs of circular plates, a base and a cover, used for growing bacteria | satellite dish a concave mirror that reflects signals sent by satellite and collected from the area of the dish onto a central receiver

disinfect to sterilise a surface, to get rid of an invasion of microbes

disinfectant a liquid that kills microbes

disintegrate to fall to pieces, to explode

disk (USA) / **disc** (UK & USA) a vinyl record, a circle cut from a flat piece of material | disk brake equipment for slowing cars which consists of a disk, to which a braking force can be applied, on the same axle as a wheel | antibiotic disks small circles of paper that have been soaked in different drugs that are placed on agar plates on which bacteria are growing so as to test how effective is each drug | compact disk (cd) a data-storage medium using the surface of a silver disk in which are tracks of binary digits | floppy disk a method of storing digital information, originally the disks were thin plastic and had to be kept in cardboard cases | slipped disk a common term to explain back pain, more properly should be said that a disk of cartilage between two vertebrae has become weakened

dislocate to move a joint away from the correct fit | dislocated hip the ball at the top of the femur has moved away from the socket of the pelvis

dislodge pushed off

disorder chaos, not forming a pattern | eating disorder unable to eat normally, an inability to digest some types of food

disparate differences are many and wide ranging

dispense to give out, to distribute

dispersal scattering, especially of seeds | animal dispersal scattering seed by using animals, either the animal eats the fruit and will later excrete the seed or the seed in a case becomes attached to the fur or feather of an animals | explosive dispersal sudden opening of the pods scatters the seed | seed dispersal scattering of seeds by wind, water or animals | wind dispersal throwing seeds out of a pod so they are scattered by the moving air

disperse to spread out, to separate

dispersed spread out, scattered | dispersed light visible radiation that has been separated into the colours of the rainbow

dispersion separating light into the colours of the rainbow, mixing two fluids together so as to give a mixture that has the same composition throughout

displace to push out, to reposition

displacement the volume or mass pushed out, a distance in a specified direction | displacement of water collection of a gas by inverting a tube full of water in a water bath then allowing the gas to collect in the tube and push out the water | displacement reaction / displaement rule a more reactive metal will push out a less reactive metal from a solution of its salt, a more reactive halogen will push out a less reactive halide

display a large size of work; to show off, especially for attracting a mate | display results to show your observations and measurements in clear fashion | display work items that are intended to be shown publicly | digital display using numbers to show information | firework display an entertainment lasting several minutes in which many brightly coloured fireworks are ignited in turn to give synchronised patterns | graphic display a picture or diagram that shows the results of an experiment | laser display making patterns in the sky using laser lights | real-time display a dial or number that shows what is occurring at the same time as the event is happening | wall display showing drawings and pictures on the wall

disposable meant to be thrown away after use

disposal getting rid of | safe disposal getting rid of material in a way that will cause no damage to the environment

dispose of to get rid of an object by throwing out

disprove to show, by experiment, that some idea is wrong

dissect to cut open with the intention of looking carefully

dissection the act of cutting open to show specific features

dissipate to scatter over a large area, to spread through a vast volume

dissipated spread out until the concentration is too low to cause any effect | dissipated energy the heat energy that is lost to the surroundings causing a tiny increase of temperature

dissipation the act of spreading (eg energy, smells, particles) over a large volume

dissolve to mix a solid into a liquid (solvent) so that the solid seems to disappear as the particles become too small to be seen

dissolved mixed into a liquid | dissolved air the gases from air (nitrogen, oxygen and carbon dioxide) that can not be seen in water, but must

be there in order for plants to grow and animals to live | dissolved gas any gas that has been dissolved in a liquid, eg carbon dioxide, under pressure, is dissolved in flavoured water to give fizzy drinks | dissolved minerals the ions, or charged particles, that will dissolve in water | dissolved oxygen amount of oxygen gas that is dissolved in water (oxygen does not dissolve in blood – the oxygen is carried by the haemoglobin in the red blood cells) | dissolved salts solids, made from metal ion and another ion, dissolved in water | dissolved solids chemicals that are in water that can be weighed when all the water has been evaporated

dissolving mixing a solid into a liquid

distance the length between two points, should be measured in metres (m) | distance multiplier a lever in which the distance moved by the load is much greater than the distance moved by the effort | distance–time graph a diagram showing the distance that an object has moved at increasing times, the gradient is the speed of movement | apparent distance the separation of two objects as seen by the eye | braking distance the length of road that is needed to stop a car once the brakes have been applied, depends on speed and tyre grip | relative distances comparing two displacements | stopping distance the total length of thinking distance and braking distance added together | thinking distance the length you travel while deciding what response to make to an incident in front of you, depends on the reaction time of the driver and the speed of the vehicle

distant a long way away

distil to heat a mixture so as to obtain a vapour that can be cooled to give a pure liquid

distillate the liquid produced when a vapour is condensed

distillation heating a liquid, removing the vapour then condensing the vapour to give a liquid made from a single chemical | distillation apparatus the equipment that is used in order to hold the liquid to be heated, the heating method and the way that the vapour is cooled | fractional distillation is used to separate chemicals with very similar boiling points, eg different parts of crude oil | simple distillation uses a heated flask attached to a condenser to purify water

distilled water water that has been obtained by boiling tap water, removing the water vapour the cooling the vapour to give water that should contain no dissolved solids

distillery a series of buildings in which the grains of a cereal are germinated, fermented and then distilled to give whisky

distilling purifying a liquid by heating the mixture, removing the vapour then condensing the vapour

distinct clear, specific, recognisable | distinct layer a thickness of material that is easily seen sandwiched between other material | distinct property a characteristic that is possessed only by that substance

distinction the feature that sets one person apart from another

distinctive clear | distinctive feature a characteristic that is possessed only by that material or creature

distinguish to tell the difference between

distinguished having at least one characteristic feature that is easily seen

distinguishing features characteristics or points of observation that allow different members to be named

distort to change in small ways so that the ideas and consequences change, often in large ways

distortion a change, a twisting

distract to divert, to be moved away from the main target

distracted not giving the attention that is required

distribute to give out, to spread around

distribution how many organisms are found in different areas | distribution of results how spread out is the data | compare distribution to look at the number and type of organism in different environments | starch distribution the areas where starch will be found in a plant

district an area | Lake District an area of north western England that has lots of sharp peaks and many valleys that are flooded

disturb to interrupt, to cause an unexpected change

ditch an open channel in the ground | irrigation ditch a channel for directing water to specific areas

diurnal follows a 24 hour cycle, often with distinct differences caused by night and day

diverge to move away from each other

diverging lines moving away from a point in many directions | diverging lens transparent material that has been shaped so as to cause light to spread out, usually a concave lens

divers (not diverse which means different) people who swim underwater, swimmers who have jumped from a board | skin-diver a scuba diver, a person who swims under-water with a tank of air on their back (self-contained underwater breathing apparatus) | sky diver a parachutist who falls for most of the distance from the plane to the ground before opening the parachute and will often perform manoeuvres in the air

diverse (not divers which means swimmers) many different kinds, a variety

diversity how many different types of organisms are found in an area | bio-diversity a measure of how many different types of organisms there are in a particular area

divide / sub-divide to break into parts

divided separated | divided by the material that prevents the separate objects from meeting

dividing separating, carrying out a mathematical operation | dividing cells the cells that are reproducing asexually

division splitting, asexual reproduction, a small part of a large organisation, the ratio of two numbers, a mathematical operation | division of labor (USA) / division of labour (UK) separating a large job into smaller parts that can be carried out by individuals | cell division a living cell divides into two | scale division the small parts of a scale between the fixed points | subdivision a smaller part

DNA [deoxyribonucleic acid] a complex very long thin molecule made from four types of units and arranged in a double helix, the arrangement of the units in the DNA provides the instructions or genes that control the cell | DNA analysis using enzymes and chemical methods to cut the genetic material into pieces that can be separated and characterised | DNA strand a long string of nucleotides, one of the two filaments that wind around each other in the chromosome

Döbereiner (Johann Wolfgang 1780–1849) was a self-educated teacher. He proposed a law of triads in which one element of each triad has properties that were very close to the average of the other two elements.

document an important text, a book, an agreement

dodo three species of flightless bird that became extinct between 1660 and 1720

doe (not dough which is used in baking) a female deer

does (not dose which is a portion) capable of carrying out an action, female deer

dog a carnivorous mammal that has been domesticated as a pet | dog whelk looks like a snail, but lives in the sea | dog whistle a tube that is blown so as to produce a sound that has a frequency above the range of human hearing but that dogs can hear

dolerite an igneous rock produced when the magma cools underground

dolomite a sedimentary rock that is a mixture of calcium carbonate and magnesium carbonate [$CaCO_3.MgCO_3$]

dolphins mammals that are adapted to living in the open water (sea or large rivers) and which can hunt by echo location

domain an area | domain model the theory that any magnet is made out millions of tiny areas of magnetic material | magnetic domain a tiny area (a few atoms) of magnetic material

dome a hollow hemi-sphere, a rounded ceiling

domestic around the house (as opposed to in-dustrial which is large scale) | domestic animals animals that live in a house alongside humans | domestic devices machine, instrument or tools that are found in a house and help improve the quality of life | domestic electricity the electrical energy that is used in the house, usually 240 volts 50 hertz alternating current | domestic environ-ment the conditions of temperature and humidity that people find comfortable and aim to achieve in their houses | domestic heat loss the amount of thermal energy that is lost from the house and which could be reduced by insulation | domestic livestock animals that are kept in the home for the pleasure they give, *eg* cats, dogs, hamsters | domestic pet an animal with which you are happy to share your home | domestic uses an object that may be used anywhere, but is employed for a purpose in the house

domesticated taught to behave in a way that is compatible with living in a house

dominant takes control, especially in genetics where parents provide different instructions for the same characteristic, but only the dominant instruction is used (the other instruction is called recessive) | dominant allele the instruction that is always expressed if present | dominant characteristic the feature that is always seen when the cells has at least one of the dominant alleles for that trait

dominate to control, to rule

donate to give away

done ended, finished | work done energy used measured in joules

donkey a small member of the horse family, a beast of burden

donor a person who gives something away | donor organism the animal that has the organ that is to be transplanted | blood donor a person who voluntarily gives some of their blood, usually 500 cm^3, to be used for medical purposes

door a hinged opening to a room or to a building | door bell a bell inside the house with the switch on the outside | door catch a mechanism for ensuring that the door will remain closed | door step the block of flat, hard stone at the base of a door in the outer wall of a building | revolving doors four doors revolve around the central axis

of a cylinder so that there is minimal exchange of air form inside and outside the building

doormouse / dormouse a small rodent similar to a mouse but with a long, bushy tail

dormancy being inactive or dormant

dormant inactive or latent | dormant structures any construction, arrangement or group of cells that are inactive, but will grow and divide when the conditions are right | dormant twigs small branches that do not seem to be alive, but, given warmth, light and water, will start to grow again | dormant volcanoes volcanoes that have not erupted for a long time, but are still able to blow their tops at some time in the future

dormouse / doormouse a small rodent similar to a mouse but with a long, bushy tail

dorsal the back | dorsal fin the large fin on the back of most fish (especially prominent in sharks!)

dose (not does which is a carrying out) a measure, a portion; to give a medicine | fatal dose the amount taken is sufficient to kill the body | overdose taking too much of a drug leading to illness or death | safe dose the quantity of a substance that can be taken each day without causing ill effects

dot a circular mark made by the tip of a pen or pencil; to add small points

dotar a musical instrument with two strings

dotted marked with small spots | dotted line a path shown by spots and spaces

double twice as much | double blind trial a method of removing bias – neither the subject nor the person making the observations will know if the subject has been given an active drug or a placebo | double circulation system having one set of vessels and a pump to move blood to and from the lungs and a second set of vessels and another pump to move the blood around the body | double cropping sowing seeds from a slow-growing plant and a fast-growing plant at the same time into the same ground then they can be harvested separately | double glazing two layers of glass that trap a layer of air, so reducing loss of heat and preventing entry of noise | double pump describes the heart as two pumps in a single organ

Double Eagle II in 1979, became the first helium balloon to cross from America to France, taking 137 hours to travel 5000 kilometres

dough (not doe which is a female deer) mixture of flour and water with or without yeast | bread dough made by mixing flour with yeast and water, then leaving to rise as bubbles of carbon dioxide are produced

dowel / wooden dowel a piece of cylindrical wood

down closer to the Earth, a fine coat of feather or hair | down feathers the fine feathers that provide insulation to birds, but are not suitable for flight | down stream the river and the river banks at any point below the stated area flowing towards the sea | breakdown the splitting into smaller parts | break down to separate into smaller pieces | broken down unable to work, damaged, turned into smaller pieces | cut down the organism fell over because the base had been chopped away | push down using weight to compress, rotate or change shape | scaling-down making smaller | slow down to move at a lower speed | wear down to rub away, to abrade, to make thinner

downwards towards the Earth | downwards force gravity, the force pulling an object towards the Earth | downwards growth the root is growing deeper into the soil

draft (USA) / **draught** (UK) a slight wind, an outline, a first attempt | draft excluder sealing material that prevents entry of cold air into a warm room | draft plan a preliminary outline, an outline of future actions

drafty (USA) / **draughty** (UK) an uncomfortable area, or room, in which cold air can easily enter and leave

drag / drag force air resistance caused by the object trying to push air particles out of the way

drain a tube for removing waste water; to remove a liquid

dramatically suddenly, forcefully

draught (UK) / **draft** (USA) a slight wind, an outline, a first attempt | draught excluder sealing material that prevents entry of cold air into a warm room

draughty (UK) / **drafty** (USA) an uncomfortable area, or room, in which cold air can easily enter and leave

draw to derive, to reach, to pull out, to extract, to produce a picture using a pencil, to pull out | draw a conclusion to use the evidence to provide a simple explanation | draw a diagram to show the information or instructions as a picture | draw a graph use the measurements, with the independent variable along the horizontal axis and the dependent variable on the vertical axis, to provide a simple curve | draw in to take inside | draw inferences to provide explanations for some observations

drawbacks disadvantages, problems

drawbridge a large plate that allows traffic to cross a ditch or moat, but which can be raised so as to prevent entry of unwanted people

drawing a diagram | drawing pin thumb tack, a small nail with a wide head | clear drawings showing important aspects | prepared drawings diagrams that are printed but need finishing off, *eg* by adding labels | scale drawing a simple picture that shows all the components in the correct proportions

drawn produced a picture using a pencil, pulled out, extracted, pulled

dray / drey a low cart drawn by a horse

dressing the act of putting on clothes, a covering that is used to protect an open wound | medical dressing the protective covering, of lint, cotton wool and cloth, that is placed over a wound to prevent infection or further damage while healing takes place

drew past tense of draw

drey / dray a low cart drawn by a horse

dried removed moisture | dried milk milk that has had all the moisture removed so it can be stored for a long time

drier / dryer less wet; equipment for removing water | spray drier equipment that injects a fine mist of liquid into a vacuum chamber so the solvent evaporates and the solute falls as a dry powder | tumble drier a heated drum that separates clothing and evaporates the water

drift to move slowly in random directions | continental drift movement of the tectonic plates of the Earth's crust

drill a pattern of activity that has to be followed many times, equipment that rotates so as to make a hole; to make a hole, to repeat a short performance | drill bit the rotating end that cuts into the material | drill string the long tube (up to 5000 metres!) that connects the drilling rig to the cutting drill bit

drink a liquid that is swallowed; to take in liquid through the mouth | drinks can the hollow cylinder of metal, sealed at both ends, that is used for storage, transport and sale of drinks | fizzy drink a mixture of water, flavours and colourings that contains carbon dioxide dissolved under pressure | high-energy drink a liquid that contains a large amount of glucose | soft drink a liquid containing no alcohol that is suitable for quenching thirst

drinkable water that is safe to drink although the taste may not be good, potable

drinking water water with sediments and microbes removed so it is safe to drink

drip a slow leak of liquid; to form drops | saline drip the sterile fluid, water containing mainly sodium chloride, that medics flow into the patient's vein in order to replace lost body fluids

dripping a liquid falling in drops

drive to push, to direct

driver equipment used for moving, a person in charge of a vehicle | **screw-driver** equipment for turning a screw

driving force the effect that is trying to make an object move in a particular direction

drone a continual, low-intensity, low-pitched sound, a male bee

drooped bent over, hanging

drop a small sphere of liquid; to fall | **sudden drop** a decrease that is both unexpected and substantial

droplets very small spheres of fluid | **tiny droplets** small spheres of water that are too small to be seen individually but large numbers cause fog, mist or clouds

dropped fallen

dropper a method, usually a long tube with a rubber teat, for delivering small amounts of liquid

dropping decreasing, descending, getting less, falling | **droppings** the faeces of animals | **dropping bottle** the stopper of a small bottle (capacity less than 10 cm^3) has a hole so drops of liquid can be released in a controlled manner | **dropping pipette** (also called a pasteur pipette) a tube into which liquid is introduced using a teat and then drops of the liquid are released by gently pressing the teat | **bird droppings** the excretion products of a bird's digestion that often will contain large amounts of phosphate

droppings the faeces of animals

dropsy swelling of the body caused by retaining fluid, death can result as the lungs are damaged by too much fluid

drought lack of water

drown to fill the lungs with water so preventing exchange of gases

drowned died as a result of flooding the lungs with water

drugs chemicals that cause a change to some cells | **drug addict** a person who needs to take a particular chemical, usually an illegal drug | **drug resistance** the microbe is not affected by that chemical, development of new strains of bacteria that are not affected by the chemical | **drug treatment** using specific chemicals to treat an ailment, using methods to try to stop a person needing to take an drug that affects the brain | **abusing drugs** taking chemicals that cause changes to the brain in quantities that will cause long-term damage | **addictive drugs** chemicals that cause a change in the chemistry of the brain and which are constantly needed | **antiviral drug** a chemical that destroys viruses | **categories of drugs** chemicals that can affect the body that are separated into groups with common features |

depressant drugs chemicals that reduce the activity of nerves | **fertility drugs** chemicals that are given in order to increase the chances of an egg being produced | **illegal drugs** chemicals that are used to give pleasure but the Government has banned from possession by the public | **legal drugs** chemicals that can cause a change the behaviour of your cells or your brain, that can be bought in a shop, *eg* alcohol, caffeine, nicotine | **medical drugs** chemicals that are given in order to cure a disease but will affect the cells of a person | **over-the-counter** (otc) **drugs** chemicals that could affect the body, which can be bought from a pharmacy without prescription | **prescription drugs** chemicals that affect the body but need special permission from a medic | **recreational drugs** chemicals that are taken voluntarily, and usually for pleasure, which cause dramatic changes to the brain

drum musical instrument made by stretching a skin over a frame | **drum brakes** a method for stopping a car in which brake-shoes are pushed against the inside surface of rotating drums | **drum skin** the material, usually an animal skin or plastic, that is stretched tightly over a circular frame | **ear drum** the stretched piece of skin at the end of the ear canal that allows sound to be transmitted to the ossicles, but prevents entry of microbes

drumlin a low mound of rock left by a glacier

drunk has taken liquid through the mouth, has lost control of the body because of drinking too much alcohol

dry absence of moisture | **dry air** the atmosphere is almost free of any moisture | **dry cell** an electric power source (cell) in which the electrolyte is in a jelly so the cell can be turned upside down without all the contents spilling out | **dry cleaners** a company that removes dirt and stains from clothes without using water | **dry cleaning** removing dirt from clothes using a solvent other than water | **dry conditions** an environment that contains very little moisture | **dry deposition** dropping smoke particles or sand that have been carried by the wind | **dry ice** carbon dioxide that has been cooled below − 60ºC, and so is a solid, will turn directly to gas (sublime) when the temperature is raised | **dry mass** the material that is left when all the moisture has been removed | **dry rot** timber decay caused by infection with a fungus | **dry skin** a lack of oil means that the dead outer layer of skin flakes off more easily | **dry spell** a period when there is no rain | **dry up** removal of water from an area that is usually wet

dryer / drier less wet; equipment for removing water | spray dryer equipment that injects a fine mist of liquid into a vacuum chamber so the solvent evaporates and the solute falls as a dry powder | tumble dryer a heated drum that separates clothing and evaporates the water

drying losing water, the act of causing loss of water | drying agent a desiccant, a chemical that removes water vapour from the air | spray drying removing water from droplets of water at very low temperature

dryness a qualitative measure of the amount of moisture that is remaining

duck a species of bird that lives on fresh-water rivers or lakes; to lower the upper body | nodding ducks / Salter's ducks equipment for using the energy from waves to produce electricity, developed by Professor Stephen Salter (born 1938) in 1976, but dammed by a biased report in 1980

duckweed a small green plant that grows on the surface of fresh water

duct a tube | alveolar duct the tiny tube connecting each air sac to the bronchiole | bile duct the tube connecting the gall bladder to the small intestine | lymphatic ducts tubes containing the fluid (lymph) that drains from between cells and is important in the immune response | oviduct (fallopian tube) carries the ovum from ovary to the womb | sperm duct the tube joining the testes to the end of the penis

ductile can be bent, hammered into thin sheets or pulled into thin wires – all without breaking

due (not dew which is condensation) expected, owed | due to caused by

dug-over ground earth that has been turned over, so breaking up the soil and moving many nutrients close to the surface

dull non-reflective, not shiny, unable to react rapidly | dull surface a covering that does not reflect light

dumb unable to speak, without independent control

dump an area that is used for collecting rubbish; to drop

dunes / sand dunes banks, mounds or ridges of loose sand

dung manure, faeces

duodenum the part of the small intestine closest to the stomach

duplicate to do an experiment a second time, using exactly the same conditions, in order to check the accuracy of the measurements | duplicate measurements carrying out the same experiment twice in order to check for accuracy

duration a continual length of time

during at the same time, over a period

dusk the time when the Sun is setting below the horizon, so there is little light or heat

dust tiny particles, usually the remains of dead skin cells | dustbins containers for rubbish | dust damage harm caused by tiny fragments of material | dust mite a tiny arthropod that lives by eating dead skin cells | dust particles the individual tiny specks | chalk dust powder produced by breaking pieces of chalk

duster a cloth that is used for removing tiny particles

dusty covered with a thin layer of fine powder

duvet a bed cover that is filled with insulating fibres

dwarf short or small compared to the rest of the population | dwarf plant a plant that has the genetic instructions to remain low | white dwarf a star with a mass greater than that of the Sun in a volume that is smaller than the Earth

dwarfism the condition of being very short

dye (not die which is to stop living) a coloured chemical that can be attached to fabric so as to produce a coloured effect | colored dyes (USA) / coloured dyes (UK) chemicals that dissolve in water and can be used to change the colour of cloth or paper | food dyes chemicals used to give colour to food and drink

dyed (not died which is no longer alive) chemicals have been used to change the colour

dying losing life, approaching death, adding colours to cloth

dyke / dike a ditch, a moat, a low dam that protects land from flooding

dynamic producing movement | dynamics the part of mathematics that deals with movement | dynamic equilibrium lots of things are happening, but there is no apparent change, eg your body weight will eventually reach dynamic equilibrium – lots of food going in, but no change of weight | dynamic model a theory in which the different parts are moving and changing | dynamic system a series of objects that cause each other to change

dynamite an industrial explosive, invented by Nobel, made by absorbing nitro-glycerine onto an inert powder

dynamo a machine for turning kinetic (moving) energy into electrical energy

dysentery a disease, caused by infection by bacteria or amoeba, that produces painful diarrhoea. The disease can be spread by carriers – people who show no sign of the disease, but can spread the microbe to others in the community

E.../ exa... (*Greek*) prefix for a million, million, million of a unit, 10^{18}

e$^-$ [electron] the atomic particle that has no mass and a negative charge

E-number the identifier that has been given to one of set of chemicals that can be added to food *eg* to change the colour (E100 – E180), to be a preservative (E200 – E299), to enhance the taste

E.coli (*Escherichia coli*) a type of bacterium that is commonly found in the gut, where it usually does no harm

each every one, separately

eagle a large bird of prey

ear organ of hearing | ear ache pain within the ear, often caused by bacterial infection | ear bones (ossicles) three tiny bones in each ear (hammer, anvil and stirrup) that transmit sound from the ear drum to the cochlea | ear canal the tube from the outside world that ends with the ear drum | ear defenders covers for the ear that reduce the intensity of sound that reaches the ear drum | eardrum / ear drum the membrane (thin sheet) that allows sound to enter, but prevents the entry of any material, *eg* bacteria, from the outside world | ear flaps the visible part of the mammalian ear that should be called the pinna | ear infection growth of microbes inside the middle ear | ear lobes extensions of the pinna of the ear that may be attached to the skull or free floating, depending on the presence of a single gene | ear muffs two circles of fur, or other insulating material, that are used in winter to cover the ears to keep them warm | earphones small equipment that fits into the ear canal and that changes electrical signals into sound | ear plugs cylindrical pieces of wax or plastic that are inserted into the ear canals so as to limit the damage caused by loud and continuous noises | ear protectors covers that fit the ears so as to reduce the intensity of sound reaching the ear-drum | ear-ring an ornament that is attached to the lobe of the ear | ear wax the essential lubricant that keeps the ear canal and ear drum flexible, but can increase in amount and lead to temporary deafness | inner ear the cochlea and semi-circular canals that are in a cavity within the bone of the skull | middle ear the space, connected to the throat by the eustachian tube, containing the ossicles | outer ear the part of the ear that you can see, the pinna, ear canal and ear drum

earlier some time before the event that is being discussed | earlier ideas the thoughts that developed before the present observations were made | earlier treatment chemicals, such as drugs or fertiliser, that have already been given, the medicines and care that were given in previous years | earlier work experiments and observations that had been carried out previously

early near the start of that particular area of study, the start of the day | early growth the changes that occur as the single fertilised cell is dividing and becoming more specialised, the first leaves that are produced by plants | early ideas the estimates, theories and guesses that were available when the amount of information available was very small | early model any theory that was put forward shortly after the observations had been made | early signs the small, almost insignificant, changes that occur near the start of an event

Earth the planet on which we live that is the third rock from the Sun, diameter is 12,750 kilometres, distance to the Sun is 150 million kilometres | Earth's core the metal sphere at the centre of the Earth | Earth's crust the thin, solid layer (up to 90 kilometres thick) that is the outside surface of the Earth | Earth year the time period taken for the Earth to orbit once around the Sun (approximately 365 Earth-days), often used to allow comparison between the year length of each planet | Earth's development / development of the Earth the change in the structure of the Earth from a cloud of dirt that came together to give the planet, through the different surface movements to the present day structure | Earth's magnetic field the Earth seems to act like a giant magnet, so that the north pole of every compass is attracted to one end of the Earth | earthquake movement of some area of the Earth's crust | Earth's surface the outer part of the Earth's crust that we are able to see and feel | earth wire the safety feature in most electrical circuits that prevents electrocution | earth worm the living organism shaped like a tube that helps the soil by providing holes and digesting leaf mould | Earth years the time period taken for the Earth to orbit once around the Sun (approximately 365 Earth-days), often used to allow comparison between the year length of each planet | development of the Earth / Earth's development changes in the structure of the Earth over millions of years | flat Earth the theory that the Earth is a plate and you could sail over the edge | restless Earth the picture that over long periods of time, the continents move relative to each other causing mountains and oceans to appear and disappear | rotation of the Earth the movement of the Earth around an axis that passes close to the Poles | spherical Earth the idea that the Earth is a sphere in space | tilted Earth the axis of rotation of the Earth is at an angle of about 70° to the solar plane

earth soil, the material in which plants will grow

earthed the equipment has one wire that is connected to the earthing circuit

ease without any effort; to make less difficult

easily without difficulty | **easily seen** obvious, stands out

east one of the four main directions on a compass, the Sun rises in the east

easy without difficulty, without great effort

eat (not heat which is energy) to take food into the mouth

eaten has ingested food

eating taking in food | **eating disorder** unable to eat or to digest some types of food

Ebola virus causes blood loss, fever and, in most cases, death. First identified in 1976, named after the Ebola river in Zaire

echinoderms marine animals with five-rayed symmetry that have a single cavity for digestion, absorption and excretion

echo (plural is echoes) a sound that has been reflected by a hard surface (soft surfaces absorb the sound energy); to reflect a sound, to re-verberate | **echo location** finding the position of an object in a place where light is not available by sending a pulse of sound and measuring the time taken for the echo to return | **echo-sounder** equipment that produces a pulse of ultra-sound, measure the time until the echo returns then calculate the distance | **echo soundings** finding the depth of water by sending a pulse of sound and measuring the time taken to return

echoes (plural of echo) reflections of sound

eclipse when one object in the Solar System prevents another body being seen | **eclipse of the Moon / lunar eclipse** when the Earth is on the line joining the Sun to the Moon so the light from the Sun is obscured by the Earth, because of the Earth's atmosphere, the Moon appears to become dark red or purple | **eclipse of the Sun / solar eclipse** when the Moon moves into the direct line between the Sun and the Earth so the shadow of the Moon falls on the Earth and the Sun can no longer be seen | **lunar eclipse** the Earth is in the line between Sun and Moon | **partial eclipse** a solar eclipse in which the Moon covers part of the Sun's brightness | **solar eclipse** the Moon is in a line between the Sun and the Earth and so casts a shadow on the Earth | **total eclipse** the Moon is in a direct line between Sun and Earth so the Sun's disc is totally covered

eco- (*Greek* house) relationship between organisms and their habitat

E. coli (*Escherichia coli*) a type of bacterium that is commonly found in the gut, where it usually does no harm

ecological relationship how different organisms affect and depend on their environment and interact with each other

ecologist a person who studies the interaction of life and the environment

ecology the study of organisms in their natural living conditions

economic concerned with money, the best balance between cost and quality

economically good quality at a cheap price | economically important affecting the amount of wealth

ecosphere the Earth's ecosystem, consisting of all the organisms that live on land, in the air or under water, a collection of different of animals and plants that are in dynamic equilibrium in a sealed container

ecosystem the life and conditions in a specific area | **stable ecosystem** the conditions and the populations of each organism has been unchanged for a long time

Ecstasy (methylene-dioxy-methamphetamine) an illegal hallucinogenic drug that is said to heighten the sense, but has led to several deaths

ecstasy a state of extreme happiness

ecto- (*Greek* outside)

ectoparasite a small organism, eg worm or insect, that lives on the outside of an animal, usually causing discomfort and harm, without providing any benefit to the host animal

edge (not a hedge which a line of bushes) the boundary | **sharp edge** a sudden change, a border that is distinctly different

Edison (Thomas Alva 1847–1931) was the most prolific of inventors, submitting a new idea for patenting every fortnight for over 60 years – yet he had almost no formal education because he had been expelled from school! He started by in-venting an electrical vote recorder then went on to revolutionise communication along the rail-ways, improved the microphone on Bell's telephone and invented the light bulb – this latter task needed him to test several thousand materials until he found one that worked – Edison was not one to give up easily! New light bulbs needed an improved supply of electricity so Edison doubled the efficiency of generators and improved power cables.

education teaching and learning (literally a 'leading out') | **alcohol education** telling people about the uses, benefits and drawbacks of drinking alcohol

eel (not heel which is at the end of a foot nor heal which is to mend a wound) a fish that looks like a snake | sand eel a fish that is long and thin, like a snake, and lives in the sand

effect the change caused; to cause, to bring about the result of a change | effects of alcohol the increased confidence and the lack of co-ordination resulting from alcohol causing changes in the brain | effects of smoking the changes (damaged lungs / smell / lack of oxygen carrying capacity) brought about in the body by smoking cigarettes | cooling effect the decrease in the average world temperature that could be caused by acid rain | environmental effects the changes in the local conditions | greenhouse effect an increase in the temperature of the Earth caused by burning fossil fuels and so increasing the concentration of carbon dioxide in the atmosphere | harmful effect the result damages cells or organisms, the result causes a change in environmental conditions | heating effect causes an increase of temperature | ill-effect a substance, which was intended to be useful, causes the recipient to feel unwell | knock-on effect changing one object will cause a change in an unrelated object or organism | long-term effects changes that occur over a long period of time | magnetic effect a change that is related to, or caused by, the phenomenon of magnetism | negative effects the end result is not good | placebo effect taking a tablet that contains no active ingredient (a sugar pill) may cause the illness or pain to disappear | potential effect a change that could occur | resultant effect the outcome related to a specific variable or input, differences that are caused by the stimulus | side effects unexpected or unavoidable changes that are not related to the desired outcome | specific effect the result is concentrated on a stated item | turning effect using a force to cause the rotation of a lever or wheel

effected (not affected which means changed by) caused by, the way a change was made

effective produce the required result | effective approaches methods that produce the measurements or changes that are desired | effective use operating an instrument with the minimum of trouble | cost-effective a process that will cost money in the short-term, but eventually provides a profit | highly effective works superbly well at that particular task

effectively productively, without waste

effectiveness an estimate of how well the process is working

effector any tissue that reacts to a stimulus | effector nerves carry the messages that cause muscles to contract or relax

effects the changes, the differences

effervesce to bubble rapidly

effervescence bubbling, especially around a solid

efficiency the ratio of output energy to input energy

efficient working effectively | efficient use the work done achieves the objective without waste | efficient way a method that achieves the desired result with the least amount of effort | energy efficient the minimum amount of energy is used to achieve the specified objective

efficiently competently, without waste

effluent the liquid that is released into rivers and lakes from sewage works

effort the force that is applied

e g [Latin *exempli gratia*] for example (literally 'example given')

egest to get rid of some material that is unchanged from when the material went in, *eg* fibre is egested from the human gut

egestion the act of getting rid of material that is unwanted because it can not be used

egg oval body laid by birds, reptiles and fishes that contains the egg cell and sufficient food for the offspring to develop | egg case the hard container that is large enough to protect an egg and to allow development of the immature insect | egg cell the female reproductive cell, or gamete, that is very large and immobile because it is full of nutrients | egg maturation the change in structure of an immature egg cell in the ovary to give a gamete that is capable of being fertilised | egg shell the hard, strong protective coat around the egg | egg tube (fallopian tube, oviduct) the very thin tube down which the ovum, or egg, is moved on its way from the ovary to the uterus | egg white albumen, the solution of nutrients that surround the yellow of an egg | boiled egg a hen's egg has been heated in boiling water so the contents have turned solid because the proteins have denatured | fertilised egg (UK) / fertilized egg (USA) a zygote, the nucleus of the female sex cell has fused with the nucleus of the male sex cell | lay eggs the production of eggs by hens | rotten eggs the contents of the egg have changed chemically so they have the horrible smell of hydrogen sulphide [H_2S] | unfertilised egg (UK) / unfertilized egg (USA) the female sex cell contains half the number of chromosomes of the mature adult cell

Ehrlich (Paul 1854–1915) hated exams, but did well enough at school to get into medicine. He started work in Berlin in 1878 and remained there for the rest of his life. His early work was concerned with white blood cells and the study of body defences, but then he had a brilliant idea. Ehrlich started from two well known observations – dyes can be used to colour (stain) specific parts of a cell for use in microscopes and the lead in lead poisoning is found in a few tissues – so why not try a similar idea in the body, find magic bullets that would target and destroy either specific cells or parts of cells? He started work in 1905 and, four years later, found that compound 606 was effective against syphilis – this was the basis of all antibiotics and led to Fleming discovering penicillin.

eight (not ate which is taking in food) number following seven

Eijkman (Christiaan 1858–1930) was asked to investigate the paralysing disease of beri beri while serving as a medical army officer in the Dutch East Indies.The obvious cause was a microbe, but Eijkman noticed that poultry with a similar disease recovered when their diet was changed, so he had to persuade the people to try eating rough rice, complete with the husk rather than the refined white rice – this was the first account of a deficiency disease and led to the recognition of vitamins by Hopkins. Eijkman and Hopkins shared the Nobel Prize in 1929

Einstein (Albert 1879–1955) had many difficulties at school and could get a job only in the Swiss Patent office after graduating. He had sufficient time to produce three papers in 1905, one explaining the random motion of smoke and pollen seen by Brown, the most famous on Special Relativity and the third on the photo-electric effect for which he was awarded a Nobel Prize. He rapidly climbed from junior lecturer to Director of a Research Institute in Berlin, but he visited California in 1933 and never returned to Germany. He was instrumental in persuading the Americans to develop an atomic bomb and was offered, but declined, the Presidency of Israel.

either a choice from two items
ejaculate to eject semen
elastic able to be stretched by a force then return to its original shape when the extra force is removed (see Hooke's law) | elastic band a loop of material that is stretched by a force then returns to its original shape when the force is removed | elastic energy the amount of energy, or the work that can be done, when an object is stretched and is trying to return to its original shape | elastic

potential energy the ability to cause a change because the object is stretched or compressed | elastic properties a quality that an object has that means it will change shape when a force is applied but return to its original shape when the force is removed

elbow / elbow joint the hinge between the lower arm and the upper arm | tennis elbow a painful inflammation of the capsule or fluid at the elbow joint

electric concerned with the flow of charge | electric bell completing a circuit causes a hammer (striker) to hit the bell repeatedly | electric blanket a layer of wires that is sealed between two sheets and can be heated by passing a current | electric buzzer the electric current causes a small vibrator to move producing a buzzing sound | electric cable a length of conducting material made from many thin strands of copper [Cu] or aluminium [Al] wire forming a thick spiral | electric cell two metals separated by an electrolyte that produces a voltage | electric charge property responsible for the effects seen with electricity; conventionally, electrons have a negative charge and protons have a positive charge | electric circuit a compete loop of power source connected to components by connecting wires | electric current (I) flow of charge, the direction of flow shown for the current is in the opposite direction to which the electrons are moving | electric fence one or more strands of bare wire that are at about 30 volts, relative to the earth, so a small current passes through any animal that touches the wire | electric fuse the weak link in a circuit that will melt if the current is too high so opening the circuit and stopping the flow of current | electric kettle a container that has an electric heater on the inside that can be used to warm water | electric motor a device that changes electrical energy into rotating kinetic energy | electric plug the object on the opposite end of a flex or wire to the electrical appliance, and which fits into an socket | electric shock a change to the muscles in the body cause by an electric current passing through the person | electric socket the pattern of holes which allows an electrical appliance to be attached to mains circuit using a plug | electric vehicle a car or transporter that uses motors to turn the wheels | hydro-electric power (HEP) producing electricity by converting the potential energy of water in a dam into kinetic energy that turns a turbine and a generator

electrical concerning or related to the use of electricity | electrical apparatus equipment that transforms electrical energy into other forms of energy | electrical appliances any machine or instrument that uses electrical energy to carry out useful work such as turning, lighting or heating | electrical branches the different parts of a parallel circuit | electrical cell two metals separated by an electrolyte that produces a voltage | electrical charge the property responsible for the effects seen with electricity; conventionally, electrons have a negative charge and protons have a positive charge | electrical circuit the path taken by the charge from the source, such as a cell or power pack, through wires and components then back to the source | electrical component any item that uses electrical energy in order to do something useful, such as producing heat or light | electrical conductivity a measure of how easily a charge will pass through a wire, reciprocal of the resistance per metre of wire | electrical conductor a metal object that is used to connect parts of a circuit | electrical device an item or component that uses electricity as the energy source | electrical energy the type of energy that uses a flow of charge in order to cause a change, the energy is measured either in kilowatt hours (kWh) or joules (J)

electrical energy	=	power	×	time
(kWh)		(kilowatts)		(hours)
(joules)		(watts)		(seconds)

| electrical generator a machine that produces electricity by rotating a coil of wire relative to a magnet | electrical hazards dangers and injuries that could be caused by using electricity – usually either a fire or electrocution | electrical heater a coil of wire that is heated by passing a current | electrical insulation / electrical insulator a non-metal that will prevent the movement of charge and so will not allow electrons to flow | electrical meter the instrument in every house that measures the amount of current and so allows calculation of the energy used and, therefore the cost to be paid | electrical power the amount of energy that is provided each second from an item that uses electricity

power	=	current	×	potential difference
(watts)		(amps)		(volts)

| electrical resistance a property of materials that slows the flow of charge and so reduces the size of the current | electrical signals changes in the size of the current that transfer information | electrical socket the set of holes into which a plug is pushed | electrical supply the source of the electrical energy, could be a mains socket, power pack or cell | electrical unit a measure of energy used to work out the cost of electricity used, a unit is one kilowatt hour (kWh)

unit	=	power	×	time
(kWh)		(kilowatts)		(hours)

electricity a form of energy that is useful in the home | electricity bill the account sent by the Distribution Companies asking you to pay for the electrical energy that you have used | electricity generator equipment for producing electricity by turning a coil in a magnetic field | electricity meter equipment for measuring the quantity (power x time) of electrical energy used | electricity sub-station an area containing equipment that reduces the very high potential difference to 240 volts for local distribution | electricity supply industry the total grouping of fuel suppliers, electricity generating companies, distribution networks and local contractors | conduct electricity / conduction of electricity to allow an electric current to flow | current electricity emphasising that the electrons are flowing so producing an electric current | domestic electricity / household electricity / mains electricity the electricity that is used by all household appliances and is 230 – 250 volts 50 hertz alternating current (50 Hz ac) in the United Kingdom | generate electricity to produce a potential difference (voltage) by spinning a dynamo | off-peak electricity the electrical energy is being supplied at a time when the majority of the population is not using electrical appliances | static electricity an area of charge that does not move, the area has a negative charge if electrons have been added, but removal of electrons leaves a positive charge | units of electricity the amount of electrical energy that has been used, measured as joules in science but as kilowatt-hours by the electricity providers

electro- (*Greek* amber) to do with electricity

electrochemical cell two different metals separated by an electrolyte will produce a potential difference

electrochemical series a list of metals in the order that they produce a voltage when used in a cell

potassium	K	3.26 V	zinc	Zn	1.11 V
sodium	Na	3.05 V	iron	Fe	0.78 V
magnesium	Mg	2.71 V	lead	Pb	0.47 V
aluminium	Al	2.00 V	copper	Cu	0.00 V

electrochemistry the study of permanent changes that are either caused by electricity, *eg* electrolysis, or that produce electricity, *eg* an electric cell

electrocute to kill by passing a large current through the organism

electrocution the killing of an organism by passing a high current through its body

electrodes conducting rods or poles that are placed into an electrolyte and connected to the electric power supply | negative electrode the cathode, the metal that has the excess of electrons, so having a negative charge, and so attract cations | positive electrode the anode, the electrode with a positive charge and so attracts anions

electrolysing passing an electric current through a fluid, so as to cause a chemical reaction

electrolysis using an electric current to cause a chemical change | electrolysis cell the assembly of the container of fluid and the electrodes | electrolysis of water passing an electric current through water [H_2O] produces twice as much hydrogen as oxygen

electrolyte the fluid (usually a liquid, but is a gas in strip lamps) that contains ions, or charged particles, and through which an electric current is passed in order to cause a chemical reaction

electrolytic a chemical change caused by an electric current | electrolytic cell equipment that allows an electric current to be passed through a liquid | electrolytic process the manufacturing method used electricity to bring about the required chemical change

electromagnet equipment made from many coils of wire wound around an iron core, the iron becomes a magnet when current flows in the coil and stops being a magnet when the current is switched off

electromagnetic effects caused by an electric field and a magnetic field together | electromagnetic switch a relay, a switch that is controlled by an electric current | electromagnetic spectrum/em spectrum any part of the spectrum including the visible colours, ultra-violet, infra-red and radio waves | electromagnetic wave any energy that is able to travel in a straight line through the vacuum of space

electromagnetism the effects caused by passing a current through a wire that is wound around a iron core

electron / e⁻ a tiny particle with a negative charge (1.66×10^{-19} C) and almost no mass (9.11×10^{-31} kg) that is found in orbitals around the nucleus of an atom, an electric current is the flow of electrons | electron beam a ray of electrons, millions of negatively charged particles moving in a continual stream | electron gun the combination of a high-temperature filament and magnets that produces the stream of electrons in a television | electron microscope uses a beam of electrons (rather than light) to look in detail at objects that are much too small to be seen with a light microscope | flow of electrons occurs when an electric current is in a wire | outer electrons the electrons in the outer shell that are important in bonding of atoms

electronics using the flow and charge of electrons to control equipment and to carry out calculations | electronic arrangement the distribution of electrons in the orbitals around the nucleus, the number of electrons in each shell | electronic balance equipment in which a change in weight of an object will cause the electrical output to change | electronic structure the distribution of electrons in the orbitals around the nucleus, the number of electrons in each shell | electronic system solid-state sensors are linked to a computer that automatically controls the output to motors and valves | electronic timer an accurate clock that is started and stopped by electrical signals | electronic timing measuring the duration of an event by electrically linking the start and stop to a clock | micro-electronics electrical circuits that are too small to be seen and are able to be used as sensors or logic circuits

electroplating is used to put a thin layer of an expensive, protective metal around an object that is made from a metal that is cheap, strong but likely to corrode. The cheap object is made the cathode in an electrolyte containing a salt of the expensive metal.

electroscope instrument for measuring the amount of charge | gold-leaf electroscope measures the amount of charge by separating a thin plate of gold from a metal mount

electrostatics concerned with charge that does not move because the charge has been placed onto an insulator | electrostatic charge the property caused by changing the number of electrons, adding electrons produces a negative charge, removing electrons leaves a positive charge | electrostatic precipitator using charged wires in a chimney in order to attract smoke particles which then fall down

element a heating wire, one of the over a hundred different materials that contain one type of atom only. Elements may be gases (oxygen, nitrogen, fluorine, chlorine, noble gases), liquids (mercury and bromine) or solid (majority of elements) at room temperature. More than 80 of the elements are metals and so will conduct electricity | artificial element an atom that is not found in nature, an atom with a proton number greater than 92 (the proton number of uranium) | common element an element that is often found in a specified type of molecule, an element that is found in large quantities at particular places | constituent elements the atoms that are found in a compound | group 1 elements the alkali metals, atoms with one outer electron | heating element the wire in a kettle or radiant heater that is heated by an electric current | metallic element an element that will conduct electricity | non-metallic element an atom that reacts with oxygen to produce an oxide that is acid in solution | pure element the material contains only one type of atom | radio-active element atoms where the nucleus is able to break down producing radio-activity and new atoms | rare-earth elements the atoms with proton number 58 to 71 that have very similar properties to $_{57}$La (lanthanum) | trace element an element that is present in very small amounts | transition elements the metals that are found between group 2 and group 3 in the periodic table

elephant the largest land based mammal, characterised by an extended nose, found in Africa and India

elicit to find out, to cause

eliminate to get rid of, eg to excrete waste material from the cell to prevent poisoning

elimination excretion, removal, extinction

ellipse an oval shape

elliptical orbit the path taken by an object moving around a star or planets is like a circle that has been flattened slightly

Elodea (pond weed) an small, freshwater plant that grows easily and is used to demonstrate that oxygen is produced during photosynthesis

elongated made longer | elongated orbit the path taken by the satellite is an oval or a squashed circle

embed to fix firmly by burying into a surface

embedded fixed firmly by burying

embryo an immature offspring that is unable to take care of itself | embryo development the change in structure and number of cells as the fertilised egg turns into a foetus that is ready to be born | embryo root the start of the root in the seed | embryo shoot the initial stages of development of the plant shoot | human embryo the developing baby in the womb up to about 6 weeks after conception, after which it is called a foetus | plant embryo a group of cells within the seed that will produce the plant at germination

emerge to appear, to come out

emergency a sudden disaster | emergency alarm a switch that can be pushed in order to show that you need help immediately, a loud, distinctive sound that indicates that a crisis has occurred | emergency services the skilled people and their vehicles that help others in a crisis (ambulance / fire / police / mountain rescues / cave rescue / lifeboat)

emergent ray the visible path of the light that is leaving a surface

emerging diseases illnesses that have been seen only in recent years eg AIDS, Ebola virus

emissions radiation such as light or radio-active particles | car exhaust emissions the gases that are produced by burning petrol or diesel fuel in an internal combustion engine | radio-active emission the radiation produced by breakdown of a nucleus

emit to give out

emitted given out, produced from a surface

emotional showing strong feelings | emotional changes difference in reaction to events | emotional needs mental and spiritual encouragement and support that is required

emotionally with strong feelings, eg of love, hate, joy

Empedocles (5th century BC) has three claims to fame: he led a revolution in his home town on Sicily but refused to be crowned as king, he developed an idea of elements, and his writings are all poems. A major idea in these poems is that life, including that of the universe, is a cycle involving the four elements of earth, air, fire and water, and the two forces of love and hate. He is said to have died in an attempt to prove he was a god by jumping into the crater of Mount Etna.

emphasis the stress, the major point

emphasise to give importance, to stress

emphysema a disease of the lung that causes the air sacs to be damaged and so they do not work properly and the patient has great difficulty breathing

empirical not based on a theory, using observations | empirical observation a feature that is known to be important, but without knowing how the affect occurs | empirical question to ask a question that is not based on theory but follows from other observations

emptied the material has been poured out

empty vacant, containing nothing; to get rid of content | empty space the universe is a vast volume of vacuum with tiny amounts of solid material

em spectrum / electromagnetic spectrum any part of the spectrum including the visible colours, ultra-violet, infra-red and radio waves

emulsification shaking a liquid that will not dissolve in water with water so as to produce very fine droplets of water suspended in the liquid

emulsifier a chemical that causes two immiscible liquids to form a suspension

emulsifying turning a layer of fat on top of water, into tiny droplets that are spread throughout a solution

emulsion a suspension of tiny droplets of one liquid (eg water) in another (immiscible) liquid, eg oil

enable to make possible

enact to bring about, to cause

enamel / tooth enamel the hard white material that covers the crown of each tooth

enclose to cover, to put into a container | enclosed box the container has a lid that can seal the box

encounter to meet, to come across

encourage to give confidence or approval to continue a task

encyclopaedia (UK) / **encyclopedia** (USA) a set of books containing all that is known on many subjects

end the finish; to finish, to bring to a halt | like ends the tips bear the same charge or the same magnetic pole | unlike ends the parts at the extremes are not the same charge or the same magnetic pole

endangered species particular types of organisms that continue to exist but may become extinct in the near future

endemic always present especially a disease which is found everywhere and all the time in that area

ending the finish, the material that is at the terminus or end of an object | nerve endings the small objects that are at each end of a nerve and transmit the message to the next part

endless never ending, without a finish

endo- (Greek within) inside

endocrine gland a set of specialised cells (a gland) that releases specific chemical messengers (hormones) into the blood | endocrine system the several glands that produce hormones and influence each other

endoscope a flexible tube, containing thousands of glass filaments, that is inserted through a small opening so as to be able to see the tissues inside the body

endo-skeleton the structure providing the support is inside the body, eg bones

endothermic to take in energy, usually heat energy, as in a thermal decomposition, but sometimes light, as in photosynthesis, or electricity, as in electrolysis | endothermic reaction any chemical change that takes in energy eg thermal decomposition, photosynthesis, electrolysis

enemy a predator, an animal that kills other species

energy work done, the physical factor that may cause or be the result of a chemical change | energy chain the energy changers involved and the route taken by energy moving from source to final usage | energy change converting one form of energy into another | energy changers transducers, components that convert energy from one form to another | energy conservation (law of conservation of energy) energy can neither be created nor destroyed – all the energy that goes into a changer must come out, but most is wasted as heat energy | energy conserving changes that have taken place so that less energy is needed in order to achieve the same affect | energy consumption how much energy is being used, especially by electrical appliances | energy content the amount of energy that is present in a food, often given on the package information panel | energy crisis a time when there will not be sufficient coal or oil for everyone who wants the fuel | energy device any instrument or component that uses energy for some useful purpose | energy efficient the minimum amount of energy is used to achieve the specified objective | energy flow movement of energy, especially heat energy, from one place to another | energy intake how much chemical energy is in somebody's diet | energy level diagram / energy profile the total energy in the bonds of the reactants, the separated atoms and the bonds of the products are shown as horizontal lines| energy output how much work will be done by that machine | energy release changing energy from one form into a form that is more useful | energy resources the supplies of energy that are available | energy sources where the energy actually started, majority of energy started with the light and heat that arrived from the Sun | energy store the method by which energy is kept until needed, animals store energy as fats, a battery is a store of chemical energy | energy supply the material that will react and provide useful energy, eg food, chemicals in a battery | energy transfer movement of energy from one place to another in order to bring about a useful change | energy transformation the changing of one form of energy into another form, usually with the production of heat | energy transformer a transducer, an object that changes energy from one form to another, eg lamps change, or transform, electrical energy into light | energy use the amount of energy that is used in causing a change | energy value the amount of energy that is needed to make or break a particular covalent bond | energy waste loss of energy, usually as heat, that could be usefully used elsewhere | alternative energy renewable energy resource that can be used to produce electricity, that does not involve the burning of fossil fuels |

atomic energy nuclear energy, the energy released when the nucleus of an atom changes and gives out radio-activity and the release of heat | biomass energy the total amount of chemical energy in a stated mass of living organisms | bond energy the amount of energy required to make or break the bond between two specified atoms for one mole of material | chemical energy the energy that chemicals possess because they have bonds joining atoms together, these bonds can be broken to form new chemicals in which the bonds have less energy | conservation of energy the total amount of energy at the start of the process is exactly equal to the quantity of energy at the end | dissipating energy to get rid of energy as waste heat and sound that causes very little change to the surroundings | elastic energy / elastic potential energy the energy that an elastic object possesses because it has been pulled tight and will produce kinetic energy when released | electrical energy the type of energy that is associated with the movement of electrons (electric current) and always produces heat and magnetic effects | flow of energy change of energy from one form to another over time | food energy the chemical energy that is stored in food | forms of energy the different types of energy (chemical, electrical, heat, light, movement, nuclear, potential, sound) | gain energy to increase that particular type of energy, could be heat, potential or movement energy | geo-thermal energy the energy of hot rocks because the mantle of the Earth is liquid rock at high temperature | gravitational energy / gravitational potential energy the energy an object has because of its height

$$\text{potential energy} = \text{weight} \times \text{height}$$
$$\text{(joules)} \qquad \text{(newtons)} \quad \text{(metres)}$$

heat energy the speed of vibration in a solid or the speed of movement in a fluid, the speed will increase, or melting or boiling will occur, if the heat energy is increased | hydro-electric energy the potential energy that is stored in a reservoir of water and can be turned into electricity using a turbine and generator | kinetic energy the energy that an object has because it is moving

$$\text{kinetic energy} = \frac{\text{mass} \times \text{velocity} \times \text{velocity}}{2}$$
$$\text{(joules)} \qquad \text{(kilograms)} \quad \text{(m/s)} \qquad \text{(m/s)}$$

light energy radiation that interacts with the eyes to allow sight (electromagnetic radiation of wavelength 380–650 nanometres) | lose energy to decrease the amount of energy in the starting form because it has been changed to another form | mechanical energy the sum of kinetic

energy and potential energy | movement energy / moving energy the energy that an object has because it is moving, also called kinetic energy | nuclear energy / atomic energy the energy released when the nucleus changes and produces radioactivity, new elements and releases heat and light energy | positional energy / potential energy the object is not moving, but a slight change will cause a lot of energy to be released *eg* the energy of a weight on a shelf or of an elastic band under tension

$$\text{potential energy} = \text{weight} \times \text{height}$$
$$\text{(joules)} \qquad \text{(newtons)} \quad \text{(metres)}$$

| quantity of energy amount of energy, measured in joules or kilowatt-hours | radiant energy / radiation energy heat or light from a surface that travels in straight lines | release energy to change energy from one form to a more useful form | renewable energy an energy source that can be used but will be replaced in a short time | solar energy the heat and light from the Sun that can be used to change temperature in a solar panel, to produce new chemicals in photosynthesis, to produce electricity in a solar cell or to enable the eye to see | sound energy vibrations | sources of energy the objects, items or places that may be used to produce the energy change | spring energy the energy stored in a compressed or tensioned spring | stored energy energy that is not being used, but is available for later use, *eg* a battery stores chemical energy that can be turned into electricity | strain energy the potential energy that is stored when a spring is pulled or pushed or a rod is twisted | thermal energy heat energy | tidal energy the energy that is available if the change in the height of water, that is the tide, is used to power a turbine | total amount of energy adding together all the different forms of energy that are used | transfer of energy the movement of one type of energy from one object to another | transform energy to change energy from one form to another | useful energy the energy that is used in carrying out the required change | wasted energy the energy that can not be used, usually the energy is lost as heat or sound | wave energy the kinetic energy of the water moving up an down as the waves move, possibly of use to produce electricity | wind energy the kinetic energy of moving air that can be used to turn windmills or wind turbines

engine equipment used to turn the chemical energy of fuel into kinetic energy | internal combustion engine machinery that burns a fuel inside the engine and this leads to circular motion of an output shaft, *eg* a car engine | model engine a small version of a full size engine that shows how the different parts react together, but is not very powerful | **petrol engine** uses petrol as the fuel which is burned inside a cylinder causing the pistons to move | **steam engine** apparatus that is used to turn steam into kinetic energy

engineer a designer or maker of machines; to change, to bring about

engineering changing | **genetic engineering** changing the instruction set, or genes, in the chromosome so as to achieve a change in the chemistry of the cell

engulf to overwhelm, to take in totally

enhance to improve

enhancing improving | **performance enhancing** chemicals that improve the speed or endurance of an athlete

enlarge to make bigger | **enlarged image** a part of the photograph is magnified so as to show more detail over a small area

enormous very, very big

enough sufficient, an adequate amount

enquire / inquire to ask questions, to seek information

enquiry (plural is enquiries) a question, a set of people investigating an incident | **scientific enquiry** asking question that can be answered by the results of simple experiments that include a control procedure

ensure to make certain

entangle to snare, to put into a net, to make into a knot

enter to go in

entirely completely, continuously

E-number the identifier given to each of the several hundred chemicals that manufacturers can add to food products

envelope a surrounding barrier, the glass part of an electric lamp, a paper cover for a letter; to surround completely

environment the area and the range of conditions (temperature, amount of water, strength and direction of wind, and availability of food) in which an organism lives | **coastal environment** the conditions, of wind, temperature and concentration of salt in the sea, that are found where sea meets land | **controlled environment** having the ability to decide, and change, conditions such as the intensity of light, concentration of moisture or the temperature | **damp environment** an area where there is lots of moisture absorbed in the solids | **domestic environment** the conditions of temperature, moisture and light that are found in a house | **greenhouse environment** a hot, moist area, similar to the environmental conditions in-

side a greenhouse | **impact on the environment** the changes in conditions that are caused by the specified process | **internal environment** the conditions of temperature, moisture and amount of nutrients that are found inside an organism | **local environment** the conditions of wind, rain, light and temperature close to a specified point | **marine environment** the oceans, the combination of salt water and stable temperatures that are found in seas | **micro-environment** the conditions of temperature, humidity, light intensity and wind speed that are found in a small area, *eg* under a fallen branch | **monitor the environment** to measure the concentration of chemicals and the temperature at regular intervals | **non-windy environment** an area that is protected from any violent or sudden movement of air | **perfect environment** the conditions of temperature, wind, light, and moisture that perfectly suit that organism | **town environment** the combination of buildings, hard surfaces, lack of open space and pollution that is typical of a large number of people who are living and working close together | **urban environment** the conditions associated with areas where there are lots of houses, roads and people | **warm environment** the temperature is above 30°C | **woodland environment** the conditions associated with an area covered by trees, especially the shadows under the branches of the trees | **working environment** the conditions under which you carry out particular tasks

environmental concerned with area and the weather conditions | **environmental aspects** discussing the local weather conditions and their effects | **environmental causes** the changes and effects that are caused by that combination of temperature, rain and wind | **environmental changes** differences in an area brought about by changing some condition | **environmental chemistry** the study of reactions that could change the conditions of an area | **environmental conditions** the volume and rate of rainfall, the temperature range and the wind strength and direction | **environmental context** discussing the number and behaviour of organisms in particular conditions | **environmental data** information concerning the area and the local weather conditions | **environmental differences** comparing the changes caused by unlike conditions | **environmental effects** changes in the area and the organisms caused by a change of temperature, amount of water or brightness of light | **environmental factors** any physical thing, *eg* rain or temperature, that could affect the organisms living in an area | environmental features measurements of rain, temperature or light in different areas | environmental groups people who believe that they can influence the decisions and ideas of others concerning the environment and the treatment of organisms | environmental health officer a local authority representative who makes sure that all health and safety regulations are followed and studies changes in the number of people who get certain diseases | environmental impact the change caused to the local conditions by an event | environmental influences changes, *eg* in temperature or rainfall, that could affect the environment | environmental issues discussion of changes that may occur in the environment and the time-scale over which these changes occur | environmental monitoring measuring the different variables *eg* rainfall, temperature, light intensity, type and quantity of chemicals, within an area | environmental probe an instrument or organism that is able to give information about the conditions in a specified area | environmental problems the questions raised about changes in local conditions that may affect the organisms that live there | environmental protection taking steps and procedures to try to ensure that the conditions within an area do not change | environmental reason a justification that is based on the effects on the wildlife | environmental science studying the way in which creatures are affected by the habitat and local weather conditions | environmental scientist a person who studies the effects of temperature, water flow and light on the organisms in an area | environmental sensors electrical items that measure specific factors such as rainfall or temperature | environmental significance the results of changes to the environment | environmental variables items, such as temperature or water flow, that could change and affect the growth and number of organisms in an area | environmental variation differences in conditions either between areas that are similar or within one area at different times of the day or year

environmentally determined some item, such as weight, that depends on the local conditions and not on the genetics of the organism | environmentally friendly changes that will not damage the environment | environmentally sensitive a bad reaction, *eg* death or lack of growth caused by a slight change in local conditions

enzyme a protein that increases the speed of a biological reaction | carbohydrase enzyme a chemical that increases the speed with which large carbohydrate molecules are turned to sugar | digestive enzymes proteins in the gut that increase the speed with which large food molecules are broken down into nutrient molecules that are small enough to be absorbed | lipase enzyme a protein that causes the breakdown of fat into glycerol and fatty acids | protease enzyme a protein that causes the breakdown of other proteins into the individual amino acids

eon (USA) / **aeon** (UK & USA) a time interval of 1000 million years

epi- (*Greek* besides), in addition

epicenter (USA) / **epicentre** (UK) the point on the surface of the Earth that is nearest to an earthquake

epidemic a sudden outbreak, affecting a large number of people in that area, of a disease

epidemologist a person who studies the trends and changes of illnesses and wealth in the human population

epidermis a thin, outer protective layer of cells on the skin of animals and the leaves of plants | onion epidermis the single layer of cells that occurs between the layers of an onion

epiglottis a thin piece of cartilage that covers the windpipe and prevents entry of food or drink during swallowing

episodes a series of events or incidents

epithelia (plural of epithelium) thin layers of cells at the surface of organs

epithelial cells the cells, which, under the microscope, look like tiles, that are found in the outermost part of skin or an organ lining

epithelium (plural is epithelia) any thin layer of cells that lines the surface of an organ

Epsom salts magnesium sulphate [MgSO4], originally prepared from a mineral spring in Epsom, Surrey

equa- / equi- (*Latin* to make even)

equal two items that are the same

equally matching, identically

equation a shortened or brief form of showing what is occurring | balanced equation showing that the number of atoms at the start of the reaction is identical to the number and type of atoms at the end, although the atoms will have formed new molecules | chemical equation a method for showing a chemical change, the names or shorthand for the reactants (starting chemicals) are on the left hand side and the chemicals that are formed (products) are on the right hand side | construct an equation to decide which chemicals need to be on each side and then balance the equation | general equation a mathematical relationship that has lots of different applications |

half-ion equations / ion equations / ionic equation show the changes that occur at each electrode in electrolysis by the movement of electrons so that atoms form ions or ions become atoms | mathematical equations show the dependent variable on the left hand side of an equals sign and the independent variables on the right hand side (several mathematical equations are given on the inside front cover) | shorthand equation writing the chemicals as their formulae and then balancing the equation for each atom so there are exactly the same number on the reactant side as on the product side | speed equation the formula relating speed to distance and time (SIDOT – speed is distance over time) | symbol equation to write out an equation, either chemical or mathematical, using symbols not words | word equation a chemical equation that shows the names of the reactants on the left hand side of the equals sign and the names of the products on the right hand side

equator an imaginary line around the Earth, mid-way between the North and South Poles, over which the Sun is directly overhead at the spring and autumn equinoxes

equatorial in the region around the equator | equatorial orbit the path taken by a satellite circling the Earth directly above the equator

equi- / equa- (*Latin* to make even)

equilibrate to reach a stage of balance where no further changes seem to occur

equilibrium appearing to stay still | atmospheric equilibrium the composition of the air does not seem to change because the removal of carbon dioxide and water by plants is balanced by the output of these two chemicals by respiration | dynamic equilibrium lots of things are happening but there is no apparent change overall, *eg* your body weight will eventually reach dynamic equilibrium – lots of food going in and energy being used, but no change of weight | stable equilibrium will not fall over unless a very big force is applied

equinox (plural is equinoxes) the day and night are exactly equal length of 12 hours each

equipment apparatus | amplification equipment the assembly of components that make the effect larger, apparatus for increasing the amplitude of a signal | analog equipment (USA) / analogue equipment (UK) apparatus in which the control or the output can take any value | appropriate equipment the apparatus is suitable for that experiment | data-logging equipment apparatus that can be used to collect and store lots of numbers especially numerical information that changes

over time | digital equipment apparatus that uses numbers | direction-finding equipment a device for establishing the line along which you should be moving | heating equipment apparatus that is used for increasing the temperature of a substance, especially the electrical heating mantles that are used for safe boiling of fluids | laboratory equipment apparatus that you would expect to find in a laboratory | mains equipment electrical apparatus that uses a 230–250 volt, 50 hertz alternating current supply | measuring equipment apparatus that is suitable for the measurement to be made, and has been calibrated

equivalent a different item or process, but has the same, or similar properties and effects

eradicate to wipe out entirely, the World Health Organisation has succeeded in eradicating smallpox (no case of small pox has been reported for 20 years)

Erasistratus / Eristratus (around 250 BC) lived at Alexandria, the site of the greatest library in the ancient world. His dissection of human brains led to the conclusion that intelligence must have something to do with the surface lumpiness. He realised that nerves carried messages to and from the brain, but believed this was the flow of liquid in tiny tubes.

Eratosthenes (of Cyrene 270–190 BC) was educated in Athens, but became chief librarian at Alexandria in Egypt. He used the difference in the angles to the Sun at two different parts of Egypt to calculate the circumference of the Earth to a value that is within a 100 kilometres of that accepted value today (38,400 kilometres)

erect upright, vertical; to build

erectile tissue the blood vessels and muscles that are involved in causing the penis to become rigid

erection firm, rigid

erode to reduce the size of a rock by breaking off fragments

eroded worn away over a long period of time because of continual contact with wind or waves | eroded land ground that has disappeared because the soil has fallen into moving water, ground from which the top soil has been removed by wind, rain and water

erosion wearing away of rocks and then carrying away the fragments by the action of wind, moving water or sliding glaciers | soil erosion the removal of fertile soil by wind and rivers

erratic irregular

error difference between identical experiments that is always present despite your best efforts, a mistake

erupt to break out

eruption a sudden or violent ejection of material | frequent eruptions the ejection occurs many times in a short period | unpredictable eruptions you are not able to say how long it will be before the next eruption occurs | violent eruptions the ejection of material occurs with a vast amount of damage over a large area | volcanic eruptions the ejection is liquid rock (magma) through gaps in the Earth's crust

erythrocyte a red blood cell, the cell that transports oxygen

escape to break free

esophagus (USA) / **oesophagus** (UK) the gullet, a flexible tube that connects the mouth to the stomach

essential needed, necessary, vital | essential nutrients small molecules that are found in food and which are necessary for good health: includes vitamins and minerals

establish to put onto firm foundations, to make certain | re-establish to form new connections, to put back in place

estimate an approximation; to make a best guess based on the evidence | estimate size to guess the length or height without using any measuring instruments

estimation a best guess

estrogen (USA) / **oestrogen** (UK) a hormone that causes many of the female characteristics

estrus (USA) / **oestrus** (UK) the time when the female is able to conceive | estrus cycle the regular changes that occur in the female from the production of one egg to the production of the next egg, this period is around 28 days in humans

estuaries (plural of estuary) the areas where rivers widen to meet the sea

estuary (plural is estuaries) where the fresh water river widens to meet the salt water sea

ethane [C_2H_6] an alkane, a hydrocarbon with no double bonds

ethanoate [CH_3COO^-] the ion produced when ethanoic acid is neutralised

ethanoic acid / acetic acid [CH_3COOH] vinegar, a weak acid originally made from wine

ethanol [C_2H_5OH] a flammable liquid that is produced by fermentation of sugar with yeast, freezing point of −117°C

ethene [C_2H_4] a hydrocarbon that is the monomer used for making polythene, the smallest alkene

ethical moral, treating others with respect | ethical issues / ethical questions problems that have no easy answer and can not be tested experimentally, eg should Jenner have injected the young boy with smallpox?

etiolated (USA) / **oetiolated** (UK) having the characteristic appearance of a plant grown in the dark, ie no green in the leaves and a long spindly stem

ery
↓
eva

Euclid (c 300 BC) worked in Alexandria (the site of the greatest library in the ancient world) and brought together all that was known concerning mathematics into a 13-volume series called *Elements of Geometry*. These volumes were translated into Arabic, then into Latin, and finally into all the languages of Europe; they dominated the thinking in mathematics for over 2000 years. Euclid attempted to prove all his theories using logical development from assumptions (axioms) that had to be stated.

Euglena a single-cell protozoan that has a flagellum for movement and chloroplasts for photosynthesis

eukaryotic having a nucleus in the cell

eureka Greek for *I've solved it,* attributed to Archimedes when he realised how to find if a crown was made from gold | eureka can a cylinder with a spout close to the top that is used for measuring the volume of irregular shaped solids

eustachian tube / eustacian tube the pipe connecting the middle ear to the back of the mouth that allows pressure in the ear to become equal to the air pressure

eutrophication the destruction of a water habitat by the addition of too many nutrients (the increase in nitrate causes growth of algae and plants leading to the increased activity of decomposers that remove all the oxygen from the water)

evacuate to take the substance, usually air, out of a container

evaluate to discuss something in detail and suggest improvements | evaluate conclusions to discuss the closing statement with regard to the ideas you put forward initially and the results you found | evaluate data to decide if the measurements are true or accurate, and where errors may occur | evaluate evidence to discuss the accuracy, relevance and importance of the observations | evaluate methods to look closely at what was carried out and to suggest where improvements could be introduced | re-evaluate to look again at the evidence and the conclusions

evaluation the final section of any report reflecting on where mistakes were made and how improvements could be incorporated next time

evaporate to turn from liquid to gas at a temperature below the boiling point

evaporating turning a liquid into a gas | evaporating basin / evaporating dish a glass bowl, approximately 5 centimetres diameter, that is used for turning liquid water rapidly into a vapour | evaporating pond a small lake of salt water that is being left to evaporate so as to obtain the salt

evaporation a liquid turning into gas at a temperature below the boiling point

evaporite the sedimentary rock produced by evaporation of water from a solution

evening late afternoon, the part of the day when the Sun is visible, but is low on the horizon so does not provide much heat

evenly uniformly, treating each part in like manner, spread to the same thickness

event an incident, a programme | geological event a sudden change that has occurred in the crust of the Earth and has widespread consequences | sequence of events the actions shown in the order in which they occurred

eventually after a long period of time, after many other events, finally

evergreen the tree or bush does not lose its leaves in winter | evergreen woodland the area is covered with trees that retain some leaves throughout the year

everyday / every day some object that is likely to be found outside the laboratory and is used frequently | everyday appliances machines that are found in most households, eg washing machine, television | everyday changes differences that are expected to occur each day, eg in the amount of light or heat | everyday context events in the normal life of most people | everyday examples applying science to equipment around the home, eg calculating the current used by a heater | everyday experiences the type of situations and events that are likely to be met by the majority of the population | everyday life the routine existence of the majority of people | everyday materials substances or objects that could be bought in a local store | everyday name the term that is used by most people to describe an object | everyday objects articles that are likely to be seen and used regularly | everyday phenomena any routine event that can be seen in normal life | everyday situations events that are likely to be seen regularly | everyday speeds the speed achieved by methods that are available to the majority of the population eg walking (up to 2 metres per second), cycling (approximately 7 metres per second), driving (maximum of 35 metres per second) | everyday uses the purposes to which an object is put in the home or on the way to work

evidence data and observations on which the conclusion is built | accumulated evidence observations and measurements have been gathered from several experiments and point to the same conclusion | additional evidence more facts / data are needed or are available | appropriate evidence the observations will answer the question that was asked | available evidence the measurements and observations that you are able to use | collect evidence to make observations and measurements | conflicting evidence two sets of observations each point to different conclusions | consider evidence to think about what the data mean | evaluate evidence to decide if the data are reliable and accurate or could be improved | experimental evidence measurements were made, and observations taken, in a practical task | fossil evidence information that has been obtained by looking at the size, age and distribution of fossils | further evidence more indicators that the theory is correct | gather evidence to bring together the measurements from several sources | historical evidence observations that were made in the past | interpretation of evidence stating how the observations will support an idea | limitation of evidence the data will help support an idea but there may be other interpretations | literary evidence the support obtained from an opinion that some person wrote | microscopic evidence observations made using a microscope | new evidence additional data that can be used to support an idea that was put forward earlier | obtain evidence to gather information, to make measurements | patterns of evidence trying to fit the measurements into simple curves or a small number of groups | photographic evidence the information is in the form of a photograph | provide evidence to show the information that will support your ideas | range of evidence a measure of how many different types of experiment were carried out | relevant evidence the data will help to answer the question that was set | reliable evidence repeating the experiment would lead to the same results | strength of evidence an estimate of how well the observations support the idea

evolution the change over time, the throwing off | evolution of gases production of gases from a reaction or a volcano | evolution of species emergence of new types of organisms that are better suited to survive in the environment | evolution of the universe change in the universe from the initial 'big bang', through formation of dust, planets and stars to wherever it goes in the future | gas evolution giving off gases

evolve to change gradually from one shape or function to a form that is similar, but that has significant differences

evolved changed, given off

evolving changing, giving off | evolving gas bubbling, effervescing, boiling

exa... / E... (*Greek*) prefix for a million, million, million of a unit, 10^{18}

exact precise, accurate

exactly precisely, perfectly correct

examination a detailed test, an assessment | microscopic examination using a microscope in order to look in detail at fibres or dust or cells

examine to study, to look at the details

examples events, people or objects that are both familiar and show the properties that are being discussed | contemporary examples using events that have been reported in recent newspapers | everyday examples objects that are likely to be familiar to the person | historical examples citing events that happened in the past

exceeding greater than

exceptions different, missing, excluded

excess more than is needed for that purpose and so is left over at the end | excess metal oxide when preparing a salt using an insoluble metal oxide, more metal oxide is used than is needed to neutralise the acid, so the extra amount can be removed by filtration

excessive too much

exchange to take in one thing and give out something else at the same place and time, to substitute | exchange gases to allow one gas in and another gas out | exchange of gases / gas exchange the movement of oxygen into the blood and the loss of carbon dioxide into the air | exchange system any set of tissues or organs that allow exchange to occur | gaseous exchange the diffusion of oxygen into the blood and the loss of carbon dioxide into the air, the function of the lungs or gills | materials exchange swapping substances across a boundary

exclude to keep out, to prevent from getting in

excluder an item that prevents entry of other material | draft excluder (USA) / draught excluder (UK) material that is used to block holes around doors and windows so as to prevent movement of air and loss of heat

excreta the waste material which is pushed out of organisms, including faeces and urine

excrete to push out waste material

excretion pushing out, secretion of waste chemicals | excretion products the names and types of chemicals that are in the waste material,

including urea (in urine) and alcohol (produced during fermentation)

excretory system the organs and vessels of the body that are involved in removing chemicals that could be poisonous

exemplar a perfect example, a model answer

exercise a practice, a repetitive task, a training, a physical exertion; to use, to practise, to carry out physical tasks repetitively in order to improve the condition of the heart and lungs | aerobic exercise repetitive movement so that the muscles have insufficient oxygen and start to produce lactic acid, so the heart rate and the breathing rate have to increase | heavy exercise carrying out physical tasks that cause the heart rate to increase substantially for long periods | regular exercise carrying out physical exertions several times over a week | vigorous exercise using muscles to move rapidly until respiration becomes anaerobic

exert to apply a force

exerted made a great effort, applied a force

exhale to breathe out | exhaled air the air that is breathed out of the lungs which contains more carbon dioxide and less oxygen than the air in the room

exhaling breathing out

exhaust the gases that are produced in an engine; to remove entirely, to tire out | exhaust fumes / exhaust gases the chemicals that are produced when fuel is burned | exhaust pipe the tube taking the products of burning away from the engine | exhaust system the series of tubes, heat-exchangers, silencers or mufflers and catalysts that allow gases produced by combustion to be released into the atmosphere

exist to have reality, to live, to be

existence the state of living

existing available, living | existing knowledge what was known up to that time | existing rocks the silt, boulders and mountains that were present before the change occurred | existing stock the amount of material or the number of animals that you know about | existing system the method that is used either today or at the stated time | pre-existing known or available before an event that causes a considerable change

exit a door leading out; to leave

exo- (*Greek* outside)

exoskeleton the hard scaffolding is on the outside of the organism

exothermic to give out energy, usually heat energy which causes the temperature to increase | exothermic reaction a chemical change that produces heat

expand to get bigger, to take up more volume

expanded polystyrene air is blown through a molten plastic which cools and keeps lots of air bubbles and so is good for insulation

expanding getting bigger | **expanding universe** the theory that all the stars are moving away from a central point

expansion getting bigger | **expansion joint** a gap in between sections of road or rails that allows the road or rail to expand without causing any damage as the temperature increases | **thermal expansion** the increase in size that occurs when an object gets hotter

expect to anticipate, to look forward to an event

expectancy hope | **life expectancy** the average amount of time for which you would predict a member of that species to live

expected likely to happen, predicted

expedition an organised journey of exploration

expel / expel from to push out

expelled pushed out, especially waste material from a cell

expensive costing a lot

experience a personal participation in events; to be part of, to be moved | **everyday experience** an event or situation that most people are likely to meet | **first-hand experience** to have taken an active part in an event | **harmful experience** an event that led to the damage to a person

experiment an investigation, the carrying out of an investigation in which you can decide the variables and make measurements; to investigate by changing variables and measuring results | **additional experiments** you carry out more practical work | **breaking bar experiment** demonstrates expansion by heating a bar, clamping the ends then waiting for the bar to contract as it cools, and eventually it breaks | **control experiment** carrying out the same practical work as the experiment, but the variable is held at a constant value, or an active ingredient is at zero concentration | **design an experiment** to plan what is going to be done, with reasons for the choice of each material and method and an idea of weights and times | **mine-shaft experiment** a demonstration of convection in which a heated candle, placed at the base of one chimney, causes hot air to rise and be replaced by cooler air flowing down a second chimney | **planning an experiment** deciding how to carry out the practical part of an investigation | **previous experiments** similar work that was carried out earlier | **rainbow experiment** mix universal indicator with sodium hydrogen carbonate in a tube then gently add hydrochloric acid and watch

a rainbow of colours | **smoking experiment** demonstration of the gases produced by smoking cigarettes in which the cigarette smoke is drawn though cotton wool, universal indicator solution and lime water | **thought experiment** dreaming about what could occur in order to decide which of several ideas is most likely, theoretical consideration

experimental practical, found by investigation | **experimental data** measurements collected in an investigation | **experimental evidence** observations and measurements that were obtained in an investigation and are used to support a conclusion | **experimental results** measurements and observations that are found in an investigation | **experimental technique** the methods and skills that are used in an experiment | **experimental variation** error, small differences that occur whenever an experiment is repeated | **experimental work** the collection of practical procedures that were used to develop an idea

experimentation the act of carrying out practical work

expert a person who has a vast amount of knowledge and experience of that particular field of study

expiration the act of breathing out

expire to breathe out, to die

explain to make clear, to give reasons | **explain observations** to show how the measurements fit into a simple theory

explanation a clarification, especially of points of disagreement | **alternative explanation** a second idea that explains the observations and measurements | **particle explanation** explaining all chemical and physical changes as being the result of change in forces between particles | **scientific explanation** an idea that builds on the simple ideas of science and allows predictions to be made

explicit clearly stated, out in the open

explode to burst in a violent, expanding, reaction

exploding moving outwards rapidly

exploration investigation of new areas of land or knowledge | **lunar exploration** sending probes and men to land on the Moon | **space exploration** sending satellites and people into space to see what can be found and seen

explore to go looking for something new

explorer a brave person who goes where no one has gone before

explosion a sudden, often violent, expansion | **population explosion** a sudden increase in the number of that species in that area

explosive a hazardous chemical that can react and cause violent expansion | **explosive dispersal**

scattering seeds by sudden opening of the pod throwing the seeds into the air | explosive volcano throwing magma (molten rock) up into the air | highly explosive detonation of the chemical would cause lots of damage

exposed open to weathering, lacking protection, had light fall on a film | exposed rock the stone or hill is open to the action of wind or water | exposed shore a beach that has no protection against the energy of the waves, wind and tide

exposure showing, opening up | time-exposure leaving the shutter of a camera open for sufficiently long that changes of position are easily seen

express very fast; to speak out, to provide

extend to get longer

extension the amount by which an item has become longer

extensive covering a wide area, large coverage

extent the size, the scope, the area

exterminate to destroy a species

external outside | external development the fertilised egg changes into independent offspring outside of the mother | external factors variables that should not be part of the experiment but may cause a change | external features characteristics that can be seen on the outside | external fertilisation (UK) / external fertilization (USA) the male and female gametes meet outside the female's body | external pressure the force per unit area that is being exerted on the outside of the craft or body

externally on the outside

extinct there are now no living members of a species that used to exist | extinct animals animals that once existed but are no longer alive | extinct groups related sets of animals that no longer exist | extinct volcano the gap in the Earth's crust has been closed by cooling rock so the volcano will no longer erupt

extinction the dying out of a particular breed or species

extinguish to put out

extinguisher equipment that will prevent further change | fire extinguisher equipment that can be used for putting out a fire

extra- (*Latin* beyond) outside

extract a short piece of text, the solution containing the chemical of interest, the material that is removed; to remove, to take out | extract information to find the important ideas and measurements | extract metals to obtain a pure metal from the metal ore | alcohol extract mixing

the substance with ethanol so that any lipids will dissolve | vegetable extract the fluid that is left when edible plants have been turned into juice then the solid parts removed

extraction taking out, removing | extraction plant one or more industrial buildings that are used to purify a metal from an ore | metal extraction obtaining pure metal from the ore

extracts short pieces of text taken from a longer passage; takes out

extrapolate predict or guess, from the evidence that you have already collected, what will happen next, to draw a curve beyond the end points, to take further

extra-terrestrial an object that originates, or is found, somewhere other than this Earth

extremes at the ends | extreme case the rare outcome that results from the inputs being unusually high or low

extrusive rock molten rock that reached the surface of the Earth then cooled

Eyam a village in Derbyshire that isolated itself after the arrival of the plague in 1565 in order to prevent spreading the disease to surrounding inhabitants

eye the organ that reacts to light and allows you to see | eye ball the sphere that is one complete eye of a mammal | eye brow the line of hairs above the eye in mammals | eye color (USA) / eye colour (UK) the colour of the iris | eye lid a flap of skin that regularly sweeps over the front of the eye | eye patch a semi-circle of light-proof material that is placed over the eye | eye-piece the lens at the top of the tube of a microscope at which you put your eye | eye protection goggles that should be warn whenever using flames or hazardous chemicals | eye sight an estimate, on an arbitrary scale, of how easily a person can distinguish a shape or a colour | eye socket area of the skull into which the eye fits | eyespot an area of skin that is sensitive to light | compound eye the visual organs of insects that have many tiny eyes in one large structure | naked eye without the use of a magnifying instrument | pair of eyes two eyes allow estimate of size and distance | stalked eye the organ of sight is at the end of a stem | unaided eye examining an object without the help of any lenses

eye-piece / eyepiece lens the lens at the top of the microscope tube

eyespot an area of skin that is sensitive to light

F fluorine, proton number 9, a halogen

°F temperature in degrees fahrenheit

f [frequency] the number of cycles each second

f.../ femto... (*Greek*) prefix for a thousand, million, millionth of a unit, 10^{-15}

F$_2$ fluorine gas, a highly dangerous gas

fabric a substance, a material

Fabrizio (Girolamo 1533–1619) was a pupil of Fallopius at Padua and he built the first operating theatre so as to demonstrate dissection to his students, including showing the valves in veins to Harvey. He started research into the development of a foetus from a fertilised egg.

face the front, especially of the head with the nose, eyes and mouth; to look towards | face magnet a thin cuboid of steel, cobalt or nickel. in which the magnetic poles are at the largest surfaces | cliff face the vertical part of a landscape | mountain face one side of a mountain, usually very steep

facet a side, a view | multi-faceted several different features or important sides

facial hair the hair that is found on the face

facilities equipment available for an experiment, buildings | useful facilities tools or equipment that could help solve a problem

facing directly opposite

fact an observation that can be repeated by other people | fact sheet a collection of related measurements that are useful, but do not need to be measured again

factor a variable, anything that could cause differences between duplicate experiments | abiotic factor a part that causes a change or influences an environment that does not involve life, *eg* amount of rain | biotic factor the influence on the environment of microbes, animals or plants | environmental factors variables, such as temperature, moisture or light intensity, that could affect or describe an area | external factors variables that should not be part of the experiment, but may cause a change | genetic factors the instructions in the genes that make you more or less likely to develop a disease or talent | identify factors to list the variables that could change the result | inherited factors instructions in the genes that you received from your parents | key factors the important variables | physical factors variables that do not involve chemicals *eg* temperature, pressure, light intensity | relevant factors variables that could influence the outcome| rhesus factor a protein in the blood that allows compatibility only between rhesus positive blood groups or between rhesus negative blood groups |

scale factor the ratio that is used to allow several objects to be drawn to the same scale

factory (plural is factories) a building that is used for the large-scale production of an object | factory-made manufactured in large numbers using a standard pattern | cheese factory place for large scale production of cheese

facts observations, measurements | basic facts / fundamental facts the observations that are at the starting point of ideas | organise facts (UK) / organize facts (USA) to place the observations into groups and the measurements into a table

factual information reporting of observations or measurements that are repeatable and can be made by anyone

fade to lose intensity

faeces (UK)/ **feces** (USA) solid waste products that are egested (excreted) from the anus

Fahrenheit (Gabriel Daniel 1686–1736) was a German glassblower working in Holland, specialising in building instruments for measuring weather conditions. He constructed the first thermometer that used the expansion of mercury along a narrow tube in order to measure temperature. The fahrenheit scale uses the lowest temperature reached by an ice-salt mixture as the zero point and the temperature of the human body (which he measured as 96°F) as the second fixed point. Fahrenheit measured the boiling points of many liquids.

fahrenheit scale method for relating hotness to temperature with the fixed point at the lowest temperature achieved by mixing salt and ice (0°F) so ice melts at 32°F and water boils at 212°F

failure a breakdown, not achieving an objective | liver failure damage to the liver so that poisons are no longer removed from the blood

fair (not fare which is a payment) treating all parts of the experiments identically | fair comparison looking in an objective way at similarities and differences between observations that are related but not identical | fair test an experiment in which one variable, or factor, is changed and all other variables are either kept constant or measured

falcon a carnivorous bird that usually captures its prey in flight

fall an accidental trip, a drop; to stumble | free-fall dropping towards a planet or a star without any attempt at slowing down so you do not have weight | rock fall an area of lumps of rock produced by the main area of rock being broken down by weathering

falling dropping | falling rain emphasising that the water is dropping form the sky

fallopian tube the oviduct, an egg canal, the tube down which the egg travels from the ovary to the womb

Fallopius (Gabriello 1523–1562) studied to become a priest but swapped to medicine and studied at Padua, the greatest of the medical schools (50 years later, Harvey attended the same university), under Vesalius. He spent many years in dissecting human bodies and discovering new structures – he described the oviduct (also known as the fallopian tube) but could not give a purpose, this was not described for a further 300 years.

fallow a farm field that has been left to grow wild flowers and grasses | fallow deer a hoofed mammal that is native to Mediterranean countries, the coat is gray in winter, turning pale brown with white spots in summer (many centuries ago, fallow meant light brown)

false not true | false-colour photographs / false-colour pictures the colours in the image are different form the colours of the object

familiar well known in everyday life | familiar contexts situations that could have occurred many times to most people | familiar metals the metals (conductors of electricity) that could be found in many homes | familiar objects any material that is likely to be found in everyday life | familiar situations events which could have occurred many times to most people

family (plural is families) a group of organisms that are very similar and are likely to be related | family tree a diagram showing the relationship between the offspring at the bottom and the parents and grandparents further up the page

famine a period when there is not sufficient food

fangs sharp hollow teeth that snakes use for injecting a poison

far a long way, distant | far point the furthest point that can be seen clearly

Faraday (Michael 1791–1867) an extraordinary man with an extraordinary life, he was considered the greatest of experimental physicists and he had a real rags to riches transition. He became a bookseller's errand boy and educated himself by reading articles in the books that were sent for binding. After attending Davy's lectures at the Royal Institution, Faraday wrote out the lecture notes, bound them and presented them to Davy together with an application for a job. After an initial refusal (he was recommended to stay as a bookbinder) Faraday became an assistant to Davy and was immediately taken on an 18 month tour of Europe. Faraday started research as a chemist, making benzene and liquefying chlorine, but started studying the effects of an electric current on solutions. Most of the words used in electrolysis, were introduced by Faraday. Following Oersted's work on a current producing a magnetic field, Faraday produced a dynamo, transformer and motor. Faraday had great charm and a major influence on physics, yet he had no students and was helped only by an ex-soldier. One legacy of Faraday – the Royal Institution Christmas Lectures, that had been started by Davy, became the most popular event of the year.

fare (not fair which is equality) money paid for a journey

farm an area and organisation that is used for raising animals or growing crops that will be sold for profit; to grow crops for profit | farm animals livestock, the animals (cows, goats, hens, pigs, sheep) that are often reared for cash | farmland the area of land given over to the raising of the crop or feeding the animals | fish farm a lake in which fish are fed and protected until ready for eating | organic farm will use manure and crop rotation to ensure a good crop (but not chemicals such as fertilisers or weed killers) | urban farm land used for raising sheep, pigs and cows in an area which is mainly housing estates | wind farm many wind turbines in one area

farmer a person who makes a living by growing crops or raising animals as food

farming growing crops or raising animals that are to be eaten | farming methods techniques that are used in order to maximise the productivity of farming | intensive farming growing a large mass of crop from a small area, often by adding lots of fertiliser | organic farming not using any artificial fertiliser, herbicide or pesticide when growing crops

farther (not father which is the male parent) further, more distant, remote

fast rapid; to starve | fast-growing the size is becoming bigger in a shorter time than expected | color-fast (USA) / colour-fast (UK) the dye will not run or fade | hold-fast the part of a water plant that holds onto rocks to prevent the plant from being swept away in a river

faster more rapidly, with more speed

fastest moving at a speed greater than anyone else

fat an object that is wider than expected; a chemical, that will float on water, but will not dissolve, used by the body as a store of chemical energy | fats chemicals that are used as a store of chemical energy in animals | fat callipers equipment for

135

measuring the thickness of fat layer in the skin | **fat cells** cells that are used for storing fat, may form a layer below the skin or produce bundles of cells in the body | **fat-soluble** chemicals that will dissolve in oil, but not in water | **fat-soluble vitamins** the small chemicals that are essential for good health, but are not soluble in water | **fat store** tissue made from cells that contain fat | **fat test / test for fat** a method for deciding if the material is fat: either fat will cause paper to become permanently translucent, or fat will dissolve in alcohol, but the alcohol solution turns white when water is added | **saturated fat** the bonds of the fatty acid are all single, an animal fat | **unsaturated fat** the oil produced by plants or fish that has some double bonds

fatal resulting in death | **fatal dose** the amount taken is sufficient to kill the body

father (not farther which is distant) the male parent; to provide the moving sex cell that will fertilise an egg and develop into an offspring

fathom a measure of water depth, 1 fathom is 6 feet or 1.8 metres

fats chemicals that are used as a store of chemical energy in animals

fatter wider, having more weight

fatty containing lots of fat or chemicals that will not dissolve in water | **fatty acids** acids that contain -COOH, the acids that are produced by breakdown of fats | **fatty foods** one, or more, parts of the meal contains a high proportion of fat | **fatty layer** fat cells that are found, like a sandwich filling, below the skin and help insulate the animal | **fatty tissue** groups of fat cells within an organ

fault a crack in a rock, a discontinuity in layers of rock because the strata have slipped, a mistake, an error, an imperfection | **fault finding** using techniques that will diagnose the problem of a broken item so that it can be fixed

faulty not working properly

favorite (USA) / **favourite** (UK) most popular, first choice, preferred option

Fe iron, proton number 26, a magnetic metal that is extracted using a blast furnace

feathers stems or shafts having barbs or fronds on each side, a characteristic of birds | **down feathers** very fine feathers that provide insulation

feathery looking like feathers, fluffy

feature characteristic or important point that is special to that event | **adult features** the proportions of the limbs and head to the body, the amount of hair and the voice are similar to those found in the mature animal | **characteristic features** marks that are found only on that type

of object or organism but on no other | **common features** points that are often found | **decorative features** characteristics that seem to serve no purpose other than to make the place, object or organism seem more attractive | **distinctive feature / distinguishing feature** mark or property that is found only on that material or creature | **environmental features** conditions (permanent, *eg* rocks, repetitive, *eg* tide or changeable, *eg* weather) that are used to describe an area | **external features** marks that can be seen on the outside surface or skin | **functional feature** a characteristic that is needed for specific tasks | **key features** the major points that are important in identifying that product or organism | **main features** the marks and points that are easily seen, are most important or are unique to that object | **observable features** characteristics that you can see | **particular feature** a point that is important in identifying that organism | **physical features** the visible marks that are important in identifying that object or place | **safety features** characteristics of that method or equipment that are intended to improve safety | **special feature / specialised feature** (UK) / **specialized feature** (USA) the property that is needed for a particular purpose | **taxonomic features** the observable characteristics that are used to divide organisms into groups | **unique feature** a characteristic that is seen only in that object, place or time | **unusual features** points or characteristics that are not often seen in that type of object | **water-feature** a garden ornament that involves flowing water

feces (USA) / **faeces** (UK) solid waste products that are egested (excreted) from the anus

fed given food, having eaten

feed nutrients that are given to a plant, a meal for a baby; to provide nutrients, to take in food

feeding taking in food, eating | **feeding level** trophic level, how many animals separate that creature from the plants | **feeding relationships** the interdependency of different life forms so that changing the number of one type of animal may affect the numbers of several other types of animals | **breast feeding** giving milk from the mammary gland to a newborn offspring | **intravenous feeding** providing a solution of nutrients directly into the bloodstream

feel to use a sense of touch

feeler a sensor on the end of a stalk

feet (plural of foot) organs at the end of the legs | **webbed feet** the thickness of the foot is reduced and the bones connected by a flexible membrane to increase the surface area

feldspar a type of rock made from silicon oxides mixed with other material

fell tripped, dropped in an uncontrolled way, an area of moorland

felt a type of fabric made from cotton or wool | felt-tip pens the writing tip is a wick of felt which is in a reservoir of coloured liquid

female the gender that produces the egg | female cell any cell from a female, in humans this means that the sex chromosomes will be XX | female flower the flower that produces the ovule | female gametes the ova, eggs or reproductive cells produced by females, these cells have difficulty moving as they have a large food store | female nucleus the 'control centre' in a female cell | female parent the parent that produced the egg | female parts the reproductive organs in a female animal | female reproductive cells ova, eggs, the gamete that can not move | female reproductive organs the organs that are essential for the female to reproduce, in women, these include the ovaries, fallopian tubes, uterus and vagina | female sex cells the gametes that contain large food stores and in humans will all have an X sex chromosome | immature female an animal that will produce eggs later in life but is not doing so at present | mature female an animal that is producing eggs and so can be fertilised

femto.../ f... (*Greek*) prefix for a thousand, million, millionth of a unit, 10^{-15}

femur the thigh bone, the long bone connecting the pelvis to the knee

fence a thin vertical structure marking a boundary | electric fence one or more wires, at a low voltage relative to earth to discourage animals crossing, that mark a boundary

ferment to change a sugar into another chemical using microbes, *eg* alcohol is produced by yeast, yoghurt is produced by bacteria changing the sugars in milk

fermentation the process by which the microbes change sugar into other chemicals | fermentation lock equipment that allows escape of the carbon dioxide produced during fermentation, but prevents entry of air

fern a type of plant that has been growing since ancient times, they reproduce sexually, but without producing flowers | giant ferns/ tree ferns plants, about 20 metres tall, that grew about 300 million years ago when the concentration of carbon dioxide was high, so good growth was possible, and the concentration of oxygen was low, so the dead plants turned to coal

ferri- / ferro- (*Latin* iron)

fertile ready to produce a crop, able to reproduce | fertile ground / fertile land an area that is rich in nutrients and with sufficient water so is ideal for growing crops

fertilisation (UK) / **fertilization** (USA) the process that is occurring when the male and female nuclei fuse together | external fertilisation the sperm meets the ovum outside the body of the mother, *eg* fish and amphibia use external fertilisation | human fertilisation the fusing of the nucleus of a human sperm with the nucleus of a human ovum | *in vitro* fertilisation (IVF) artificial external fertilisation in which the ovum and the sperm are mixed together in a dish, the fertilised egg is then placed in the wall of the uterus for the necessary 9 months gestation | internal fertilisation the sperm meets the ovum in the body of the female *eg* used by birds and mammals | self-fertilisation the male and female gamete are provided by the same parent

fertilise (UK) / **fertilize** (USA) to unite the nuclei of the male and female reproductive cells | fertilised cell / fertilised egg cell the zygote, the nucleus of the male gamete has fused with the nucleus of the female egg | fertilised eggs the large spheroids laid by hens and amphibians that will develop into offspring

fertiliser (UK) / **fertilizer** (USA) a chemical that is added to the soil in order to improve the growth of plants | nitrate fertiliser a powder containing calcium nitrate, potassium nitrate or sodium nitrate that is used to give nitrogen to plants | plant fertiliser a mixture of simple chemicals that is spread on the soil in order to improve the growth of the plant

fertility drugs chemicals that are given to a woman in order to increase the chances of an egg being produced

fertilization (USA) / **fertilisation** (UK) the process that is occurring when the male and female nuclei fuse together | external fertilization the sperm meets the ovum outside the body of the mother, *eg* fish and amphibia use external fertilization | human fertilization the fusing of the nucleus of a human sperm with the nucleus of a human ovum | *in vitro* fertilization (IVF) artificial external fertilization in which the ovum and the sperm are mixed together in a dish, the fertilised egg is then placed in the wall of the uterus for the necessary 9 months gestation | internal fertilization the sperm meets the ovum in the body of the female, *eg* used by birds and mammals | self-fertilization the male and female gamete are provided by the same parent

fertilize (USA) / **fertilise** (UK) to unite the nuclei of the male and female reproductive cells | fertilized cell / fertilized egg cell the zygote, the nucleus of the male gamete has fused with the nucleus of the female egg | fertilized eggs the large spheroids laid by hens and amphibians that will develop into offspring

fertilizer (USA) / **fertiliser** (UK) a chemical that is added to the soil in order to improve the growth of plants | nitrate fertilizer a powder containing calcium nitrate, potassium nitrate or sodium nitrate that is used to give nitrogen to plants | plant fertilizer a mixture of simple chemicals that is spread on the soil in order to improve the growth of the plant

fetal (USA) / **foetal** (UK) concerned with the life form that is developing in the uterus | fetal blood stream the blood that flows around the foetus, to the placenta and then back to the foetus

fetus (USA) / **foetus** (UK) the young organism that is developing in the womb | developing fetus the embryo in the womb becoming larger and the specialised cells and organs form getting ready for birth

fever an increase in the body temperature to well above its usual 37.4°C | glandular fever a disease caused by the Epstein–Barr virus; this virus is present in almost everybody without ill effect, but sometimes causes flu-like symptoms over a long period, the symptoms may occasionally be more serious | hay fever an allergic reaction, seen as runny nose, wet eyes and difficulty in breathing, caused by a reaction to the presence of plant chemicals, usually the pollen of wind-pollinating plants such as hay | yellow fever an illness, Finlay discovered that the cause was infection by a microbe found in mosquitoes

few not many

fewer less than a specified number

fiber (USA) / **fibre** (UK) roughage, part of the food that passes through the gut (alimentary canal) without being absorbed and so is egested unchanged, a filament, any long strand of material | fiber glass a cloth made from very thin filaments of glass, a hard material produced by allowing millions of long glass filaments to be set in resin | fiber optic a thin glass tube in which light is transmitted from one end to the other by internal reflection | carbon fiber a filament of pure carbon that is very strong and flexible | cloth fiber a part of one of the millions of thin strands of cotton or wool that cross over each other to produce a material | cotton fiber a single filament of cotton | man-made fiber plastics that are spun as filaments then used to manufacture cloths and materials | natural fibers filaments that are made from material that is grown, *eg* wool, cotton, silk | nerve fiber the long part, or axon, of a nerve cell | optical fiber a thin filament of glass through which light can be passed either to transmit a picture or to convey information

fibre (UK) / **fiber** (USA) roughage, part of the food that passes through the gut (alimentary canal) without being absorbed and so is egested unchanged, a filament, any long strand of material | fibre glass a cloth made from very thin filaments of glass, a hard material produced by allowing millions of long glass filaments to be set in resin | fibre optic a thin glass tube in which light is transmitted from one end to the other by internal reflection | carbon fibre a filament of pure carbon that is very strong and flexible | cloth fibre a part of one of the millions of thin strands of cotton or wool that cross over each other to produce a material | cotton fibre a single filament of cotton | man-made fibre plastics that are spun as filaments then used to manufacture cloths and materials | natural fibres filaments that are made from material that is grown, *eg* wool, cotton, silk | nerve fibre the long part, or axon, of a nerve cell | optical fibre a thin filament of glass through which light can be passed either to transmit a picture or to convey information

fibrous behaves as though the material was made from filaments mixed together | fibrous structure an arrangement of different materials that contains long threads

fibula the thinner of the two bones that join the knee to the ankle (the thicker bone is the tibia)

fiction a story that has been made up from the imagination | science fiction stories that are set in the future, a tale containing at least one idea that is currently considered to be scientifically impossible

field an area of land, a subject to be studied, the volume of space in which an effect can be measured | field guide a book which illustrates and describes the types of organisms that are found in an area | field lines paths that are formed between two magnetic poles that can be shown using iron filings | field mouse (plural is field mice) a type of small mammal that lives in grassland | field of view the area that you are able to see under the restrictions that have been given | field strength / magnetic field strength the size of the force that attracts opposite magnetic poles or repels similar poles | field work experiments and observations that are carried out in an area away from the laboratory | crop fields large areas of land that are used for producing that type of food | Earth's magnetic field the Earth seems to act like a giant magnet, so that the north pole of every compass is attracted to one end of the Earth | gravitational field the area over which the mass of one body has an attractive effect on another body | magnetic field the area around a magnet that will attract another magnet, iron, nickel or cobalt | oil field the area of land, often vast, below which is found the reservoir of oil | playing field an area of grass that is marked out for ball games | treating fields adding material to large areas of land so they produce a better crop

fighters people who resist | fire fighters the people who are skilled at putting out large fires

fighting struggling, attempting to destroy, setting out in opposition

filament a thin strand | filament lamps a bulb that produces light by passing an electric current through a thin piece of wire | tungsten filament thin strands of tungsten that are used in electric lamps because the metal has a high melting point

filamentous green algae a long, thin fresh water organism that has chlorophyll for photosynthesis

filings (not fillings which are put into teeth) thin shavings | iron filings iron that is produced as a powder

fill to pack, to pour in a liquid to the top

filled loaded to the top

fillings (not filings which are thin shavings) packing materials, *eg* tooth fillings

film paper on which is made a permanent image; to take a series of pictures | film case an opaque cylinder that is used for storing photographic film | film material the object is a very thin sheet covered with light-sensitive chemicals, a fabric | cling film sheets containing a plastic that melts at about 35°C so the plastic is melted by hand heat, then moulded to a shape that remains when cool | photographic film the paper sheet that is coated on one side with chemicals that change when exposed to light

filter to pour a fluid through cloth or paper so as to allow only the liquid part through | filter bed a tank containing layers of rocks of different sizes that allows sewage water to be pumped onto the top and clean water to leak out underneath | filter funnel a piece of plastic or glass that has a wide top and a narrow stem | filter paper the paper through which a solution is poured in order to separate the solids from the liquid | filter screen a mesh that prevents large material entering tunnels carrying water | color filter (USA) / colored filter (USA) / colour filter (UK) / coloured filter (UK) a glass or plastic plate that allows certain parts of the spectrum through and absorbs the other wavelengths | daylight filter transparent material that transmits different colours to different extents so the spectrum of a light bulb is similar to that of the Sun | green filter a piece of material that allows only green light to pass through | red filter a piece of glass, Perspex™ or other transparent material, that has a coating or contains chemicals so that only red light is able to pass through

filtering cleaning by passing through a sieve | filtering blood passing blood through a special matrix so as to separate the blood cells from the plasma

filtrate the liquid that passes through a filter paper

filtration the process of separating solids from a liquid using a filter paper

fin a thin membrane stretched between supports that is used for swimming, the tail part of an aeroplane, the dorsal organ of a shark; to move through water by moving a membrane | dorsal fin the large fin on the back of most fish (especially prominent in sharks!) | pectoral fin the fin on the side of the body of the fish, immediately behind the gill slits

final last, ultimate | final proof the evidence that shows the theory must be correct

find / find out to discover, to observe

findings your observations and measurements | fault finding using techniques that will allow a broken item to start working again | preliminary findings measurements that are taken near the start of the project

fine small, thin, delicate, a financial penalty | fine detail observations of every part, no matter how small or insignificant | fine focus the small changes that are needed to provide an image with sharp edges | fine structure details of what an organism or a rock looks like | fine tubes capillaries, very small canals that can be seen with a microscope

finely in tiny pieces | finely crushed / finely ground pressure was used to turn an object into a powder

finger one of the extensions at the end of a hand, a digit | finger length an old measure of length that was the length of the first finger | finger nail the plate of horny material found at the end of each digit each grows approximately 1 millimetre per week | fingerprints the marks left by the raised lines on the ends of your fingers | fingertips the area of skin at the end of the fingers | clamp fingers the parts of a clamp that are like two fingers that can be closed to hold apparatus | index finger the finger next to the thumb

fig

↓

fin

finish the end; to end, to complete | photo-finish the contestants in a race finished so close together that a photograph needed to be examined to establish who won

finite must end sometime or somewhere | finite speed the distance covered per second can be measured

Finlay (Carlos Juan 1833–1915) was the son of a Scottish father and a French mother who practised medicine in Cuba, fortunately, he was a good linguist! After 20 years, he concluded that yellow fever must be transmitted by one type of mosquito – he was so convinced that he would feed a mosquito on the blood of a yellow fever victim then try to pass the disease onto another patient – fortunately for the patient, this was unsuccessful, but seemed to disprove Finlay's idea. Finlay was right in his idea, but it took others to prove that the yellow fever had to be in the mosquito for about 20 days before the infection could be passed onto the next victim.

fins thin membranes, stretched between supports, that are used for swimming

fir (not fur which is hair) / **fir tree** a tall plant that is an evergreen and produces cones

fire combustion, burning, a chemical reaction in which heat is given off, flames and smoke will be seen if the combustion is incomplete; to shoot | fire blanket a flame-resistant sheet that can be wrapped around a burning object so as to smother the flames by preventing movement of oxygen | fire break an area from which all material capable of burning has been removed | fire extinguisher equipment that can be used for putting out a fire | fire fighters the people who are skilled at putting out large fires | fire fighting attempting to put out a fire by removing any of the three parts of the fire triangle (heat, oxygen and fuel) | fire place an area in which a fire may be lit safely in the home | fire prevention taking precautions so that a fire is unlikely to start | fire-proof will not burn | fire triangle the three parts that are essential for a fire – heat, fuel and oxygen | fireworks controlled explosions that are used to give visual pleasure | bar fire an electrical heater in which a wire is wound around a porcelain rod that is placed at the centre of a semi-circular reflective metal plate | ring of fire the edges of the Pacific ocean which are the sites of many active volcanoes

fired projected at high speed by an explosion | fired clay the clay has been heated so as to retain its shape | oil-fired the fuel that is providing the heat energy is a hydrocarbon

fireworks controlled explosions, often contain metal compounds that burn with different colours | firework display an entertainment lasting several minutes in which many brightly-coloured fireworks are ignited in turn to give synchronised patterns

firm definite, hard, fixed | firm conclusion the observations are reliable and fit the theory very closely | firm prediction foretelling exactly what will happen and when

firmness hardness

first initial, a start | first-hand information that you obtained, experiences that have occurred to you | first-hand data information and observations that you have made yourself | first-hand experience you were part of the scene that took place | first-hand observation you made the measurements and actually saw what was happening

fish (plural is fish or fishes) one of the five divisions of animals that have backbones (vertebrates) distinguished by having gills and scales | fish farm a lake in which fish are fed and protected until ready for eating | fish gills thin plates at the side of the head that allow a fish to remove oxygen from the water | fish scales thin plates that cover the outside of fish | fish stock the population of each species of fish in the specified area | goldfish a fresh-water fish that grows up to 30 centimetres long and is bred to give a wide variety of colours | shellfish sea creatures that have an external skeleton such as mussels, prawns, crabs or lobsters

fisherman a person who catches wild fish for pleasure, for eating or for selling to make a living

fishes a rarely used plural of fish

fishing line a string that is very thin and is strong, a strong filament that is used with bait to catch fish

fission breaking into parts | binary fission breaking into two parts | nuclear fission breakdown of the nucleus of an atom to produce new elements

fissure a crack which may be tiny, because it is in a tooth, or very large, for example in a rock

fit the right size, able to do exercise then the heart rate quickly returns to resting level; to match sizes | best fit with least error so most points lie near to the curve

fitness the heart rate returns rapidly to a resting level after exercise | fitness center (USA) / fitness centre (UK) a building containing equipment that will measure variables such as heart rate and weight, then provide exercise that will improve your heart rate and blood pressure | fitness program (USA) / fitness programme (UK) exercises taken in order to reduce the heart rate and blood pressure and make you better able to recover from exercise

fittest best suited to particular circumstances | survival of the fittest the animals that are still alive after there has been competition for resources such as food or mates

five kingdoms the five major divisions of life *ie* animals / fungi / monera / plants / protoctista

fixation a habit | nitrogen fixation the changing of unreactive nitrogen gas [N_2] into ammonium [NH_4^+] and nitrate ions [NO_3^-] that can be absorbed by plant roots

fixed not changing | fixed air the name given in the eighteenth century to the gas (carbon dioxide) produced by fermentation | fixed boiling point the temperature at which a liquid turns to gas and is unchanging for that liquid | fixed composition the proportion of the several components never changes | fixed height the vertical distance between two items is stated and is not allowed to change | fixed joint a junction between bones that can not move, *eg* in the skull | fixed melting point the temperature at which a solid turns to liquid is unchanging for a pure substance, *eg* ice melts at 0°C | fixed period the time taken or needed is stated and then not allowed to change | fixed points temperatures used to calibrate a thermometer – the position of the alcohol or mercury in the stem is marked at 0°C and 100°C | fixed position the place or point is not allowed to move | fixed proportion the ratio of one thing to another remains the same, *eg* hydrogen and oxygen are in fixed proportion of 2:1 in water [H_2O] | fixed temperature the temperature is not allowed to change | fixed volume you decide how much liquid is to be used then use that same volume throughout the experiment

fizz to give off lots of gas in a solution, carbon dioxide dissolved under pressure in a fluid

fizzes droplets of liquid are being thrown into the air by the movement of air bubbles in the liquid

fizzy a liquid with many bubbles | fizzy drink a mixture of water, flavours and colourings which contains carbon dioxide dissolved under pressure | fizzy water carbon dioxide is dissolved under pressure in water and forms bubbles when the pressure is reduced

flaccid loose, limp, deflated

flag a cloth with a pattern that represents a country, an emblem; to become tired

flagella (plural of flagellum) look like hairs sticking out of a cell, but they can be controlled and moved like muscles

flagellum (plural is flagella) a very thin whip that can be controlled like a muscle and is used for moving some microbes

flake a thin fragment, a chip | snow flake a single piece of snow that looks like a circle of six flat fronds

flame the visible sign that a fuel is burning | flame color (USA) / flame colour (UK) may tell you the temperature of the flame, yellow being coolest and invisible being hottest, or may show the presence of metal ions, *eg* copper ions produce a green flame | flame-proof to treat a material so it will not catch fire | flame test spraying the material into a colourless flame and measuring the intensity and wavelength of the colour | blue flame the flame produced when there is lots of oxygen, because the hole at the base of the bunsen burner is fully open, so combustion is complete | cold flame there is not enough oxygen (the hole in the bunsen burner is closed) so there is less heat | naked flame a flame that is not protected by a shield such as glass or gauze | safe flame a highly visible, yellow flame produced by closing the air hole of a bunsen burner | yellow flame a highly visible flame produced when there is not enough oxygen for complete combustion

flammable (also called inflammable) able to catch fire | flammable liquid the liquid is able to catch fire, *eg* petrol | flammable material any substance that can be burned | highly flammable catches fire very easily

Flamsteed (John 1646–1719) was frequently absent from school, through ill health, but this did not prevent him going to Cambridge University and starting to publish original research, while still a teenager! He was created Astronomer Royal in 1675 with the task of constructing accurate data on every star. His desire for accuracy meant that he was not prepared to publish very much information, and this led to a major argument with Newton. Eventually, the magnificent astronomical catalogue, showing the position of 3000 stars, was published in 1725 – just 50 years after the work had started.

flap a small opening that is self-closing, a disorganised manner; to wave a flexible object | catflap a swing-door that is sufficiently large to allow a cat to pass through

flare a bright light, a container which has chemicals that react to produce bright light and is used by sailors or mountaineers

flash a very short time, a brief, high-intensity light; to move rapidly | bright flash a source of light that has a high intensity for a brief period of time

flask a jar or bottle in which the diameter of the neck is less than that of the main part of the bottle | **conical flask** glassware that is in the shape of a cone with a short neck | **Dewar flask** a storage jar with two parallel walls, usually made from glass, that are separated by a space in which there is a vacuum | **flat-bottom flask** the container is almost spherical, but with a flat bottom opposite the neck so it can stand on a bench | **round-bottom flask** a piece of glassware that looks like a sphere with a neck so it will not stand upright but is suitable for heating liquids | **side-arm flask** a conical flask with an open glass tube welded to the neck | **Thermos™ flask / vacuum flask** (also called a dewar vessel) a bottle with walls made from two layers of glass that are painted silver, the air has been removed from the space between the two walls so heat loss is minimised

flat level | **flat battery** a structure that would be expected to provide a voltage, but does not because the chemicals have all changed | **flat-bottom flask** the container is almost spherical but with a flat bottom opposite the neck so it can stand on a bench | **flat Earth** the theory that the Earth is a plate and you could sail over the edge | **flat mirror** a reflective surface that is perfectly flat, a plane mirror | **flatworm** an invertebrate animal that is flat like a sheet of paper or a tape measure

flavor (USA) / **flavour** (UK) taste

flavoring chemicals (USA) / **flavouring chemicals** (UK) substances that are added to foods in order to improve or enhance the taste

flaw (not floor which is a base) a break, a crack, a theory that is based on a wrong idea

flea (not flee which is to run) a small insect without wings that lives on the skin or hair and feeds on blood

fledgeling / fledgling a bird that is developing its first set of flight wings and has yet to learn to fly

flee (not flea which is an insect) to run away in a panic

fleet fast, rapid; a collection of ships or aircraft

Fleming (Sir Alexander 1881–1955) started as a shipping clerk but a legacy allowed him to study medicine at St Mary's Hospital in Paddington – where he remained until his retirement. In the First World War he tried to improve methods to prevent infection of wounds, this led to his work on lysozyme and then on to antibiotics, especially penicillin – he used the well-known fact that bacteria will not grow near to certain fungi to deduce that the fungus must be excreting an antibacterial chemical. A multinational team led by Fleming (Scottish), Florey (Australian) and Chain (German) working in England isolated the penicillin and were jointly awarded the 1945 Nobel Prize for Medicine

flesh the muscles of an animal, meat

flew (not flu which is a disease, nor flue which is a chimney) departed, the past participle of to fly

flex a cable, a wire covered with a flexible insulator, a group of insulated wires in a sheath; to bend | **flex grip** the part of a plug that can be adjusted so as to hold the flex tightly, therefore preventing any tension on the individual wires | **three-core flex** the three insulated wires inside a plastic sleeve that connects the mains electricity plug to the equipment

flexible able to bend easily without breaking

flick to move rapidly outwards

flight the ability to make controlled and extended journeys through the air

flip chart a large block of paper on an easel

flipper a modified limb that allows some mammals, eg seals, to move efficiently in the sea

float to remain on the surface of a liquid, to rise upwards | **milk float** a vehicle powered by batteries that is used for transporting bottles of milk in large numbers

floatation device / flotation device equipment that prevents other bodies from sinking

floated remained at the surface

floating moving upwards through air, remaining on the surface of a liquid because of buoyancy | **floating objects** any material that remains on the surface of a liquid with some part of the material below the surface | **floating plants** plants that grow in water and do not need to put roots down into soil

flood a vast amount of water covering areas that are normally dry land; to increase the amount of water so the land becomes covered with water | **flood-lights** high intensity lamps that flood the area with light | **flood-lit** a wide area is brightly illuminated by high-powered lamps

flooded covered with water

flooding adding vast amounts so the barriers are overcome

floor (not flaw which is a crack) the horizontal surface on which you walk

floppy flaccid, unable to hold its shape | **floppy disc** (UK & USA) / **floppy disk** (USA) a method of storing digital information, originally the discs were thin plastic and had to be kept in cardboard cases

Florey (Howard Walter 1898–1968) started by studying lysozyme, an antimicrobial chemical that had been found by Fleming in tears. He was joined by Chain in 1935 and together they isolated sufficient pure penicillin to carry out clinical trials. Production of penicillin increased rapidly so many casualties of the D-Day landings survived infections that would have killed them in previous years.

flotation device / floatation device equipment that prevents other bodies from sinking

flour (not flower which is the part of a plant) a powder produced by grinding the seed of a cereal plant that is used in baking, *eg* making bread

flow movement, usually in one direction | flow chart / flow diagram a picture to show the movement of energy, chemicals or information, but without any details of the processes involved | flow of blood movement of blood through the blood vessels | flow of charge an electric current, may be movement of electrons or of ions | flow of electrons occurs when an electric current is in a wire | flow of energy movement of energy through a system such as a food web | flow of heat conduction, the movement of thermal energy from the hot end of a solid to the cool end | flow rate the speed with which a movement occurs, *eg* the flow rate of blood in the blood vessels | blood flow the movement of blood through vessels and capillaries | current flow emphasising that something, water or charge, is moving in a particular direction | energy flow movement of energy, especially heat energy, from one place to another | heat flow movement of energy from a region of high temperature to an area of lower temperature | lava flow movement of the molten rock that has erupted from a volcano | water flow the rate of movement of the liquid

flower (not flour which is a ground corn) the reproductive organ of plants that use insects to transport pollen; to produce an organ that will attract insects | flower bed a patch of earth that is used for growing lots of flowers | flower color (USA) / flower colour (UK) the colour of the petals that should attract insects and so may reflect light that is beyond human vision | flower structure the tissues, such as stamen, ovules and petals, that make up the flower | composite flower the head of the flower is many tiny flowers packed closely together, *eg* a daisy | female flower the flower that produces the ovule | garden flower a type of flower that is planted in the garden for a specific purpose, such as looking or smelling really good | male flower the part of the plant that

produces the pollen, or male sex cell | wind-pollinated flower a plant, *eg* grasses, that scatter their pollen onto the wind

flowering plant an organism that is able to make sugars by photosynthesis and produces a flower | non-flowering / non-flowering plant an organism that lives by using photosynthesis, but does not produce a flower and so pollination will not involve an insect

flu / influenza (not flew which is to fly nor flue which is a chimney) a virus that causes a disease, with an increased body temperature, feeling sick and sleepy, which is usually not fatal, but occasionally special types of flu arrive that kill people, especially the elderly or very young

flue (not flew which is to fly nor flu which is a disease) a chimney

fluff-out to raise the feathers so as to improve insulation by trapping more air

fluff-up to change the direction of the feathers so that they are more upright and so trap more air and help the bird retain body heat

fluffed-up the feathers are almost vertical to the skin

fluid a group or set of particles that is able to flow, not only are liquids and gases fluids, but also sand, flour and any powder | fluids liquids that are drunk in order to ensure that the body has adequate amounts of water | fluid motion movement of the bulk or majority of a fluid, carrying everything with the fluid | fluid resistance resistive force that slows down any object trying to move through a fluid because the particles have to be shifted out of the way as the object moves | amniotic fluid the liquid in which the foetus floats and which provides protection | cooler fluid the liquid or gas is at a lower temperature | hot fluid any liquid or gas that feels hot to the touch and may damage the skin | hydraulic fluid the liquid, with a high boiling point and that is difficult to compress, which can be used in hydraulic systems | synovial fluid the liquid that separates the ends of a joint | tissue fluid the liquid surrounding cells in animals, a liquid similar to blood plasma

fluidised (UK) / **fluidized** (USA) breaking a solid into tiny particles that then act almost like a liquid | fluidised bed a layer of powder behaves like a liquid when a continuous stream of air is blown through the base

fluorescent absorbs light of one frequency and emits light of a lower frequency – often absorbs ultra-violet (invisible) light and emits a colour | fluorescent light / fluorescent tube a light source in which an alternating current produces ultra-violet rays which are turned to visible light by the glass envelope

fluoridated a fluoride salt, usually sodium fluoride [NaF], has been added to the water

fluoride / fluoride ion [F⁻] the charged particle formed by a fluorine atom gaining an electron, the ion that is needed in the diet to ensure that the teeth are strong | potassium fluoride [KF] a white crystalline solid that looks like common salt

fluorine (F, proton number 9) the most reactive of the halogens; [F_2] an incredibly reactive gas, boiling point −188°C

flush to wash out, to turn the skin red

flute a musical instrument in the shape of a tube, played by blowing across an air hole

fly an insect; to move through the air | green fly aphid, a small insect that feeds on plants and is used by ants

flypast the path of a space probe that passes close enough to an object that photographs can be taken

flywheel a large, heavy wheel that can store energy by rotating

foam lots of air in bubbles of soap | foam plastic/ plastic foam a springy solid that is made from plastic and contains many small bubbles of air | insulating foam a layer of solid sponge that is used to prevent heat movement | shaving foam a soap that prepares a skin for cutting of hair growth

focus the point to which parallel rays are directed after passing through a lens the underground location of an earthquake; to bring light rays to a point so as to give a sharp picture | focus control the method for changing the distance between object and lens in a microscope so the image is sharp and details can be seen | focus knob the rotating control that changes the distance between object and lens in a microscope so the image is sharp | coarse focus moving the objective lens relatively large distances, so as to approach a sharp image | fine focus the small changes that are needed to provide an image with sharp edges | in focus the image is sharp, there is no blurring

focused / focussed brought to a point, concentrated

fodder the plants that have been harvested then stored for later feeding to cattle or horses, *eg* hay, straw

foetal (UK) **/ fetal** (USA) concerned with the life form that is developing in the uterus | foetal blood stream the blood that flows around the foetus, to the placenta, where chemical exchange occurs, and then back to the foetus

foetus (UK) **/ fetus** (USA) the young organism that is developing in the womb of a mammal | developing foetus the embryo in the womb becoming larger and the specialised cells and organs form getting ready for birth

fog a suspension of tiny water particles in air

foil a very thin sheet of metal | aluminium foil (UK) / aluminum foil (USA) thin sheets of aluminium, often on a roll | shiny foil a thin metal sheet that will reflect light and heat

fold a bending in a layer of rock; to deform a stratum of rock, to bend

folded bent over on itself, cables or layers that have been deformed | folded membrane the cell membrane appears to have ripples so as to increase the surface area | folded rocks the layer of rock has buckled and bent by the movement of the surrounding strata

folic acid a vitamin that helps with the absorption of iron

follicle a pit, an opening, a tube | hair follicle the tube through which a hair grows on the skin

following chasing, after an event, subsequent; a sequence

food chemicals that an organism eats in order to get the nutrients that are essential for life | food additives chemicals that are added to food so that the taste, appearance or shelf-life are improved | food-borne diseases, such as food poisoning, that are transmitted in food | food chain a line or sequence of organisms that starts with a producer and finishes with the top consumer | food chemistry the study of the chemicals that humans eat, including the storage, preparation and digestion of such chemicals | food coloring (USA) / food colouring (UK) a chemical that is added to food in order to change the colour | food components the different types of plants and animals that go into a meal | food constituent any chemical that is found in food | food crop a plant that is grown with the intention that it will be harvested and sold as food | food dyes chemicals that change the colour of food | food energy chemical energy, released during respiration, and used by the organism for movement and growth | food manufacturer a company that turns a plant or animal into a form that you are willing and able to eat | food mixer electrical equipment that uses rotating paddles to mix ingredients | food molecule any chemical that is found in the food that you eat | food packaging the boxes, cartons and wrappings that are used to keep food looking fresh and free from dirt | food poisoning an illness caused by eating food that contains microbes that produce chemicals which cause you to be sick and to feel ill | **food preservation** treating food so that the food remains edible for a long time, such treatment includes pickling in salt or vinegar and storing in a concentrated sugar solution | **food processing** changing food on a large scale so that the food is either easier to prepare or to eat | **food product** a substance that is made from different foods and which is then eaten, *eg* ice cream is made from eggs and cream | **food production** farming, making edible dishes from raw materials | **food pyramid** the triangle shape produced by consumers needing to eat vast amounts of food in order to produce a small amount of growth | **food reserves** the amount of fat in an animal or oils in plants, that can be used in the absence of new food, the amount of food that is kept in a store for emergency use | **food resources** the number, amount and type of animals and plants that are available for eating | **food retailer** person or shop that sells food and food products | **food safety** making and storing food in such a way that foreign bacteria can not get in and start to breed | **food sample** a small quantity of the meal has been taken for examination | **food science** the investigation of the changes that occur when food is prepared, cooked and stored | **food scientist** a person who studies the effects of different foods or the methods for preparing and storing food | **food source** the types of organisms and where they are found that are eaten by a consumer (animal or microbe) | **food storage** keeping food at a temperature and humidity that minimises decay | **food store** a collection of nuts that is hidden from other animals, a chemical, or parts where chemicals are stored, that can be used later | **foodstuff** any material that goes into making a meal | **food supply** the amount and type of food at that place and that time of year | **food tests** specific reactions that show which nutrients are in a food | **food type** a class of nutrients that have common chemical properties | **food web** a diagram that shows, in a simplified form, the different animals that may eat one type of prey or plant and the number of different food sources used by each animal | **availability of food** whether nutrients are present in a form that the animal can eat | **cattle food** the plants and crops that are suitable for feeding to cows | **chilled food** meals that have been prepared then frozen rapidly | **digested food** the mash produced by the pummelling of the stomach, the hydrochloric acid and the many digestive enzymes | **fatty foods** one, or more, parts of the meal

contains a high proportion of fat | **gnawed food** the material to be eaten has been crushed between molar teeth | **home-grown food** crops that are grown by a person for their own consumption | **hot food** usually refers to the temperature of the food, usually above 50°C, but may mean very spicy and hot to the taste | **intravenous food** giving nutrients to a person by direct introduction of a solution into the bloodstream | **low-energy food** food that does not provide many calories / joules of energy, although it may contain lots of essential nutrients and vitamins | **moldy food** (USA) / **mouldy food** (UK) food on which an area of coloured fungi are visible - possibly producing harmful chemicals | **organic food** crops that have been raised without either adding any artificial chemical to the soil or spraying the crop with chemicals | **pet food** a meal that is intended to be eaten by a domestic animal | **plant food** nutrients, especially NPK fertiliser or manure, that are added to the roots of a growing plant | **preserving food** treating food in such a way that the food remains edible for a long time, *eg* by using pickling, producing a jam or sealing into a tin | **snack foods** edible materials that need no further preparation other than heating | **solid food** material that is eaten and needs chewing before it can be swallowed | **undigested food** substances that have been eaten, but has passed unchanged through the digestive tract and is egested as faeces

fool a person who lacks common sense; to mislead | **fools' gold** iron sulphide [FeS_2], a compound that looks just like gold, but reacts violently with hydrochloric acid

foot (plural is feet) the part of the body adapted for moving over ground by pushing, the lowest part, a length of approximately 30 centimetres | **foot bones** (metatarsals) the long bones in the feet | **footpath** a track for use by walkers only | **foot-print** the mark left by standing, the area needed for an activity | **athlete's foot** a disease of the foot caused by infection with a fungus, itching is caused by the hyphae (roots) of the fungus growing under the skin

footpath a track for use by walkers only

for (not fore, which is at the front, nor four, which is a number) because, on behalf of

forage to look for food that may be covered

force something that tries to change the speed or direction of an object

force = mass × acceleration
(newtons) (kilograms) (metres / sec / sec)
| **force arrows** arrows that show the direction

and size of a force | force diagram a representation showing the size and direction of the forces | force-meter / newton-meter an instrument for measuring the size of a force | force multiplier a machine (usually a lever or hydraulic pump) in which the force that is applied to the load is greater than the force that you put in | force of attraction any force, *eg* those produced by charge, magnetic fields or gravity, that causes objects to move closer together | force of gravity the weak attraction between any masses but important for astronomical bodies such as stars or planets | amplifying force increasing the effort applied to the load compared to the force that you applied *eg* in a lever or a car jack | applied force the effort, the push or pull that is trying to cause a change of direction or speed | attractive force causes two or more objects to become closer | balanced forces two equal forces are trying to change the direction or speed of an object but the two forces are in opposite directions and so cancel out | bending force a push or pull that is applied to a rod that is held at the opposite end, resulting in the object changing shape | constant force the push or pull is unchanging | downward force a push that is applied in the direction of the gravitational field | drag force the wind resistance slowing down a speeding object | driving force the push that is trying to make an object move at a faster pace in a particular direction | frictional force the force between two surfaces moving over each other that causes the two surfaces to try and stick together | g-force measuring an acceleration relative to that expected for Earth | gravitational force the movement produced because of the attraction of a nearby large body | hydrostatic force the push produced because a liquid is being pushed, either by a piston in a cylinder or the weight of fluid above that position | inward force pushing towards the inside, trying to compress | magnetic force the change in movement caused by the presence of a magnet | moment of a force a torque, a turning force, the applied force multiplied by the distance to the pivot | pushing force a force, that if opposed, will cause compression, otherwise it causes the object to move forward | reaction force the push in the opposite direction to the applied force that opposes any movement | resistive force the force that opposes your attempts at changing speed *eg* friction, wind resistance | resultant force the overall force, in size and direction, that results when more than one force is applied to an object | retarding force / stopping force the force that

tries to slow the object, *eg* brakes | thrust force a push that causes the object to move forward | transmit force to apply a force at one part of a hydraulic or mechanical system, which is then applied to a position that is at a distance and in a different direction | turning force (moment, torque) a push or pull that results in a rotation

turning force = applied force × distance to pivot
(newton-metres)   (newtons)   (metres)

| unbalanced forces two forces are opposing, but one is larger so they do not balance and movement occurs | unhelpful forces pushes and pulls that hinder progress | universal force something that causes a change of velocity and is found everywhere | upward force a push that lifts an object against gravity | useful force a push or pull that causes a helpful change | variety of forces different ways in which attempts are made to change speed or direction | weak force the push or pull is not sufficiently strong as to be important at that distance

forceps tweezers, small pairs of levers used for picking things up without using fingers

fore- (not for, which is a reason, nor four, which is a number) (*Anglo-Saxon* at the front)

fore-arm the part of the arm between the elbow and the wrist

forecast to predict, to say what is expected to happen | weather forecast a prediction of what the temperature, wind speeds and rainfall are likely to be in a particular area

forecaster a predictor | weather forecaster the person who tells you what the temperature, rain and wind conditions are likely to be in the near future

foreign not native to that area | foreign antigen the chemical causing the immune response is from a cell that is not normally found in that animal

forelimb an arm, a front limb

forensic investigation looking at tiny details using scientific methods in order to develop a picture of a past event | forensic science analysis of material and evidence that could be used in a court of law

foreskin the skin that covers the head of the penis

forest a hunting ground, an area with lots of trees | forest clearance to cut down the trees so the land can be used for some other purpose | northern forest the type of woodland that is found near the Arctic circle | rain forest large areas of trees and undergrowth associated with lots of rain, spread through the year, together with high temperatures | sustainable forest new trees are planted to replace the trees that have been cut down | tropical forest large areas of tree and bushes that are subject to almost continuous rain and high temperatures

foreword (not forward which is a direction) the words at the start of the book that outline the contents

fork an implement with two or more prongs at one end, a division of a path into smaller paths; to split into two parts | tuning fork an implement that has two prongs that vibrate at a known frequency

form a sheet of paper that can be completed with information, a type; to make into a shape, to produce | appropriate form suitable type of table (a form), the general presentation | diagrammatic form to show a process or structure in a simplified drawing | inactive form the structure of a chemical that has all the atoms of the active form (a chemical that will bring about a change), but will become active only after it has a few minor changes | landform any feature that is seen on the surface of the Earth | life form any type of life that could be found in that environment | standard form representing a number as a digit between 1 and 10 multiplied by a power of 10 | wave form the shape of a wave which can be square, saw tooth or sine

formal following expected conventions or agreements of dress and behaviour

formaldehyde [HCHO] a chemical that has been used to preserve bodies or to destroy bacteria, but is now rarely used because it probably causes cancer

format style, arrangement | appropriate format general appearance and sequencing of the writing| suitable format the presentation is appropriate for that occasion or experiment

formation making, a structure, an arrangement | fossil formation means by which the body of a dead animal was turned into a permanent rock structure | image formation a diagram showing the rays of light from the object to the image | process of formation the method by which an article is made | rock formation the changing of material into a specific type of rock | seed formation the changes that occur in the ovule between the pollen tube reaching the ova and the seed being released | shadow formation producing dark areas by placing a solid object between the light source and the wall | soil formation method by which rocks, dead plants and leaves and manure are broken down by wind, water and worms to produce material suitable for growing seeds

Formica™ a polymer of urea and formaldehyde that is sold as decorative, impermeable sheets

formic acid [HCOOH] methanoic acid, the irritant that is injected when an ant bites

forming making, becoming | rock forming the processes, involving change of temperature and pressure, by which rocks are produced

forms kinds, types, paper that has to be completed with information | forms of energy the different types of energy (chemical, electrical, heat, kinetic, light, nuclear, potential, sound) | forms of insulation different methods that can be used to prevent movement of heat

formula (plural is formulae) an exact method of showing a structure or a change, a shorthand method of showing the atoms in a chemical | formula triangle placing the three variable of most simple equations into a triangle so that covering the unknown allows a decision as to the next mathematical operation eg the speed equation can be written as

$$\text{speed} \quad = \quad \frac{\text{distance}}{\text{time}} \quad \text{or} \quad \frac{d}{s \mid t}$$

| balance formula the law of moments (moment = force x distance to pivot)

$$\text{sum of clockwise} \ = \ \text{sum of anti-clockwise}$$
$$\text{moments} \qquad \qquad \text{moments}$$

| chemical formula using the chemical shorthand to show the exact number and type of atoms in a compound | mathematical formula shows the dependent variable on the left-hand side of an equals sign and the independent variables on the right-hand side of the equation

formulae (plural of formula) relationships between variables, the chemical shorthand for compounds

formulate to produce a plan

fort (not fought which is to have had a fight) a group of buildings surrounded by a high wall that is for defence, a castle

forth (not fourth which is used in counting) forward, out into view

fortnight a period of two weeks, ie 14 days

fortune a large amount of money

forward (not foreword which is an introduction) moving in the direction that is in front | forward thrusters rocket engines that eject hot gases in the direction of travel so as to reduce the speed

fossil a rock that has been produced by fine silt filling the space left by a decaying organism and then turning hard | fossil evidence information that has been obtained by looking at the size, age and distribution of fossils | fossil formation method by which the remains of a living organism are turned into the rock that is a fossil | fossil fragments parts of a creature that have formed fossils | fossil fuels fuels that were produced long, long ago when there was less oxygen in the atmosphere and then buried underground; coal was originally plants, such as the giant fern, and oil was from sea creatures, gas is found with both coal and oil | **fossil specimen** a fossil that shows special and important features

fossilised (UK) / **fossilized** (USA) becoming a fossil, looking like a fossil

Foucault (Leon 1819–1868) studied medicine then moved over to physics where he measured the speed of light in air and under water, showing that light must be a wave. He made pendulums – big pendulums – there is one in the London Science Museum which is about 30 metres high. Foucault hung a 67 metres pendulum from the dome of the Pantheon in Paris – the swing of the 28 kilogram ball on the end showed that the Earth must be rotating.

fought (not fort which is a castle) to have been involved in an interaction of physical violence

foul (not fowl which is a bird) horribly smelly, stormy; an act against a rule; to make filthy

found discovered, measured

four (not for which is a reason, nor fore which is at the front) the number between three and five

fourth (not forth which is forward) three others are in front | **one-fourth** a quarter, $\frac{1}{4}$

fowl (not foul which is smelly) poultry, hens

fox (plural is foxes) a canine mammal with a pointed nose and bushy tail that seems to be able to live comfortably in any surroundings – including towns

foxglove a tall, biennial flowering plant, the original source of the heart drug called digitalis

FP / fp / f.pt. [freezing point] the temperature at which the liquid turns into a solid

fraction a part of a whole

fractional a part | **fractional distillation** separating a mixture into pure components by heating a liquid then passing the vapour up a column packed with porous material that reduces convection

fractionating column a tube filled with porous material, that is used to separate components by boiling point | **fractionating tower** the large cylinder in which hot, crude oil is separated into fractions by boiling point

fracture a break; to come apart, to splinter

fragment a small part that has broken; to break into small pieces | **angular fragments** the broken pieces have sharp edges | **fossil fragments** pieces of a single fossil, a few pieces of the many fossils that are made from the many bones in a body | **rock fragments** parts of a rock that have broken off and so are more easily transported

fragmental pieces that show sharp edges and corners | **fragmental rock** sedimentary material that has been produced by rocks breaking apart

fragmentation broken into pieces with sharp edges | **rock fragmentation** breaking of rocks into many smaller pieces, possibly caused by water freezing in cracks and then thawing

frame an outline, a boundary; to put into a skeleton | **frame a question** to ask a question in a very precise manner that can be answered by experiment | **window frame** the wood or metal surround that holds the glass into the window

framework the outline, the supporting skeleton, the limitations

Franklin (Benjamin 1706–1790) had three separate and very different careers, he made a fortune as a printer/ journalist, he then became interested in electricity and finally he was active politically, helping to draft the American Declaration of Independence. His famous experiment, flying a kite into a cloud to see if electricity could be conducted to Earth led to the fixing of lightning conductors to most buildings and to the death of most people who tried to repeat his experiment.

Franklin (Rosalind 1920–1958) graduated from Cambridge University, worked for a while in Paris then returned to London. Her x-ray photographs of DNA were essential in allowing Watson & Crick to develop the idea that DNA is a pair of spirals wound around each other.

freckles small light-brown spots in the skin

free not restrained, missing, unrestricted | **friction-free** two surfaces appear to meet but do not affect each other because they are separated by a thin layer of lubricant

free-fall dropping towards a planet or a star without any attempt at slowing down so you, and any objects around you, appear not to have weight

free-swimming animals creatures that are able to move themselves through the water

freely without opposition | **freely moving** able to be moved easily and the movement continues without further force being applied | **freely pivoted** the junction or joint between the rotating part and the static part produces no friction and so no slowing down | **freely rotating** able to move around a pivot without any measurable frictional slowing

freeze to turn a liquid into a solid at constant temperature

freeze-thaw cracking / freeze-thaw cycle the freezing of water in a small crack, followed by expansion of the ice then by melting, will break a rock into many parts | **freeze-thaw weathering** the breakdown of rocks caused by liquid water getting into small cracks, the water freezes, expands and enlarges the crack then the ice melts

freezer equipment for achieving low temperatures, a cupboard which is kept at temperatures well below 0°C | **freezer temperature** the temperature used in a food freezer, which should be −20°C for household freezers

freezing turning from liquid to solid at a constant temperature | **freezing conditions** the weather is sufficiently cold that any water will turn to ice | **freezing mixture** a mixture of two chemicals that cause a drop in temperature, commonly use salt added to crushed ice | **freezing point** the temperature at which a liquid turns into a solid | **freezing temperature** freezing point, the temperature at which the liquid turns solid | **freezing temperatures** the weather is sufficiently cold that water will rapidly turn to ice | **freezing water** water with a temperature below 0°C which is very cold compared to body temperature

Freon™ one of several chloro-fluoro-carbons that have been used as the cooling fluid in refrigerators

frequencies (plural of frequency) the different rates of vibration

frequency (plural is frequencies) the number of times a wave move up and down each second, measured in hertz | **frequency diagram / frequency graph** bar chart, pie chart, a drawing showing how often an event occurs | **frequency of sound** the pitch or note of a vibration in the air (sound) | **highest frequency** the maximum rate, the highest pitch | **lowest frequency** the wave with the highest wavelength

frequent often, happening many times, at short intervals | **frequent eruptions** the volcano emits ash and hot gases many times each year

frequently happens many times with a short time interval between each event

fresh newly made, just picked, new | **fresh air** air that is free to mix with most of the atmosphere | **fresh fruit** fruit which has been picked in the near past and so is not marked or bruised | **fresh leaves** the leaves have just been removed from a growing tree | **fresh peas** the peas have been picked and the pods are still firm | **fresh samples** small amounts that have been taken directly from the bulk material | **fresh water** water that is suitable for drinking as it contains no salt

freshener a chemical that makes material appear as new | **air freshener** a solid or liquid that gradually turns to vapour that will mask any unpleasant smells

fresher more recent

freshly cut the separation has occurred very recently

fret a marker on the fingerboard of a guitar; to worry

friability the ability of a solid to retain its structure and not turn to powder when crushed or rubbed

friable the solid will easily form a powder

friction the force between two surfaces which prevents them moving across each other | **friction-free** two surfaces appear to meet, but do not affect each other because they are separated by a thin layer of lubricant | **contact friction** emphasising that the loss of speed and production of heat is caused by two surfaces touching | **reducing friction** using a lubricant, such as air or oil, to separate the two surfaces so that there is less friction | **sliding friction** the slowing force when a body is moving across a surface | **static friction** the reaction force produced between two surfaces that are not moving and which prevents the object form starting to move

frictional force the braking force that is applied in order to cause slowing down | **frictional resistance** the size of the force between the two surfaces that is slowing the movement

frictionless the movement of one surface is not slowed by the supporting surface | **frictionless pulley** there is very little force resisting the rotation of the wheels of the pulley, da Vinci invented a frictionless pulley in about 1500 | **frictionless surface** a very smooth surface that will allow other items to slide easily

fridge a refrigerator, equipment for keeping food cold | **fridge magnet** a decorative picture with a magnet on the back

friend a person who enjoys your company and who is prepared to help you through good and bad times

friendly helping each other, being sympathetic | **environmentally friendly** changes that will not damage the environment

frightening shocking, causing alarm, fear and possibly nightmares

fringes edges

frogs fresh water amphibious creatures that reproduce by external fertilisation in the water

from moving away from a source | **derive from** to work out from previous knowledge | **different from** comparing two items that share many features, but show some important differences | **expel from** to push out

frond a leaf-like structure of fern, palm and some sea-weeds

front forward, first, where one weather system meets another system | **front limbs** arms | **cold front** the mass of moving air is at a lower temperature than the volume of static air, often leading to rain | solvent front the moving line which shows the movement of the solvent on a chromatography paper | warm front the mass of moving air is at a higher temperature than the volume of static air | weather front the line where a body of air at one temperature, humidity and pressure meets a body of air with different characteristics

frost the thin layer of ice that is produced when dew is frozen | frost damage the breakages produced when the temperature is so low that water turns to ice

frozen turned to solid | frozen meat the meat has been stored at a temperature below −20°C | frozen peas the peas were dropped into liquid nitrogen within a few hours of being picked and may then be stored in a freezer for several months without change

fructose a sugar similar to glucose

fruit part of a plant that contains the seed and a store of food that could be useful in either dispersing the seed or helping the seed to grow | fruit carton a box made from paper, used for storing fruit juice | fruit crop fruit such as apples, pears or berries that are grown in order to be sold at a profit | fruit juice the liquid that is obtained by crushing a fruit | fruit squash a concentrated form of fruit juice that must be diluted with water before drinking | citrus fruit oranges, lemons and grapefruit, fruit with a thick skin that contains citric acid | fresh fruit the object either has just been picked or has the taste, appearance and smell similar to a fruit that has just been removed from the tree | ripening fruit the change that occurs in colour, texture and chemicals inside a fruit between initial formation and when the fruit is dispersed

frying cooking food in hot oil | frying pan a flat, metal pan intended for cooking with fat

fuel a chemical that reacts rapidly with oxygen to release heat | fuel cell an object that reacts fuel with oxygen at room temperature producing electrical energy | fuel conservation using as little fuel as possible so the energy source will last for longer | fuel consumption the mass or volume of fuel, usually petrol or diesel, that is used by a vehicle travelling a stated distance | fuel tank the container in which the fuel is stored or carried | aviation fuel the hydrocarbon that is burned in the jets of aeroplanes | bio-fuel anything that grows and can be used to give light and heat by burning | burning fuel most fuels are the remains of living material eg plants, wood or fat, that react with oxygen with the intention of producing heat or light | clean fuel a chemical the reacts with oxygen, releasing heat, but the

products do not pollute the environment, eg hydrogen is a clean fuel that burns to produce water | common fuels materials that are often burned to provide heat, eg coal, wood | fossil fuels fuels that were produced long, long ago when there was less oxygen in the atmosphere and then buried underground; coal was originally plants such as the giant fern, and oil was from sea creatures, gas is found with both coal and oil | liquid fuel a chemical that is able to flow and to fill tanks and which can react with oxygen, releasing heat energy | non-renewable fuels the chemicals have been made and will burn, but can not be made again, mainly the fossil fuels of coal, oil and gas | nuclear fuels (a misuse of the word fuel as no chemical is burned) the radio-active materials that are used to provide heat that is used to generate electricity | range of fuels several different materials, all of which react with oxygen and produce heat | renewable fuels materials, such as trees or grass, that can be burned but will be replaced within a few years | rocket fuel the chemical that is to burned in the rocket's engines in order to produce the thrust | smokeless fuel material that burns without producing carbon particles, solid smokeless fuel is achieved by heating coal or wood in the absence of air so the material is a porous solid of dry carbon | solid fuels material that keep their shape but can be burned, usually refers to coal or coke, but could mean wood

fulcrum the pivot of a lever

full moon the Moon is on the opposite side of the Earth to the Sun and so the whole face is illuminated

full-range universal indicator the liquid or paper that has many colours between pH 1 and pH 14

fully without restriction, completely | fully movable / fully moveable able to move in any direction

fume a vapour, an exhaust chemical in the air; to give off small amounts of unpleasant gases | fume cupboard a box with tough glass sides and an extractor fan in the roof that is used for experiments where toxic gases might be produced | acid fumes a vapour containing particles of a strong acid | dangerous fumes a vapour that will cause illness or death if breathed in | exhaust fumes the waste gases produced by an engine

function the use of some equipment, the purpose, a mathematical equation; to work in a particular way | function of cells the main purpose of that type of cell in helping the organism remain alive | cardiovascular function the work carried out by the heart (cardio) and the blood and blood vessels (vascular) | cell function the main purpose of that type of cell in helping the organism remain alive | different function a separate and distinct purpose | particular functions the special jobs that are to be carried out | specialised function (UK) / specialized function (USA) a use that can only be carried out by that object, the particular purpose | specific function the only process, a single use

functional in working order, able to carry out the task

functionally dependent the component will complete the task only if other components are working

functioning working, carrying out the task

fundamental basic, important | fundamental facts the observations that are at the starting point of ideas

fungal caused by a fungus | fungal disease an illness that is caused by infection with a fungus

fungi (plural of fungus) one of the major kingdoms of life, characterised by the cells having a nucleus and a cell wall, but the cell wall is not made from cellulose. Fungi do not have any chlorophyll and so are unable to carry out photosynthesis, they live mainly on dead organisms

fungicide a chemical that kills a fungus

fungus (plural is fungi) one of the five kingdoms of life (the others are plants, animals, monera and protoctista) which have nuclei and cell walls but live by absorbing nutrients from dead material

funnel equipment that is wide at one end and narrow at the other; to move from a wide part to a narrow part | filter funnel a funnel that is used, with a filter paper, to separate solids from a suspension | separating funnel a glass cylinder with a stop-cock at the bottom | thistle funnel a small vessel on the top of a glass tube, the structure looks like the outline of a thistle | Tulgren funnel / Tullgren funnel tube with a wide neck and a gauze base so insects can be studied

funny bone the nerve on the outside part of the elbow connecting the hand and lower arm to the spine

fur (not fir which is a type of tree) a thick covering of hair

furnace an oven that is capable of heating to temperatures above 1500°C | blast furnace manufacturing process for the extraction of iron using a vast tower which is kept at high temperature by vast amounts air being blown in at high speed

furniture objects that allow tasks to be carried out in comfort | office furniture desks, tables and other solid items that are found in the work place

furred up the inside surface of a tube is covered with unintended deposits thereby decreasing the bore of the tube

furry (not fury which is anger) covered with soft hair | furry coat an insulating covering of thick hair

further additional, a longer distance | further apart the distance is greater | further evidence more indicators that the theory is correct

furthest most distant

fury (not furry which is hairy) extreme anger, rage

fuse a weak link in an electrical circuit that melts if the current is too high; to melt the weak link in an electrical circuit, to cause two cells or nuclei to become one | fuse box an enclosure that contains the fuses that are used by each electrical circuit in a house | fuse wire the filament that is used in a fuse that will melt if the specified current is exceeded | blown fuse the fuse wire has melted so current can no longer flow | cartridge fuse a standard size of component for plugs, a glass tube with metal ends that are joined by a thin wire within the glass tube | electric fuse the component that is designed to melt, so breaking the circuit and stopping the flow of current

fused a weak link has been inserted into the circuit, the weak link has melted, joined together

fusion two objects coming together and producing one new object | cellular fusion two reproductive cells (gametes) join together to form a new off-spring | nuclear fusion means that two nuclei have joined together to become one nucleus, this could be in sexual reproduction (where the nuclei of two sex cells join together) or the fusion of two atomic nuclei to give a new element and release heat energy

future the time and ages that have yet to come

fuzzy blurred, not clear

G a constant used in astronomy, that relates mass and distance to gravitational force

G... / giga... (*Latin* giant) prefix for a thousand million of a unit, 10^9

g [gram] a unit of mass, 1000 gram is a kilogram

g [the acceleration due to gravity] usually referring to the value of 9.81 m/s^2 that is found for Earth | g-force measuring an acceleration relative to that expected for Earth

(g) (gas) a state symbol to show the chemical is a gas or a vapour

gabbro an igneous rock that cooled while still underground so the crystals are large

gabbroic rock a rock with crystals larger than 0.5 millimetre diameter, and mainly magnesium or iron

Gagarin (Yuri 1934–1968) joined the Russian Air Force in 1957 and, four years later, became the first man to orbit the Earth; he shared the Galabert Astronautical Prize with Glenn (the first American astronaut) in 1963. Gagarin was killed on a training flight.

gain an increase; to increase | gain energy to give an object more energy, often heat or movement energy | gain mass to give more mass to an object, *eg* planets gain mass by attracting dust from space | heat gain the increase in thermal energy | height gain an increase in the height of an organism, the vertical distance that an object moves upwards | weight gain the increase in weight of an organism

galaxies (plural of galaxy) there are estimated to be several hundred million galaxies in the universe

galaxy (plural is galaxies) a cluster of millions of stars, our star (the Sun) is in a collection of 100 million stars called the Milky Way | spiral galaxy a collection of millions of stars that looks like a whirlpool or a Catherine Wheel

Galen (Claudius c130–201) born in Turkey, educated in Egypt and Greece then the medical attendant to four emperors in Rome. Galen wrote continually on any matter medical or philosophical (over 300 books), these writings were used as standard textbooks for the next 1200 years

galena lead sulphide [PbS], an ore of lead

Galileo (Galilei 1564–1642) (unusually – Galileo was his first name and Galilei was the family name) studied medicine, but became professor of mathematics in 1589 – a post he held for 20 years. Although unmarried – he did have a companion for a decade by whom he had two daughters and a son. He started to use a tele-scope with more than one lens in 1610, and published his ideas in *Sidereal Messenger*. He studied the Moon, he realised that the moons of Jupiter orbited the planet and therefore not every object orbited the Earth – this teaching was deemed heretical and led to house arrest for the last ten years of his life. He did not appreciate that staring at the Sun through a telescope would lead to blindness. Galileo studied the time period of a pendulum, using his pulse as a clock, found that balls would fall with an acceleration that did not depend on mass (but not by dropping balls from the leaning tower of Pisa) and a new type of thermometer. The method of working used by scientists today, in which any idea must be based on careful observation, was developed by Galileo

galileo a global positioning system, that should be ready by 2010, that has been launched by Europe

gall bladder a small organ, under the liver, that stores a surfactant (a type of washing up liquid) called bile

gallon a unit of volume, unfortunately there is a US gallon (3.78 litres) and an Imperial gallon (4.55 litres)

Galton (Sir Francis 1822–1911) a scientist in London and Cambridge, Galton explored widely over North Africa. He had sufficient money that he did not need to work, but was active in many learned Societies. He believed that any obser-vation should lead to measurements and count-ing. He was the first to map the weather over Europe at a particular time – leading to our every day weather forecasts. In 1859, a book by his cousin Charles Darwin, led Galton to investigate the contribution of hereditary and upbringing (nature and nurture) to the development of adult human beings. The lack of data and methods for dealing with this information meant that Galton had to devise totally new mathematics for analysing populations. Some of his ideas as to how to improve the genetics in humans were used to justify the mass killings in the 1930s.

Galvani (Luigi 1737–1798) became Professor of physiology at Bologna at the age of 25 He took a well-known observation (that fixing dead frogs by brass skewers to an iron bar led to leg twitching) and began systematic studies ending with his idea that animals produced a new kind of electricity. Have you ever been galvanised into action – this term is named after Galvani

galvanic cell two different metals separated by a fluid that will allow charge to move and so produce an electric current

galvanise (UK) / **galvanize** (USA) to produce a hard layer of oxide on a metal using electricity

galvanised steel (UK) / **galvanized steel** (USA) the alloy of iron and other metals has been covered with a layer of zinc to prevent corrosion

game a pastime, an enjoyable way of competing | Olympic Games competitions that were originally held between Greek City States then banned in 393 AD, the modern Games were started by Baron de Coubertin in 1896

gamekeeper a person who ensures suitable conditions for the raising of pheasants, deer or other animals that are to be hunted

gamete a reproductive cell (sex cell) that contains half the adult number of chromosomes | female gametes the reproductive or sex cells that are very large, because they contain nutrients for the developing offspring, and so are unable to move | male gametes the sex cells that are able to move and will move towards the female gamete

gamma / γ the third letter of the Greek alphabet | gamma radiation / gamma rays a type of radioactivity that is very dangerous, the high frequency electromagnetic radiation that is produced when radio-active nuclei break down

gap a hole, where something is missing

garage a construction or 'building' intended for the storage of a car, a shop that sells car fuel, a shop that repairs car engines and bodywork

garden an outside area set aside for enjoyment, often next to a house | garden beans the variety of beans that can be grown in ground near the house | garden center (USA) / garden centre (UK) a business that sells anything that could help you grow better plants | garden flowers the types of flowers that are planted in the garden for a specific purpose, such as looking and / or smelling nice | garden roller a heavy cylinder that is used to flatten and compact soil | garden soil the mixture of sand, clay and rocks that is likely to be found in land that has been used for growing flowers | botanical garden land where new plants are developed, grown and studied and is open to the public | zoological garden an area where animals are kept both for scientists to study and for other people to observe for enjoyment and education

gardener a person who looks after an area in order to grow flowers or herbs

gardening growing plants and fruit for pleasure

gargoyle a stone spout for removing rainwater, often in the form of animals or faces

garlic clove a sub-division of a bulb of the *Allium*, which is used in cooking

garment an item of clothing

gas (plural is gases or gasses) the state where the particles, atoms or molecules, are moving rapidly in all directions and they are well separated, the fuel that is used in ovens and bunsen burners; the word gas was introduced by Helmont from the Greek word *chaos* | gas bubbles small volumes of gas (bubbles) that are seen in a liquid or rock | gas cylinder a strong container, in the shape of a tube, in which gas is stored and transported under pressure | gas evolution production of gas from a chemical or biological reaction | gas exchange where one gas goes in and a different gas comes out, there is gas exchange in the lungs and in the spongy layer of leaves | gas generator equipment that produces a specific gas by allowing reaction of two chemicals only when the gas is required | gas giants the four planets that are very large and seem to be made from gas (Jupiter, Saturn, Uranus and Neptune) | gas-guzzler vehicles that travel no more than 4 kilometres for each litre of fuel | gases in air air is 80% nitrogen, 19% oxygen, 0.04% carbon dioxide and variable amounts of water vapour | gas jar a glass cylinder that has a flat lip, which can be sealed using a plate of glass | gas pressure the force per centimetre squared on a container caused by the molecules of gas bouncing off the surface | gas syringe a large syringe that is gas tight and is used for measuring the volume of gas | gas tap a valve used to control the flow of a gas, often refers to the tap that controls the flow of inflammable gas to a bunsen burner | gas thermometer the volume (or pressure) of a reservoir of air is used to measure temperature | acidic gas a vapour that will produce a pH below 7 when dissolved in water | balance of gases the concentrations of carbon dioxide and oxygen in the atmosphere remain constant as a result of the rates of respiration and of photosynthesis being similar | biogas the fuel gas produced by breakdown of biological material, usually methane [CH_4] | coal gas the fuel that is produced when coal is heated strongly in the absence of air (leaving coke behind) | collecting gas taking a sample of gas by suction into a syringe, directing the gas into an inverted boiling tube filled with water | common gases the chemicals that are easily obtained in the form of gases, such as nitrogen, oxygen, hydrogen and carbon dioxide | compressed gas the pressure has been increased so, following Boyle's law, the volume must be less | dissolved gas the gas is dissolved in a solvent and so seems to have disappeared | evolution of gas / evolving gas a chemical or biological reaction that produces a gas |

exchange gases / exchange of gases the process that occurs in the lungs where carbon dioxide is lost from the blood and oxygen diffuses into the red blood cells | exhaust gases the waste gases that are produced from burning fuel in an engine | greenhouse gas the gas in the atmosphere that prevents the heat from leaving the Earth at night, the two common greenhouse gases are carbon dioxide [CO_2] and methane [CH_4] | harmful gas a chemical that can diffuse through the air then kill when inhaled by an animal | hydrogen gas used to emphasise that the hydrogen is in the form of the gas, H_2, rather than hydrogen atoms | inert gas a gas that will not react, especially the group 0 column of elements | laughing gas nitrous oxide [N_2O], was used by dentists as an anaesthetic | liquefied gas (UK / USA) / liquified gas (USA) the chemical is usually a gas at room temperature, but is stored as a liquid either because of high pressure or a low temperature | liquid petroleum gas (LPG / lpg) many hydrocarbons are gases at room temperature, but form liquids when pressure is applied and can then be transported easily in tanks | main gases the important gases (such as oxygen in respiration or carbon dioxide in photosynthesis), the gases that exist in large amounts (such as nitrogen and oxygen in air) | natural gas the inflammable gas, called methane [CH_4], that is found with oil and coal and is produced by decaying vegetation | nitrogen gas used to emphasise that the chemical is the stable gas, nitrogen or N_2, rather than the atoms of nitrogen, nitrogen was isolated in 1772 by Scheele, in Sweden, and by Rutherford, in Scotland | noble gases the group 0 column of elements that are totally unreactive, but are superb in producing coloured light, all the noble gases were isolated by Ramsay | oxygen gas the molecule O_2 | poisonous gas a chemical that will kill if breathed into the lungs | pollutant gases the gases that change the composition of the atmosphere in a specified area, especially the oxides of sulphur, phosphorus and nitrogen (gases that cause acid rain) or carbon dioxide (the greenhouse effect) | town gas any fuel that is distributed from a central point to the many houses in a town, originally this was coal gas, but is now usually natural gas (methane [CH_4]) | useful gas the vapour or gas that is produced will be used in another process

gaseous the gas that was dissolved in a fluid is forming bubbles | gaseous exchange the function of lungs and gills, the diffusion of oxygen into the blood and the loss of carbon dioxide into the air

gases (plural of gas) producies a gas, fizzes | gases in air air comprises 80% nitrogen, 19% oxygen, 0.04% carbon dioxide and variable amounts of water vapour | atmospheric gases the gases that are found in high concentration in the air around a specified planet | common gases the chemicals that are easily obtained in the form of gases, such as nitrogen, oxygen, hydrogen and carbon dioxide | waste gases the gases that are produced in an industrial process, such as the blast furnace, which can not be sold but could contaminate the atmosphere

gasoline (USA) / **petrol** (UK) a mixture of hydrocarbons, with 5–8 carbon, the liquid fuel that is used in the internal combustion engine

gasses (plural of gas) producies a gas, fizzes | gasses in air air comprises 80% nitrogen, 19% oxygen, 0.04% carbon dioxide and variable amounts of water vapour | atmospheric gasses the gases that are found in high concentration in the air around a specified planet | common gasses the chemicals that are easily obtained in the form of gases, such as nitrogen, oxygen, hydrogen and carbon dioxide | waste gasses the gases that are produced in an industrial process, such as the blast furnace, which can not be sold but could contaminate the atmosphere

gastric concerned with the stomach | gastric juice the liquid, produced by the lining of the stomach, that contains enzymes and hydrochloric acid

gastro- (*Greek* the stomach)

gate a structure that marks the entry through a boundary, an electrical component that can perform some change | AND gate the output is positive only if both inputs are positive (set to 1) | light gate a lamp and detector that is able to detect when an object passes between them | logic gate an electronic component that is able to perform a logical function such as AND, NOT or OR | NAND gate a logic circuit that is OFF only if both inputs are ON | NOR gate a logic circuit that is ON only if both inputs are OFF | NOT gate turns an ON to an OFF or turns an OFF to an ON | OR gate if either input is positive (1) then there is a positive output

gather to bring together | gather evidence to bring together the data, measurements and observations from several experiments in order to prove an idea

gauge an instrument for measuring the height or depth; to estimate a measurement | pressure gauge equipment for measuring the pressure (force per unit area) | rain gauge an instrument for measuring the depth of water that has fallen as rain

gauze a sheet formed by fibres running in one direction going over and under fibres in the other direction, the fibres could be metal wire, giving the gauze suitable for heating, or could be cotton so giving a gauze bandage | gauze cage an enclosure made from metal with lots of holes that is used to contain small animals

GDA [guideline daily amount] the mass of each nutrient that is the required daily intake by a healthy adult

gear a cog, a toothed wheel | protective gear clothing that is worn so as to provide safety and avoid injury

Geiger counter equipment used to measure the amount of radio-activity

gel a state somewhere between a solid and a liquid – the material will keep its shape but is easily penetrated, a jelly | agar gel material that is extracted from seaweed then used for growing microbes

gelatin / gelatine a mixture of proteins that are produced when animal parts, eg skin, bone, are heated with water

gen- (*Greek* birth) to be born

gender sex – male or female

gene an instruction that is encoded in the sequence of DNA in the nucleus and defines the structure of a protein | gene sequence the order in which the instruction sets are found on a chromosome | useful genes instructions in the DNA of the chromosomes that are thought to help survival

general what is expected from previous experiments | general anaesthetic (UK) / general anesthetic (USA) a chemical that causes the patient to lose consciousness and so should be unable to feel pain | general equation a mathematical relationship that has lots of different applications | general knowledge information that should be known by most people even if they have not been formally taught | general pattern a trend that is often seen and so will be expected to occur again

generalisation a statement that moves an idea from the particular data and information to the whole world

generalise (UK) / generalize (USA) to take particular examples and turn into a wide-ranging rule

generally usually, almost always, normally

generate to produce | generate electricity to produce electricity by turning a coil in a magnetic field | generate graphs to draw the information as a graph | generate heat to produce heat energy, so leading to an increase in temperature | generate sound to produce vibrations

generating station the building in which some form of energy is turned into electricity

generation the production of energy such as electricity, sound or heat, relationship between parents and children in a family | generation of heat the production of thermal energy | electricity generation the production of electricity, usually from kinetic energy | spontaneous generation a sudden production of new life forms from a place where they did not seem to exist previously

generator a machine for producing electricity from kinetic energy | electrical generator / electricity generator a machine for producing electrical energy from moving energy by turning a coil in a magnetic field | gas generator equipment that produces a specific gas when required, by allowing reaction of two chemicals | motor-generator equipment that will produce movement if an electric current is applied, but will generate electricity if the centre is rotated | signal generator a machine for producing changes in an electrical output that can be used to drive a loudspeaker, with a frequency and amplitude that can be controlled | simple generator there is a single coil of wire rotating between opposite poles of a magnet | van de Graaff generator a machine for producing and collecting electrical charge

genes instructions that are encoded in the sequence of DNA in the nucleus

genetic anything to do with the instruction set, or genes, that are in the chromosome | genetic code the arrangement of atoms in the DNA that ensures the correct proteins are made at the right time | genetic diagram a punnet square, a grid that shows the alleles for each pair along the axes then the boxes show the possible genetic combinations | genetic engineering changing the instruction set, or genes, in the chromosome so as to achieve a change in the chemistry of the cell | genetic factors an instruction in the cell that makes the cell permanently different from others and may help or hinder survival | genetic information the instructions that cause specific developments in a cell, the known sequence of DNA that will allow diseases to be treated | genetic makeup that sum of all the different effects caused by the genes | genetic map the position of every gene on the chromosome | genetic material the chemicals that are found in the chromosome, especially the DNA that encodes the instruction | genetic relationship how one organism is related to another, not through appearance or behaviour, but by looking at the sequence of instructions in the chromosome | genetic variation differences between similar organisms caused by differences in the chromosomes

genetically concerned with the information on the chromosome that was obtained from the parent | genetically identical two or more organisms with identical genes | genetically modified changing one or more of the instructions in the chromosome so as to improve the crop | genetically modified organism (GMO) a living thing in which the instructions in the chromosome have been chemically changed so as to try and bring about a change in the organism | genetically unique the genes, or instructions, are found only in that one organism

genetics the study of the DNA sequences and the factors that affect inheritance

genome the sequence of all genes, or instructions, that are in the nucleus

genotype the set of genes in a nucleus

gently softly, with care

genus a taxonomic group of closely related organisms

-geny (*Latin* from) production

geo- (*Greek* the Earth)

geo-centric model an idea that the Earth (geo) is at the centre of the universe and all the stars and planets orbit the Earth

geographic poles the two points through which the axis of rotation of the Earth seems to pass

geologic activity any movement or change in the crust of the Earth

geological related to the study of the Earth | geological ages the long periods into which geologists have divided the time since the Earth was formed | geological changes differences in the structure of the Earth over time, *eg* raising and lowering of sea levels and continental drift | geological event a sudden change that has occurred in the crust of the Earth and has widespread consequences | geological map a diagram showing the distribution and depths of rocks near the Earth's surface | geological processes methods by which the shape of the land or the appearance of rocks have been changed | geological section a diagram showing a cross-section of the Earth's crust between specified points, with the identity of the different strata | geological survey examining rocks on the surface and underground so as to give the three-dimensional arrangement of the rock

geologist a person who studies rocks and the Earth

geology the study of rocks and rock strata, where they came from and how they change

geo-magnetism the magnetic field found on the Earth that starts near one geographical pole and ends near the other

geophone equipment for detecting the sound and echoes of an underground explosion

geostationary appearing to remain still when viewed from the Earth | geostationary orbit the track taken by a satellite that has an orbital period of 24 hours | geostationary satellite equipment in orbit around the Earth that seems to be remaining over the same spot on the equator because the orbital period is exactly the same as the rotation period of the Earth

geosynchronous / geosynchronous satellite a space craft that is orbiting the Earth with an orbital period of 24 hours, a geostationary satellite

geothermal to do with the hot rocks | geothermal energy / geothermal power obtaining heat from the rocks

geotropism growth of a plant is affected by gravity – so the root grows down and the shoot grow up

gerbil a rodent similar to a mouse but with long back legs and a long, furry tail

germ any microbe (bacterium, virus or fungus) that causes illness | germ cell (nothing at all to do with bacteria or illness) a non-specialised cell that is produced during the early stages of development following fertilisation of the egg by the male sex cell

German measles (rubella) an illness caused by a virus, which normally will not cause death, but can cause damage to an unborn foetus – so young women (but not young men) are often vaccinated; part of the MMR (measles, mumps & rubella) vaccine given to all babies

germicide a chemical that is intended to kill harmful microbes

germinate to grow, to change a seed so the plant starts to grow | germinated grains moisture and warmth have caused the seeds of a grass to start the changes that will lead to shoots and a root

germinating / germinating seeds the changes that occur when a dormant seed starts to produce a shoot and a root

germination changing of a seed, usually caused by water, so the plant starts to grow

germs microbes (bacteria, viruses or fungii) that cause illness | household germs microbes that are likely to be found in any home and usually cause no ill effects

gerontology the study of the causes and effects of ageing

gestation the act of carrying, being carried | gestation period the time from fertilisation of the egg to the birth of the offspring, this period is nine months in women

get to obtain, to prepare, to acquire

ghost an object that does not seem to be real | Pepper's ghost putting two images on top of each other, *eg* a flame in a jar, by using a sheet of glass at 45° to each object

giant big – very big! | giant ferns the plants that grew millions of years ago, when the concentration of carbon dioxide was high and ferns could grow 20 metres tall | giant stars stellar, objects that turn nuclear energy into heat and light, that are very, very big, *eg* stars with a diameter similar to that of the orbit of Mars | giant structure a chemical that is millions of atoms strongly bonded together, *eg* diamond is one molecule made from millions of carbon atoms | giant windmill (more properly should be giant wind turbine) is a very tall tower, maybe 200 metres tall, with giant vanes for turning wind energy into electrical energy | gas giant any of the four planets that are very large and seem to be made from gas (Jupiter, Saturn, Uranus and Neptune) | red giant a star that has a diameter greater than the orbit of the Earth and the surface temperature is approximately 2000°C and so glows red

giga... / G... (*Latin* giant) prefix for a thousand, million, 10^9, used as a prefix for 2^{30} in computing

gigajoule (GJ) a thousand, million joules, 10^9 joules of energy

Gilbert (William 1544–1603) studied at Cambridge then settled in London and became physician (medical doctor) to Queen Elizabeth I. Gilbert discovered how to turn pieces of iron into magnets by stroking them with a lodestone. He studied the Earth's magnetic field and he introduced the term 'magnetic pole'. His book *De Magnete* (1600) is considered to be the first great science book written in England. Galileo called him the 'father of experimentation'. Gilbert also studied the effects of electricity and introduced more new words, *eg* electricity and electric force from the Greek for amber, which can be charged by electricity

gills / fish gills the organs used by fish to extract oxygen from the water, the covering of the gill openings on each side of the fish's head

gill slits the perforations on the sides of a fish that allow water to pass over the gills so the fish can obtain oxygen

ginger a colour similar to orange, a plant with a root that is used as a hot spice

girder a steel beam

girls young female humans, young women who are not yet sexually mature

girth the distance around an object, especially waists and trees

give off to produce a gas

given a present, a gift, a value or object that can not be changed | given length the distance between the points is specified

gizzard the second stomach of birds

glacier a large piece of ice that fills a valley and is gently sliding downwards

gland any small organ that produces a chemical (a hormone) that causes a long-term and wide-ranging effect | gland cells the cells that produce a secretion such as a hormone or an enzyme | adrenal gland a group of cells above the kidney (ad - renal) that reacts to danger by producing adrenaline, the fight-or-flight hormone | endocrine glands small organs that produce hormones, chemical messengers that cause large-scale and / or long-term changes | mammary glands / milk glands the characteristic feature of female mammals – the tissue in which milk is produced for feeding the young offspring | oil glands a group of cells at the base of each hair in the skin that produces an oil | pituitary gland a small gland at the base of the brain that helps control most of the other endocrine glands | prostate gland the small sac near the base of the bladder that adds liquid to the sperm to produce semen | salivary glands small sacs in the lower jaw that produce the saliva in your mouth | scent gland the group of cells that releases a chemical into the air with the intention of announcing your presence to other members of the same species | sebaceous glands a group of cells next to each hair follicle that produce a grease or wax-like chemical | sweat glands groups of cells, in the skin, that produce a salt solution that evaporates in order to keep the skin cool | tear glands sacs near the corner of each eye that produce a liquid that keeps the eye moist and clean | thyroid gland a gland in the neck that helps to regulate body weight and activity

glandular fever a disease caused by the Epstein–Barr virus (EBV); this virus is present in almost everybody without ill-effect, but sometimes causes flu-like symptoms over a long period, the symptoms may occasionally be more serious

glass a molten mixture of sand, soda and other chemicals is cooled to give a clear solid that is easily shattered, glass is chemically unreactive but easily formed into many shapes simply by heating | glass beaker a cylinder made of glass with an open top that is used for mixing or heating chemicals | **glass block** a large piece of glass that usually has at least three flat surfaces | **glass cover** a sheet of glass is used to protect the object from dust, dirt or prying fingers | **glass-like** shiny surface that allows light through, which may behave like glass and shatter to give sharp edges | **glass prism** a block of glass that is triangular with a flat, rectangular base | **glass probe** a tube of special glass that will react to the presence of specified chemicals | **glass rod** a length of glass that is used for stirring any liquid | **glass stopper** a block of glass that appears almost cylindrical, but is part of a cone that is used to seal bottles | **glass thermometer** any method of measuring temperature that depends on a reservoir of liquid attached to a transparent glass capillary tube | **glass tube** a hollow tube, made from glass so the shape is easily changed by heating | **glassware** any of the laboratory apparatus, such as beakers, flasks or tubes, that is usually made from glass | **glass wool** filaments of glass that have been loosely mixed together | **borosilicate glass** a type of glass that can be heated to high temperatures | **burning glass** a large magnifying glass that was used to focus the rays from the Sun, to give a high temperature, before the invention of the bunsen burner | **fiber glass** (USA) / **fibre glass** (UK) a thick cloth made from very thin filaments of glass, a hard material produced by allowing millions of long glass filaments to be set in resin | **ground glass** the shiny surface of the glass has been removed by scratching or sand-blasting | **magnifying glass** a circular piece of glass with curved edges so the image appears larger than the object | **pane of glass** a large, flat piece of glass | **thick glass** a glass that is sufficiently deep for the effects of refraction to be obvious | **watch glass** a circular piece of glass that has a shape suitable for fitting over the face of a very large watch

glassware any of the laboratory apparatus, such as beakers, flasks or tubes, that is usually made from glass

glassy properties similar to glass, hard material with shiny surfaces that will not bend

glazing inserting glass into a frame, a pane of glass | **double glazing** two layers of glass that trap a layer of air so reducing loss of heat and preventing entry of noise | **single glazing** the windows have one layer of glass

glide to move without any apparent effort, especially through air or water

glider the carriage that rides on an air track, an aircraft without any engines

global over the whole Earth, taken together from many sources | **global changes** differences that will affect everything on Earth | **global positioning system (GPS)** using several geostationary satellites to give accurately your position on the Earth | **global temperature** an average of the temperature at all points on Earth | **global warming** the increase in average temperature of the Earth that has been recorded over the past fifty years, probably caused by increasing concentrations of carbon dioxide [CO_2], and is likely to lead to massive climate changes

glossary a list of important words with their meanings

gloves covering worn over the hand and fingers | **surgical gloves** the protective gloves that are worn by most medical personnel in order to prevent infection when examining a patient

glow a low intensity red light; to radiate heat

glowed was giving out a low-intensity red light

glowing giving off heat, having a red colour | **glowing splint** a piece of wood that is sufficiently hot to glow, but there is no flame – a glowing splint will relight when put into oxygen

glucose [$C_6H_{12}O_6$] the carbohydrate produced by plants in photosynthesis | **glucose solution** a liquid made by dissolving glucose [$C_6H_{12}O_6$] in water | **glucose tablet** a pill made from sugar and eaten so as to give an immediate increase in blood-sugar level

glue a substance that is used to hold surfaces together; to bond, to join two solids with a liquid that sets hard | **polystyrene glue** an adhesive, usually polystyrene dissolved in an organic solvent, that is used to join polystyrene pieces together | **superglue** a bonding agent that will stick to most surfaces

glued two objects joined by a material that was liquid when applied then turned solid

glycerol [$CH_2OH.CH_2CH_2OH$] produced when fats are digested, used as anti-freeze

glyco- (*Greek* sweet) related to sugars

glycogen the large molecule produced by joining thousands of sugar molecules allowing storage of excess sugar

glycol [$(CH_2OH)_2$] ethyl glycol, a chemical that is used as an antifreeze in car radiators

GMO [genetically modified organisms] usually plants that have had a gene changed to enhance a desirable characteristic, *eg* the crop is easier to grow or the fruit stays fresher longer

gnat small flying insect

gnaw (not nor which is and not) to wear away by biting with teeth

gnawed food the material to be eaten has been crushed between molar teeth

gnawing using teeth to crunch, to pull and to bite the limbs of an animal

gneiss a metamorphic rock with a characteristic layered appearance

gnomon the upright triangle or rod that produces a shadow in a sundial

go to leave, to depart

goat a four-legged mammal that has been domesticated for the production of wool and milk

goblet a cup without a handle | **goblet cells** lining cells within the body that produce a liquid

goggles a strong, transparent material *eg* Perspex™ or polycarbonate, used in a holder to protect the eyes | **safety goggles** eye protectors

gold (Au, proton number 79, melting point 1060°C) a yellow coloured metal that is very un-reactive, shiny and expensive | **goldfish** a fresh-water fish that grows up to 30 centimetres long and is bred to give a wide variety of colours | **gold jewellery** (UK) / **gold jewelry** (USA) ornaments made from gold which are worn by people | **gold leaf electroscope** two thin sheets of gold are each attached by one edge to the bottom of a metal rod and they separate when an electric charge is brought close to the rod

Gold Rush one of several mass movements of people following the discovery of gold, *eg* to California in 1849, to Colorado in 1858, or to Alaska in 1896

gonads reproductive organs, *eg* testes, ovaries

gondola the cabin of a large hot-air balloon

gone disappeared, left | **gone off** when some food, *eg* milk or meat, has become contaminated with bacteria so it is no longer safe to eat

gong a circular metal dish that is suspended then struck with a hammer so as to produce a loud musical note

good useful, suitable, more than adequate | **good conductor** a metal, a substance that will allow heat or electricity to move with little resistance | **good insulator** material that prevents the movement of heat or electricity

gorge a deep pass through mountains; to eat a vast amount

gorilla the largest of the apes, growing to over 1.8 metres tall

got obtained, achieved, aquired

Governmental organisation (UK) / **Governmental organization** (USA) a group of people employed by the Government

GPS [global positioning system] using several geostationary satellites to give your position on the Earth as an accurate point

de Graaf (Reiner / Reigner 1641–1673) trained as doctor in France, then returned to his native Delft in Holland, where he met Leeuwenhoek. de Graaf investigated the detailed structure of ovaries and the pancreas and recognised that meeting of sperm and ovum was essential for conception to occur.

van de Graaff (Robert Jemison 1901–1967) studied in America, Paris and Oxford – it was in Oxford that he realised that a hollow metal ball could be used to store charge, and where he constructed his first electrostatic generator. He developed the idea into the van de Graaff accelerator, which is an essential tool in studying the parts of an atom.

gradation a small step, a scale

grade a boundary that shows the level of knowl-edge, a measure of size of solid; to divide into groups, to change gradually

gradient slope, rate | **temperature gradient** the difference in temperature over a stated distance

gradual a low rate, slow | **gradual changes** changes, that are too small to be noticed, take place over a long time period

gradually small changes that continue over a long time

graduation obtaining a degree, a mark to show the extent of a change

graft the piece of tissue that is added; to add a new piece, to work hard | **burns graft** the piece of skin that was damaged by the heat is removed and replaced by a healthy piece from elsewhere on the body | **tissue graft** replacing any damaged tissue or organ with a healthy replacement

grafting replacing one part of an animal or plant with a similar part that has more desirable properties | **tissue grafting** moving groups of healthy cells to replace those damaged at another site

grain in geology, the grain is any particle or frag-ment, the seeds of any type of cereal such as oats or wheat, the direction that is up or down a tree | **grain shape** one of the characteristics of different rocks is the shape of particle that is in the rock | **grain size** the size of particles or fragments in the rock is another characteristic that defines different types of rock | **grains of sand** individual particles of sand | **alignment of grains** the general direc-tion in which he particles are seen in a rock | **compacted grains** small rocks that have been pushed together | **compacting grains** the change of shape and size of rock particles as a result of high pressure and temperature | **germinating grains** the seeds of a cereal are starting to develop so the root and shoot are just beginning to appear | mineral grains tiny particles of rock that contain a compound, usually the oxide, of a metal | pollen grain one male reproductive cell from a plant | sand grains the fragments of silica rock | sediment grains small fragments of rock, rock particles that have become cemented into other rocks | size of grains the size of the individual grains in a rock | starch grains clumps of starch that are found in plant cells and show clearly as islands when iodine is added | tiny grains regular structures that are visible only with the aid of a microscope

Gram (Hans Christian1853–1938) worked mainly at Copenhagen, but devised a method for staining and classifying bacteria while on a visit to Berlin. He found that bacteria formed two classes, the Gram positive could be stained, and the Gram negative could not be stained.

gram (UK & USA) / gramme (UK) a small unit of mass, the standard unit of mass is 1 kilogram which is 1000 grams

Gram stain a mixture of chemicals that colours the cell membrane of many types of bacteria

gramme (UK) / gram (UK & USA) a small unit of mass, the standard unit of mass is 1 kilogramme which is 1000 grammes

Grand Canyon an enormous gorge (350 kilometres long, up to 25 kilometres wide and sometimes as deep as 2 kilometres) in Arizona that is the result of erosion by the Colorado River

granite a common form of igneous rock, usually found near volcanoes or the edge of continents, containing lots of tiny crystals of quartz

granodiorite a very hard rock that is produced by the magma turning solid near the bottom of the crust

granulated crushed to given small fragments, turned into grains

granule a powder with particles that have rough surfaces and shapes and which are up to a millimetre in diameter | anti-bump granules / anti-bumping granules fragments of pot, glass or wood that allow many small bubbles to form in a boiling liquid

grape a fruit that grows on vines, contains a lot of sugar and can be turned, by fermentation, into wine | seedless grape the fruit from a vine with flowers that have not been fertilised

graph- / -graph (Greek to write) drawn

graph a diagram drawn using pairs of data points to show any relationship or trend; to draw | graph scales the choice of range and division of the lengths of each axis | appropriate graph the axes are correct for the information that is being sought | bar graph used with discontinuous variables in which the area or height of each bar shows the value of that variable | bar-line graph a graph in which the height of the bar represents the value of the dependent variable | block graph a bar chart | construct graphs to take the data and produce a graph with labelled axes | distance–time graph a diagram showing the distance that an object has moved at known time intervals, the gradient represents the speed of movement | draw a graph to take a table of data, draw and label the axes then put each point on to the diagram | frequency graph the vertical axis indicates how often the item occurs that is defined by the horizontal axis | generate a graph to produce a graph from some data | growth graph a table, graph or line that shows the height that boys and girls are expected to achieve at different ages | interpret a graph to look at the distribution of the data and decide what it means | line graph the picture is simplified by drawing a best-fit curve | linear graph the data can be joined by a single, straight line | micrograph a picture taken of the sample on the stage of a microscope | plotting graphs putting the data points on to a graph then drawing the best fitting line | predator–prey graph a diagram with time along the bottom (x) axis, population size on the vertical axis (y) and individual lines for the number of predators and prey in a given area | produce a graph to draw a graph from a set of numerical results | scatter graph each pair of ordered data is indicated by a symbol | seismograph the line that shows the movement of the Earth's crust as detected by a seismometer | sketch a graph to show the general shape of the graph that is expected without putting any numbers on the axes | speed–time graph the speed, on the vertical axis, is measured at different times, so time is along the horizontal (x) axis | thermograph a picture produced by using the infra-red or heat radiation | velocity–time graph a diagram, showing time along the bottom axis and velocity up the vertical axis, in which the slope gives the acceleration and the area under the curve represents the distance moved

graphic diagramatic representation, picture, lots of sharp details | graphic display a picture or diagram that shows the results of an experiment | on-screen graphics pictures or diagrams that are shown on the monitor

graphically a simple display that is memorable

graphite a form of carbon in which the carbon atoms form flat plates that are easily rubbed off

grass (plural is grasses) a plant that is used to give a green cover to large areas of ground, reproduces by wind pollination | grass-eating animals herbivores, animals that obtain most nutrients from grass, *eg* cows, sheep, rabbits | grass seedlings the grass seeds have produced the shoot and roots | grass verge the edge of the hard area is covered with grass | blade of grass a long, thin leaf of grass

grater (not greater which means larger) a sheet of metal with lots of ridges that can take small parts off a softer object

graticule a fine ruler that is inserted into the lens of a microscope so as to show the true length of an object that is being viewed

gravel pieces of rock that are larger than sand, but smaller than boulders

gravimeter equipment that is used to measure the force of gravity

gravitation a force of attraction between any objects, the force increases with the size of each object and also increases as they approach closer together

gravitational attraction a force pulling masses closer together | gravitational energy potential energy, the work done by changing the height of an object | gravitational field the area over which the mass of one body has an attractive effect on another body | gravitational field strength the size of the attraction at a given position | gravitational force the attractive pull caused by the mass if each body | gravitational potential energy the work done in lifting a weight through a height, the energy released when an object falls

potential energy (joules)	=	weight (newtons)	×	height (metres)

| gravitational pull the attractive force between masses

gravity an attractive force that occurs between any pair of bodies, the force produced by gravity is increased as the two bodies get nearer and as either of the bodies gets more mass | acceleration due to gravity / g the change of speed caused by the attraction of a nearby large body especially the Earth | center of gravity (USA) / center of mass (USA) / centre of gravity (UK) / centre of mass (UK) a point at which all the mass of the object appears to be, this point will lie directly below the pivot if the object is suspended freely from a pin | force of gravity the size of the attractive force between two masses | specific gravity the ratio of the density of the liquid to the density of pure water at the same temperature | zero gravity the measurement is taken sufficiently distant from a star or planet that any gravitational attraction is too small to be measured

gray / grey a tint of black

graze a wound in which the top layers of skin are removed; to eat small amounts at frequent intervals, to eat grass for most of the day

grazing eating continuously | grazing animals herbivores that eat plants continuously

grease a lubricant that can be spread or pushed into place, but will not flow easily

greaseproof paper a paper that has a wax-like coating that prevents any grease passing through the paper

greasing applying a lubricant

greasy slippery, slidey, covered with a layer of oil

Great Plague the epidemic of 1665, which killed probably half the population of England and led to Newton leaving Cambridge and Eyam shutting itself off from the world. The disease is caused by a bacterium that is found in the fleas that infest rats and mice

great tit a species of bird

greater (not grater which is used for making thin pieces) larger than, more important

greatest biggest, best, tallest, first, most significant | greatest proportion largest fraction, highest ratio, the majority

grebe a diving bird

greedy wanting more, even when an adequate amount has been obtained

Greek a person who lives in Greece, the language used in Greece | ancient Greeks the people who lived in the land of the Eastern Mediterranean in the five centuries before Christ was born

green a colour to which the human eye responds (the other colours are red and blue) | green algae a set of organisms, some single-celled and others are multi-cellular, that are considered part of the kingdom protista, although they carry out photosynthesis using chlorophyll | green filter a piece of material that allows only green light to pass through | green fly aphid, a small insect that feeds on plants and is used by ants | greenhouse a glass structure that allows plants to grow in an environment that is warmer and less windy than the surrounding area | green parts the sections of a plant that contain chlorophyll | green pigment chlorophyll, the chemical that is essential for photosynthesis | green plants plants that contain chlorophyll for use in photosynthesis

greenhouse a glass structure within which conditions are warmer and less windy than the surrounding area so can be used for raising plants that would die in the open air | greenhouse effect the increase in world temperature caused by an effect similar to that in a greenhouse – heat can get in during the day, but the Earth can not cool down at night | greenhouse environment the temperature, moisture and other conditions that are found in a greenhouse | greenhouse gas any gas that prevents the Earth from losing heat at night, *eg* burning fuel produces carbon dioxide, and cattle produce methane | commercial greenhouse very large glass building that may be kept warm to nurture delicate crops

grew became bigger

grey / gray a tint of black

grid two sets of parallel lines are at right angles to each other | National Grid the network of pylons, wires and transformers that allows electrical energy to be transmitted from the power station to the homes, shops and factories

grill equipment that cooks by radiation of heat; to cook using radiant heat

grind to break a solid down into small pieces or a powder, to sharpen by friction, to crush teeth together

grinding crushing, pulverising,

grip to hold tight in the hand | cable grip / flex grip the strap or teeth in an electrical plug that prevent the sheath of a cable from moving

ground an area of land, broken down into a fine powder | ground glass the shiny surface of the glass has been removed by scratching or sandblasting | ground level the approximate height above sea level of that the area of land | dug-over ground earth that has been turned over so breaking up the soil and moving many nutrients closer to the surface | fertile ground land that contains the nutrients and water that plants need for healthy growth | finely ground crushed to a powder | plot of ground an area of land set aside for a particular purpose | porous ground land made of soil through which water is able to percolate | school grounds the fields belonging to a school

group a set, a collection, several objects with some common feature; to put into a set | group 1 elements / group 1 metals the alkali metals | group activity where several people co-operate to complete an experiment | group plan the idea which has been discussed by all members of the group and to which they are working | group together put items into sets with common characteristics | age group people who are approximately the same age, whether it be a year group at school or anyone over 65 years old | blood group a characteristic of blood determined by the presence or absence of particular proteins, the common groups are the ABO set and the

rhesus set | environmental group people who argue for a particular way of living so as to minimise the effects on the local environment | extinct group organisms that have died out | investigative group the set of people who use a variety of skills and techniques in order to answer specific questions | subgroup a section of the whole set | target group the people who are expected to respond to an advertisement | taxonomic group a set of organisms that share common characteristics that set them apart from other organisms

grouped placed into sets so each member has common characteristics | grouped together moving items so that objects with similar features are physically close

grouping putting objects into sets with similar properties, a set of objects that are similar

grow to become bigger, to produce larger cells, to increase, to develop more cells, to specialise

growing getting bigger, becoming more | growing bacteria adding a bacterium to a suitable liquid so that the microbe repeatedly grows and reproduces to give you millions of identical offspring | growing plants the plants are becoming larger and producing more leaves | growing season the number of months for which a crop will grow before producing fruit or seeds | fast-growing the size is becoming bigger in a short time

grown mature, having reached full size

growth one of the characteristics of life – either to get bigger or to produce more | growth chart / growth graph a table, graph or line that shows the height that is achieved or expected for boys and girls at different ages | growth pattern the way in which the cells rearrange themselves at various times during growth | growth problems questions that can occur because a body is increasing in size and maturity, disease that can hinder natural development | growth spurt a time period in the early teens, when the change of height becomes more rapid | abundant growth lots of different plants in an area, an organism produces lots of new branches | annual growth new material that an organism, such as a plant, adds each year | bacterial growth usually refers to the number of a type of bacterium in an area, the number can double every 20 minutes | crystal growth turning from a solution into a solid, rapid growth usually provide small crystals | downwards growth the root is growing deeper into the soil | early growth the changes that occur near the start, especially after fertilisation | healthy growth growth under normal conditions attaining the expected landmarks in their lives |

limits of growth the maximum number of organisms that can grow in that area before the amount of water, nutrient, space, light or air prevents further increase in population | microbial growth an increase in the number of microbes, colonies of microbes are starting to become visible | plant growth the height, spread or number of branches or leaves of a plant | prevent growth to stop an organism from growing | rapid growth a large change in total size over a short time period | sideways growth parts of the root are growing horizontally so as to increase the volume of soil from which nutrients are available | uncontrolled growth an increase in numbers or size which is getting faster | wheat growth the increase in size of the cereal plant over a year

grub a maggot, a stage in the life of an insect; to uproot a tree

guard cells pairs of cells that control the opening of the stomata of leaves

guess to make a judgement without any guidance or data, to estimate

guessed (not guest which is a person) estimated with an incomplete amount of information, judged without using data

guest (not guessed which is estimated) a person who is being entertained or offered hospitality

guidance a pointer, given direction

guide a person giving directions, a book containing instructions; to point out the correct way | guidelines a set of instructions | guide lines / honey guides tracks on the petals of flowers that show insects the direction of the nectary | field guide a book that illustrates and describes the types of organisms that are found in an area

guillotine a sharp blade is held by guides so the positioning is accurate even though the force is high

guilty judged to have committed the crime

guitar a stringed instrument, usually with six strings

gull an omnivorous sea bird

gullet the oesophagus, the tube connecting the mouth to the stomach

gum a sticky material produced by trees, the fleshy area around the teeth and jaw bone; to put glue onto a surface | gums the material covering the jaw bone through which the teeth protrude

gun an instrument for firing a bullet down a barrel, equipment for accelerating a small mass to high speed in a short distance | gun powder the mixture of chemicals that will burn rapidly, thereby producing an explosion | electron gun the combination of a high-temperature filament and magnets that produces the stream of electrons in a television | radar gun the tube and meter that give the speed when pointed at a moving vehicle | starter's gun the equipment used by the person starting the race that not only gives an audible bang, but produces an electrical signal that is used to start the electronic timer

gut the organs in the digestive tract or alimentary canal between the mouth and the anus | gut muscles the radial or longitudinal muscles that change the shape of the intestine in order to push food along, the abdominal muscles | model gut using plastic bags and semi-permeable tubing to mimic the chemical changes that occur in the gut

gutter a tube or canal that is intended to carry water away

gymnast a person who is able to carry out exercises to demonstrate strength and agility in the human body

gymnastics exercises for the purpose of increased strength and agility, a competition between people to show agility and timing

gymnosperms plants in which the seed develops outside the ovary, eg conifers

gypsum [$CaSO_4$] calcium sulphate, plaster of Paris, a fine, white powder that reacts with small amounts of water to produce a solid plaster when dry

H hydrogen, proton number 1

h / hr [hour] a unit of time, 24 hours comprise one day

H₂ hydrogen gas, a gas with low density that can be used in balloons, but explodes easily

habit a routine, a custom, an addiction | **smoking habit** smoking cigarettes regularly and being unable to stop

habitable conditions are adequate for living | **habitable planet** a planet (which means any natural satellite of a star) that has an atmosphere, temperature and gravitational acceleration that is similar to those found for Earth

habitat the place where organisms live | **aquatic habitat** conditions that are found in and around water | **contrasting habitats** the environmental conditions are very different in two or more areas | **different habitats** several places with a variety of climates | **natural habitat** the place where a particular type of creature prefers to live when in the wild | **open habitat** an area that lacks any protection of trees, shrubs or rock, so is likely to be windy and possibly hot | **particular habitat** a specified place that is suitable for some creatures | **range of habitats** several different types of places, with a variety of sunlight, shade, wind and water, where that creature is able to live | **shaded habitat** an area where the heat and light of the Sun can not reach and so is less suited for plants | **terrestrial habitat** land that is suitable for that organism

Habsburg lip a characteristic shape that was seen in many of the Habsburg family over a period of four centuries

had (not add which is to sum) the past parts of the verb *to have*

haema- (*Greek* blood)

haematite (UK) / **hematite** (USA) the most important ore of iron, a mixture of iron oxide and sand

haemoglobin (UK) / **hemoglobin** (USA) the protein in red blood cells to which oxygen attaches in order to be carried around the body | **oxy-haemoglobin** the molecule produced when oxygen links to haemoglobin in the red blood cell

haemophilia (UK) / **hemophilia** (USA) a disease in which the blood will not clot so there is a danger of bleeding to death

haemophilus influenza B the virus that causes influenza (flu)

hail rain that has cooled sufficiently to form solid pellets of ice | **hailstones / hail stones** spheres of frozen rain

hair (not air which is the gas we breathe, nor hare which is an animal) a very long protein that is pushed out of the skin and is found only in mammals | **hair care** using soaps and liquids intended to keep hair clean, shiny and free from nits | **hair color** (USA) / **hair colour** (UK) the colour of your hair, as determined by your genes | **hair follicle** the small pit in the skin through which the hair appears | **hair muscle** a small muscle in the hair follicle that contracts and causes the hair to stand more upright | **body hair** visible hair that grows on any part of the skin | **facial hair** hair that grows on the face, more obvious in men | **pubic hair** the hair that grows from the skin of the pubic region, in front of the pelvis | **root hairs** long thin extensions from the cells of the plant root that increase the surface area for absorbing water

hairy appearance caused by hairs growing long and close together

half (plural is halves) the parts of an object that has been divided into two equal pieces | **half-ion equations** show the changes that occur at each electrode in electrolysis by the movement of electrons so that atoms form ions or ions become atoms | **half-life** the time taken for the activity to be reduced to half of the initial value | **half-moon** the appearance, similar to a filled semi-circle, of the Moon when it is mid-way between no visible moon and a full moon

halides ions (charged particles) produced by an atom in group 7 of the periodic table gaining an electron

Halley (Edmond 1656–1742) was rich, good looking and charming – he made important discoveries in statistics, meteorology, tides, the Earth's magnetic field and colour vision. He also estimated the size of the atom. He is remembered principally for his comet – this was one of 24 comets for which he worked out the orbits and predicted the date when Halley's comet would return. As Clerk and Editor of the Royal Society, he paid for the publication of Newton's *Principia* in 1687. He succeeded Flamsteed as Astronomer Royal at the age of 63 and began to observe the 19 year lunar cycle – a task which he successfully completed.

hallucination a dream that appears to be real

hallucinogen a chemical that affects the brain so your dreams and imagination seems to be the real world

halogen any of the atoms or elements that are in group 7 of the periodic table

halve to cut into two equal portions

halves (plural of half) the two equal sized portions

hammer one of the three tiny bones (ossicles) that connect the ear drum to the cochlea, the striker that hits a bell, a hand tool with an iron head; to hit

hamster a small rodent that lives in burrows and can store food in pouches in the mouth

hand the part at the end of the arm, a distance of 4 inches (almost 10 centimetres) used as the unit to measure the height of a horse; to give | hand bones (metacarpals) the long bones in the hand | hand lens a shaped piece of glass, up to approximately 10 centimetres diameter, that can be used to give an image that is much larger than the object | hand-span the distance across the palm of the hand | hand warmer a metal canister that fits into the hand and containing either chemicals that produce heat when mixed or pieces of carbon that will burn slowly | bare hands without using any equipment, not wearing gloves | first-hand information that you obtained, experiences that have occurred to you

handkerchief a piece of cloth that is used when clearing the nose

handle an extension that is used for holding a pan or kettle; to use your hands to carry out a task | handle bars the length of metal that has a hand grip on each end and makes the steering of the wheel much easier | pan handle / saucepan handle an extension that is made from a heat insulator so the pan can be heated while the handle remains cool | pump handle the long bar that is moved up and down in order to deliver water from a lower reservoir

handling holding an animal or item, moving an object between terminals | data handling collection of information and standard methods for changing or presenting that information

hand warmer small equipment that uses a chemical reaction to heat the hands safely

hang to suspend

hangar (not hanger which is a hook) a building for protecting aircraft

hanger (not hangar which is a building) a hook used for suspending weights

hanging suspending from a hook or rope, an abrupt end, incomplete

happen to occur, to take place

happened occurred, took place

hard not easily marked or bent, with great force, difficult | hard hat a protective covering for the head | hard magnetic material metal that will retain its magnetic properties for ever | hard parts the parts of an animal that will not rot away easily, *eg* bones, teeth, nails and claws | hard water will form a foam with soap only with difficulty because the water contains dissolved salts of calcium and magnesium and leave solids

behind when evaporated | magnetically hard the metal is not easy to magnetise or to demagnetise

harden to turn from liquid to solid because of a chemical change

harder more difficult, less easily scratched | harder material the substance is more difficult to scratch

hardness firmness, a measure of how difficult the material is to scratch or to bend; a measure of how difficult it is to form a foam with hard water

hardware the equipment that is being used

hare (not hair which is fur) a mammal that looks like a rabbit, has long ears and long back legs

harm the damage; to cause damage, to injure

harmful a substance that may cause damage to the cells if inhaled, touched or swallowed, damaging | harmful allele the instruction encoded at that gene position in the DNA is likely to lead to ill health or the early death of that organism | harmful effect the damage that results | harmful experience an event that causes damage either immediately or over a long time | harmful gas the material can be breathed in and will then cause illness or death | harmful substance a chemical that can cause damage, especially to a body | potentially harmful could cause damage to health or illness if the substance is not handled safely

harmless not hurtful, unlikely to cause an injury

harness a combination of metal pieces and straps that fastens a horse to a cart; to control

harpoon a long spear that is used for killing fish or whales; to fire a spear

Harrison (William 1693–1776) was a carpenter's son who had almost no formal education. He entered his first chronometer (accurate clock) for a competition that had been held to find a time piece that would gain or lose a few seconds over a period of a year, this would allow ships to find their positions accurately. He was already experienced at making very accurate long clocks but what was needed was a clock that would keep time in the roughest of seas. This first clock was not considered good enough, but over the next 20 years another four designs were submitted and eventually Harrison received all the prize money – by the age of 80!

hart (not heart which pumps blood) a male deer, a stag

Hartsoeker (Niklaas 1656–1725) was born in Holland, but in 1678, he moved to Paris where he made the lenses and mirrors for the Paris Observatory. He developed the microscope and, in 1692, he drew the homunculus, or tiny man, that he saw inside the sperm.

harvest the crops that have been picked and stored; to pick a large amount of a crop | **harvest time** the time of year that a particular crop is to be picked

Harvey (William 1578–1637) studied medicine at Cambridge and Padua then returned to London and became physician to the King. By dissection and experiment, Harvey showed that the valves in the heart and veins would allow blood to flow only in one direction, and that one half of the heart supplies the body, whilst the other half directs blood to the lungs. He proposed that blood circulated round the body, an idea that was immediately ridiculed (everyone thought Galen was the only true authority on blood), but this idea was eventually accepted

hat a covering for the head | **hard hat** a covering for the head worn to protect against falling objects

hatch (plural is hatches) a small opening in a roof; to break out | **hatch out** to break out of the shell of the egg

Hauksbee the Elder (Francis 1666–1713) a self-educated Englishman who may have been an assistant to Boyle, but was known to be a shop-keeper from 1687 to 1703, selling pumps and scientific instruments. In 1703, he was employed by The Royal Society to give demonstrations (a post similar to that previously held by Hooke) one of which involved causing a globe containing mercury to glow – the same effect as is used in neon lights.

Hauksbee the Younger (Francis 1687–1763) a nephew to Hauksbee the Elder, a name and relationship that has led to some confusion. Adding further to the confusion is that both made and sold scientific instruments, such as air pumps and telescopes, and both worked for the Royal Society.

have to need, to possess, to obtain | **have young** to give birth

hawks a group of carnivorous birds that includes eagles | **sparrow hawk** a small bird of prey that kills other birds in the air

hay grass which is cut, dried and stored for use as animal food

hay fever symptoms, such as difficulty with breathing, runny eyes and a streaming nose, caused by the body reacting to the air borne pollen of grasses, including hay or other allergens

hazard something that may cause damage unless care is taken | **hazard labels / hazard warning labels** paper or card that is put on a chemical container so as to emphasise possible dangers |

hazard sign / hazard warning sign paper or card that is placed near the position where a dangerous situation may occur | **hazard symbols** diagrams that show the harmful affects that may be caused by the chemical | **biohazard** damage or death may occur if these living organisms are allowed to escape | **common hazards** dangers that are always found with some activities such as heating water or using electricity | **electrical hazard** the dangers that may arise from the misuse of electrical equipment, *eg* electric shock, fire | **low hazard** very little danger | **recognise hazards** (UK) / **recognize hazards** (USA) to notice where accidents could occur and take steps to make the procedure safe

hazardous dangerous, likely to result in damage | **hazardous activity** a dangerous pastime | **hazardous chemicals** materials that may become dangerous (*eg* explosive or poisonous) if they are not stored and handled safely | **hazardous reaction** the starting materials are usually safe, but mixing them could cause a fire or an explosion | **hazardous substance** a dangerous chemical that could be explosive or poisonous

hazcards A5 sizes posters that outline the dangers associated with the named chemical and steps that should be taken to minimise damage if an accident occurs

hazchem symbols / hazchem system pictures that show the dangers associated with a particular substance (or HAZardous CHEMical)

Hb [haemoglobin] the protein in red blood cells that produces the red colour and carries oxygen

He helium, proton number 2, an inert gas that was detected in the Sun before being found on Earth

head the part of the body that contains the ears, eyes and brain, the part of a sperm that contains the nucleus; to go in a direction | **head of liquid / pressure head** the pressure produced by a height of liquid | **match head** the chemical on the end of the match stick that burns easily when heated by friction | **recording head** the part of a tape player that transfers the electric signal to the magnetic domains of the tape

header / heading a title for a column or a page

headlamps /headlights the main lamps or bulbs that are used to light up the area in front of a car

Heaf test a skin test to see if you are immune to tuberculosis

heal (not eel which is a long fish, nor heel which is part of a shoe) to restore to good health

health the general condition of the mind or body | **health organisation** (UK) / **health organization** (USA) a group of people who look after a particular part the medical service | **health professional** a person whose job is to look after the physical or mental wellbeing of people | **health promotion** advertising and publicity that encourage people to change to a healthier life style | **health services** systems for providing the public with the individuals and buildings that can help keep good health | **health warning** advice that an action may cause damage to a body or mind | **environmental health** understanding the causes and effects of illnesses that occur when many people live in a small area, and taking steps to prevent these diseases | **personal health** the height, weight, and illnesses that are shown by one person – usually yourself | **public health** an understanding of the causes of illnesses and methods of preventing disease among a population of people

healthier has a lower heart rate, breathing rate and blood pressure than another person

healthily living well, eating a diet that is adequate and nutritious, taking reasonable exercise

healthy a state where all organs and tissues seem to be working properly | **healthy bones** the bones are rigid and able to withstand bending and hitting, and the bone marrow will produce a sufficient number of blood cells | **healthy diet** eating sufficient of each nutrient, and not too much of any one chemical, so the body enjoys good health | **healthy growth** a change of size, shape, colour or other measure that indicates that all the organism is working properly | **healthy heart** a heart that is beating rhythmically and can cope with the increase in rate caused by normal exercise | **healthy individual** a person who is able to exercise without any signs of stress | **healthy plant** a green plant that is growing with a good colour and an acceptable number of new leaves | **healthy teeth** the teeth are strong, not chipped and without bacterial growth or plaque

heap a mound, a pile; to put items into a pile without any order | **compost heap** a mixture of dead plants and waste material that is able to be broken down by microbes then returned to the soil

hear (note here which is a near place) to listen

heard (not herd which is a group of cattle) the past tense of hearing – your ears' response to a sound

hearing (not earring which is an ornament) listening to a particular sound, having the ability to respond to sound | **hearing ability** a measure of how sensitive is the ear to different frequencies or pitch | **hearing aid** equipment to help a person to hear more clearly | **hearing impaired** a person who finds difficulty in understanding a sound because they are not sensitive to all the frequencies

that could be expected | **hearing loss** a measure of the difference between the sound sensitivity of a healthy individual and that person | **hearing protectors** material that is placed over the ears in order to reduce the intensity of sound reaching the ears and so prevent hearing loss | **hearing range** the difference between the lowest frequency that a person can hear and the highest frequency to which they are sensitive | **hearing sensitivity** a measure of how loud must be a particular pitch in order to be heard | **acute hearing** the ability to hear sounds of very low intensity | **damaged hearing** the range of frequencies to which the ear responds or the sensitivity of the ear has been affected by an accident | **poor hearing** the ear is not very sensitive to low intensity sounds | **range of hearing** the frequencies of sound, from the lowest to the highest, to which a animal will respond | **range of human hearing** the frequencies of sound which a person is able to hear | **science of hearing** studying how organisms are able to detect the vibrations of sound and then to make sense of the many frequencies

hearsay a report without supporting evidence, gossip

heart (not hart which is a male deer) the muscular organ in the chest that pumps blood around the body | **heart attack** a sudden change to the control of the heart so that the pumping of blood either stops or is ineffective | **heart beat** the thumping sound that is the result of the rhythmic contraction and relaxation of the heart | **heart condition** a disease of the heart leading to a loss of the effectiveness with which the blood is pumped around the body | **heart disease** a change in the structure or control of the heart so that the heart can not respond to the body's demands for blood | **heart–lung machine** equipment that is used to pump the blood and allow exchange of gases while a surgical operation is carried out on the heart or lungs of a patient | **heart massage** rhythmic pumping of the chest, or directly of the heart, in order to encourage the heart to start working again | **heart muscle** the special cells that make up the heart and are able to contract and relax at approximately once each second for a hundred years | **heart rate** the number of times, each minute, at which the heart contracts or relaxes | **heart strings** threads in the heart that prevent the valves from turning inside out | **heart valves** structures inside the heart that prevent the blood from flowing in the wrong direction | **artificial heart** a small pump that is intended to be placed in the chest so as to replace the patient's own heart | **healthy heart** a heart that is beating rhythmically and can cope with the increase in rate caused by normal exercise

heart valves structures inside the heart that prevent the blood from flowing in the wrong direction | **artificial heart-valve** a construction of plastic and metal that replaces one of the valves in the heart

heat (not eat which is to take in food) the amount of vibrational or movement energy within an object | **heat capacity** the amount of energy that is needed to increase the temperature of an object, often heat capacity will be specified for a 1 gram of material changing by 1°C | **heat conduction** movement of the vibrations of the outer electrons from one end of a solid to the other | **heat conductor** solid material through which heat moves rapidly | **heat energy** emphasising that the type of energy is the vibration of the outer electrons | **heat flow** movement of energy from a region of high temperature to an area of lower temperature | **heat gain** the increase in the energy of an object caused by an increase in temperature or a change of state | **heat loss** the reduction in the amount of vibrational energy caused either by a lowering of the temperature or a change of state | **heat movement** the changes in temperature that are seen when the vibrational energy moves from one place to another | **heat production** the energy that is released from a chemical reaction produces an increase in temperature | **heat-proof mat** a square of material that is placed under a heat source so as to prevent movement of heat to the table | **heat radiation** loss of heat energy (wavelength from about 600 to 2000 nanometres) from a surface that is at a temperature above the surroundings | **heat sensor** a structure, that could be biological or physical, that is affected by heat and causes a change | **heat shield** the material on the base of space capsules and the Shuttle that protects the craft from the heat generated by moving rapidly through air | **heat source** the point or object that is providing the heat | **heat strongly** to use a source of heat energy that gives a high temperature | **heat transfer** movement of heat energy from one object to another, using conduction, convection, radiation or evaporation / condensation | **heat transmission** the directed movement of heat from an area of high temperature towards a specific object | **absorption of heat** to take in heat and either increase in temperature or change state | **body heat** the energy that the organism produces in order to keep the

body temperature constant | **conduct heat / conduction of heat** to move heat through a solid by causing the outer electrons to vibrate | **flow of heat** movement of heat energy from an area with a higher temperature to a cooler region | **generate heat / generation of heat** producing heat energy from some other form of energy, *eg* friction causes moving energy to turn into heat energy | **latent heat** the amount of energy that is needed to change state at the boiling point or freezing point, heat is exchanged but there is no change of temperature | **loss of heat** the movement of thermal energy from the area at a higher temperature | **moving heat** occurs whenever there is a difference in temperature, heat tries to move from the hot region to the cooler area | **red heat** a piece of iron that has been heated to about 600°C and so glows red | **transfer heat** to move heat from a hot area to a place which is cooler

heated warmed, increased in temperature

heater an electrical component that gets hot as an electric current is passed through it | **chemical heater** mixing of two or more chemicals, producing sufficient heat energy to boil water, but there is no flame | **electrical heater** a piece of wire that produces heat when an electric current is passed through it, useful in a kettle | **immersion heater** a coil of wire near the bottom of a tank of water that is used to produce hot water for domestic purposes | **low-voltage heater** equipment that uses a potential difference that is safe for humans to touch (up to 24 volts), but produces heat when a current is flowing | **radiant heater** equipment in which a wire is wound around an insulating rod, then a current is passed through it, which raises the temperature of the wire to about 600°C and the wire glows red hot

heating increasing the amount of heat energy leading either to an increase of temperature or to a change of state | **heating apparatus / heating appliance** equipment that can be used to heat a material | **heating curve** the graph of temperature against time as a substance is heated, the flat parts of the curve show the temperature at which a change of state is taking place | **heating effect** the result of passing a current through a wire is to increase the temperature | **heating element** the wire in a kettle or radiant heater that is heated by an electric current | **heating equipment** apparatus that is suitable for the safe heating of a substance | **heating wire** a long thin piece of metal that safely transforms electrical energy to heat energy and is intended to be hot | **off-peak heating** producing heat by using the capacity that is available for generating electricity at periods when very few people want electricity | **solar heating** using the heat from the Sun to warm a house or water | **strong heating** using a large flame at high temperature

heavenly bodies anything that can be seen in the sky at night, the stars, planets, comets and asteroids that are in space

heavier having more weight

heaviest the object with the most weight

heavily highly, a lot of, involved with enthusiasm

heavy large weight | **heavy exercise** lots of muscle movement, leading to sweating and tiredness | **heavy industry** the production of raw materials such as iron, steel, oil or plastics | **heavy rain** a large amount of water falling in a very short time

hectare an area of 10,000 square metres, one hectare is 2.47 acres

hedge (not edge which means boundary) a line of bushes or trees that marks a boundary | **hedge cutters** equipment for removing the growing tips so the surface of the bush or tree is as smooth as possible

hedgehog a small mammal, covered with spines, that lives mainly on insects and worms

heel (not eel which is long fish, nor heal which is to restore to health) the back part of the foot, the back part of a shoe; to lean to one side | **stiletto heels** long, thin blocks on heel of some ladies' shoes

heifer a young cow

height vertical distance | **height-weight chart** a graph, table or line showing the height and weight for young people at different ages | **height changes** the differences that occur in the height of an organism over a period of time | **height gain** an increase in the height of an organism, the vertical distance that an object moves upwards | **constant height** the distance from a specified level does not change | **fixed height** the distance from the ground is either kept constant or is given before the start of the experiment

heli- / helio- (*Greek* the Sun)

helicopter a flying machine that uses a large horizontal rotor and does not have wings

heliocentric model a description of the universe in which the Sun (helios) is at the centre with the planets, comets and meteors in orbit around the Sun | **heliocentric orbit** the path taken by the object is a closed curve, *ie* circle, oval or ellipse, around the Sun

helium (He, proton number 2, melting point −269°C) an inert gas that was first discovered in the Sun (hence the name – from helios) with a density about 15% that of air | **helium balloon** a bag filled with helium and so has buoyancy and will float

helmet a protective cover surrounding most of the head

heav

↓

hem

Helmholtz (Hermann 1821–1894) has been called the last of the true scholars because his work ranged over almost the whole field of science and he was also a skilful musician. He trained to be a doctor, because grant money was available to pay for that medical course. He became professor of biology at Konigsberg (1849), Bonn (1855) and Heidelberg (1858) where Bunsen was professor of chemistry, he was then appointed professor of physics at Berlin in 1871. He extended the work of Joule on energy, developed the ophthalmoscope that is still used for examining the retina of the eye and deduced that the cochlea in the ear must be able to distinguish different frequencies. He provided help to Maxwell, and Hertz was one of his pupils

Helmont (Jan Baptista 1579–1644) a wealthy man, Helmont studied classics and theology before turning to chemistry. He measured the growth of a willow tree, the initial weight was 5 pounds (2 kilograms) which increased to 169 pounds (77 kilograms) after five years, a change which he said was due to the water; the importance of fixed air (carbon dioxide) was not realised until Priestley over a century later.

helped aided, supported, given guidance

helpful giving aid, useful

helter-skelter a spiral chute from the top of a tower, up to 20 metres tall, to the ground down which a person slides

hematite (USA) / **haematite** (UK) the most important ore of iron, a mixture of iron oxide [Fe_2O_3] and sand

hemi- (*Greek* half)

hemispheres the halves (hemi) of a ball (sphere), division of the Earth into two halves | **Northern hemisphere** the part of the Earth that is north of the equator | **Southern hemisphere** the part of the Earth that is south of the equator

hemoglobin (USA) / **haemoglobin** (UK) the protein in red blood cells to which oxygen attaches in order to be carried around the body | **oxy-hemoglobin** the molecule produced when oxygen links to haemoglobin in the red blood cell, this chemical is bright red

hemophilia (USA) / **haemophilia** (UK) a disease in which the blood will not clot, so there is a danger of bleeding to death

HEP (hydro-electric power) producing electricity from the potential energy of water stored in a dam

hepatic concerned with the liver | hepatic portal vein the blood vessel taking material that has been absorbed in the small intestine to the liver | hepatic vein the vessel (tube) that returns blood from the liver to the heart

hepatitis any disease that affects the liver

herb- (*Latin* grass) concerned with plants

herb a plants that is used in cooking to add flavour or fragrance to food

herbaceous any plant in which the parts above ground regularly die back

herbicide a chemical that kills plants | selective herbicide a chemical that kills certain types of plants, but leaves others alone

herbivore a animal that is able to eat only plants

herbivorous a diet that comprises only plants

herd (not heard which is related to sound) a group of domesticated mammals, *eg* cattle, horse, elephants

hereditary coming from the parents in the genes | hereditary disease illness caused by a particular gene, *eg* sickle-cell anaemia

heredity inherited, given by parents

hermaphrodite a living organism that develops both male and female reproductive organs, *eg* an earthworm

hermit crab a crab-like crustacean that has a soft body and that uses an empty snail shell as portable protection

Hero of Alexandria (c 62 AD) may simply have been a recorder of ingenious devices as shown in the only two of his books to survive, *Pneumatics* and *Mechanics*, or he may have been a prolific inventor and expert at mathematics. He described a coin-operated slot machine, a fire engine, and automatic fountains. The only invention attributed to Hero is a steam engine that uses opposing jets of steam to rotate a cylinder

heroin a drug, similar to morphine, that is used to get rid of pain – so highly addictive that heroin is no longer legally used in the USA

heron a bird that has long legs and a long neck and feeds by wading through shallow water | heron population the number of herons in that habitat

Herschel (Caroline 1750–1848) trained as a singer in Germany then moved to join her brother in Bath in 1772. She claimed to be his housekeeper but she was also his co-worker (possibly given less credit because she was female) who made many of the measurements for the star catalogues and discovered eight new comets

Herschel (Sir Frederick William 1738–1822) was a freelance musician – playing music for who ever would pay, who was appointed organist at Bath. He was a perfectionist, who had to grind his own mirrors for his telescope. That first telescope needed more than 200 mirrors to be produced before he was satisfied with the accuracy. This precision allowed him to discover Uranus in 1781 – the first new planet for over 3000 years. He was made Court Astronomer so he had the money to build a bigger reflecting telescope with which he found that both Uranus and Saturn had satellites. His incredibly careful observations included catalogues of 800 double stars and of 5000 nebulae. Herschel proposed the idea that the Sun is moving through the universe and he discovered infra-red radiation by holding a thermometer in the spectrum of sunlight.

Hertwig (Oskar 1849–1922) studied medicine and zoology in Germany. He established, in 1875, that fertilisation involved both sperm and ovum.

Hertz (Heinrich Rudolf 1857–1894) was assistant to Helmholtz before becoming Professor of Physics in 1885, three years later, he demonstrated that the waves given out by an electric spark could be detected 20 metres away, thus proving Maxwell's theoretical ideas. Further experiments showed that these waves behaved exactly like light, but have wavelengths of about a metre. Hertz died of blood poisoning at the early age of 36, in the same year as his old master.

hertz / Hz unit of frequency measured as cycles per second

hetero- (*Greek* other)

hexagon a figure with six lines joined to form a circuit, the six lines are usually all the same size

hexagonal having six sides | hexagonal prism a solid transparent object that has faces made from six rectangles of equal size

Hg mercury (hydro gentium) proton number 80, the only metal that is liquid at room temperature

hibernate to spend the winter in a deep sleep in which the heart rate is much reduced

hibernating lowering the rate of breathing and heart-beat in a special sleep over winter

hibernation a sleep-like existence that some animals use in order to avoid the cold period of winter when food is scarce

hide a small enclosure that allows animals to be observed without the observers being seen by the animals; to put out of sight, to take cover

hierarchical in a definite sequence that allows progress from the lower levels upwards | hierarchical organisation (UK) / hierarchical organization (USA) groups of people in which there is a definite ladder from the lowest to the person in charge

high above or greater than some accepted level | high altitude a large vertical distance above the Earth's surface | high blood pressure the heart pumps blood out at a pressure that usually varies between 120 millimetres and 80 millimetres of mercury – blood pressure that is higher may indicate a need for treatment | high crop yield work out how many tonnes of a crop could be obtained from an area – if this is higher than expected for ground of that type, then the yield is high | high current any current that is likely either to damage a person or to cause a fire | high-energy drinks liquids containing large amounts of glucose so your body can rapidly absorb the sugar and use the chemical energy | high mountains any rocks which are large, with steep sides and long drops | high pitch sound with a frequency above 2000 hertz | high power any equipment that uses or produces, a lot of energy in a short time | high pressure in weather forecasting, any pressure above 1000 millibars | high quality an item that is likely to last for a long time without failing | high speed going faster than normal, *eg* a high-speed train is 70 metres per second, but a high-speed plane would fly at 700 metres per second | high temperature if it directly affects you, then any-thing above 50°C, otherwise any temperature that is higher than normal for that activity | high tide the highest position reached by the sea before the height starts to decrease as the tide goes out | high voltage a potential difference that provides a current that is dangerous either by damaging you or causing a fire | high winds movement of air that can cause damage – higher wind speed causes more damage | high yield a chemical process that turns most of the reactant into useful product, a large quantity of the crop from one plant

higher further from the ground, frequency has increased, more of | higher organism the creature shows more specialisation, development and the use of intelligence | higher pitch the frequency of that note is higher than others | higher reactivity the metal is further up the reactivity series and will therefore replace the

lower metal | higher temperature the material feels or looks hotter

highest furthest, best | highest frequency the maximum rate, the highest pitch

highlight the best part; to make plain, to emphasise, to bring attention to

highly… very… | highly effective works superbly well at that particular task | highly explosive detonation of the chemical would cause lots of damage | highly flammable catches fire very easily | highly porous allows fluid through at high speed | highly reactive add another chemical with care – there is likely to be a lot of heat produced | highly sensitive able to react to a very low intensity signal

Highway Code a booklet, produced by the Government, that gives guidance as to the expected behaviour of anyone who uses the public roads / highways

hill (not ill which is unwell) an area of higher ground, a small mountain, an upwards slope | upland hills the hills that are inland from the coastal plain

hilly the countryside changes height several times in all directions, an undulating landscape

Himalayas several ranges of gigantic mountains between India and China, produced by the Indian tectonic plate crashing into China

hind at the rear, a female deer | hind limbs the back legs

hinge two sheets of metal that are joined along one edge and are able to rotate about that edge | hinge joint the junction of two bones that is able to move in one direction only, *eg* the elbow joint, the knee joint

hint a suggestion, an indication; to give a clue

hip the part of the body below the waist and around the pelvis | hip joint a ball-and-socket joint where the femur, or thigh bone, meets the pelvis | hip replacement to remove the damaged hip joint and replace with a ball and socket made from metal or synthetic materials | dislocated hip the ball at the top of the femur has moved away from the socket of the pelvis

Hippocrates (460–377 BC) is said, by legend, to have been small and born on Kos. He taught that moderation and cleanliness are essential and that disease is the result of an imbalance in the *humours* of the body.

histo- (*Greek* web, tissue)

histogram a bar chart used for displaying measurements of discontinuous variables

histology the study of cells, using a microscope to examine the structure of cells

historic an event that is worthy of being recorded, having lasting importance, linked with the past | pre-historic occurring before the development of permanent written records

historical in the past | historical evidence observations that have been recorded many years ago | historical examples using facts and observations that were made long ago

history perspective on past events

hit (not it which is a pointing word) a bang; to thump, to collide

hitting beating, reaching, achieving

HIV [human immuno deficiency virus] a virus that causes damage to the immune system so the person is very easily damaged or killed by infection

Hofmann voltameter glass tubing, of a crosspiece and two vertical tubes, with an electrode at the base of each upright tube, passing an electric current through water produces two volumes of hydrogen and one volume of oxygen

hold to keep in one place, to prevent from moving | hold together to push into close contact, to prevent from falling apart

holder fingers, equipment that is used for gripping equipment safely | battery holder an insulated pack in which electrical cells can be held and connected together | bulb holder the plastic collar containing electrical contacts into which a lamp is placed | test-tube holder looks like a very long clothes' peg and is used for grasping a test tube when it would be dangerous to use fingers

holdfast a modified sucker that stops a water-dwelling plant from being swept away

hole (not whole which means everything) a gap | hole in ozone layer ozone [O_3] forms a layer near the top of the atmosphere, the thickness varies and is thinnest above the poles – sometimes so thin that there is no ozone above the South Pole | air hole the gap near the base of a bunsen burner that allows air to mix with the gas, a gap in the ice at which Arctic sea mammals can breathe | black hole a star that is so dense that light can not escape | microscopic hole a tiny puncture through which air can move, but which is too small for water to pass through | pin hole a tiny puncture, a small perforation | plug hole an exit hole that can be blocked by a plug | pot hole a cave, an underground passage | tap hole an opening at the bottom of a vessel that is usually kept closed with a removable bung

hollow a depression, vacant, empty | hollow stem a trunk or stalk which has a hole down the centre

holly / holly bush a small evergreen tree which produces red berries near the start of winter and has leaves that are very spiky

home (not ohm which is the unit of electrical resistance) the place where a creature lives and feels most comfortable | home-grown food that has been raised in the garden, geographically close | typical home the type of dwelling in which a particular group of people or animals would be expected to live

homo- (Greek same)

homunculus the tiny person that was thought to be in the sperm | homunculus theory the idea that the sperm contained an exact replica of the adult, but in a miniature form

honey a sweet solution produced by bees for the benefit of their grubs, it is used as food by humans and is delicious on toast | honey guides the lines on a petal that guide the bee to the nectary, guide lines

hoof (plural is hoofs or hooves) the natural covering of the feet of some animals

hook a length of curved material, often metal: to capture

Hooke (Robert 1635–1703) started studying for the church (his father was vicar), but was in such poor health that he became a scientist! In 1662, he helped found The Royal Society (so prestigious that it needs no other title) and became the Curator – charged with demonstrating three or four considerable experiments each week. He carried out some measurements using springs, leading to Hooke's law, and used this knowledge to improve the accuracy of watches. Hooke was not the first to use microscopes, but he refined the lenses, and in 1665 he published *Micrographia* which for the first time contained the word 'cell'. Hooke was so busy that he had lots of might-have-been discoveries, he almost found that light is waves, he almost discovered oxygen a hundred years before Priestley and he almost described Newton's law of gravity.

Hooke's law the extension of a spring or elastic material depends directly on the force applied and the material will return to its original length when the force is removed

hooves (plural of hoof) the horny coverings of animals feet

hop to jump on one leg, to make a giant leap

Hopkins (Sir Frederick Gowland 1861–1947) has been called the 'father of British biochemistry' because of his belief that every chemical reaction in a cell is understandable in terms of normal chemistry. This title came to him late in life – he left school at 17, worked as an insurance clerk and analyst, he did not enter Medical School until he was 27 and then worked so hard that he had to retire in 1910. Fortunately he recovered and, at age 50, began the work on vitamins and nutrition for which he was awarded the Nobel prize, together with Eijkmann, in 1929

horizon as far as you can see, where sky meets land or water

horizontal parallel to the ground | horizontal period / horizontal row sets of elements forming the rows in the periodic table that have the same number of orbitals

hormonal system / humoral system the set of cells producing hormones, including the gland producing the hormone, the chemicals to which the gland is sensitive and the cells that respond to the hormone

hormones chemical messengers that are produced in a set of cells in one part of the body and produce long-term changes, *eg* growth hormone, or wide-spread changes to the body *eg* adrenaline | hormone concentration the amount of the specific hormone in each litre of blood | circulating hormones the chemical messengers that are to be found in the blood | sex hormones chemicals produced by the ovaries and testes that cause the body to develop organs and a shape that is characteristic of that gender

horny very hard and with a grain, bundles of keratin fibres | horny pad the flat pad that replaces the upper front teeth in some herbivores

horrific terrible, shocking, awesome, disgusting

horse a mammal with four legs that is sufficiently large and docile that it may be used for pulling a carriage or for riding by adults and children

horse-shoe magnet a piece of iron or nickel that is in the shape of an incomplete circle

hose / hosepipe a flexible tube for delivering water; to spray with water

hospital a building which houses the experts and the equipment that should be able to heal sick and damaged people | hospital laboratory the area of the hospital where tests are carried out and the amounts of chemicals in body fluids are measured

host the organism in which a parasite lives

hot a qualitative measure of temperature, usually anything above 50°C – hot materials can damage the skin | hot air any air that is warmer than the surrounding gas | hot-air balloon a bag filled with air that is heated so the air expands, the density goes down and the balloon goes up | hot fluid any liquid or gas that feels hot to the touch and may damage the skin | hot food usually refers to the temperature of the food – above

50°C, but may mean very spicy and hot to the taste | hot links icons or alpha-numeric displays that allow rapid connection to the specified web site | hot magma emphasising that rock is at a high temperature and so is able to flow easily | hot water any water with a temperature which could be painful to your skin | hot-water cylinder the circular tank in which heated water is stored | red hot the material is at a temperature above 600°C | white hot the temperature is so high that the material is producing white light

hotter higher temperature

hottest highest temperature

hour (not our which shows ownership) a period of time that is $^1/_{24}$ of a day or 60 minutes | daylight hours day time, the time during which the Sun is above the horizon | kilometres per hour (kph) a measure of speed that is used for cars | kilowatt hours (kWh) the amount of energy used by an electrical appliance

energy used   =   power   x   time
(kilowatt hours)   (kilowatts)   (hours)

| miles per hour (mph) the unit of speed that is used for transport

house the building in which people live; to place people into a building suitable for living | greenhouse a glass structure that is warmer and less windy than the surrounding area, used to protect growing plants | lighthouse a tower with a powerful lamp on top that can be used to warn shipping of hazards | model house a miniature version of a human dwelling place, possibly with decorations and working lamps, but without heating or running water | nocturnal house a building, the inside of which is 12 hours out of step with the real world, so that animals that are active usually only at night may be observed by visitors during the day

household any item that could be expected to be found in the home | household acids acids, such as ethanoic acid (vinegar) or citric acid (lemon juice) that could be found in a home | household appliances equipment that use energy and are found in most houses | household chemical any chemical that could be bought at the local supermarket | household device equipment found in the home | household electricity the electricity that is used by all household appliances and is 230–250 volts 50 hertz alternating current (50 Hz ac) in the United Kingdom | household germs microbes that are found in homes and cause very little problem | household items any material that is easily obtainable and is often found in the house | household liquids fluids that are found in the home | household materials any substance that could be expected to be found in a house or is easily bought from a local shop | household products materials that are likely to be used in the house | household waste the dirty water that is flushed down the toilet or the sink and the solid material that is put into the rubbish bin | smoking household a home in which many members of the family smoke cigarettes

hover to remain suspended in the air without any visible support

hovercraft a vehicle, invented by Cockerell in 1955, that was lifted by a cushion of air so the bottom surface was a few millimetres above the ground or water and there was no friction

how in what way? using what means? the way chosen

hr / h [hour] a unit of time, 24 hours in a day

hub the central part of a wheel, often with spokes radiating outwards, the centre of activity

Hubble (Edwin Powell1889–1953) was trained in law and became a successful athlete and boxer, but spent most of his life studying the stars. In 1923, Hubble proved that the Andromeda galaxy was not part of the Milky Way but a separate galaxy. By 1929, he had measured the distance and speed of 18 galaxies, and found that those furthest away were moving fastest, these observations supported the idea of an expanding universe and then led to the big bang hypothesis

Hubble telescope a large reflecting optical telescope that was put into orbit in 1990 in order to see the stars without the distortion and loss of clarity caused by the atmosphere

huge very, very big, enormous

hum a sound of constant pitch and loudness; to produce a sound with the mouth closed

human relating to people | human activity any change which is caused by the people being there | human body the organs, tissues and cells that make up a person | human arm emphasising a structure in which there is an upper arm bone, a joint then a pair of lower arm bones | human body systems the sets of tissues and organs that perform particular functions, such as circulating blood or digesting food | human breath the air that is expelled from the lungs of a person | human characteristic features and behaviours that are associated with people | human contact touched by other people, interacted with people | human diet the types of food and nutrients that a person needs to eat in order to stay healthy | human embryo the group of cells that develops inside the womb of a woman | human fertilisation (UK) / human fertilization (USA) the fusion

of the sperm, from a man, with the ovum from a woman | Human Genome Project a worldwide collaborative task to find the position of every atom in the 46 chromosomes of the human cell | human immuno deficiency virus (HIV) a disease that causes the immune system to stop working and so the person is more susceptible to disease | human interference the presence of people has caused the change to the habitat | human life cycle the changes that occur from the baby growing up, through the maturing and reproduction of the adult to old age | human organs the organs, or groups of tissues, that are found in a person | human powered using a person's arms and leg movement in order to move a vehicle | human reproduction the changes that occur in going from the isolated sperm and ovum to the birth of the baby | human skeleton the bones (over 200 of them!) and the way they are arranged in the human body | human sperm the male gamete has been produced by a man | human subjects experiments involve the direct response of people

humane causing least amount of distress to an animal, without damage | humane trap a method for capturing an animal without causing pain or damage

humerus (not humorous which is funny) the bone connecting the shoulder to the elbow joint

humidity amount of moisture in the air relative to the saturated air at that temperature

humoral system / hormonal system the tissues and glands that produce the hormones, or chemical messengers in animals

humorous (not humerus which is a bone) funny

hump a mound especially that on the back of a camel which is a store of fat

humus decomposed plants

hundred the number between 99 and 101, abbreviated to centi... or c...

hunt the act of finding prey; to follow an animal in preparation for killing and eating, to search

hunter an animal that has to find and kill other animals for food

hunting using skill, patience and surprise to kill another animal for food

hurricane locally, a high speed wind, globally, a swirling mass of fast moving air

husk the dry shell of some fruit

Hutton (James 1726–1797) studied law in Edinburgh then medicine in Paris and Leyden, he returned to the family farm in Scotland and made a fortune by extracting ammonium chloride from soot. He is remembered for his ideas in geology.

Hutton proposed that the processes leading to changes in rock formation and structure that we see today, are exactly the same processes that have been occurring since the start of the Earth.

Huygens (Christian 1629–1695) studied Law in his native Netherlands before turning to Physics. He observed Saturn, using telescopes that he had constructed himself, and both described the rings and discovered Titan. He explained refraction, using his idea that light is a wave, developed new equations in mathematics and made a vary accurate pendulum clock. Huygens was considered second only to Newton in the breadth and depth of his discoveries.

hyacinth a plant with many flowers on a single stalk and a strong scent | water hyacinth a fast-growing freshwater plant that may help to reduce chemical pollution of water, but may clog water channels

hybrid a cross between two items that takes some characteristics from one and some from the other

hydra a fresh-water microscopic animal that fixes itself to a surface

hydrangea a flowering shrub that produces large flowers with colours that depend on the pH of the soil, the flowers are blue on acid soil, and pink on alkaline soil

hydrated with water added | rehydrated water has been added to activate a dried powder

hydraulic using liquids | hydraulic brakes pushing a piston at one end causes an increase in pressure in the fluid that can be used to apply pressure to the brake pads | hydraulic fluid the liquid, with a high boiling point and that is difficult to compress, which can be used in hydraulic systems | hydraulic jack a method for raising vehicles by putting pressure onto a liquid in a piston | hydraulic lever equipment in which the force applied to one piston is different from the force that is felt at the second piston | hydraulic system any method using pressure in a liquid to cause a change

hydraulically operated moved by means of pressure in a pipe

hydrazine [$NH_2.NH_2$] a colourless liquid, boiling point 113°C, that reacts violently with oxidising agents and so is used as a propellant for rockets

hydride / metal hydride a compound between the named metal and hydrogen

hydro- (*Greek* water)

hydrocarbon a molecule that contains carbon and hydrogen only, *eg* cooking gas, oil, diesel and petrol

hydrochloric acid [HCl] a strong acid that contains a chloride ion [Cl^-] bonded to a hydrogen ion [H^+], hydrochloric acid always produces chloride salts

hydro-electric energy the potential energy stored in a lake of water, the energy obtained by allowing water to flow from a reservoir through a turbine under gravity | hydro-electric power (HEP) electricity that has been generated using the potential energy stored in a dam of water

hydro-electricity a potential difference or voltage that has been produced using movement of water out of a reservoir

hydrogen (H, proton number 1) the simplest atom; [H_2] a gas with a very low density that forms an explosive mixture with air (*pop!* test), boiling point −253°C | hydrogen balloon a gas-proof sack that is filled with hydrogen (a gas that is less dense than air) so as to give uplift in air | hydrogen carbonate indicator a coloured dye that changes from red to yellow if carbon dioxide is dissolved in the liquid | hydrogen carbonate / hydrogen carbonate ion [$HCO_3^=$] an ion with a negative charge that decomposes easily to give an oxide and carbon dioxide | hydrogen cyanide [HCN] a gas that is said to smell like almonds, but causes death | hydrogen gas [H_2] a gas with a very low density that forms an explosive mixture with air (*pop!* test), boiling point −253°C | hydrogen ion [H^+] the positively charged particle produced by a hydrogen atom losing an electron | hydrogen peroxide [H_2O_2] a liquid that slowly breaks down to produce water and oxygen | hydrogen sulfide (USA) / hydrogen sulphide (UK) [H_2S] bad egg smell, produced if acid is added to iron sulphide | liquid hydrogen hydrogen that has been compressed and cooled so the gas turns into a liquid | test for hydrogen the *pop!* test, a lighted splint will go *pop!* or *squeak*

hydrolysis reaction of a chemical with water to produce new compounds

hydrophone a tube with a funnel on the end so you can listen to sounds underwater

hydrostatic force the force produced within a liquid, the force could be because of height, as in a reservoir of water, or because a force is applied, as in a hydraulic brake system | hydrostatic pressure the force per unit area, either in the depths of water or in a hydraulic system

hydro-tropism growth of roots towards water

hydroxide / hydroxide ion [OH^-] an oxygen atom and a hydrogen atom are bonded by a strong covalent bond and can then link to a metal, the hydroxide is never found by itself but must be bonded to another element | ammonium hydroxide [NH$_4$OH] the chemical produced by dissolving ammonia in water | calcium hydroxide [Ca (OH)$_2$] slaked lime, a weak alkali that forms when calcium or calcium oxide is mixed with water | metal hydroxide a metallic element ionically bonded to a hydroxide | potassium hydroxide [KOH] potash, caustic potash, a white material that is strongly alkaline and corrosive in solution | sodium hydroxide [NaOH] soda, caustic soda, a white chemical that is strongly alkaline in solution and is produced by dropping sodium onto water or the electrolysis of salt solution

hygiene preventing the spread of germs by keeping every item clean

hygrometer an instrument for measuring the amount of moisture in air

hyper- (*Greek* above, beyond)

hypo- (*Greek* under, below)

hypothermia the body temperature has fallen well below the expected value

hypotheses (singular is hypothesis) ideas that explain the results, but the predictions have not been fully tested by experiment

hypothesis (plural is hypotheses) an explanation that has not been proven by experiment | capture hypothesis the idea that the Moon was a large rock in space that was attracted by the Earth's gravity | collision hypothesis the speculation that the Moon resulted from a large body hitting the Earth

hypothesising (UK) **/ hypothesizing** (USA) producing ideas or theories that could explain the data

Hz / hertz unit of frequency of a wave, the number of times that a wave goes up and down each second

I iodine, proton number 53, a halogen

I [current, because currents used to be induced by moving a wire through a magnetic field] measured in amps

I$_2$ iodine, a shiny solid that turns directly to a gas

I-beam a structural steel joist that has an I or H shape when cut across

Ibn al-Nafis (also known as Al Quarashi, Ibn Rushd or Averroes 1126–1198) a polymath who studied theology, maths and medicine before becoming a judge in his home town of Cordoba, Spain at the age of 35. He became the personal physician to the Caliph of Morocco for 13 years but was sent into exile because of his writings. He had written extensive commentaries on the work of the Greek philosopher Aristotle (384–322 BC) and attempted to synthesise the Arabic and Greek traditions of thinking. He also wrote books on medicine, astronomy and grammar.

ice the solid form of water that occurs as the temperature falls below 0°C | Ice Age one of the several periods when the Earth was sufficiently cold that ice covered most of the surface, the last Ice Age ended about 10,000 years ago | ice bath a container containing ice floating in water that is used to ensure that samples remain at 0°C | ice caps the very cold areas of a planet near to the Poles | ice cold any temperature below 0°C, sufficiently cold that any water would turn to ice | ice crystals the regular shaped objects that appear when water is frozen slowly | ice cube a container of water that has been frozen, usually at about –20°C | ice skating moving on a surface that is almost friction free because the high pressure of the skates causes the ice to melt | ice-salt mixture ice forms at 0°C but adding salt causes the ice to melt and the temperature to drop down to as low as –20°C, which is also 0°F | dry ice pellets of solid carbon dioxide, at –60°C or below, that turn directly from solid to gas without ever forming a liquid (called subliming) | melting ice the slush that forms when ice is left at temperatures above 0°C | permanent ice areas of the Earth's surface that remain below 0°C throughout the year | smooth ice frozen water that has a polished surface | solid ice emphasising that the temperature is so cold that melting will not occur

iceberg a large mass of frozen water floating on the surface of the sea but with 90% of the bulk under the water | iceberg lettuce a variety of lettuce with a compact head

Ichthyosaur / Ichthyosaurus a dinosaur, with many similarities to a fish, that lived 200 million years ago

icing sugar very finely ground sugar

ICT [information communication technology] the use of electronic components, computers, wires and wireless to gather, analyse and distribute data

icy the air temperature is sufficiently low that any dew or water freezes to form a slippery layer of ice

-ide the ending that is used when a non-metal is bonded to a metal eg oxide [O$^=$], chloride [Cl$^-$]

idea a thought that might explain some observation or provide the basis for further experiments | change ideas to start with one thought as to how something happened, but new evidence means that a rethink is required | clarify ideas to make the thoughts clearer and simpler | collate ideas to bring several thoughts together then try to put them into an order of probability and importance and look for patterns | combine ideas to bring the thoughts of several people into one explanation | develop ideas to improve and extend a thought | different ideas alternative suggestions, various explanations, contrasting opinions | earlier ideas the explanations that were put forward some time ago | early ideas the thoughts that were expressed when the observations were first being made and explained | key ideas the few important thoughts that are crucial to the development of an explanation | modern ideas suggestions and theories that have been put forward in the recent past | new ideas ways of explaining the observations that had not been suggested previously | organise ideas (UK) / organize ideas (USA) to take many thoughts and decide which are important and which need further work | refine ideas to look critically at a thought to see how the explanation can be made both more simple and more wide-ranging | related ideas explanations that are similar but often are based on different experiments | review ideas to look again at the ideas especially in the light of new observations | scientific ideas explanations, theories and hypotheses that are based on observation and are able to suggest new experiments and predict further measurements | test ideas to carry out experiments that will show if the ideas are valid

ideal perfect, suitable, could not be better

identical the same in every detail | identical chromosomes the sequence of genes and the DNA is exactly the same in the two cells | identical copy a second object that can not be distinguished from the original | identical offspring the daughter cells or the young of an organism all have identical genes | identical twins two people that have exactly the same genes because the fertilised egg split into two and each half developed as a foetus | **genetically identical** the instructions in the nucleus are the same in all respects | **non-identical** similar but with important differences

identifiable marked or changed so as to be unique, having unique markings

identification classification, defining an individual | **identification booklet** a small book that allows many similar, but distinct, species to be identified | **identification sheet** a display that highlights the characteristics of several organisms

identified detected, recognised, found who or what was responsible

identify to highlight, to point out, to recognise, to distinguish | **identify differences** to compare objects and point out things that are not the same | **identify difficulties** to point out the items that may cause problems | **identify factors** to state the variables | **identify key points** to point out the crucially important variables | **identify key variables** to point out the items that could have an important affect on the results | **identify limitations** / **identify the limitations** to point out boundaries or the area over which the experiment or results are valid | **identify patterns** to discuss the trends and size of the results | **identify similarities** to point out where the objects are almost the same | **identify variables** to find which items are able to change and so should be specified or controlled for a fair test

identifying trying to establish what is important

identity (plural is identities) the unique and specific features that characterise an organism

ie [Latin *id est*] that is

igneous with fire | **igneous intrusion** a sheet of rock formed by injection of magma under pressure between existing layers of rock | **igneous rocks** any material that has been produced from magma or molten rock

ignite to set on fire

ignition starting a fire, starting a car | **ignition circuit** the cables and components that cause the engine plug to produce a spark | **ignition temperature** the temperature at which a substance will start to burn | **ignition tube** a small, glass test tube that can be used for burning chemicals safely

ignore to disregard, to pass over without noticing, to neglect

ileum the lower part of the small intestine

ill (not hill which is a slope) poorly, unwell | **ill-effect** a substance, which was intended to be useful, causes the recipient to feel unwell

illegal against the law, unlawful | **illegal drugs** chemicals that could be used recreationally, but that the Government has banned from possession by the public

illness (plural is illnesses) sickness, disease, the body is not working properly | **incidence of illness** the number of times that a particular disease occurs | **range of illnesses** many different types of disease | **smoking-related illness** damage that is caused to the body that can be traced back to the habit of smoking cigarettes | **specific illness** a named disease

illuminate to light up with a lamp, to shed light, *eg* on a theory

illuminations lots of lights that are used outdoors to produce pictures and the appearance of movement

illusion what you think you are experiencing is different from what is really there, *eg* a mirage | **optical illusion** what you see differs from the object, often the difference is intentional, *eg* in a film

illustrate to draw a diagram that simplifies a feature, to use an example that shows a common application of an idea

illustrating showing, using a diagram or an example

illustration a diagram, an example

illustrative material examples that are given in order to make the idea more clear

im- / in- (*Latin* not) without, lacking

image the picture that you see in a mirror or on a screen | **image formation** lines to show how light from the object behaves so as to form an image | **enlarged image** the picture you see is larger than the original object | **inverted image** the picture you see is upside down | **Landsat images** pictures of parts of the Earth produced using satellites in space | **mirror image** the picture you see is the right way up, but everything that is on the right side of the object appears on the left side of the image | **real image** the image can be projected onto a screen | **reflected image** a picture that is formed because light bounces off a shiny surface | **virtual image** you can see a picture, but you can not project the picture on to a screen

imagination the ability to dream, to capacity to think of solutions to problems

imagine to think, to dream

immature not yet ready for the purpose, unable to reproduce | **immature female** the organism that will produce the eggs is not ready to reproduce | **immature male** the organism that provides the sex cell that moves (sperm or pollen) is not yet producing the gametes

immerse to cover completely

immersion to push completely under the surface | immersion heater an electrical heater that is in the container of liquid – often refers to the electrical heater in a tank full of household water | immersion thermometer a tube for measuring temperature in which the whole tube must be in the fluid for a valid measurement

immiscible two liquids are unable to mix and so form either two layers, *eg* oil and water, or a suspension, *eg* an emulsion paint

immovable / immoveable in fixed position, can not be pushed

immune able to defend itself against a microbe so the bug does not cause an illness | immune memory the body has produced antibodies to a microbe so the instructions for that antibody are now present and available for later use | immune system the several organs and tissues that are responsible for producing the white blood cells and antibodies that try to prevent infection

immunisation (UK) / **immunization** (USA) injection of an organism with the weakened strain of a virus in order to protect the creature from infection | routine immunisation the injections that are given to most children, *eg* the MMR (measles, mumps, rubella) or tetanus vaccines

immunise (UK) / **immunize** (USA) to vaccinate, to inject with a dead or inactivated microbe or with part of a microbe in order to encourage the body to withstand an active infection

immunity able to defend yourself, especially against invasion by microbes | artificial immunity causing the body to produce antibodies by injection with part of a microbe so the person can resist infection by that microbe | improve immunity to increase the ability of the body to defend itself against infection | natural immunity you have had a mild form of a disease so you are better able to resist subsequent infection by that microbe | passive immunity you have been helped by being injected with antibodies to the microbe

immunization (USA) / **immunisation** (UK) injection of an organism with the weakened strain of a virus in order to protect the creature from active infection with that virus | routine immunization the injections that are given to most children *eg* the MMR or tetanus vaccines

immunize (USA) / **immunise** (UK) to vaccinate, to inject with a dead or inactivated microbe or with part of a microbe in order to encourage the body to withstand an active infection

impact the coming together; to hit | impact on the environment the change to the living conditions | impact strength the pressure at a surface when it stops a moving object | environmental impact the change that would be caused to the local conditions if a project were carried out | minimal impact causes almost no change to the surroundings

impair to damage, to reduce in effectiveness

impaired working, but not very well | hearing impaired a person who is less sensitive to sound than would be expected and so has difficulty hearing | visually impaired a person whose eyes are damaged and so is not able to see as well as expected

impairment a change that causes a loss of effectiveness

impartial neutral, not on one side or the other

imperial concerned with the British Empire | imperial system an agreed set of measurements including the feet and inches for length, and pints and gallons for volume

impermeable will not allow material to pass through | impermeable layer a stratum of rock that will not allow fluids to pass through

implant an item that is hidden under a surface; to bury beneath a surface

implantation an item that is buried beneath the skin

implanted hidden within the cells of the lining

implicated the evidence or results point to the involvement of another factor

implication the outcome of a discussion or observation | practical implication an outcome that changes the way that an experiment can be carried out

implies hints, suggests

imply to hint, to suggest

importance the significance, the reason something matters, the meaning

important outstandingly significant | important issues ideas that are worthy of long and detailed discussion | important organs the collections of tissues that are essential for the maintenance of life | economically important contribute much either to the money or to the jobs in that area

impossible can not be achieved, unable to succeed

improve to get better | improve immunity to make the body more capable of rejecting infection

improvements changes or developments that make the item more suited to its purpose

improving getting better

impulse a sudden change that rapidly returns to the original state | nerve impulse / nervous impulse the message that is sent down a nerve cell

impure a mixture of the important chemical with one or more other chemicals

impurity (plural is impurities) a different chemical that should not be present in the pure material

in- / im- (*Latin* not) without, lacking

in addition furthermore | in contact communicating, touching | in focus the image is sharp, not blurred | in parallel running next to each other; in electrical circuits, this means there must be pairs of junctions | in series one after another | *in situ* leaving in position, not moving | *in vitro* carrying out the procedure in a tube or a dish | *in vitro* fertilisation (UK) / *in vitro* fertilization (USA) the nuclei of the egg and the sperm are fused in a petri dish | *in vivo* the investigation is carried out on the whole cell or in the animal

inaccuracies errors, mistakes, deviations from the facts

inaccurate not fitting into the pattern, wrong, not correct

inactive not showing signs of life, but will start to respond when the conditions are appropriate | inactive form the structure of a chemical that has all the atoms of the active form (a chemical that will bring about a change) but will become active only after it has a few minor changes

inadequate not sufficient, not enough | inadequate amount not enough for the purpose | inadequate diet the food that is taken over time either is too low in all quantities or is lacking some of the vitamins, minerals, energy and amino acids | inadequate supply an insufficient amount

inanimate without life, never having possessed life (and so is different from dead), not showing any signs of being alive

inappropriate not acceptable in that context at that period | inappropriate diet the amount or type of food was wrong for that person or animal

inaudible can not be heard, either because the sound is outside the frequency of hearing or the energy is too low to affect nerve endings

incense a substance that is burned to produce a pleasant smell

inch (plural is inches) the imperial unit of length, one inch is approximately 2.54 centimetres, there are 12 inches in a foot

incidence the direction of a ray, a measure of how often an event will occur | incidence of disease / incidence of illness where, how often and when did a disease occur | angle of incidence the angle between the ray meeting the surface and the normal to that surface

incident an event, an occurrence | incident beam the light that is shining on to the surface | incident ray a thin beam of light, or a drawing to represent a thin beam that is approaching a surface

incisors / incisor teeth the teeth at the front of the mouth that are used for cutting

incline a hill, a slope; to lean

include to make part of a group or set

incomplete not finished, more information is needed | incomplete circuit there is a gap in the wires joining the components so no current will flow | incomplete combustion the amount of oxygen is not sufficient to allow the fuel to burn completely so smoke and carbon monoxide also form | incomplete knowledge not knowing enough, not seeing the complete picture

incompressible applying pressure does not cause any decrease in volume

incorporate to include an idea or observation into another idea or set of observations

incorrect unsuitable, false, untrue

incorrectly wrongly, inaccurately

increase to get bigger, to go up

increasing becoming bigger, getting larger, more | increasing quantity more material is either available or is needed | increasing speed accelerating, getting faster | increasing temperature heat energy is being added so the material is hotter

incubate to allow a microbe to grow at the optimum temperature, to develop

incubation allowing an organism to develop | incubation period the time taken for the organism to grow sufficiently to become self-supporting

incubator a box that allows the inside volume to be kept at constant temperature, used for looking after sick or premature babies or for growing microbes

indefinite uncertain, unclear, not known precisely

indefinitely without end, for an unspecified period

independence not reliant on the power or resources of others

independent separate, not dependent on others | independent research working by yourself | independent variable the factor whose value you can decide before the experiment

index a list of topics with the page numbers | index finger the finger next to the thumb, also known as Peter Pointer

indicate to show, to suggest, to demonstrate, to point out

indication a sign, a pointer | appropriate indications correct or suitable pointers and information

indicative showing, directing, suggestive

indicator a chemical that changes colour in specific conditions, commonly the colour will change at a known pH | indicator lamp a bulb that shows when the equipment is switched on |

indicator organism a form of life that reflects the environment in that small area, especially useful for showing pollution | indicator solution a liquid that changes colour in response to a specific stimulus, eg universal indicator solution is red in acid but blue in alkali | bicarbonate indicator / carbonate indicator / hydrogen carbonate indicator a liquid that changes colour depending on the concentration of carbon dioxide | pH indicator a chemical that changes colour at a particular pH value | pollution indicator either an organism that is able to live in polluted conditions, the presence of, or the absence of an organism that requires a clean environment | universal indicator a mixture of chemicals that give different colours at each pH

indigestible can not be broken down into simpler materials by the enzymes that are available

indigestion feeling ill in the stomach region | indigestion remedies chemicals that claim to relieve the stomach ache | indigestion tablets small solid blocks containing chemicals that remove the discomfort of stomach ache

indigo one of the colours of the rainbow or spectrum, indigo is between blue and violet

indirect going through two or three steps instead of directly by a single step | indirect methods measuring one variable by looking at the change in other variables, eg finding resistance by measuring current and potential difference

individual one person, a single or particular organism | individual animal one animal by itself | individual plant one specific plant in isolation | different individuals two or more organisms are selected and studied in detail | healthy individual the person has low blood pressure and heart rate and soon recovers from exercise | unique individual one person, emphasising the specific characteristics of that one organism

induce to cause, to bring about | induced current the flow of electrons (current) caused by moving a wire between the opposite poles of a magnet

induction production of a current in a wire by moving the wire between the poles of a magnet and at a constant distance from each pole

industrial large-scale production | industrial context the effect of moving the reaction or process onto a much larger scale | industrial device equipment that is large and/or expensive | industrial plant machinery that can be used to carry out a large-scale process | industrial pollution chemicals and heat that are wasted into the atmosphere on a large scale, causing a change to the environment | Industrial Revolution a period when many manual tasks start to be taken over by machines, the Industrial Revolution in Europe started approximately 1775 with the mechanisation of the cotton and woollen industries | industrial waste material that is produced, which can not be sold, but is likely to cause pollution of the environment

industry (plural is industries) the commercial producer | electricity supply industry the total grouping of fuel suppliers, electricity generating companies, distribution networks and local contractors | heavy industry the production of raw materials such as iron, steel, oil or plastics | light industry the production of finished goods, eg cars, washing machines | pharmaceutical industry the people involved in the research, development, testing, manufacturing and selling of chemicals that can affect the body or treat disease | textile industry the factories and people that are employed either to make cloth from wool or cotton, or to make clothes from the material

inedible can not be eaten

inefficient loses lots of energy, inept

inert will not react, noble | inert gases group 0, the six different atoms that will not react with any other material and are very difficult to liquefy | inert metals the expensive metals, such as gold or platinum, that are not very reactive | inert state unchanging at present, but is capable of becoming active

inertia the force needed to change the speed at which an object is spinning

inevitable must occur, can not be avoided

infancy a child from birth to about eight years old

infect to cause, or allow, a microbe to enter another organism

infected a microbe has invaded an organism and is reproducing, although there may be no symptoms

infection a microbe has got into your body, is multiplying and could be making you feel ill | ear infection growth of microbes inside the middle ear | intestinal infection a microbe has got into your intestine and is making you feel ill | microbial infection emphasising that the organism that is in the body and making you feel ill is a microbe | middle-ear infection a microbe has infected the space occupied by the ossicles and is starting to reproduce | water-borne infection any microbe that spreads between organisms through the water

infectious capable of giving the microbe to other people | infectious agent a small organism that is able to live inside another organism, usually causing some feeling of ill-health | infectious disease an illness, caused by a microbe, that can be passed between people simply by breathing

infective able to pass the microbe, that causes an illness, to another person

infer to interpret one observation as being caused by another event

inference a conclusion that is not supported by direct evidence | draw inferences / make inferences provide explanations for some observations

infertile unable to have offspring | infertile couple two people who are unable to conceive a child by intercourse

infertility lacking the ability to have offspring

infinite without end, extending forever

inflammable (also called flammable) able to catch fire

inflate to increase in size, to blow up

inflexible firm, not able to be bent, taking a fixed position

influence the affect; to change | environmental influences the effect of temperature, amount of light, nutrients or moisture and air movement of the surroundings on an organism

influenza / 'flu' feeling ill because of an infection by an influenza virus

in focus the image is sharp, not blurred

information relevant knowledge, data collected by experiment | information card a small sheet that contains specific information, often concerning safety | information leaflet a sheet of paper that describes the properties of a particular product | information sheet the paper that gives you guidance as to how an activity should be carried out | information source the place or item from where you able to obtain information | information storage the method used to keep a permanent record of your measurements | additional information further data that are collected in order to check the accuracy, or extend the range, of the original information | appropriate information the observations or measurements that are needed to support or demolish an idea | binary information data that are produced as a string of 0s or of 1s | collect information to gather data from any source | comparative information similar data has been obtained by a different method or from other sources | compare information to check your observations against other data and observations taken at other times or by other people | dietary information advice as to the type and amount of foods that would best suit your lifestyle | digital information data, knowledge that is transmitted as a string of digits (binary is 0s and 1s, hexadecimal is from 0 to 16) |

extract information to draw out the important pieces of data or observations | factual information measurements of data, rather than an opinion of an event | genetic information the data in the chromosome that controls the cell | inherited information the genes that you must have obtained from your parents | interpret information to give meaning to some observations | locate information to find the measurements or observations | nutritional information the quantity of different nutrients (fats, sugars, minerals, vitamins) that are present in a food | organise information (UK) / organize information (USA) to put the data into order, to arrange observations into a sequence | relevant information the data that may be important to the question you are trying to answer | reliable information data that you can be sure are accurate and will be obtained every time | scientific information data that were obtained by a fair test and help to explain the world around you | select information to decide which observations and conclusions are important and should be used | source of information the place or item that can provide datum that is relevant to your problem and is reliable | synthesise information (UK) / synthesize information (USA) to produce data without an experiment, to take the results of several experiments into one explanation | transmit information to send measurements and data to other places | useful information data and observations that may help you solve a particular problem | visual information observations that can be seen

informed told details, made aware of other situations | informed consent giving permission after all the advantages and drawbacks have been explained

infra-red / ir the part of the spectrum that has a longer wavelength than red so is not visible to the human eye | infra-red camera is used to take pictures using the heat that is being given off by an object | infra-red radiation / infra-red wave heat that is given off from a surface

infrequent not very often, not regular | infrequent ovulation the egg is released occasionally, an ovum is produced at intervals much longer than is usual (28 days is usual in humans)

ingest to take into the digestive system or into a cell

ingestion the act of taking food into the gut or a cell

ingot a bar of metal

ingredient component, constituent, a part of the whole

inhabit to live in an environment

inhabitable suitable living conditions

inhalation an intake of breath

inhale to take air into the lungs

inhaled taken a gas into the lungs | inhaled air the air that is taken into the lungs, usually 20% oxygen, 80% nitrogen plus traces of water and 0.04% carbon dioxide

inhaler equipment used for introducing a drug directly into the lungs, a person who breathes a substance into the lungs

inhaling taking air into the lungs

inherit to gain possessions from a parent, to have features caused by genes

inheritance goods and substances provided by the parents

inherited from the parents | inherited causes the reasons for the change are to be found in the genes | inherited characteristics any feature, such as eye colour or hair colour, that is caused by the instructions in the nucleus of your cell and so must have been provided by one of your parents | inherited deafness lack of hearing caused by information missing from a gene | inherited differences each individual has different genes given by their parents | inherited factor any gene received from a parent that allows an organism to react to the environment | inherited information the genes in your cell, that control all your actions, were provided by your parents | inherited variation differences between related organisms caused because there is a random chance as to which parent will provide which gene

inhibit to hinder a process, eg to slow a chemical reaction, to reduce the activity of a microbe

inhibition the slowing down of a process, not permitting something to take place

initial original, starting | initial acceleration the rate of change of velocity near the start of the experiment | initial size measurements at the start of the experiment

initially at the start, originally

inject to push in a liquid under pressure

injection a procedure, using syringe and needle, for introducing liquid into muscle or skin | booster injection a further dose of a disabled microbe so as to increase resistance to the live microbe and therefore prevent the disease

injury (plural is injuries) damage | sports injury / sports-related injury damage to a tissue or organ caused by taking part in a physical activity

ink coloured liquid that can be used to write on paper | blue ink a solution of blue dye in water that can be used for writing

inlet a river mouth, a small bay, a pipe that fills a container | water inlet the position at which water enters the equipment

inner on the inside, within | inner core a solid sphere of nickel and iron, approximately 2500 kilometres diameter, at the centre of the Earth | inner ear the part of the ear that is inside the skull and contains the cochlea and the semi-circular canals | inner planets the four planets nearest to the Sun, all of which are made from rock (Mercury, Venus, Earth and Mars)

inoculate to inject a small amount of a microbe, often used to prevent more dangerous infection by that microbe

inoculation an injection of a small amount of microbe | inoculation loop a small circle at the end of a wire that is used to transfer microbes

in parallel running next to each other; in electrical circuits, this means there must be a pair of junctions

input the variable that can cause a change | input data the information put into a computer; to put information into a computer | input variable the value that you can change or decide upon | analog input (USA) / analogue input (UK) the signal that enters the equipment is able to vary continuously | digital input the data arrives as a stream of numbers, often 0s and 1s only

inquire / enquire to ask questions, to seek information

insect an invertebrate animal with six legs and an outside skeleton (exoskeleton), the largest and most diverse class of multicellular organisms, with at least a million different species | insect bite a tiny wound produced by an insect attacking the skin | insect pest an insect that damages a valuable material such as crops | insect-pollinated plant a plant that reproduces by enticing insects to carry the pollen from one flower to another | insect-pollination method for moving the plant sex cell using insects

insecticide a chemical that will kill insects, but should not affect other organisms

insemination placing sperm into the vagina | artificial insemination (AI) to collect sperm from the male, store, and then use tubes to place the sperm into a female

in series one after another

insert an item that is placed inside another; to push one object into another

inside within

in situ remaining in place

insoluble unable to dissolve in that liquid | insoluble chemical / insoluble material any substance that will not dissolve in that particular liquid | insoluble molecules material that will not dissolve in that solvent | insoluble solids material that will not dissolve and can be removed by filtration

inspiration the act of taking air into the lungs; to have a sudden idea that explains a lot of observations

inspire to take a breath into the lungs, to cause somebody to do an exceptional act

installation the act of fixing in place

instantaneous in a fraction of a second | instantaneous speed travels a long distance in almost no time

instantaneously immediately, with no measurable interval

instantly immediately, without delay

instruct to tell, to teach, to guide

instruction an order telling you what to do | instruction set /set of instructions several directions that together, will allow a complicated procedure to be carried out in simple steps

instrument musical equipment that is used for producing music, a tool that is used for careful work | brass instrument a musical instrument made from brass, *eg* trumpet, trombone | measuring instrument equipment that is used for finding the size, speed or weight | musical instrument equipment that can be used to produce sounds for enjoyment | string instrument a musical instrument that produces sound from a vibrating string, *eg* guitar, violin, piano | surgical instruments equipment that is used for cutting into the body of living people | wind instrument musical equipment that produces a sound by blowing, *eg* flute, recorder

insufficient not enough | insufficient data there is not enough information or measurements to allow a conclusion to be drawn

insulate to cover with material that will prevent movement of energy, to reduce heat loss | insulated wire a piece of metal covered with plastic

insulating preventing the movement of heat or electricity | insulating foam a layer of solid sponge that is used to prevent heat movement | insulating jacket a closely fitting coat that is layered over a hot-water cylinder in order to retain the heat | insulating material any fabric, *eg* cotton wool, fibre glass, that prevents the movement of heat

insulation / insulation material any substance that prevents the movement of heat or the flow of electricity | insulation technique the method that is being used to prevent the loss of heat or the flow of electricity | cavity-wall insulation foam or fibre that is injected into the space

between two walls in order to prevent loss of heat | electrical insulation a non-metal that will prevent the movement of charge and so will not allow electrons to flow | forms of insulation different methods that can be used to prevent movement of heat | loft insulation / roof insulation layers of material that are put into the roof space in order to prevent heat loss | sound insulation absorbent material that prevents the transmission or reflection of sound | thermal insulation material, usually a non-metal containing trapped air, that prevents heat from moving | wall insulation material that is attached to, or inside, the wall of a building to prevent loss of heat

insulator material that prevents the loss of heat or the flow of electricity | electrical insulator material that will not allow a current to flow | good insulator material that prevents the movement of heat or electricity | poor insulators substances that could be used to slow down the flow of heat or electricity, but are not a good choice | thermal insulator material that prevents the movement of heat

insulin a hormone, secreted by the pancreas, that regulates the level of glucose in the blood

intact whole, unbroken

intake the input, the area where material may be entered | energy intake how much chemical energy is in the diet that a person eats

integrate to bring together individual parts so as to make a whole that is greater than the sum of the parts

integrated joined together to make a whole, especially the joining of many different items into one package | integrated circuit all the components that are needed for that circuit are on one piece of material, usually silicone

intense with lots of energy, bright, loud, concentrated

intensity the amplitude or energy of a wave | light intensity the amplitude, or brightness, of visible light | sound intensity the loudness of sound, the amplitude of the wave

intensive thorough, with lots of energy, concentrated, focused | intensive farming growing a large mass of crop in a small area, often by adding lots of fertiliser

intensively with lots of energy, focussed | intensively managed extra resources have been used so as to increase the yield, *eg* of a crop, in a specified period or area

intentional deliberate, knowing the consequences

inter- (*Latin* between)

interact to affect other people at the same time as they are affecting you

interaction how one item or variable can cause a change in a second item | complex interactions the web of cause-and-effect that is produced when each member not only affects every other member, but is also affected by changes in other members

intercept to cross paths, to be in the same place at the same time

interconnect to join together

intercostal muscles the muscles that are found between the ribs

intercourse the act of transferring sperm from the male to the female

interdependence explaining how the value of one variable depends on another factor

interdependent two, or more, variables where changing one variable has an affect on the other factors

interesting causing thought, worthy of further investigation

interface the area between two materials or ideas

interfere to become inappropriately involved, to cause a change in direction

interference intervention from an unwanted source, causing loss of focus | human interference the presence of people has caused the change to the habitat

interfering causing a loss of signal, contaminating

interlocking a mixture in which projections from one type of particle fit into the holes of other particles so the whole mass is solid | interlocking textures rocks with grains of different sizes that lock together

intermediate a half-way stage, material or people that are between the extremes

intermingle to mix together

intermittent at odd intervals, random, erratic, now and then

internal inside | internal combustion engine the fuel is burned inside the machine, *eg* a car engine | internal development the embryo grows inside the womb of the mother | internal environment the conditions of temperature, moisture, nutrients and chemicals that are found inside the object | internal fertilisation (UK) /internal fertilization (USA) the male and female sex cells (sperm and ovum) meet inside the body of the female | internal organs the structures, each with a special function, that are hidden inside the body | internal reflection the light bounces off an inside surface | internal structure an item that has definite shape and position inside a body, organ or cell

internally inside, within

internet a worldwide source of information that is accessible by computer

interplay the action and reaction of several bodies or events

interpret to give the meaning | interpret data to state what the results mean and to what accuracy they support your predictions | interpret evidence to give meaning to your observations and data compared to a previous idea | interpret a graph / interpret graphs to look at the accuracy and trends in a graph | interpret information to say what the observations mean | interpret observations to give meaning to something that has caused a change

interpretation the meaning, an explanation | interpretation of evidence explaining how the observations, data and measurements can be used to support an idea

interrupt to stop for a while, to suspend for a time

intersect to draw a line across another line

interval a period between two events | time interval the period between taking measurements

interview a meeting; to discuss, to ask questions

intestinal concerned with the parts of the gut below the stomach | intestinal infection a type of microbe is growing in the gut, which causes an illness rather than the help that most microbes provide

intestines the long tube from the stomach to the outside world, along which passes the squished-up, half-digested food that is to be fully broken down and then digested | intestine wall the layers of cells and blood vessels that are between the muscles and the inside lumen of the intestine | large intestine the final part of the intestines, a short, wide tube in which water is absorbed | small intestine a thin tube, about 5 metres long, in which food is broken down by enzymes, and the nutrients absorbed

intra- (*Latin* within)

intravenous inside the vein | intravenous feeding continuous dripping of a solution containing nutrients into a vein

introduce to add, to emphasise the importance, to make known | re-introduce to replace, to put an object or organism back into an area from which it had disappeared

introduction making known, a formal giving of names, the start, the insertion

intrusion invasion | igneous intrusion a sheet of rock formed by injection of magma under pressure between existing layers of rock | minor intrusion a small amount of magma has penetrated the solid rock, then cooled slowly

intrusive rocks rocks that were formed by the magma breaking into a solid rock and then cooling inside the rock

intuitive instinctive understanding, ability to see an idea without the need for a long explanation or proof

Inuit the Eskimo people of Canada

invade to enter an area, usually in large numbers, causing damage

invader a foreign species that is in an area where it can grow and will probably cause damage, *eg* a microbe or a parasite

invasion occupying an area that does not belong to that organism

invent to produce a design or idea that has never been seen before

invention a new machine, or a new use of an existing device

inventor a person who thinks up a new piece of equipment or a new use for existing equipment

inverse the opposite | inverse proportions relates two variables – as one item increases then the other factor goes down

inversion turning upside down | lateral inversion left and right seem to have swapped position – the image in a mirror is laterally inverted

invert to turn upside down

invertebrate animal / invertebrates an animal without a backbone, *eg* a worm

inverted turned upside down | inverted image what happens to the picture in a camera or on the retina of your eye where the image is upside down | laterally inverted everything that was on the left side of the object appears on the right side of the image and anything that was on the right side of the object is on the left of the image

investigate to find out what has happened and why by carrying out experiments and collecting data

investigation an examination, a research task, an enquiry, asking lots of questions | biological investigation any experiments involving living creatures | class investigation several groups in a school class either carry out different parts of the investigation or all carry out the same experiment so as to check for errors | controlled investigation an experiment in which there are adequate control experiments with which to compare the effect of changing one variable | forensic investigation looking at tiny details using scientific methods in order to develop a picture of a past event | laboratory investigation experiments that can be carried out in a specially equipped room | method of investigation the technique or process that is used to solve that problem | national investigation research that involves collecting information from the whole country | scientific investigation using existing knowledge to make predictions then carrying out controlled experiments, observing carefully and comparing the results with the prediction | systematic investigation being thoughtful and using several experiments, observing the effects of changing one aspect at a time, to reach an understanding of a process | yeast investigation experiments to see how changes in environmental conditions changes the rate of growth of yeast

investigative questioning, research | investigative group the set of people who use a variety of skills and techniques in order to find the answer to specific questions | investigative methods the techniques that are used in researching a topic | investigative skills the ability to ask a simple question that can be answered and provide new information | investigative workers researchers, investigators

investigator a person who is trying to answer a problem by observation and by asking lots of questions

invisible can not be seen, well hidden

in vitro experiments involving living tissue grown in culture, tested using chemical equipment, using glassware | *in vitro* fertilisation (UK) / *in vitro* fertilization (USA) the nuclei of the egg and the sperm are fused in a petri dish

in vivo any process that occurs within the living organism

involuntary without thought | involuntary action a change in the action of muscles that you are not able to control consciously, *eg* movement of the heart or gut

involved complex, fascinated, concerned, taking part

involving concerning, comprising, including

inwards towards the inside | inward force pushing towards the inside, trying to compress

iodide / iodide ion [I^-] the charged particle that is produced when iodine reacts with a metal | potassium iodide [KI] a solid that looks like common salt, but helps dissolve iodine into water

iodine (I, proton number 53) a halogen; [I_2] a solid, melting point 114°C, boiling point 184°C, that looks like small silver crystals, but turns directly to a beautiful purple gas when heated | iodine solution iodine is dissolved in potassium iodide solution to give a yellow coloured antiseptic solution that will turn black with starch | iodine test add yellow iodine solution to starch and the material turns black or to a very dark blue

ion (not iron which is element number 26) a particle with an electric charge | ion equations show the changes that occur at each electrode in electrolysis by the movement of electrons so that atoms form ions or ions become atoms | acetate ion [CH_3COO^-] ethanoate ion | ammonium ion [NH_4^+] the charged particle produced when ammonia [NH_3] forms salts | bicarbonate ion [HCO_3^-] hydrogen carbonate, an ion that is always found attached to metals, produces carbon dioxide when heated or acid is added | hydrogen ion [H^+] the charged particle produced by a hydrogen atom losing an electron | iodide ion [I^-] the charged particle that is produced when iodine reacts with a metal | nitrate ion [NO_3^-] the charged particle produced from nitric acid | oxide ion [$O^=$] the charged particle produced by oxygen gaining electrons | silicate ion [$SiO_3^=$] a group of silicon and oxygen atoms that do not exist alone, but are found combined with metals | sulfate ion (USA) / sulphate ion (UK) [$SO_4^=$] the charged particle produced from sulphuric acid

ionic to do with atoms that have achieved a charge by losing or gaining electrons | ionic bond joining of atoms in which some atoms gain electrons, other atoms lose electrons and the particles that have opposite charge are attracted to each other | ionic compound a chemical in which the atoms are held together by ionic bonds | ionic equation the chemical equation that shows the reaction involving specified ions, the equation must be balanced for atom and for charge | ionic lattice a regular structure, often giant, that is made from alternating two types of particle – one with a positive charge and the other with a negative charge | ionic structure the solid comprises ions joined together by attraction between opposite charges and so has a regular shape and a high melting point

ionisation (UK) / **ionization** (USA) removal or addition of electrons to an atom so as to give a charged particle

ionising (UK) / **ionizing** (USA) turning from a neutral particle (atom or molecule) to a charged particle | ionising radiation rays, caused by the breakdown of the nucleus of an atom, that may cause a molecule to lose or gain electron, *ie* to form ions

ionosphere the part of the atmosphere between a height of 50 kilometres and 1000 kilometres, where most particles are ions

ions atoms that have a charge because they have gained or lost electrons

ipilipil a very fast growing tree that could provide renewable biomass energy

IR / ir [infra-red] heat radiation

iris the coloured ring in the eye that changes shape so as to ensure that the optimal amount of light gets through the hole called the pupil

iron (Fe, proton number 26, melting point 1530°C) (not ion which is a charged particle) a metal that is one of three that are magnetic (the others are cobalt and nickel), extracted in large quantities using blast furnaces and used extensively as the structure for buildings, railways and road transport | Iron Age the last of the Ages of prehistory (the others are Stone Age and Bronze Age) which started in the Middle East over 3000 years ago | iron armature the piece of metal that is attracted to a magnet | iron core the middle part of an electromagnet that is made from iron | iron filings pieces of iron that are so small that they appear like dust | iron nail a nail made from iron | iron nitrate [$Fe(NO_3)_2$] a soluble salt of iron | iron oxide [Fe_2O_3] also called rust – a reddish powder produced when iron reacts with damp oxygen | iron rich rocks that contain a lot of iron – usually as iron oxide | ironstone a sedimentary rock that contains iron compounds and has lots of what look like tiny eggs | iron strip a ribbon made from iron [Fe] | iron sulfate (USA) / iron sulphate (UK) [$FeSO_4$] forms green crystals | iron sulfide (USA) / iron sulphide (UK) [FeS] called fools' gold because it looks like small chips of gold - just add hydrochloric acid and you will smell the difference | cast iron the type of iron that flows from a blast furnace, the iron contains 4% carbon and is brittle | molten iron iron at a temperature above 1700°C is liquid | native iron the iron is found in rocks as the metal rather than as rust | scrap iron objects made from iron that were useful, but now need melting back into liquid iron before using in a new form | soft iron iron which is easily magnetised in a coil but very rapidly loses its magnetism when removed from the current | wrought iron an early form of steel, iron mixed with a small amount of carbon that is less brittle than cast iron

irradiate to expose an object to light or radioactive radiation

irradiation exposure of an object to radioactive rays either on purpose, to sterilise the item, or by accident, leading to cell damage

irregular random, with no visible pattern

irreversible one way only, can not change direction | irreversible change creating a permanent difference, a chemical reaction in which products are formed that will never re-form the reactants, *eg* when egg white is boiled and turns solid

irrigate to direct water through tubes and channels so that crops always have an adequate supply

irrigation providing water to farm land for growing crops | irrigation channel / irrigation ditch a small canal for directing water to specific areas | **irrigation water** the water that is transported to be distributed over farm land

irritable moody, easily upset, responds disproportionally to a small stimulus, easily made painful

irritant a chemical that causes discomfort or damage to the skin

irritate to annoy, to make worse

irritation soreness, stress, anger

iso- (*Greek* equal) the same

isobar a line on a map joining points of equal pressure

isolated by itself, alone

isotherm lines joining points of equal temperature

isotonic the osmotic pressure (ion concentration) is the same in two liquids

isotopes forms of an atom that have the same proton number, and so have identical chemical properties, but differ in number of neutrons and so have different mass numbers | **radio-active isotope** an atom that is one of a family of elements with identical proton numbers but different mass numbers, and whose nucleus will change so as to produce alpha-, beta- or gamma-radiation

issue the idea that is to be discussed, offspring; to pour, to give out | **cultural issues** problems that arise from the ideas, values and faiths of people with different backgrounds | **current issue** a question that is likely to be discussed in newspapers and on television | **environmental issue** a problem caused by people needing to live com-fortably and so using lots of resources and producing much pollution that could change a habitat and damage the environment | **ethical issues** problems that have no easy answer and can not be tested experimentally, *eg* should Jenner have injected the young boy with small-pox? | **important issues / main issues** ideas that are worthy of long and detailed discussion | **moral issue** a question involving a judgement that depends on values and prior experience | **public-health issue** a discussion concerning the occurrence, the spread and the prevention of disease | **scientific issue** questions that can be answered by using observation and experiment | **social issues** problems that are caused by, or affect, the society around you | **specific issue** the particular problem, the precise question

it (not hit which is a blow) a word that is used to replace a noun, a word that directs your attention to a specific point

itchy irritating, sore, needs to be scratched or soothed

item an object, an article | **household item** any material that is easily obtainable and is often found in the house

IVF [*in vitro* fertilisation] artificial external fertilisation in which the ovum and the sperm are mixed together in a dish, the fertilised egg is then placed in the wall of the uterus for the necessary 9 months gestation

ivy a plant that grows vertically by clinging to other plants or walls

J / joule the unit of energy or work done – 1 joule of work is done when a force of 1 newton pushes for a distance of 1 metre

jab an injection into the body, a vaccination | BCG jab an injection that will cause the body to produce antibodies to tuberculosis (BCG is the abbreviation for *Bacillus Calmette-Guérin*)

jack a mechanism for increasing force | car jack a tool that is used to raise a car from the ground | hydraulic jack a machine that uses pressure in a liquid in order to change the size and direction of a force

jacket a coat, a cover | insulating jacket a closely fitting coat that is layered over a hot-water cylinder in order to retain the heat | life-jacket a buoyancy aid, a set of floats worn around the body so as to prevent drowning | water jacket a flow of water around a pipe or tank in order to keep the contents of the pipe at constant temperature

jagged having sharp peaks, uneven

jamming making a preserve of fruit by heating with sugar, preventing a signal from being received

Janssen (Hans and his son Zaccharias 1580–1638) Dutch spectacle makers who claimed to have invented the compound microscope in 1595.

jar a cylinder, a round container | bell jar a container, usually made from glass, that is in the shape of a bell with straight, parallel sides | gas jar a glass cylinder, the top edge is flattened then ground so that the jar is gas-tight when a flat plate is placed over the top

jaundice an illness that causes the skin to appear yellow because the liver is not working properly

jaw the front, lower part of the face | lock jaw (tetanus) a disease caused by infection with a *Clostridium* bacterium from the soil, the bacterium produces a toxin that causes every muscle in the body to go into painful contraction

jawbone the bone that moves up and down in the joint at the bottom of the skull | lower jawbone mandible, the part of the jaw that moves while chewing

jelly (plural is jellies) a gel, a substance that will keeps its shape, but is easily penetrated, a type of food made using gelatine and flavourings, the liquid in the eye ball | jellyfish a sea creature that has the shape of a bell without any solid skeleton, but does have many tentacles that sting | jelly layer a thin, protective layer on the outside of the membrane of an ovum | agar jelly the extract of *Agar agar* (a seaweed) suspended in water | petroleum jelly a grease-like substance that is used as a lubricant or as a base for some ointments

Jenner (Edward 1749–1823) started to study medicine, as an apprentice, at age 13 and, ten years later, started his own country practice where he carried out major research on cuckoos and bird migration. Dairy maids have always had a reputation for having fair skin – despite the fact that everyone else would be disfigured by small pox. In 1796, Jenner took the brave, or foolish, step of injecting a young boy with cowpox (*Vaccinia*) using a thorn and then six weeks later deliberately giving the young boy smallpox – and the boy did not develop the disease. Vaccination became compulsory in 1853 and by 1980 small pox was officially declared extinct in the world.

jerk a sudden movement; to move sharply

jet a deep black form of coal, a stream of fast-moving fluid that has been pushed out of an opening | water-jet a continuous stream of water leaving a hole at high speed, a boat that is pushed by a stream of high-speed water

jewellery (UK) / **jewelry** (USA) objects that are worn, which look beautiful and are of value, especially to the person who is wearing them | gold jewellery (UK) / gold jewelry (USA) ornaments that are made from gold

jiggle to move randomly from side to side

jiggling moving in short paths with sudden changes of direction

job a task, the work | special job a task that can only be carried out by an operator with unusual talents | specific job the stated type of work

jog to run at a pace that can be kept up for many minutes, to jerk, to knock

jogging running at a slow pace in order to keep the body fit

join to bring together, often with the idea of the parts sticking together

joined having been brought together

joining bringing together

joint the section where there is a meeting of two objects, each with fixed shape, so as to allow the two objects to move relative to each other | joint of meat a lump of flesh for eating that is sufficient for several portions | ball-and-socket joint the end of one bone has a ball, the end of its partner has a cave or socket into which the ball can go – this allows a rotating joint | damaged joint an accident has caused one, or more, components in a joint to be damaged so the joint no longer allows free movement of the bones | elbow joint the area where the bone of the upper arm (humerus) meets the two bones of the lower arm (radius and ulna) | expansion joint a gap between two railway lines or two sections of a bridge that will allow the solid parts to expand with an increase of temperature without damage to the structure | fixed joint a junction between bones that can not move, *eg* in the skull | hinge joint a junction, such as the elbow or knee, where the two parts can move in one plane only – like the hinge at the edge of a door | hip joint the movable section formed by the ball of the femur sitting in the socket of the pelvis | knee joint the joint between the bone of the upper leg (femur) and the bones of the lower leg (tibia and fibula) that also involves the knee cap (patella) | meat joint a lump of flesh for eating that is sufficient for several portions | partly-movable joint / partly-moveable joint the bones have a limited amount of movement, *eg* the spine | pivot joint a junction of two bones that allows movement in one plane only, *eg* the knee joint | replacement joint cutting off the ends of the bone and replacing them with plastic or metal parts that work better than the parts they are replacing | shoulder joint a ball-and-socket joint between the upper arm and the body | weak joint a joint that is easily damaged | wrist joint the set of tendons, ligaments and small bones that allows the hand to move relative to the lower arm

jointed able to bend or rotate at a specific point | jointed leg a limb used for walking that has a hinge joint near the middle

Joule (James Prescott 1818–1889) was too delicate to go to school and so was tutored at his home in Manchester by Dalton. Joule was fascinated by heat and developed accurate methods for measuring temperature and deduced a connection between current and heat produced. He showed that different forms of energy are related and, in 1848, gave an estimate for the speed of particles in a gas.

joule / J the unit of energy or work done – 1 joule of work is done when a force of 1 newton pushes for 1 metre

joulemeter an instrument for measuring the amount of electrical energy that has been used

journey the movement involved in going from one place to another spot; to move from one place to a distant part

judge to decide on the basis of evidence presented, to weigh up each side of an argument

judgement the decision that is reached after considering all the evidence

juice the liquid that has been squeezed from something, *eg* fruit | digestive juice the liquid found in the stomach (containing enzymes and hydrochloric acid) that breaks down food | fruit juices liquids obtained by squeezing fruit | gastric juice the liquid, produced by the lining of the stomach, that contains enzymes and hydrochloric acid | lemon juice the liquid produced by squeezing a lemon | orange juice the liquid produced by squeezing an orange | pancreatic juice the liquid that is produced by the pancreas and contains enzymes | pure orange juice a liquid that should contain nothing but the juice produced by squeezing oranges

jumble to mix up, to put in random order | jumble sale a sales event where people give what they consider to be useless items but which other people are prepared to buy

jump to push yourself suddenly away from a surface, to leap

junction where two or more tubes, paths or wires join together

Jupiter the largest planet in the Solar System, the father of the gods in Roman mythology

justify to give reasons with evidence

juvenile young, sexually immature

K potassium (*Swedish* kalium), proton number 19, an alkali metal

K / kelvin a unit temperature using the kelvin scale

k... / kilo... (*Greek* a thousand) prefix for a thousandth of a unit

kaleidoscope three rectangular mirrors of equal size meet to form a tube, producing an image that is a repeating pattern

KE [kinetic energy] the energy that a body has because of its mass and the speed with which it is moving

kinetic energy = mass × speed × speed / 2
(joules)   (kilogram)   (metres / sec)^2

keep to retain, to continue

keeper a piece of steel that is placed across the opposite poles of a magnet, a caretaker of a zoo | timekeeper a person who measures and records the time taken for an event | zoo keeper a person who cares for and feeds the animals in a zoological park

keeping holding, storing, unchanging, preserving | keeping warm preventing loss of heat, using exercise to produce heat

kelp a very large sea weed that grows rapidly

Kelvin (Baron Kelvin of Largs / William Thomson 1824–1907) was one member of an intellectual family – his father had started as a farm labourer and ended as professor of mathematics, and his brothers were each distinguished in science. He started studying at Glasgow, left to travel, and then returned as professor of physics – a post he held for 53 years. Thomson showed that heat and electricity flowed in similar ways and showed that electricity should be transmitted at high voltage, his house was amongst the first to be lit by electricity (1881). He made a fortune by directing the laying of the first successful transatlantic cable (1866) and he took up sailing with enthusiasm – which meant he had to develop new navigational instruments. His work on the expansion of gases led to methods for producing very cold liquid gases and the idea of an absolute temperature scale that is measured in kelvin, this work allowed Ramsay to discover and isolate three noble gases

kelvin scale a scale for measuring temperature which moves the Celsius scale by 273, so absolute zero is 0 K, the freezing point of water is 273 K and water boils at 373 K

Kepler (Johannes 1571–1630) had smallpox at age 3 which damaged his hands and his eyesight. He studied under Copernicus and, after a spell at Graz in Austria, he joined Brahe in Prague. Brahe died two years later, leaving 20 years of observations to be analysed by Kepler. These results showed that planets must move in elliptical or oval orbits.

kerosene / kerosine paraffin, a mixture of hydrocarbons with 11 or 12 carbon atoms, the fuel that has been used both in heating homes and as a fuel for jet planes

kettle a container for heating water and allowing safe pouring of the hot water | electric kettle a container that has an electric heater on the inside that can be used to heat water to boiling point

key important, a method for identifying items, a item for opening locks | key characteristics features or behaviours that are important or will define that organism | key differences significant differences | key fact cards pieces of paper that contain the major ideas concerning a subject or object | key factors variables that should either be measured or kept constant | key features important properties | key ideas the thoughts and theories that are considered an essential part of science | key phrase the important few words | key points the few ideas that must be known | key principles ideas or laws that must be followed and should never be broken | key process the one fundamental method for changing from one position or chemical to another | key questions the very few queries that must be answered in order to prove or disprove the solution to a problem | key skills the particular abilities that a person must develop if they are to survive and prosper | key stages the important points or processes along a path leading from the starting position to a finishing line | key terms the main words that describe an object, event or process | key trends a description of the movement of important variables | key variables conditions or concentrations that, if changed, will almost certainly affect the end result | key words the very few words that must be included in a description or method in order to show understanding | binary key a method for writing information as a series of 0s and 1s only

kg [kilogram / kilogramme] the fundamental unit of mass that is kept near Paris

kick sample in a stream – disturb the bed by kicking then examine some of the muddy water

kid a young goat, (*slang* a child)

kidneys a pair of organs, found in the middle of the lower back, that control the concentration of salt and water in the blood and produce urine

kill to end a life

killers factors that cause death | pain killers chemicals that prevent pain being felt |

weed killers chemicals that prevent the growth of undesirable plants

kiln an oven that can reach over 1000°C, a furnace used to dry clay | lime kiln a very hot oven in which limestone or chalk is decomposed by heat to give calcium oxide [CaO] (lime)

kilo... /k... (*Greek* a thousand) prefix for a thousand, used as a prefix for 2^{10} (1024) in computing

kilocalorie a thousand calories (confusingly – also written as Calorie!), the energy needed to raise the temperature of 1 kilogram of water by 1°C

kilogram (UK & USA) / kilogramme (UK) / kg the fundamental unit of mass, kept near Paris

kilojoule / kJ 1000 joules, one joule is the energy changed or work done when a force of one newton moves one metre

kilometer (USA) / kilometre (UK) / km 1000 meters; the meter is the fundamental unit of length | kilometers per hour (kph) a measure of speed that is used for cars

kilometre (UK) / kilometer (USA) / km 1000 metres; the metre is the fundamental unit of length | kilometres per hour (kph) a measure of speed that is used for cars

kilowatt / kW 1000 watts, which is the unit of power | kilowatt-hour/ kWh the unit of energy used by electricity producers and consumers

kind considerate, thoughtful, type

kine- (*Greek* moving)

kinesthetic related to movement

kinetic moving | kinetic energy the energy associated with the speed of the object

kinetic energy = mass × velocity × velocity/2
(joules)   (kilogram)   (metres/sec)^2

| kinetic theory the idea that everything is made from tiny particles that may be in fixed position (solid), moving closely around each other (liquid) or widely separated and moving at high speed (gas)

kingdoms the major divisions into which all of life is divided (animal, fungi, monera, plant and protoctista) | animal kingdom living creatures whose cells have a nucleus, but do not have a cell wall | plant kingdom living items whose cells have a nucleus and a cell wall containing cellulose or lignin | five kingdoms the five divisions of life – they are animals, fungi, monera, plants and protoctista

kiss a gentle contact, contact with the lips; to touch gently, especially with the lips | kiss of life the blowing of the air form one person into the mouth and lungs of another person who is unable to breathe themselves due to injury

kit a set of related items, a collection of parts for a specific purpose | soil-testing kit a set of equipment and chemicals which can be used to measure the pH, drainage time and other characteristics of soil

kite a carnivorous bird, a covered frame that is flown on the end of a length of string | kite diagram a method of data presentation used in ecology in which the distribution of plants along a line is shown as a curve above the y-axis and a mirror image of the distribution is shown below the y-axis

kJ / kilojoule a unit of energy equal to 1000 joules

Klaproth (Martin 1743–1817) was apprenticed as a pharmacist, moving between several towns in Germany, ending at Berlin University. He was the first to isolate several elements including uranium, in 1795, named in celebration of the discovery of Uranus by Herschel, and chromium, in 1798, independently of Vauquelin.

km / kilometre a unit of distance of 1000 metres

knead (not need which is an essential) pushing, pulling and pummelling dough when making bread

knee the joint in the middle of the leg which allows the lower leg to move | knee cap (patella) a circular bone that covers the front of the knee joint and prevents the lower leg from bending forwards | knee joint the joint between the bone of the upper leg (femur) and the bones of the lower leg (tibia and fibula) that also involves the knee cap (patella)

knew (not new which is unused) having the information, recognised

knife (plural is knives) an instrument with a handle and a long sharp blade that is used for cutting

knitting turning a long thread into a cloth by interlocking of loops | knitting needles a pair of long, thin cylinders with a point at one end that are used for producing material from wool

knives (plural of knife) metal instruments that are used for slicing and cutting

knob a control that can be rotated, a small part that is pushed out | focus knob the rotating control that changes the distance between object and lens in a microscope so the image is sharp

knock to hit, to bang

knock-on effect a consequence of one action on another

knocked has been hit

knot (not not which is a negative term) appears to be pieces of string joined together or actually is where two pieces of string are joined, a speed of 1 nautical mile per hour

know (not no which is a negative) to be familiar with some information, to recognise

knowledge information or data | existing knowledge the information that you know before beginning the experiment | general knowledge information that has been received from the newspaper and television and is expected to be known by the majority of the population | incomplete knowledge you are familiar with some of the information, but there are important parts missing | scientific knowledge information or data that has been obtained by experiments and is consistent with accepted ideas

known data you already possess | known mass you measure the mass (or weight) of the chemical | known values data that are available in books

knows (not nose which is the organ of smell) has the information

Koch (Robert1843–1910) studied medicine and became a district medical officer in Germany. Koch is one of the founders of modern bacteriology. He used dyes to stain, or colour, bacteria so they were more easily seen, he introduced the use of agar for growing bacteria (Petri was his assistant) and he used steam to kill bacteria. He made discoveries about anthrax, he identified the bacterium responsible for tuberculosis (TB), he did major work on cholera, bubonic plague, malaria, and sleeping sickness. He was awarded the Nobel Prize in 1905.

kph [kilometres per hour] a measure of speed that is used in everyday life

Kr krypton, proton number 36, an inert gas

Krakatoa a volcanic island, near Indonesia, that erupted with such force in 1883 that ash was thrown 80 kilometres into the air and the sound was heard 3200 kilometres away

krill small, shrimp-like crustaceans, each of which is no longer than 50 millimetres, yet are so plentiful that they form the main food for many types of whale

krypton (Kr, proton number 36, melting point $-157°C$) a group 0 element, an inert gas

Kuiper belt a vast belt of particles, in the size range from dust to planets, that extends beyond the orbit of Neptune, the inner part of the Oort cloud

kW / kilowatt the unit of power equal to 1000 watts or 1000 joules per second

kwashiokor an illness that is caused by eating sufficient carbohydrates, but almost no lack of protein

kWh / kilowatt-hour the unit of energy used by electricity generating companies for costing

l / litre a volume of 1000 cm³

(l) (liquid) the state of the chemical is a liquid

lab laboratory, the scientists' workshop | **lab pack** an electrical power supply used in a laboratory that provides a variable potential difference (voltage)

label the information card that is attached to an object; to put a name or information card onto an item | **hazard label / hazard warning label** a sheet of paper that is stuck on to jars of chemicals in order to emphasise the dangers associated with using that chemical

labeling (USA) / **labelling** (UK & USA) giving information, putting a label on to a container | **labelling system** a process for making sure that each object has the important information in a form that can be easily understood by others | **food labelling** the information on the packet or container that shows the amount of several nutrients in a standard portion of the food

labor (USA) / **labour** (UK) work, delivery of a child; to work | **division of labor** the separation of a large job into small parts that can be carried out by different people

laboratory (plural is laboratories) a room in which experiments can be safely carried out, usually having sinks, water, mains electricity and a gas supply | **laboratory acids** the acids that are commonly found in laboratories *viz* hydrochloric acid, nitric acid and sulphuric acid | **laboratory equipment** objects that are usually found only in a laboratory, *eg* tripod, bunsen burner, clamps, that allow experiments to be carried out safely | **laboratory investigation** a series of experiments that can be carried out in a suitably equipped room | **hospital laboratory** the rooms in a hospital where the tests are carried out on important fluids (urine, blood, saliva) and tissue material | **microbiological laboratory** a room which is specially equipped for growing and testing microbes such as bacteria | **school laboratory** a room that is equipped with water supplies, sinks, electricity and gas, so that experiments can be carried out safely by a large number of young people

labour (UK) / **labor** (USA) work, delivery of a child; to work | **division of labour** separating a large job into small parts that can be carried out by different people

labrador a breed of dog that is often used by fire services and as a guide for blind people

lack missing, dearth; to be without something

lactic acid the acid that is produced when milk turns sour | **lactic acid bacteria / lactobacilli** (plural of *lactobacillus*) the microbes that live on milk and produce lactic acid so the milk tastes sour and forms solids

lactose a carbohydrate found in milk that produces two glucose molecules

ladle a deep spoon with a vertical handle; to distribute portions, *eg* of soup

ladybird a flying insect with a wing cover that is red with black spots

lager a beer produced using a yeast that prefers lower temperatures

lagging falling behind, insulating covering

lagoon an area of water that is enclosed by land for at least half the periphery

lair (not layer which is a thickness) a den, the resting place for an animal, the nest of a wild animal

lake an area of non-salty water that is not visibly moving | **acidic lake** an area of fresh water that has a pH below 5 and so is unsuitable for many fish or plants | **brine lake** a pond of water containing a concentration of salt that is so high that crystals may form | **soda lake** a body of water that is corrosive because the solution is rich in sodium carbonate, resulting in a very high pH

Lake District an area of north-west England that has lots of sharp peaks and many valleys that are flooded

lamp a source of light, a bulb | **bench lamp** an electrical item that is sufficiently small to be placed on a desk or bench and give out light that is directed in one direction | **colored lamp** (USA) / **coloured lamp** (UK) an object that gives out light of a particular colour rather than the whole visible spectrum | **filament lamp** an electrical bulb, equipment that uses an electrical current to heat a thin piece of wire (a filament) that then glows brightly | **headlamp** the bright light at the front of a car | **indicator lamp** a light that shows when the equipment is switched on | **lava lamp** an ornamental light in which bubbles of a oil will rise and fall through a cylinder of coloured liquid | **mains lamp** a light source that is designed to work safely at 240 volts | **street lamp** a source of illumination that lets you see where you are walking at night

land ground, an area of the Earth's crust; to return from flight to ground | **land animals** consumers that live, forage and reproduce on the ground | **landfill** the rubbish that is put into a hole in the ground so the hole disappears | **landform** any feature that is seen on the surface of the Earth | **landmarks** features on the surface of the Earth that are easily distinguished | **land owner** the person who owns, or possesses, some land | **landscape** the form, shapes and colours of the area | **landslide** downhill movement of a very large area of soil or mud |

land speed record the fastest that any person has travelled while supported by wheels | land usage the purpose to which a specified area of ground is put | agricultural land an area that is used for growing crops or raising animals for later sale at a profit | arable land ground that is suitable for growing crops or food | arid land desert, a dry area, a region that receives little or no rain | eroded land ground that has disappeared because the soil has fallen into moving water, ground from which the top soil has been removed by wind, rain and water | farmland the area of land given over to the raising of crops or feeding animals | fertile land ground that contains all the nutrients that a plant needs and is ideal for growing crops | meadow land an area of grassland suitable for wildlife and for cattle to feed on | moorland exposed areas of hill that are covered with heather and bushes | waste land an area where life does not seem to exist, barren, an area of land, in a town, that seems to have no particular purpose | woodland an area in which trees are close together

landed moved onto solid ground after flying or swimming

landfill the rubbish that is put into a hole in the ground so the hole disappears | landfill site the place where the hole that is being filled with rubbish is to be found

landing the period when an aircraft is returning to the ground, the area at the top of a stairs

Landsat a satellite that is used to observe the surface of the Earth | Landsat images pictures of parts of the Earth produced using satellites in space

landscape the view of a country | limestone landscape the type of hills, undergrowth and trees that are associated with areas that are high in limestone

language the speech and expressions that are used to communicate between people and with or between computers | language of science the special and specific words (thousands of them) that allow people to describe and explain their experiments | appropriate language using special words that are precise in context and can be understood by the person listening | appropriate scientific language using the special words of science in a way that is understandable by the people listening | scientific language the words that scientists use that are precise and specific in meaning

lantern a box with glass walls in which is placed a candle or an oil lamp to give out light

lap a stage of a race, a part of a journey, the area between your knees and hips, when seated

Laplace (Marquis Pierre Simon de 1749–1827) helped Lavoisier to study chemistry before moving on to astronomy and finally becoming a minister in the French Government. He developed the mathematics that predict the position and movement of the planets, and frequently wrote "it is obvious that" although the idea was understood by no one else. He was a member of the commission, that also included Lavoisier and Coulomb, who developed the metric system for measurements.

laps (not lapse which is to fall) stages in a race

lapse (not laps which are stages) a gap in your concentration; to fall back, to make a mistake

lard the fat produced when the meat from pig is baked

large big in comparison with other items of this particular type | large animals consumers that are big in comparison to the others in that area | large bowel the large intestine, part of the human gut where water is absorbed | large crystals the big version of regular, shiny solids, usually easily seen and easy to handle | large intestine the lower part of the gut is a tube with a larger diameter than the upper part, water is absorbed in the large intestine | large molecule many atoms are bonded to produce a single molecule, eg DNA is a large molecule composed of many millions of atoms | large numbers many, often refers to a significant proportion of a population | large pressure a force per unit area that is sufficiently high as to need special precautions | large–scale the size is big for that project, possibly industrial

larger / larger body the bigger of two objects

largest biggest, the most extreme when comparing the sizes of three or more objects

lark a type of bird that starts to sing just before dawn breaks

larva (not lava which is hot rock) (plural is larvae) immature form of some invertebrates that change radically as they mature, eg a caterpillar, which turns into a butterfly

larvae (plural of larva) immature forms of some invertebrates

larynx the voice box, the area of the windpipe where sound is produced

laser equipment that will produce light of a single frequency, a beam of light in which every wave has the identical frequency | laser beam the light that is produced by a laser source | laser display moving beams of light, produced by lasers

last final, ultimate; to continue, to survive

late occurring after the time that was expected, dead

latent heat the amount of energy that is needed, or released, to change state (which occurs at constant temperature, *eg* from ice to water at 0°C

later after an event, some time in the future

lateral inversion changing the left for right and the right for left

laterally inverted everything that was on the left side of the object appears on the right side of the image, and *vice versa*

latex a white fluid that is present in the trunks of many trees but, importantly, the rubber trees provide latex that can be turned into rubber

latitude lines drawn on a map that are parallel to the equator

lattice a grid, an open structure made by intertwining thin strips | **ionic lattice** a regular structure, often giant, that is made from alternating two types of particle – one with a positive charge and the other with a negative charge

laughing gas nitrous oxide [N_2O], an anaesthetic

launch the start, the beginning; to send off

lava (not larva which is an immature form) the molten rock that is pushed out of a volcano | **lava flow** movement of the molten rock that has erupted from a volcano | **lava lamp** an ornamental light in which bubbles of a oil will rise and fall through a cylinder of coloured liquid | **basalt lava** the usual type of magma that erupts through volcanoes at the fringes of the major plates, a dark coloured rock with a fine grain is produced on cooling | **liquid lava** the viscous fluid of melted rocks that flows out of a volcano | **streaming lava** magma that has erupted and remains sufficiently fluid that the molten rock can flow swiftly

Lavoisier (Antoine Laurent 1743–1794) studied law in Paris, and was elected to the Royal Academy at age 25 for his work on the first geological map of France and for proposing a method for street lighting. He became a tax collector and, at age 28, he married a 14 year old – a marriage that lasted until his death. He improved the water supply in Paris, showed that air is a mixture of oxygen and nitrogen and that combustion requires the chemicals to react with oxygen. From 1776, he was in charge of the Royal Arsenal (helped by E.I. du Pont, who emigrated to America and founded a massive chemical company) but managed to find time to improve public education, taxation and even old age pensions. In 1789, in *An Elementary Treatise on Chemistry,* he proposed the modern method for naming chemicals.

Unfortunately, the tax business that he had been involved with for 25 years made him a target for the guillotine.

law (not lore which is a story) a brief description of one of the processes that occur in the universe and which must always be followed | **law of conservation of mass** the total amount of material at the start of the experiment is exactly equal to the total amount of product at the end, mass can never be created nor destroyed | **laws of magnetism** the magnetic field lines take the shortest route from the North pole to the South pole and never cross | **law of moments** a beam or lever is balanced when the sum of the clockwise moments (also called torque or turning force) exactly balances the sum of the anticlockwise moments | **laws of motion** three laws proposed by Newton

1. every body continues at constant velocity unless a force is applied
2. the change of velocity is proportional to the force applied
3. every action has an equal and opposite reaction

| **law of reflection** the angle of reflection (measured from the normal) is exactly equal to angle of incidence | **law of refraction** the direction of movement of a wave bends towards the normal if the speed slows down and bends away from the normal if the speed increases | Hooke's **law** the extension of a spring or elastic is dependent directly on the force applied, and the material will return to its original length when the force is removed | **mathematical laws** the unbreakable rules of the universe that are shown as mathematical equations | Ohm's **law** for material at constant temperature, the potential difference (in volts) equals the current (in amps) multiplied by the resistance (in ohms)

lawn an area of tended grass; a thin layer of microbes

lay to place, to deposit | **lay eggs** the production of eggs by hens

layer (not lair which is an animal's den) a thickness, stratum or sheet; to provide a cover | **layers of air** trapped pockets of air that provide insulation | **layer of sediment** a thickness or stratum of rock, sand or soil that has been deposited from water | **alternate layers** two types of sheet in the sequence sheet 1: sheet 2: sheet 1 : sheet 2: . . . | **coal layer** a thickness or seam of coal | **dead layer** the outermost layer of cells in the skin | **deep layer** a stratum of rock that is found a long way from the surface | **distinct layer** a thickness of material that is easily distinguished from the strata above and below | **fatty layer** fat cells that are found below the skin and help insulate the animal | **impermeable layer** a stratum of rock that will not allow fluids to pass through | **jelly layer** a thin, protective layer on the outside of the membrane of an ovum | **outer layer** the membrane or sheet that is nearest to the outside | **ozone layer** a thickness of ozone [O_3] that is found high in the atmosphere, and provides protection from harmful ultra-violet radiation | **protective layer** a sheet of material that prevents injury to the material underneath | **rock layer** a stratum | **sedimentary layer** a thickness or stratum of rock, sand or soil that has been deposited from water | **spongy layer** the bottom half of a leaf is a loose collection of cells through which carbon dioxide can diffuse | **waterproofing layer** a thin sheet that prevents movement of water | **waxy layer** a thin coating on the top of leaves that prevents loss of water by evaporation

layered / layered structure the object shows planes of different materials

lazy not putting in any effort, prefer to do nothing

lb abbreviation for a pound weight, originally called a *libra*

LDR [light-dependent resistor] an electrical component in which the resistance depends on the intensity of light reaching the component

leach (not leech which is creature similar to a slug) to pull, to suck out

leached sucked out, removed by seepage of water

lead the first, a connecting wire with an insulating sheath; to go in front | **stacking lead** a connecting wire that has a terminal that can both be plugged into a connector and have another connector plugged into it

lead (Pb, proton number 82, melting point 328°C) an unreactive metal that was used extensively in making pipes | **lead–acid battery** several lead–acid cells joined in series in a single container | **lead–acid cell** an accumulator, a cell made from plates of lead in sulphuric acid that can be changed chemically by an electric current | **lead nitrate** [Pb NO_3] a soluble salt of lead | **pencil lead** a mixture of powdered graphite (carbon) and clay that is the thin cylinder that will write on paper

leaf (plural is leaves) the flat, green outgrowth in which photosynthesis uses light energy to turn carbon dioxide and water into sugars | **leaf cells** the cells, individual growing units, that are found in the leaf | **leaf litter / leaf mould** the brown remains of dead leaves that line the ground in autumn | **leaf shedding** the dropping of leaves during autumn | **leaf size** the area of an individual

leaf | **leaf stalk** the thin tube or stem connecting the leaf to the trunk or main stem of the plant | **leaf structure** the arrangement of cells to give the tissues inside the leaf | **leaf surface** the outside area of a leaf that you can see and feel | **leaf veins** tubes that both provide support for the leaves and contain the phloem and xylem tubes | **scale leaf** a small dry or hard leaf

leaflet a small leaf that is one of many from a single stem, a sheet of paper with information | **advisory leaflet** a sheet of paper that recommends a course of action | **information leaflet** a sheet of paper with relevant data

leak (not leek which is a plant) the place where water loss is occurring; to lose water in an uncontrolled manner

leaky particles are able to escape, water is able to enter

lean thin, without fat; to stand at an angle, to rest against an upright

leaned /leant (not lent which is loaned) inclined, moved from a straight line

leap a jump; to jump | **leap year** a year which has 366 days (an extra day in February) so that the longest day will continue to occur very close to June 21

leaped / leapt jumped outwards as far as possible

learn to acquire knowledge

learned / learnt having obtained knowledge or a skill

learning trying to understand the world around you

least the lowest number

leather the skin of an animal that has been cleaned then soaked in tannin

leave holiday; to depart

leaves (plural of leaf) the flat (usually green) tissue of plants that turn light energy into chemical energy using photosynthesis | **copper beech leaves** the leaves of a copper beech tree are that colour because the main chemical used in photosynthesis is xanthophyll, not chlorophyll (which is green) | **fresh leaves** the leaves have just been removed from a growing tree | **oak leaves** the leaves of an oak tree | **rhubarb leaves** the large leaves, containing high concentrations of oxalic acid at the end of the edible rhubarb stalks | **variegated leaves** leaves that show areas of different colours, dependent on the amounts of chlorophyll present

LED [light emitting diode] an electronic component that will allow the current to flow in one direction only and will then give out light

leech (not the same as leach which is to suck out) a type of worm, found in damp environments that sucks blood from vertebrates, including people, and used to be used medicinally

leek (not leak which is a loss) a vegetable similar to an onion

Leeuwenhoek (Antony van 1632–1723) was apprenticed as a draper and opened a shop in his home town of Delft. Leeuwenhoek has been called *The Father of Microscopy* because of his detailed investigations of tissues, organs and fluids. He made tiny lenses of high quality, each of which could be held between metal plates – he is reputed to have made over 400 lenses. Encouraged by de Graaf, he sent his observations of blood cells, bacteria and sperm as a series of several hundred letters to The Royal Society, where Hooke was using a microscope with two lenses to make similar observations.

left opposite side to right, not taken, remaining | left behind a residue

leg a limb used for walking, a part of a journey | leg muscles the muscles or tissues that cause movement in the lower limb | jointed leg a limb used for walking that has a hinge joint near the middle

legal allowed by the laws or courts of that country | legal drugs chemicals that can be bought in a shop that can cause a change in the behaviour of your cells or your brain, *eg* alcohol, caffeine, nicotine | legal limit the highest value that can be tolerated as decided by law

Lego™ a construction game that uses brightly coloured plastic bricks of different shapes and sizes that inter-lock to produce models

legs usually the limbs that are used for walking, but tables and electronic components have long bits sticking out that are also called legs

legumes plants that produce seeds in pods and usually have nodules of nitrogen-fixing bacteria on the roots *eg* peas

leisure center (USA) **/ leisure centre** (UK) an area or a building that provides lots of facilities for physical activities such as squash or football

Lemaître (Abbe Georges Edouard 1894–1966) trained as a priest and an astronomer in Belgium, England and America, before returning to Louvain as professor of astronomy. His solution to Einstein's equation showed that the universe should be expanding – this was confirmed experimentally by Hubble. Lemaître then showed that moving back in time would lead to all matter being in a small volume which would lead to a Big Bang

lemon a yellow colour, the citrus fruit that is sour (citric acid) and is yellow

lemon juice the liquid obtained by squeezing a lemon

length the shortest distance between two points, should be measured in metres | length of year the amount of time taken for the Earth to orbit once around the Sun | day length the amount of time between one noon and the next time the Sun is at its highest in the sky, artificially divided into 24 hours, the duration between the rising and the setting of the Sun | finger length an old measure of distance that was the length of the first finger | given length a distance that is decided before you begin the experiment | year length the amount of time taken for a planet to orbit the Sun

lengthen to make longer

lens (plural is lenses) a curved piece of transparent material, such as glass or plastic, that causes the rays of light to produce an image | concave lens the centre of the lens is thinner than the material at the edges, a diverging lens | converging lens / convex lens a shaped piece of material that is much thicker at the centre than at the edges, the beam passes through the lens then forms a point at the focus | diverging lens a shaped piece of glass that causes the beam of light to spread out, a concave lens | eyepiece lens the lens at the top of the microscope tube | hand lens a single shaped piece of glass or plastic, with a diameter between 2 and 10 centimetres, that can be held by hand and used to produce an enlarged image | magnifying lens a piece of curved glass that will increase the size of the image several times compared to the size of the object | objective lens the lens that is nearest to the stage in a microscope | semi-circular lens a half a circle cut from a thick piece of glass or plastic

lenses (plural of lens) curved pieces of transparent material, that cause the rays of light to produce a focus

lent (not leant which is inclined) allowed to be used by another person for a short period

leopard a type of large cat with a distinctive pattern of spotted coat, that is found everywhere from Siberia to Africa | leopard seal a marine mammal that lives in the Antarctic and feeds mainly on penguins

leprosy a contagious disease caused by a bacterium that attacks the nerves causing loss of feeling and consequent damage to the limbs

less smaller, lower, fewer | less dense the density (mass / volume) of one material is lower than that of the other material | less harmful pesticides chemicals that are used to get rid of one type of organism and are said to cause little harm to other organisms | less reactive when using the reactivity series (of metals or halogens), less reactive materials are lower down the series

lessen (not lesson which is an instruction) to make smaller, to reduce, to cut down

lesser smaller, lower, fewer | **lesser mass** the mass is lower

lesson (not lessen which is to reduce) instruction, an exercise taught to pupils, imparting of information

let to allow, to lease

letter one of the characters in an alphabet, a sheet of paper on which is written a message to a specified person

lettuce the green leaves are edible and used without cooking (curly, cos and iceberg are different varieties of lettuce) | **lettuce varieties** types of an edible plant that have distinct characteristics of shape and flavour

leucocyte (UK) / **leukocyte** (USA) a type of white blood cell, part of the immune system

leukaemia (UK) / **leukemia** (USA) an illness in which the marrow produces millions more white blood cells than usual

level the intensity of sound or light, the height, the concentration, the height of water, horizontally stable | **level of magnification** the ratio of the size that you see through a microscope to the actual size of the object | **antibody level** the concentration of a specific antibody in the blood | **feeding level** how many animals separate that creature from the plants in the food chain | **ground level** the approximate height above sea level of that the area of land | **low oxygen levels** the amount of oxygen in the mixture is approaching the minimum concentration needed to keep something alive | **moisture level** humidity, the amount of water vapour | **noise levels** the intensity of unwanted sound, measured in decibels | **oxygen level** the concentration of oxygen in a mixture such as air or the blood | **power level** how much energy is being produced or used each second | **resting level** the measure of activity observed when nothing is being exerted, *eg* heart beat or breathing rate | **sea level** the starting position for measuring heights of land, an average of the height of the sea at high tide and at low tide | **sound level** intensity of sound | **sound power level** the amount of sound (vibrational) energy at a point | **trophic level** the position of a creature in a food web as a producer, primary consumer or secondary consumer | **water level** the distance from a point to the surface of a body of water

lever a rod or beam, moving around a pivot or fulcrum, which can be used to change the size or direction of a force | **lever arm** the longer of the two sides of a lever | **hydraulic lever** equipment using pressure in a liquid so that the force and direction of the output can be very different from the size and direction of the applied force

levitate to float in air without any visible means of support

levitating magnets method of using opposing electromagnets so as to allow a large mass to be raised

Li lithium, proton number 3, the least reactive of the alkali metals

lice (plural of louse) insects that live on animals by drinking blood

lichen two creatures living intimately together – a fungus and a blue-green bacterium | **shrubby lichen** a composite organism, of a fungus and an alga living together, that looks like a very small bush, shrubby lichen is easily killed by pollutants such as acid rain

lid a cap, a top, a cover | **crucible lid** the cover that goes over a crucible and prevents loss of chemicals | **eye lid** a flap of skin that regularly sweeps over the front of the eye

Liebig (Baron Justus von 1803–1873) was appointed to a small university in Germany where he remained for most of his life. He developed rapid, simple methods for the analysis of organic chemicals and worked on the chemistry of animals and plants. Equally importantly, he introduced systematic training of graduate students so that his department dominated the thinking of chemistry in Europe for many years.

Liebig condenser two concentric tubes, water flows between the tubes so cooling the vapour that moves down the inner tube

lies untruths, rests horizontally

life (plural is lives) organisms that show the seven characteristics of a living organism (able to move, to respire, to grow, to reproduce, to excrete, to sense and to feed) | **life cycle** the changes that occur in most organisms in going from immature juvenile, through the sexually mature adult and then decay, a change that may take from a few days, for butterflies, to thousands of years for some trees | **life expectancy** the average amount of time for which you would expect a member of that species to live | **life forms** different types of organisms that vary in characteristics such as size, amount of movement, age, colour, sensitivity | **life-jacket** buoyancy aid, a set of floats worn around the body so as to prevent drowning | **life processes** the seven characteristics (movement, respiration, growth, reproduction, excretion, sensing and nutrition) that are associated with living organisms | life-span the expected time interval from birth to death | life style usually referring to people – the balance between different activities, such as work, play, exercise and feeding | life-support systems the pipes, bottles and tubes that are needed to keep alive either a person who has suffered massive damage or an adventurer who is exploring the sea or space | life time the period from birth to death | characteristics of life the important features that all forms of life should show, MR GRENS (movement, respiration, growth, reproduction, excretion, nutrition and sensing the surroundings) MRS GREF (moving, respiring, sensing, growing, reproducing, excreting, feeding) | daily life / everyday life the type of activities that most people would expect to carry out on several days of the week | half-life the time taken for the activity to be reduced to half of the initial value | kiss of life the blowing of the air form one person into the mouth and lungs of another person who is unable to breathe themselves due to injury | map of life the arrangement of every atom in the DNA of the 46 chromosomes of a person | marine life the type of life found in the sea | plant life producers that use the energy from the Sun for photosynthesis and have cells walls strengthened by cellulose | pond life the types of organisms that are found in long-lasting, small bodies of water | quality of life how happy or satisfied you are with your style of life | shelf life the amount of time for which a product, especially food, can safely be displayed before sale | urban life the types of organisms that are found where lots of people live close together | wild life the organisms that are found living naturally in a given habitat | woodland life the type of organisms that are usually found in a habitat that contains large numbers of trees

life cycles the changes that occur in most organisms in going from immature juvenile, through the sexually mature adult stage and then towards senility and death | human life cycle the changes that occur from the baby growing up, through the maturing and reproduction of the adult to old age

lifestyle usually referring to people – the balance between different activities such as work, play, exercise and diet | lifestyle changes a new pattern of work, play, exercise and diet

lift a box that can moves goods up and down; to move to a higher level | up-lift the force causing an object to rise

lifting taking above ground level | lifting magnet an electro-magnet, so the power can be turned

on and off, that is found at the end of a crane and so can be used for lifting large amounts of iron

ligament a band of tissue that holds the bones together at a joint

ligature a thread that is tied around a blood vessel in order to prevent blood loss

liger offspring of a male lion and a female tiger

light not heavy, the visible radiation that allows our eyes to see; to set on fire | light beam a section of light, that is thicker than a line or ray, that is easily seen | light bulb a lamp, a filament of metal, in a sealed envelope of glass, that is electrically heated to white heat | light-dependent resistor (LDR) an electrical component in which the resistance depends on the intensity of light reaching the component | light-emitting diode (LED) an electronic component that will allow the current to flow in one direction only and will then give out light | light energy emphasising that visible light is a form of energy that can bring about changes in plants, photographic films and solar cells | light gate an electronic component, with a light source in one limb and a detector in the opposite limb, that is used to start and stop a clock | lighthouse a bright beacon or lamp set on top of a tall structure; the lighthouse at Pharos was one of the seven wonders of the Ancient World | light industry the production of finished goods, eg cars, washing machines | light intensity the amount of visible light energy | light metal a metal with a low density, eg sodium floats on water | lightmeter an instrument for measuring the intensity of light | light microscope an instrument, using two or more lenses to provide a magnified image, that uses visible light to illuminate the specimen | light-minute the distance that light travels in 60 seconds in a vacuum, a distance of approximately 18 million kilometres | light path lines on a diagram to show the expected track of the light beam | light pipe an optical fibre, a thin tube of glass down which light is transmitted from end to end | light-proof no light is able to pass through the material | light rays very thin beams of light, used in diagrams to show the path that the light beam will take | light receptors the cells, cones and rods, at the back of the eye that are able to respond to light | light scattering a well-defined beam of light meets a surface or a suspension and the light is reflected in all directions | light-second the distance that light travels in one second in a vacuum, approximately 300,000 kilometres | light sensitive the size of some property will change if light is shone |

light-sensitive cell / light-sensitive spot any cell that responds rapidly and specifically to light | light sensor a component that changes properties when light is shone, maybe as simple as a light-dependent resistor or as complex as the retina at the back of the eye | light source an object that gives out visible radiation | light speed the speed with which electromagnetic radiation will travel, all wavelengths travel at 300,000 kilometres per second in a vacuum | light spot an area on the head of worms that is able to detect light | light-tight the surfaces completely cover a space and prevent entry of any light | light travelling / light travels the movement of light from a source | light treatment using ultra-violet light in order to cure a disease, used with young babies who are jaundiced | light-up to increase the brightness, especially of a given area | lightweight smaller than expected, having a weight below a specified limit | light-year the distance travelled by light in one year (approximately 9 million million kilometres) | absorb light to take in the light so that no light is reflected | beams of light similar to rays of light, but tend to be wider | black light ultra-violet radiation, part of the spectrum that has a wavelength shorter than visible light | Christmas tree lights a string of small lamps that is placed around a fir tree at Christmas time | coloured light (UK) / colored light (USA) energy that is a mixture of the primary colours, red, blue, green, but is not white | coloured lights (UK) / colored lights (USA) objects that give out light of a particular colour rather than the whole visible spectrum | day light the intensity at each frequency in the light provided by the Sun | dim light the amount of light is sufficient to see black and white but not enough to distinguish different colours | dispersed light light that has been passed through a prism and so shows the colours of the rainbow | flood-lights high intensity lamps that flood the area with light | fluorescent light a light source in which an alternating current produces ultra-violet rays which are turned to visible light by the glass envelope | headlights the main lamps that are used to light up the area in front of a car | night light a dim light, often a small candle, that will last at least 8 hours and so can be left on overnight | path of light the track, or path, that a ray of light will follow from the light source, off objects to a sensor | ray of light a thin beam of light | re-light to ignite the flame again | reflected light the light that is seen after it has bounced, or reflected, off an object or mirror | reflecting light a surface, often shiny, that causes a beam of light to be reflected |

scattered light the effect caused by reflection at a rough surface so a beam of light that was travelling in one direction is scattered in all directions | speed of light the speed at which light travels, 300,000 kilometres per second in a vacuum | spotlight a high intensity beam of light | star light the visible radiation produced by a nuclear change in a star | street lights lamps that are placed above ground level so as to light up the surroundings at night and so people can see where they are walking | strip light a lamp in which the glass envelope is a cylinder | sufficient light adequate amount of visible electromagnetic radiation | sun-light the visible light energy that arrives from the Sun | tea light a small, wide candle that will burn for several hours, also called a night light | ultra-violet light the part of the spectrum below blue, electromagnetic waves with a wavelength less than 400 nanometres | visible light part of the spectrum (wavelengths from 380 nanometres to 650 nanometres) that causes a change in the eye and so can be seen – there are other parts of the spectrum, such as ultra-violet and infra-red that can not be seen | warning light a lamp that indicates a potential danger | white light energy that is seen by the eye (light) and appears to be white because it contains the three primary colours – red, blue and green – that are seen when the light is passed through a prism

light
↓
↓
light

lighted splint a thin piece of wood which has a flame on the end | lighted splint test checking to see if a gas is hydrogen which is shown by a lighted splint producing a squeaky *pop*!

lightening (not lightning which is a flash in the sky) becoming brighter, becoming less heavy

lighter less dense than some other item or medium, having less weight, paler in colour | cigarette lighter equipment designed for easy transport and producing an instant flame

lighthouse a bright beacon or lamp set on top of a tall structure; the lighthouse at Pharos was one of the seven wonders of the Ancient World

lighting equipment for supplying visible light | lighting conditions the intensity and colour of the visible light | colored lighting (USA) / coloured lighting (UK) use of coloured lights to give a particular effect | street lighting lamps that are placed at intervals and have a brightness that allows safe passage through a street in the dark | strip lighting a lamp in which the glass envelope is a cylinder

lightning (not lightening which is to become brighter) a flash in the sky caused by electric charge moving between the ground and the cloud | lightning conductor a method for protecting buildings that was said to be invented by Franklin, a thick copper bar has a spike at the top, to attract the lightning, and the other end is buried in the ground

light-proof no light is able to pass through the material | light-proof box a container with solid walls that will not allow any light to enter

lights sets on fire, illuminates, gives out visible radiation

light-sensitive the size of some property will change if light is shone | light-sensitive chemicals substances that undergo a chemical reaction when exposed to light, eg silver nitrate | light-sensitive cell / light-sensitive spot any cell that responds rapidly and specifically to light |

lightweight smaller than expected, having a weight below a specified limit

lignin a large molecule that holds bundles of cellulose in place in the plant cell wall

lignite brown coal, a coal that crumbles easily

like similar; to enjoy, to have affection for | like charges each area has the same charge as the other positions | like ends the tips bear the same charge or the same magnetic pole | like poles magnetic poles that are the same, either both are north or both are south

likely probable, believable

limb the illuminated edge of the Moon | artificial limb an arm or a leg, made from metal, plastic or wood, that replaces the limb that has been badly damaged or removed | forelimb / front limb an arm, a front leg | hind limb a back leg

limbs arms and legs, side pieces, branches of a tree

lime [CaO] calcium oxide, a white powder that glows brilliantly white when heated, a fruit similar to a lemon, but green in colour | lime kiln a very hot oven in which limestone or chalk is decomposed by heat to give calcium oxide [CaO] | limestone a rock, made entirely of calcium carbonate [$CaCO_3$], which is a harder form of chalk | lime water calcium oxide mixed with water, a small amount of the solid will dissolve as calcium hydroxide | lime water test carbon dioxide [CO_2] will turn clear lime water to a milky suspension of chalk | quick lime calcium oxide [CaO], another name for lime | slaked lime calcium oxide mixed, usually in large quantities, with water to give calcium hydroxide [$Ca(OH)_2$] | soda lime [Na_2O] sodium oxide

limestone a rock, made entirely of calcium carbonate [$CaCO_3$], which is a harder form of chalk | limestone caves holes underground produced by the rain water removing parts of the limestone | limestone landscape the type of hills, under-

growth and trees that are associated with areas that are high in limestone | limestone pavements rocks and boulders of limestone that are close to each other and have been weathered to the same height | brown limestone the metamorphic form of chalk that contains lots of iron and so appears as a rusty colour

liming / liming soil spreading lime (calcium oxide [CaO]) onto soil in order to increase the pH of acid soils and to improve the drainage of clay soils

limit a level or line, beyond which you are not supposed to go | limits of growth the maximum number of organisms that can grow in that area before the amount of water, nutrient, space light or air prevents further increase in population | legal limit the level that has been set by the law | over-the-limit above the level specified by the law, may be too much alcohol, or a speed that is too fast | speed limit the maximum speed that is permitted on the highway

limitations the boundaries to which the observation or ideas will apply | limitation of evidence the observations are restricted to a small range so the idea may not apply over a larger range | identify limitations / identify the limitations point out boundaries or the area over which the experimental results are valid

limited restricted, confined | limited number a restricted or known amount | limited period a given period of time

limp flaccid, slack, an awkward way of walking because part of one leg is damaged; to walk awkwardly

limpet a type of snail that attaches itself to rocks between the low and high tide lines

Lind (James 1716–1794) became apprenticed to a surgeon at age 15. In 1747, he divided a crew of sailors with scurvy into several groups and gave each group a different diet; he found that oranges and lemons would cure scurvy within a week, but it took him seven years to write about his findings. Cook used a supplement of citrus fruit in the 1770s, but it was not until 1795 that lime juice became part of the sailors' diet. Almost a 150 years later, Hopkins studied deficiency diseases and in 1928, vitamin C was isolated by Szent-Gyorgi

line a path, may be straight or curved | line of best fit the curve, going in a single direction (up or down), that minimises the differences between the line and the actual measurements | line graph the data is plotted as X–Y pairs and a single curve is drawn so as to minimise the error between the curve and the data | lines of longitude the imaginary lines that pass through the Poles of the Earth and are used to divide the Earth into 360 segments | lines of magnetic force the pattern of non-intersecting lines connecting the poles that are seen when iron filings are sprinkled on to a magnet | line up to put several objects into a straight line | best-fit line the curve, going in a single direction (up or down), that minimises the differences between the line and the actual measurements | coast-line where the land meets the sea | construction line a very fine line that helps to construct a drawing, although it will not be visible in the final diagram | date line an imaginary line between the Poles and running through the Pacific Ocean | dotted line a path shown by dashes and spaces | fishing line a long, thin string that is sufficiently strong to land a struggling fish | guide lines markings on the petals of flowers that guide the bee to the nectar | number line a single axis, calibrated like a ruler, along which items can be fitted | field lines / magnetic field lines the shape that shows when iron filings are sprinkled near a magnet | pipeline a very large diameter tube that carries hot oil from the oil-well to the terminal or refinery | Plimsoll line the International Load Line, a line on the hull of every large ship that shows the weight of cargo that can carried safely, introduced by Samuel Plimsoll in 1875 | power lines thick metal cables, usually aluminium, that carry high voltage electricity | railway lines parallel pairs of iron girders on which trains can travel | straight lines the shortest distance between two points | temperature line a diagram of the temperature at which an event, such as boiling, occurs in different substances | timeline a band or line that shows the date at which events occurred

linear in a straight line, a simple progression | linear chromatography a method for analysing the components in a mixture, the solvent flows through the sample spot and the components appear as a line of oval shapes | linear graph the data points all lie on a straight line | linear motion moving in a straight line | non-linear the path or graph is not a straight line

lining a thin layer | lining cells the cells that are found on the inside of tubes, canals or ducts in the body | thermal lining an extra layer, of clothes or a wall, that reduces the loss of heat | uterus lining the cell on the inside wall of the womb into which the ovum is implanted and which is lost each month during menstrual bleeding

link one repeating piece in chain; to join together, including joining ideas in a chain of logic |

hot links icons or alpha-numeric displays that allow rapid connection to the specified web site
linked joined together, two ideas that are related
linking joining together, including ideas
links (not lynx which is a big cat) joins together, connects, relates

Linnaeus (Carl 1707–1778) was the son of an enthusiastic gardener, he started to train as a doctor but ran out of money, and fortunately was offered a post lecturing in botany – under his guidance, the number of pupils increased nearly tenfold! In the early 1830s, Linnaeus travelled throughout Europe, studying plants, and eventually settled in Holland and started training again to become a doctor; at the same time, he published *Systema Naturae*. In 1749, Linnaeus introduced the idea of a binomial naming, a system that is still in use today.

lion a large type of cat that is found in the grasslands of Africa, the male has a mane of long, dark hair
lioness an adult female member of the lion family
lip an edge, a sudden change, tissue surrounding the mouth | lip reading understanding what someone says by watching the movement of their lips | Habsburg lip a characteristic shape that was seen in many of the Habsburg family over a period of four centuries
lipase / lipase enzyme a protein that causes the breakdown of fat into glycerol and fatty acids
lipids chemicals that are soluble in petrol or nail varnish remover
lips the fleshy opening to the mouth
liquefied (UK & USA) / **liquified** (USA) condensed, a gas has been turned into a liquid by applying pressure
liquefied gas (UK & USA) / **liquified gas** (USA) a material, usually found as a gas, but has been turned into a liquid either by increasing the pressure or by lowering the temperature | liquefied petroleum gas (LPG) the liquid produced by applying high pressure to a hydrocarbon that is a gas at room temperature
liquefier (UK & USA) / **liquifier** (USA) equipment that is used to turn plants into a liquid by using a rotating blade
liquefy (UK & USA) / **liquify** (USA) to turn a gas into a liquid
liquid material that is able to flow and to fill a container from the bottom upwards, the particles in a liquid are tiny, close together, but not joined | liquid air a mixture of oxygen and nitrogen at approximately –200°C | liquid fuels chemicals that are intended to provide heat, that are found

as liquids | **liquid-in-glass thermometer** an instrument for measuring temperature in which a large volume of liquid, usually alcohol or mercury, expands up a narrow glass tube | **liquid hydrogen** hydrogen that has been compressed and cooled so the gas turns into a liquid | **liquid lava** the viscous fluid of melted rocks that flows out of a volcano | **liquid oxygen** oxygen that has been cooled below its boiling point (–183°C) and so can be transported as a liquid | **liquid paraffin** mineral oil, a transparent, colourless, odourless oily liquid, a mixture of alkanes with boiling points in the range 180° – 210°C | **liquid magma** rock that is so hot that it has melted | **liquid nitrogen** nitrogen is cooled below its boiling point of –196°C and so becomes a liquid that is easily transported and stored | **liquid oxygen** oxygen, normally a gas, is cooled below its boiling point of –183°C and so turns into a liquid | **liquid petroleum gas** (LPG / lpg) many hydrocarbons are gases at room temperature, but form liquids when pressure is applied, and can then be transported easily in tanks | **liquid rock** magma, rock that is sufficiently hot that it becomes fluid and will flow | **liquid thermometer** any thermometer that uses the expansion of liquid as a measure of temperature | **liquid water** used to emphasise that the water must be a liquid | **acidic liquid** a solution that has a pH below 7, a liquid that will turn universal indicator to red | **clear liquid** a transparent fluid, light can pass through | **flammable liquid** a liquid that easily catches fire (but the vapour is the chemical that reacts with the oxygen *ie* burns) | **head of liquid** the height of a liquid, often water or mercury, that is pushing down | **household liquids** liquids that are available in supermarkets | **neutral liquid** a solution that has a pH of 7 ie is neither acid nor alkali | **pure liquid** a liquid that is made from a single chemical and does not contain any dissolved material | **red liquid** a solution of a red dye in alcohol that is used in thermometers | **washing up liquid** a fluid that is added to the water to help remove grease from dishes

liquidiser (UK) / **liquidizer** (USA) equipment for rapidly chopping a suspended solid into tiny, tiny pieces

liquified (USA) / **liquefied** (UK) condensed, a gas has been turned into a liquid by applying pressure

liquified gas (USA) / **liquefied gas** (UK) a material, usually found as a gas, but has been turned into a liquid either by increasing the pressure or by lowering the temperature | **liquified petroleum gas** (LPG) the liquid produced by applying high pressure to a hydrocarbon that is a gas at room temperature

list short notes or single words that emphasise the important points | **component list** a table containing the equipment that is to be used

listen to pay attention to what is being said, to hear

listening trying to work out the importance of the spoken word or some noise

Lister (Baron Joseph 1827–1912) started studying art in London, but turned to medicine and qualified as a surgeon. About half of all operations in those days ended with the patient dying from some infection; following the work of Pasteur (1865), Lister made the giant leap by realising that this infection was due to microbes being introduced into the wound. He insisted that all the staff washed their hands and instruments in carbolic acid (phenol) and a carbolic acid spray was used in the operating theatre – these steps dramatically decreased the incidence of infection.

listerosis food poisoning caused by the bacterium *Listeria*

lit a flame, illuminated | **flood-lit** a wide area is brightly illuminated by high-powered lamps

-lite (*Greek* stone, rock)

liter (USA) / **litre** (UK) unit of volume that is 1000 cm^3 | **milliliter** (ml) a thousandth part of a litre, the same as 1 cm^3

literary evidence using information obtained from a published source

literature any work that has appeared in a printed form, including books, magazines and the Internet

lithium (Li, proton number 3, melting point 180°C) the least reactive of the alkali metals | **lithium cell** an electrical cell in which lithium is one electrode

litho- (*Greek* stone)

lithosphere the crust and outer mantle of the Earth

litmus a chemical, extracted from a fungus, that is red in acid, below pH 7, and blue in alkali, above pH 7 | **litmus paper** paper that has been dipped into litmus solution and then dried | **litmus solution** a liquid containing litmus

litre (UK) / **liter** (USA) unit of volume that is 1000 cm^3 | **millilitre** (ml) a thousandth part of a litre, the same as 1 cm^3

litter material on the ground, which was discarded by people, and is unlikely to be broken down easily, a set of offspring born to one parent (*eg*, a dog or a cat) | **leaf litter** the layer of dead leaves that is found on the ground in autumn

little small, tiny, not large

live to exist as a living organism in an area | **live wire** the wire in a circuit that carries the current from the generator to the house and then to the appliance, and should be coloured brown |

live young the offspring are developed sufficiently to live independently of the mother when born, although they may be immature

liver an organ of the body, found just below the diaphragm, that removes chemicals that could be dangerous to the body and breaks down old red blood cells | liver cell any cell from the liver | liver failure the liver stops functioning and so poisonous chemicals build up in the body

liverworts non-vascular plants similar to mosses

livestock the cattle, sheep or pigs that a farmer will raise in order to sell at market | domestic livestock animals (pets) that are kept in the home for the pleasure they give, *eg* cats, dogs, hamsters

living existing and capable of the characteristics of life (MR GRENS – movement, respiration, growth, reproduction, excretion, nutrition, sensing) or MRS GREF (moving, respiring, sensing, growing, reproducing, excreting, feeding) | living cells cells, the basic units of life, that show the ability to respire, to grow and to reproduce | living community a collection of different producers, consumers and decomposers that are likely to be dependent on each other | living creatures any consumer that shows many or the life processes (MR GRENS) | living materials a substance that has been taken from a creature for examination, but is unlikely to survive on its own | living organisms any object that is able to exist, possibly for a short time, in isolation from other life and shows many of the characteristics of life | living plants emphasising that the producer is able to use the sunlight and grow | living processes the functions (MR GRENS) that are carried out by an object that is alive, these are movement, respiration, growth, reproduction, excretion, nutrition and sensing | living systems the collection of producers and consumers that live in an area | living things any object that is made from cells and shows many of the characteristics of life | non-living the object is not capable of growing or reproducing, although it may once have been alive | once living the species used to exist, but now is either extinct or no longer found in that area

lizards one of the four orders of reptiles and so are cold blooded, live on land and lay eggs

load a burden, the object that you are trying to move, material carried by a river; to put an object where it can be moved

loam a soil that is not only easily drained, but is also rich because of its mixture of sand, clay and organic material

lobe an outcrop, a section | ear lobes extensions of the pinna of the ear that may be attached to the skull or free floating depending on the presence of a single gene

local in the neighbouring area, near to a particular place | local anaesthetic (UK) / local anesthetic (USA) a chemical that is applied so as to remove all feeling from that area | local diseases illnesses that are usually found in that area because of the environmental conditions | local environment the living conditions, *eg* temperature, moisture, wind, light, in a small area | local monitoring measuring the value of the some variable in order to check that it does not go too high | local population the number of the specified species (usually people) that live in the area | local soil the type of rock that is found near to a particular spot

localities (plural of locality) areas near a specific feature

locality (plural is localities) area around a place

locate to find | locate information to find data

location an area | city location area where lots of people (and cats, dogs, mice and rats) live closely together | echo-location using the time between producing a sound and listening to the echo in order to measure distance, a means of finding food that is used by bats and by dolphins | suitable location an area that is fit for that specific purpose

lock a bolt, a device for preventing movement; to prevent movement | lock jaw (tetanus) a disease caused by infection with a *Clostridium* bacterium from the soil, the bacterium produces a toxin that causes every muscle in the body to go into painful contraction | fermentation lock equipment that allows escape of the carbon dioxide [CO_2] produced during fermentation, but prevents entry of air

locusts a type of grasshopper that may form massive swarms that can eat every piece of vegetation over a very large area | plague of locusts millions of locusts descend on any plant, including crops, and will eat everything in that location, leaving behind devastation and consequent starvation

lodestone a rock that is naturally magnetic and can be used as a compass

loft the space between the ceiling of the rooms on the top floor and the roof | loft insulation layers of material that are put into the roof space in order to prevent loss of heat and so save energy

log a large piece of wood, a diary in which events are recorded; to collect and record information

logger / data logger an instrument for automatic collection and storage of measurements

logging collecting data, felling trees

logic moving from one statement to another using ideas that can be tested and examined | logic gate an electronic component that changes its output dependent on the input, the common logic gates are AND, OR and NOT

long a far distance, a large period of time | long-lasting continuing for a substantial period of time, persistent, stable, not easily broken down | long molecule a compound that is made from many units joined end to end and so appears like a piece of string | long sighted able to see objects that are a long distance away, but unable to focus on objects that are close | long-term a long period of time

longer drawn out, increased in length, more time

longest has the greatest length takes the most time

longitude position on an imaginary line that circles the globe and appears to pass through the Poles | lines of longitude the imaginary lines that pass through the Poles of the Earth and are used to divide the Earth into 360 segments

longitudinal cutting along the longest or main axis | longitudinal wave a vibration in which the movement of the particles is in the same direction as the energy is travelling, eg sound waves

long-term a long period of time | long-term data information that has been obtained over a long period of time | long-term effects changes that are seen a long time after the stimulus that causes the effect and are not easily cured | long-term studies collection of information over a long period of time

look (not luck which is good fortune) to see, to find

looking using your eyes to gather information

looks appears, seems

loop a semi-circle on finger prints; to move in a circle | inoculation loop a small circle at the end of a wire that is used to transfer microbes

loose (not lose which is to disappear) not tight

lore (not law which is a rule) a story, a fairy tale

lorry a wheeled vehicle for moving large quantities of material

lose (not loose which is not tight) to get rid of, to be unable to find | lose energy to reduce the ability to cause a change

losing getting rid of, lowering in a way that is difficult to prevent | losing energy unwanted reduction in the amount of energy in a system

loss (plural is losses) the material that has been lost | loss of blood the volume of blood that is lost after blood vessels have been cut | loss of heat the movement of thermal energy from the area at a higher temperature | loss of water the amount of water inside the system or organism is reduced |

domestic heat loss heat is being lost from a house, eg through the walls, by draughts | hearing loss becoming less sensitive to sound, either or both of the loudness or the frequency range | heat loss a change of temperature caused by losing heat because of conduction, convection or radiation | prevent heat loss use an insulator to try to keep the temperature constant | reduce heat loss to add insulation so that less heat energy is moved | water loss the movement of water out of an organism, eg from the leaf to the air or from an animal as sweat or urine

lost not there – and you do not know where it is | lost mass material that is no longer in the liquid because it has either evaporated or been removed by fizzing

lotion a liquid that is applied to the skin | calamine lotion a mixture of zinc carbonate and iron (III) oxide in suspension, a pink liquid that soothes the skin

lots many, a large amount, a high number

loud high intensity | loud noise high intensity sound that is unwanted, often occurs suddenly and for a brief time | loud sounds high intensity vibrations that have recognisable frequencies

louder with more intensity, greater amplitude

loudest highest intensity, greatest amplitude

loudness intensity of sound, measured in decibels (dB)

loudspeaker equipment for turning electrical signals into sound

louse (plural is lice) a type of small insect that attaches itself to the hair of an animal

low close to the ground, close to the bottom end | low birth-weight the weight of the baby at birth was at the low end of what is expected | low-calorie diet the food that you are eating contains very little energy | low-energy foods materials that you eat that but will not provide much energy | low hazard there will not be much damage even if there is an accident | low lying the average ground level is very close to the local sea level | low magnification the image is a few times larger than the object | low orbit circling around the Earth at a height of less than 200 kilometres | low oxygen levels the concentration of oxygen is less than is needed for comfort | low pH the amount of acid is sufficient to produce a pH below 3 | low pitch the frequency of sound is below 100 hertz | low polar orbit the satellite is flying over the Poles at less than a thousand miles high | low power the amount of energy released each second will not cause any damage; the magnification is less than ten times | low pressure the force per area is so low that damage will not result | low sperm count the number of sperm in the semen is sufficiently low that pregnancy is unlikely | low temperature cold, the temperature is low for that situation | low tide the average height of the sea is at the lowest for that day | low voltage the power output is a few volts – not sufficient to cause you any harm | ultra-low very, very low

lower less than; to drop safely | lower arm the part of the arm between the elbow and the wrist, contains two bones – the radius and ulna | lower body the part of the human body below the waist | lower jaw bone mandible | lower reactivity reaction of that metal with acid, water or oxygen will be much slower than the first metal | lower shore the land next to the sea that is covered and uncovered at almost every tide | lower surface the underside, the area that is below the main structure | lower temperature the material is less hot

lowered became less, controlled descent

lowest minimum, at the bottom | lowest frequency the wave with the highest wavelength

low-level technology machinery that can be made using a few, simple tools, not complicated

low voltage the power output is a few volts – not sufficient to cause you any harm | low-voltage supply a source of electrical power that produces a potential difference (voltage) that is too low to cause damage | low-voltage heater equipment that turns electrical energy into heat energy, but uses a potential difference below 24 volts

LPG / lpg [liquefied petroleum gas] the liquid produced by applying high pressure to a hydrocarbon that is a gas at room temperature

LSD [lysergic acid diethylamide] a drug that causes weird dreams, discovered in 1943

lubricant a fluid that reduces friction

lubricate to reduce the friction between two surfaces

lubricating adding the fluid that will separate two surfaces | lubricating oil hydrocarbon with a boiling point in the range 250–300°C

lubrication using a fluid to reduce friction

luck (not look which is to examine) good fortune

lukewarm feels comfortably warm to the touch

lumbar (not lumber which is wood) the lower region of the spine

lumber (not lumbar which is part of the body) wood for building; to move clumsily

lumen the inside of a tube, a unit of light intensity

luminous giving out light | luminous object anything that gives out its own light | non-luminous not giving out light, seen by reflected light

lump a swelling, a mass of indefinite shape; to put together | sugar lumps cubes made by compressing small crystals of sugar

lunar concerned with the Moon | lunar cycle the different appearances of the Moon from the crescent of a new moon through waxing and waning | lunar eclipse where the Earth prevents the Sun's light reaching the Moon so, for a few minutes, the Moon is no longer seen | lunar exploration using men and machines to find what there is on the Moon | lunar month the time taken, approximately 28 days, for the Moon to travel once around the Earth | lunar orbit the path taken by the Moon around the Earth

lunch (plural is lunches) a small meal that is taken around noon; to eat a small meal

lung an organ for removing carbon dioxide from, and getting oxygen into, the blood | lung cancer an uncontrolled growth of cells in the lung | lung damage changes that occur to the air sacs, making them less effective at exchanging gases | lung structure the parts of the lung (bronchi, bronchioles and alveoli), their size and number and how they are arranged | lung volume the amount of air that can be contained in the lungs

lungs organs in the chest cavity that are used for the exchange of gases

lymph a liquid, similar to the plasma of blood, that is important in protecting the body from infection

lymphatic ducts tubes containing the fluid (lymph) that drains from between cells and is important in the immune response

lynx (not links which is connections) a member of the cat family

lysozyme a protein, found in tears, egg white and many cells, that causes bacteria to burst open

M... / mega... (*Greek* great) prefix for a million of a unit, 10^6

m / meter [USA] **/ metre** [UK] the unit of length

m... / milli... (*Latin* a thousand) prefix for a thousandth part of a unit, 10^{-3}

m² [metre squared, square metre] an area

mA [milliamp] 10^{-3} A or a thousandth part of an amp

m/s / mps [metres per second] the measure of speed that is used in science

machine an instrument, a device; to change the shape of a material | heart–lung machine equipment that is used to pump the blood and allow exchange of gases while a surgical operation is carried out on the heart or lungs of a patient | smoking machine equipment that allows a cigarette to be burned and the chemical products collected | weather machine describing how the energy from the Sun affects the atmosphere so that air moves and rain falls

machinery equipment

Macintosh (Charles 1766–1843) was a Scottish chemist looking at ways to use the waste products of coal gas. He found that naptha could dissolve rubber and then the solution could form a waterproof material with cloth. These early macintoshes were waterproof, but they leaked at the seams, went sticky in summer and became very stiff in winter.

macro- (*Greek* long) large

macro-molecules large numbers of atoms joined together in a definite pattern, *eg* starch, DNA, cellulose

made (not maid which is a young lady) caused, shaped, formed | factory made manufactured in large numbers using a standard pattern | man-made artificial

MAFF [Ministry of Agriculture, Food & Fisheries]

magazine a container for bullets or shells, a journal, a newspaper in which the pages are glossy, in colour and stapled together | magazine cutting a paper on which is printed relevant and important information, that has been cut from a newspaper

Magendie (Francois 1783–1855) graduated in medicine in Paris in 1808. He studied the effects of plant poisons on animals and then on himself, in this way, he studied strychnine, morphine, codeine and quinine. By 1816, he had shown that specific chemicals must be part of a diet in order to ensure good health

magenta plum coloured, the secondary colour produced by mixing red and blue

maggots larvae of flies

maglev magnetic levitation, a method for reducing friction by supporting the object on a magnet that is repelled above the same pole of another magnet

magma rock that is sufficiently hot that it is a liquid, found in the Earth's mantle | magma chamber an underground reservoir of liquid rock that is less than 10 kilometres below the surface | cooling magma igneous rock is thrown out of a volcano as a hot liquid which cools to give lava, pumice and other solid rocks | hot magma the rock from the mantle is at a temperature above 300°C | liquid magma emphasising that the hot rock is a liquid and so free flowing

magnesia magnesium oxide [MgO] | milk of magnesia a suspension of magnesium oxide or magnesium hydroxide in water that is effective in neutralising the acid in the stomach

magnesium (Mg, proton number 12, melting point 649°C) a silver coloured, shiny metal that is reactive, but not dangerous | magnesium carbonate [$MgCO_3$] the form in which magnesium occurs in many ores such as dolomite | magnesium chloride [$MgCl_2$] the salt formed by reacting magnesium with hydrochloric acid | magnesium oxide [MgO] a white powder formed when magnesium burns, used as part of many indigestion medicines | magnesium ribbon / magnesium strip a convenient way for storing magnesium – as a ribbon approximately 6 millimetres wide | magnesium sulfate (USA) / magnesium sulphate (UK) [$MgSO_4$] the salt formed by neutralising sulphuric acid with magnesium oxide

magnet a piece of iron, nickel, cobalt or nickel, which has been treated so that it will repel one end of another, similarly treated piece; magnets will attract opposite poles and any mixture containing iron, nickel or cobalt | bar magnet a magnet in the shape of a block or cuboid | ceramic magnet a permanent magnet that uses a form of iron in a high-melting-point material – this type of magnet is very powerful for its size, but is easily broken | electro-magnet a coil of wire around a piece of iron, the iron becomes a magnet while a current is flowing through the coil | face magnet a thin cuboid of steel, cobalt or nickel in which the magnetic poles are at the largest surfaces | freely pivoted magnet a magnet that is able to spin around on a bearing that is as friction free as possible | fridge magnet decoration that has a thin sheet of magnetic material and so will stick to the steel of a refrigerator | horse-shoe magnet a magnet that is in the shape of an horse shoe | levitating magnets method of using opposing electromagnets so as to allow a large mass to be raised | lifting magnet an electromagnet that is attached to the end of a crane so that iron can be lifted and then dropped as required | permanent magnet a piece of iron, steel, cobalt or nickel that remains magnetic | temporary magnet a coil of wire that is magnetic only while an electrical current is flowing

magnetic any property related to the behaviour of a magnet, *ie* one pole attracts iron or an opposite pole | magnetic attraction a force, caused by the magnetic effect, that pulls items closer together | magnetic behaviour the response that a material has to a magnetic field | magnetic catch a magnet and a piece of steel – one is on a door or flap, and the other is on the surroundings, so the door is kept closed, but is easily opened | magnetic compass a piece of steel that has been turned into a permanent magnet and will align itself north–south if suspended and able to turn freely | magnetic devices equipment and instruments that depend on the strength of a magnetic field | magnetic dip the angle between the horizontal and the Earth's magnetic field | magnetic domain the micro-magnets that are formed by the particles of iron, nickel or cobalt either alone or in alloys | magnetic effects the changes that are seen, *eg* attraction of an opposite pole or of iron, when a magnetic field is present | magnetic field the area over which the effect of the magnet can be measured | magnetic force the strength of the attraction or repulsion | magnetic materials solids that are affected by a magnetic field or can produce their own magnetic effect | magnetic metals the three metals (iron, cobalt and nickel) that are affected by a magnetic field | magnetic north the point, currently in northern Canada, to which compasses point as North – this point is drifting randomly at a speed of approximately 15 kilometres each year | magnetic particle a tiny piece of iron [Fe], nickel [Ni] or cobalt [Co] that is a permanent magnet, the powdered iron that coats a recording tape | magnetic poles the two ends of a magnet – opposite poles will attract, similar poles will repel | magnetic properties the characteristics associated with a material that is affected by a magnetic field | magnetic recording tape the ribbon of plastic that is coated with a thin layer of powdered iron and can be used for recording signals | magnetic repulsion pushing apart by the similar poles of two magnets | magnetic rocks stones that are naturally magnetic and will point towards the Earth's magnetic poles, lodestones | magnetic shielding a sheet or box of iron or nickel that blocks the effects of a magnet | magnetic strength the intensity of the

magnetic effect | magnetic strip a length of steel that is a weak, permanent magnet | magnetic tape a very long strip of plastic that has been coated with a thin layer of very fine iron powder and can be used for recording information | magnetic train transport that runs on rails using electromagnetism to raise the train above the rails and to provide the force that changes the speed | magnetic variation the angle between magnetic north and true north

magnetic field the area over which the effect of the magnet can be measured | magnetic field lines the shapes that are seen when iron filings are scattered near a magnet | magnetic field pattern the arrangement of lines that are obtained when fine iron filings are scattered near a magnet | magnetic field strength the intensity of the magnetic affect at that position | circular magnetic field the shape of the magnetic field that surrounds a single wire, the lines of magnetic force form circles around the wire with their centres in the wire | Earth's magnetic field the Earth seems to act like a giant magnet, so that the north pole of every compass is attracted to one end of the Earth | non-magnetic not affected by a magnetic field

magnetic force the strength of the attraction or repulsion | lines of magnetic force the pattern of non-intersecting lines connecting the poles that are seen when iron filings are sprinkled onto a magnet

magnetic materials solids that are affected by a magnetic field or can produce their own magnetic effect | hard magnetic material metal that will retain its magnetic properties for ever | soft magnetic material metal that will become magnetic when surrounded by a current in a coil but loses its magnetic field when the current is switched off

magnetically hard the metal is not easy to magnetise or to demagnetise | magnetically soft the metal is easy to turn into a magnet but rapidly loses its magnetism

magnetise (UK) / **magnetize** (USA) to cause a magnetic field to be produced – often around a piece of iron, so the iron becomes a magnet

magnetism the force, usually attracting but could be repelling, that is associated with a magnet | electromagnetism / electro-magnetism the effects caused by passing a current through a wire that is wound around a iron core | geo-magnetism / geomagnetism the magnetic field found on the Earth that starts near one geographical pole and ends at the other | laws of magnetism the magnetic field lines take the shortest route from the North pole to the South pole and never cross

magnetite lodestone, an ore of iron with a strong magnetic field

magnetize (USA) / **magnetise** (UK) to cause a magnetic field to be produced – often around a piece of iron, so the iron becomes a magnet

magnification the ratio between the apparent size of the image and the real size of the object | level of magnification how much bigger is the image compared to the object | low magnification the size of the image is only a few times bigger than the object

magnified made to look larger, a bigger image so more detail can be seen

magnifier a piece of curved glass that can give an image that is larger than the object

magnify to make bigger

magnifying glass / magnifying lens a lens that will increase the size of the image several times compared to the size of the object | magnifying power the enlargement that is made by that lens or combination of lenses

magnitude an idea of size | order of magnitude a factor of ten, ten times larger, or a tenth of the size

maid (not made which is prepared) a young lady who is a servant or does manual work such as milking cows

mail (not male which is a gender) the postal service; to send by post

main (not mane which is hair around the head) important, the predominant feature | mains circuit the arrangement of wires, switches, lamps and sockets that are found in a house | mains electricity the potential difference of between 230 volts and 250 volts alternating current that is used by most households | mains equipment machinery that is designed to be driven safely by a potential difference of 240 volts | main features important characteristics | main gases the gases that make up a major fraction of a mixture | main issues important items that are to be discussed | main nutrients the important chemicals in the food that are necessary for good health | mains plug a fitting with prongs that allows safe connection to electricity of 240 volts | main points important ideas | mains power a general term for any equipment associated with, or using, the standard household electrical supply of 240 volts alternating current | mains supply mains voltage, electricity at the domestic potential difference | mains voltage the potential difference that is delivered by the thick cables to your house – should be between 230 volts and 250 volts and

alternating at 50 hertz | mains voltage lamps light sources that are designed to work safely at 240 volts | ring main the way that cables are arranged through the house in the distribution of the mains electricity, the wires within the cable start at the distribution box, are laid around the house, and then returned to the starting point

mains / mains electricity / mains voltage the potential difference that is delivered by the thick cables to your house – should be between 230 volts and 250 volts and alternating at 50 hertz | mains plug a fitting with prongs that allows safe connection to electricity of 240 volts

mains voltage the potential difference that is delivered by the thick cables to your house – should be between 230 volts and 250 volts and alternating at 50 hertz | mains voltage lamp a light source that is designed to work safely at 240 volts

maintain to keep a system in working order, to save

maintaining repairing, remaining the same

maintenance the steps taken to keep a system in working order

maize (not maze which is a puzzle walk) a cereal that is native to North America, called sweet corn in Europe and corn in the USA

major important, significant, the largest part

majority the part that is more than half

make a type; to provide, to change, to construct | make comparisons to find details that are similar and items that are different | make inferences to deduce, to reach a conclusion using the evidence | make measurements carrying out the tasks that allow you to find the size or extent of some item | make observations watch and measure what is happening then record these events in detail | make predictions to say what is likely to happen if your theory is correct | make sense to put lots of different observations and measurements into a simple theory | make-up powders and creams that are used to improve the appearance; to invent, to improve presentation, to settle an argument

make up to invent, to improve presentation | genetic makeup that sum of all the different effects caused by the genes

making producing, constructing | bread making allowing a dough of flour, yeast and water to rise, and then baking in an oven

mal- (Latin badly) an illness

malaria a disease caused by infection with a microbe that is found in the gut of a mosquito and transmitted to humans by biting

malarial mosquito the type of mosquito (there are over 2000 different species) that is able to transmit the malaria parasite into humans

male (not mail which is the post) the half of the species that will produce the sex cells that have to move in order to fertilise the female gametes | **male cell** any cell that contains the chromosomes that are associated with male characteristics | **male flower** the part of the plant that produces the pollen, or male sex cell | **male gametes** sex cells that are able to move freely | **male nucleus** the control centre of the cell that contains the chromosomes that will produce male offspring | **male parent** the parent that provided the male sex cell | **male parts** the organs that will produce the male sex cell | **male reproductive cell** the special cell, or gamete, that contains half the usual number of chromosomes and is capable of movement in order to meet the female sex cell | **male reproductive organs** the sets of tissues, or organs, that produce the male sex cells | **male sex cells** the special cells (sperm in animals, pollen in plants) containing half the normal number of chromosomes, that will move to meet the female sex cell | **immature male** the organism that will eventually have the capability of producing male sex cells, but the sex organs have not yet developed | **mature male** the organism that is able to produce and deliver the male sex cells

malfunction to go wrong | **cell malfunction** something has gone wrong with the cell, usually indicating that an essential instruction is missing

malic acid a sour-tasting chemical that is found in unripe fruit, especially apples

malignant uncontrolled growth | **malignant tumor** (USA) / **malignant tumour** (UK) an uncontrolled growth of cells that both invades neighbouring tissues and releases cells that grow elsewhere in the body

malleable able to change shape, like putty or Plasticine™

malnourished having a diet that is not adequate to keep you healthy

malnutrition not having a balanced diet, usually essential vitamins or proteins are missing, leading to illness

Malpighi (Marcello 1628–1694) became professor of medicine at age 25 and started to publish work using a microscope with a single lens. He used frogs' lungs to show that capillaries connect the veins to the arteries, so complementing the work published by Harvey in 1628.

mammal a warm-blooded animal, with hair, that produces live young which are fed by the female from mammary glands

mammalian reproduction method by which mammals reproduce, ie internal fertilisation and the birth of live young

mammary glands organs that produce milk as food for the offspring, a characteristic of mammals

mammoth enormous, giant, large | **woolly mammoth** a large mammal, similar to the elephant, that was found through most of the northern hemisphere but became extinct about 12,000 years ago

man (plural is men) a general term for describing the human species, a male human | **man-made** synthetic, artificial, manufactured, not found in Nature

manage to direct, to be able, to supervise, to cope | **intensively manage** to use extra resources so as to increase the yield, eg of a crop, in a specified period or area

management directors, method of care | **stock management** looking after animals in order to maximise their productivity

mandible the jaw bone, the part of a jaw that is able to move

mane (not main which is important) the long hair around the head of animals such as lions and horses

maneuver (USA) / **manœuvre** (UK) to change direction, to move around with a specific purpose

manganese (Mn, proton number 25, melting point 1220°C) a transition metal | **manganese oxide** [MnO_2] a black powder that increases the speed with which hydrogen peroxide [H_2O_2] breaks down to give oxygen [O_2] and water [H_2O], used as the centre electrode in dry cells

mangled torn, crushed, spoiled

mango an evergreen tree, grows 20 metres tall and produces a fruit called the mango

manhole an entrance to the tunnels containing the underground pipes and cables of a city | **manhole cover** an iron lid that is level with the road, which is easily removed for access to the underground pipes

manipulate to change, to reorganise | **manipulate data** to change the information so that the idea, trend or relationship becomes clearer

manipulative skills ability to use your hands to carry out a task safely, rapidly and accurately

man-made synthetic, artificial, manufactured, not found in Nature

manned a person is at the controls

manœuvre (UK) / **maneuver** (USA) to change direction, to move around with a specific purpose

mantle the part of the Earth between the solid crust and the core, the mantle is made from liquid rock or magma

manual by hand; an instruction book | **manual operation** using a person to provide the power and decisions

manually operated worked by hand, not under automatic control

manufacture to make, to produce

manufacturers large-scale makers or producers | manufacturers' claims the advantages of a product as told by the producer | food manufacturer a company that turns a plant or animal products into a form that you are willing and able to eat

manufacturing making on a large scale | manufacturing processes methods for the large-scale production

manure organic matter (faeces or dead plants) that is rotting down and will be recycled into the earth

many lots, more than seven

map a diagram showing the relative positions of important places | map of life a diagram of human DNA showing the position of every instruction | concept map a diagram showing observations linked by ideas | genetic map an outline of the position of genes, or instructions, on each chromosome | geological map a diagram that shows the types and depths of rock and their relative positions | mind map a diagram showing ideas and facts linked by logical statements | weather map a diagram showing the pressure, temperature, wind strength and direction and amount of rainfall

marathon a long running race, a race over a distance of 42,195 metres (26.2 miles) | marathon runner a person who takes place in a race covering a distance of 42,195 metres

marble a metamorphic rock made from calcium carbonate [$CaCO_3$], originally the sedimentary rock of chalk which turns to limestone, then marble as a result of high temperatures and high pressure, a small glass or porcelain sphere used in the game of marbles

Marconi (Guglielmo 1874–1937) spent all of his life in improving radio communication and technology. At age 21, he developed a radio based on the demonstrations of Hertz that worked over a range of nearly 2 kilometres. Three years later, he was transmitting over the English Channel and, in 1901, he gained international fame by sending a signal from Cornwall to Newfoundland. In 1909, he was awarded the Nobel Prize, and from 1921 he used his steam yacht *Electra* as his home and mobile research laboratory

margarine a product, looking similar to butter, that is manufactured from vegetable oil or skimmed milk

margin edge, junction

marine concerned with the seas or oceans |

marine animals consumers or animals that live in the sea | marine environment the conditions of salt water and temperatures that are found in the oceans | marine life any living organism that is found in the sea

mark a written symbol, a result on an agreed scale; to scratch

marked signed, scratched, important

marker a point that is used to show a specific distance or event | marker pen a writing instrument that can be used on most surfaces

markings visible variations on the skin or fur that help identify an individual animal

married a man and a woman have publicly agreed to live together until one partner dies

marrow the mushy centre of a bone, a large fruit | bone marrow the network of cells in the middle of the bones that provide additional strength and where blood cells are produced

Mars the Red Planet, named after the Roman god of war, the fourth planet from the Sun, the planet that is very similar to Earth in size

marsh a bog, land permanently covered with a layer of water

marshmallow a spongy sweet made from sugar

marsupial / marsupial mammal an animal in which the offspring is born at a very immature state and must move to a protective pouch immediately after birth for development to continue

mash to mix to a pulp

mask a thin covering for the face; to hide by covering | protective mask a thin gauze worn over the mouth and nose to prevent entry of pollutant gases

mass (plural is masses) a fundamental unit in physics that is related to the amount of force needed to change velocity, the mass of 1 kilogram was defined by a French committee that included Lavoisier; a litre of water has a mass of approximately 1 kilogram | mass number / atomic mass relative atomic mass (ram), the mass of an atom or part of an atom on a scale in which a proton has a mass of 1 dalton (1 Da) or 1 atomic mass unit (1 amu) | air mass a large volume of the atmosphere with its own temperature and pressure | biomass the total weight of the specified type of organism in a stated area | body mass the mass of the animal | center of mass (USA) / centre of mass (UK) the point through which all the mass of an object seems to fit, when hung freely, the centre of mass is always directly below the pivot | conservation of mass the idea that however much you had at the beginning, then you will have exactly the same total amount at the end | constant mass the weight does not change despite repeating the heating or the drying | dry mass the amount of material that is left when all the water is removed | gain mass to increase the amount of material | known mass the amount of material has been measured and recorded | lesser mass a smaller amount of material | lost mass the amount of material at the end is less than was there at the start, often because a gas has been produced | molecular mass the sum of the masses of atoms in a molecule | pyramid of mass in a food chain, there is a vast amount of producer, a few consumers and very few secondary consumers | relative atomic mass (ram) the mass number, the mass of an atom or part of an atom on a scale in which a proton has a mass of 1 dalton (1 Da) or 1 atomic mass unit (amu) | total mass adding together all the different materials from several sources

massage to rub parts of the body so as to improve circulation | heart massage rhythmic pumping of the chest, or directly of the heart, in order to encourage the heart to start working again

masses (plural of mass) two or more amounts, lots

massive usually means very large in size, but should refer to a very large amount of material, *eg* many stars are massive but each has a small diameter

master the controller; to learn | master cylinder the equipment in which the piston is pushed so that a braking force is transmitted through the brake fluid to the brake cylinders

mat (not matt/matte which is dull) a protective covering | heat-proof mat / safety mat a layer of material that prevents damage to the surface

match (plural is matches) a means of starting a fire using friction; to compare two items and show they are identical | match head the chemical on the end of the match stick that burns easily when heated by friction

matches shows that two items are identical; sticks with chemicals at one tip that are used for starting fires

matching showing that two sets of data refer to the same cause

mate a partner, especially for sexual reproduction; to come together with the intention of the sperm fertilising the ovum

material component, substance, object | materials exchange moving substances across a boundary, *eg* in lungs, carbon dioxide is released by the blood, and oxygen is absorbed by red blood cells | materials scientist a person who studies the preparation and properties of substances | absorbent material a solid that will soak up large amounts of another material | animal

material any substance produced by animals | biological material any product that has been produced by a living organism from a simple chemical, such as urea, to complete organs | building materials substances that are used in the structure of a house | burning material a substance that can react with oxygen to produce heat | ceramic material the product, made when clay is baked at high temperature, that is a hard, strong insulator, but often brittle | cleaning materials chemicals that dissolve grease and dirt leaving a clean surface | common materials substances that are easily found in many households or shops | different materials emphasising that substances with different properties are to be used | everyday materials substances that are likely to be found in most households | film material the object is a very thin sheet, a fabric coated with light-sensitive chemicals | flammable material any substance that can be burned | food material ingredients that go into the cooking of a meal | fossilised material the structure formed when a substance forms a fossil | genetic material the DNA that contains the genes or control instructions for the cell | harder material the substance that will scratch or mark other substances | household materials chemicals that would be expected to be bought in a local hardware shop | illustrative material the picture, diagram or photograph that highlights and demonstrates a special point | insoluble material solid substance that will not dissolve in the liquid that is being used as a solvent | insulating material / insulation material substances, usually non-metals, that prevent the transfer of heat or the movement of electricity; most heat insulators are layers or bubbles of trapped air | living materials chemicals and substances that are found with animals and plants that are growing | magnetic material any mixture containing iron, cobalt or nickel, that is affected by a magnet or may become magnetic | microbial material chemicals that are found where microbes are growing | natural materials useful chemicals that are easily extracted form an animal or plant, substances produced by living organisms | new materials substances that have been made which were not available before | non-magnetic material substances that are not affected by a magnet | opaque material a substance that will block light | organic material chemicals that contain carbon and are often associated with life | persistent material chemicals that are not easily changed and so will kill many members of a food web over a long period of time | plant material the chemicals, cells, roots and shoots that are associated with plant growth | preparing material getting the substances weighed out and cleaned ready for use | preserved material items that should have rotted away, but have retained their shape, colour and structure for many years because of the environmental conditions | processing materials changing substances from one form to another, especially on a large scale | range of materials many different substances that have some properties in common, but show differences | raw materials the substances and chemicals that are present in the land or air and will be used in an industrial process | reference material written text that reports some measurements; a well-characterised item, such as the international standard mass, to which all other measurements are traced | resource materials the substances that may be available for that experiment | rock material any substance that is found on the surface of a planet including the Earth | shelly material thin plates | smooth material the surface of the material has no visible imperfections | soft material rocks that crumble easily, cloth that changes shape easily | softer material a substance that is more easily scratched | starting materials the reactants, substances that are present at the beginning, but will be changed | stiff material a substance that is not bent easily | stimulus material ideas that are given in order to start a discussion | supporting material the evidence that helps to prove an idea | synthetic materials chemicals that are not usually found in Nature, but have been made in the laboratory | toxic materials chemicals that are likely to kill some forms of life | unconsolidated material loose rocks and sand that can change shape easily | undigested material food that has passed through the digestive canal without change | unreacted material chemicals that are left at the end of a chemical reaction | useful materials components that can be used to make life easier or more pleasant | waste material substances that are not needed and are often poisonous | written material ideas or evidence that have been written on paper

mates has intercourse

mathematical equation / mathematical formula shows the dependent variable on the left hand side of an equals sign and the independent variables on the right hand side | mathematical laws the unbreakable rules of the universe that are shown as mathematical equations

mathematically collecting numerical information with the intention of using the data in equations

mathematics the study of relationships between variables, leading to ideas that have wider application

mating copulating, the act of bringing the male and female gametes together

matt (UK & USA) / **matte** (USA) (not mat which is a covering) a surface that is dull and will not reflect any light | matt black (UK & USA) / matte black (USA) a surface which will not reflect any light

matter material, substance; importance | states of matter the three possible ways that particles are arranged so as to produce a gas, liquid, solid | theory of matter an idea that all the properties of a substance can be explained by assuming that every substance is made from tiny particles

maturation development from a juvenile to the adult that is capable of reproducing | egg maturation the changes that occur in the immature eggs before they are released from the ovary | physical maturation changes that occur in the shape and weight of the body when ageing from juvenile to adult

mature ready, developed, ripe, sufficiently old | mature female the organism has reached an age when her eggs are ready to be fertilised | mature male the organism that is able to produce the male gamete | pre-mature earlier than expected

maturity having the brain and body of an adult

mauveine the original purple colour produced by Perkin in 1856

maw (not more which means another) the throat, a mouth

maximise (UK) / **maximize** (USA) to make the best use, to reach a high point

maximum the highest, the largest, the biggest, the most | maximum-and-minimum thermometer an instrument for measuring temperature that has two pointers, one to show the highest temperature and the other to show the lowest temperature reached | maximum concentration the greatest amount that can be dissolved in the volume of solvent, the greatest amount that can be tolerated or used | maximum speed fastest rate of travel

Maxwell (James Clerk 1831–1879) was nicknamed Dafty at school, which may have been a cause of his shyness. His research into colour vision began before he entered Cambridge as a student, and continued while he was professor at Aberdeen, where he produced the first colour photographs using the three colour process that is still used today. He moved to London and began a theoretical description of electromagnetic waves and deduced that light must be such a wave – a fact confirmed by Hertz in 1888. He also developed the kinetic theory that uses particles in motion to explain gases, liquids and solids. He retired briefly, on the death of his father, but was persuaded to become the first Professor of Experimental Physics at Cambridge, and died five years later of cancer

maze (not maize which is corn) a set of pathways forming a puzzle

mb [millibar] a thousandth part of a bar, used as the common unit when measuring atmospheric pressure

mcg (µg) [microgram] a millionth of a gram, 10^{-6} grams

meadow /meadowland an area of uncultivated grassland suitable for wildlife and for cattle to feed on

meal different foods are served on your plate | barium meal a liquid containing barium sulphate that is swallowed and provides a medium that strongly absorbs X-rays as the meal passes through the gut | microwave meal a balanced selection of foods that can be cooked in a microwave oven | typical meal the most common combination of foods that you have had over the past month

mean the average; to provide an idea, to interpret | means the method

meaning the idea, the purpose, the explanation

means the method | biological means using growth of living organisms to bring about a change | chemical means causing a change by adding new reactants | physical means using changes in temperature or kinetic energy to produce a change

measles a common childhood illness that is caused by a virus, and presents little difficulty in well-nourished children, but may kill sufferers in under-developed countries | German measles rubella, a disease caused by a virus that produces slight illness in children, but is very dangerous to pregnant women as it can cause the foetus harm – hence every girl in Britain is vaccinated against rubella

measles / mumps / rubella vaccine (MMR) vaccination, an injection containing weakened forms of the three viruses that will give protection against each disease

measurable change a difference that is sufficiently large that it can be observed and quantified

measure an accepted volume or length; to find the size | measure angles to use a protractor to find the size of an angle accurately | measure temperature to use a thermometer to see how hot is a material | preventative measures the

steps taken to stop an event taking place | tape measure a piece of cloth or paper that has been calibrated for length

measured an instrument was used to find the size

measurements data, information, size | accurate measurements the information has very low error | angular measurements using a protractor to measure an angle | appropriate measurements collecting data that is suitable for that experiment | direct measurements collecting data by observation rather than using an instrument | duplicate measurements to do again or to repeat, in order to check for errors | making measurements to find some data by experiment | number of measurements how many measurements were taken | precise measurements data that is accurate and with very low error | present measurements to show your data in an organised form | range of measurements highest and lowest data points; the number of different assessments | repeat measurements to duplicate or to do again so as to check for errors | set of measurements the data that describe several changes in an experiment | specific measurements the small amount of data that is important for that experiment | sufficient measurements enough data | systematic measurements taking lots of assessments or measurements following an agreed plan | trial measurements the first attempts at seeing if a method works | unit of measurement the agreed values that are used in measurement, *eg* metres for length, kilogram for mass and seconds for time

measuring finding the size | measuring cylinder a tube that has been calibrated to allow accurate measurements of liquid volume | measuring equipment apparatus that is calibrated and is suitable for the measurement to be made | measuring instruments lines, scales and meters that are used to find the size | measuring problems difficulties that are encountered when trying to find the amount of a material

meat (not meet which is to come together) the flesh of an animal that is to be eaten | meat protein the types of protein (a long chain of amino acids) that are found in the muscles of animals | meat quality the smell, feel and touch of some muscle that is to be eaten | joint of meat / meat joint a lump of flesh for eating that is sufficient for several portions | frozen meat the meat has been stored at a temperature below −20°C | raw meat the flesh that is to be eaten has not been cooked

mechanical automated, using moving parts | mechanical breakdown using teeth or stomach

movement to change food into smaller bits |
mechanical energy the ability to do work
associated with either position, called potential
energy, or with movement, called kinetic energy

mechanically by machine, repetitively, without
thought

mechanisation (UK) / mechanization (USA)
replacing a task that was done slowly by hand
with machinery that is faster

mechanisms methods | defence mechanisms
methods by which the skin prevents microbes
from invading and damaging the body, then the
white blood cells and the antibodies try to digest
any microbe that gets into the blood | suspension
mechanism the method by which an object is
prevented from falling

mechanization (USA) / mechanisation (UK)
replacing a task that was done slowly by hand
with machinery that is faster

media (plural of medium) materials that allow
movement of energy; chemicals on which
microbes are grown; methods for transmitting
news | media reports accounts or summaries
that appear in newspapers, on radio or on tele-
vision | denser media substances that have a
higher density than other material

median the middle figure when the data are put in
size order

medical concerned with treating ailments with
the aim of achieving a healthy body | medical
advances new procedures and methods that
allow improved treatment | medical develop-
ments increases in knowledge that allow better
treatment of a disease | medical dressing the
protective covering, of lint, cotton wool and cloth,
that is placed over a wound so as to prevent in-
fection or to protect from further harm | medical
drugs chemicals that will affect the body and are
given in order to cure an illness | medical prepar-
ations chemicals that are used by health workers
such as nurses or doctors | medical purposes the
intention is to improve the health of the patient |
medical record a permanent account of illnesses
and treatments that you have had | medical
treatment the technique or instructions that will
lead to improved health | medical use utilising a
method or substance so as to prevent illness, to
cure disease or to reduce pain

medicines drugs, chemicals that are taken or
ingested in order to prevent or to treat an illness |
modern medicines the drugs and treatments
that have become available during the past fifty
years | otc medicines / over the counter
medicines chemicals that will affect the body,
but can be bought without a prescription |

p.o.m. / prescription only medicines drugs that
can be authorised only by a medical practitioner

medium (plural is media) material or substance
through which energy travels; the mix of chemicals
on which microbes are grown | denser medium a
substance that has a higher density than another
material, the material will not allow light to
penetrate | transparent medium material that
allows light through | uniform medium a sub-
stance that is the same throughout

medulla the collection of nerve cells between the
brain and the spinal cord that controls many of
the unconscious actions such as heart rate,
breathing and blood pressure

meet (not meat which is animal flesh) to join; to
come together face to face

meeting reaching an objective; a gathering of
people, coming together for a purpose

mega... / M... (Greek great) prefix for a million,
10^6, used as a prefix for 2^{20} (1 048 576) in
computing

meiosis the type of cell division that leads to the
formation of gametes, ie daughter cells that have
half the usual number of chromosomes

melanin a range of brown and black chemicals
that give colour to the skin

melt to change from solid to liquid at a specific
temperature (the melting point)

melted was solid, but the temperature was
increased and so the material is now liquid

melting changing from solid to liquid | melting ice
a mixture of ice and water in which the amount
of ice is getting less | melting point the temp-
erature at which a pure material changes from
solid to liquid, identical to the freezing point

melting point the temperature at which a pure
material changes from solid to liquid, identical
to the freezing point | fixed melting point the
temperature at which a solid turns to liquid is
unchanging for a pure substance, eg ice melts
at 0°C

melts changes from solid to liquid at a specific
temperature (the melting point)

members individuals belonging to the same class
or set because they have lots in common

membrane a thin sheet of material | cell
membrane / cell surface membrane the thin
lipid layer on the outside of the cell through
which chemicals must pass to enter or leave the
cell | folded membrane the cell membrane
appears to have ripples so as to increase the
surface area | nuclear membrane the thin layer
of material that surrounds the nucleus and controls the entry and exit of chemicals to the
nucleus | surface membrane a substance that

marks the boundary between a liquid and the surrounding environment | **synovial membrane** the material surrounding a joint preventing loss of the synovial fluid

membranous bag a thin sack

memories (plural of memory) (not memorise which is to learn) thoughts of past events

memorise (not memories which is past dreams) to learn facts by rote

memory (plural is memories) the ability to learn and to recall information | **immune memory** the body has produced antibodies to a microbe so the instructions for that antibody are now present and available for later use

men (plural of man) more than one male person

mend to restore to usable condition, to repair

Mendel (Gregor Johann 1822–1884) became a monk at age 21, failed to qualify as a teacher, but was elected Abbott to the monastery in 1868. Most of his work was carried out in the 1850s working with seven characteristics of peas (including height, seed shape and colour, and flower colour) he grew about 21,000 plants in order to develop the idea of genes working in pairs. He sent his results to be discussed and was told that more data were needed so he should grow more plants. His work was rediscovered, and proved very useful, in 1900.

Mendelayef / Medeleef (Dmitri Ivanovich 1834–1907) grew up in Siberia as the youngest of 14 children. He must have inherited some genes for forceful behaviour from his mother – she re-opened a local glass factory in order to make some money – as he was known to be incredibly outspoken and argumentative. When he was 14, his father died, the factory burned down and Mendeleef was sent to St Petersburg, although he also worked for a while with Bunsen. The idea for the periodic table arose when Mendeleef was 34 and developing his thoughts in preparation for the writing of a text book – he found that the 60 known elements would almost form a pattern if they were organised by atomic mass, his inspired contributions were that not all elements had been discovered, so he left gaps, and the order of some elements should be reversed. This table has shaped and simplified ideas in chemistry, and yet Mendeleef was never admitted to the Imperial Academy of Sciences. He married twice, the second marriage occurred while he was in the process of divorcing his first wife so he was a bigamist.

meningitis a viral or bacterial infection of the membrane surrounding the brain (meninges)

leading to inflammation and possibly brain damage or death

meniscus the top surface of a liquid, which is usually curved at the edges

menopause the time during which a woman ceases to produce menstrual bleeding

menstrual bleeding the monthly loss of blood from women of childbearing age | **menstrual cycle** the regular changes that occur in a woman during the month

menstruation the passing of blood from the uterus wall on a monthly basis, a period | **menstruation date** the first date of the last menstruation

mental concerned with the brain, thinking | **mental activity** the amount by which the brain is being used | **mental state** how a person feels and reacts to specific events, especially when compared with expected behaviour

mentally involving the brain

mention to tell, to say

Mercury the planet nearest to the Sun; the messenger of the Gods in Roman mythology

mercury (Hg, proton number 80, melting point – 39°C) a metal that is liquid at room temperature, also called hydragyrum or quicksilver | **mercury barometer** uses the height of mercury in an inverted tube to measure air pressure | **mercury poisoning** Minamata disease, the effects, such as paralysis or brain damage, caused by inhaling mercury vapour or by eating fish containing mercury salts | **mercury thermometer / mercury-in-glass thermometer** a large volume of mercury is kept in a glass reservoir and can only expand up a thin glass tube, so the length of mercury in the tube is a measure of temperature

mesa a flat-topped hill

mesh a net, a grid | **mesh bag** a sack made from string, cotton or twine, which can hold large items, but has lots of holes | **coarse mesh** a net with large holes | **metal mesh** a grid made from wires, a metal plate from which the majority of the metal has been punched out, leaving holes | **wire mesh** a net made from strands of wire

mesophyll middle layer of cells in a leaf | **palisade mesophyll** the layer of tall cells, immediately below the epidermis, where photosynthesis takes place | **spongy mesophyll** the cells near the bottom of a leaf, which are separated by gaps so gases can diffuse between the cells

messages communication of orders, ideas, information

messenger something or someone who carries instructions or information | **messenger RNA / mRNA** the long chain of nucleotides (with ribose as the sugar) that carries the instructions from the DNA molecule of the chromosome to the cytoplasm | chemical messengers hormones, chemicals that are released from a small organ in one part of the body and cause widespread, often long-term, changes to the body

meta- (*Greek* between, among)

metabolism cells changing chemicals, such as fat or sugar, into new cells, movement and heat

metacarpals the long bones of the hand

metal an element, or mixture of elements, that conducts electricity | metal bar a long block of metal, could be round or square | metal base a small sheet of heavy metal that is used to give a stable foundation; chemically, emphasising that a metal oxide is basic and will neutralise an acid | metal block a shaped piece of metal, could be a cylinder or cuboid | metal can a storage box made from metal, usually with a lid | metal carbonate a compound that is a metal bonded to a carbonate ion [$CO_3^=$] | metal chloride a compound made from a metal bonded to a chloride ion [Cl^- | metal compound any molecule that is a metal bonded to other atoms | metal corrosion the reaction of a metal with air or water to give metal compounds so that the desirable properties, such as strength and ability to bend, are lost | metal extraction chemically changing an ore (a metal compound mixed with soil and sand) so as to obtain pure metal | metal hydride a compound between the named metal and hydrogen | metal hydroxide a metal bonded to a hydroxide, *ie* OH^- | metal mesh a sieve or filter made from wires crossing at right angles | metal object any article that is made mainly from a metal | metal ore the form in which the metal is found underground – usually as a metal compound in sand and soil | metal oxide a compound of a metal bonded to oxygen | metal railings a fence made from vertical and horizontal metal rods | metal rod a long thin cylinder made from a metal | metal salt the metal has replaced the hydrogen from an acid | metal washer a flat ring of metal that provides a firm surface for a nut | metal wire emphasising the strand or filament is made from a metal | alkali metals the group 1 elements that react vigorously with water to produce solutions that are strongly alkaline, the salts are very soluble | alkali earth metals the group 2 elements that produce basic oxides, the compounds of these elements are usually insoluble so these metals are found in earth as sulphates or carbonates | bare metal metal without any paint or grease on the surface | base metal (different from a metal base) the metal, usually cheap, but easily corroded, that is used to produce the bulk of an object, a final layer of expensive metal then makes the object look pretty | displacing metals the metal in a salt will be pushed out by a more reactive metal | extract metals to obtain a pure metal from the metal ore | familiar metals the metals that are used for household or personal items, such as iron, aluminium, silver or gold | inert metals the expensive metals, such as gold or platinum, that are not very reactive | light metal a metal with a low density | magnetic metals the three metals, iron, cobalt and nickel, that can be used to produce a permanent magnet | native metal the ore contains pieces of the metal mixed in with sand and soil | noble metals metals that will not react, *eg* gold or platinum | non-metal a solid which shows none of the properties of a metal | polished metal a metal surface that has been rubbed to remove any imperfections and so reflects lots of light | precious metals unreactive metals that cost a lot of money because they are available only in small amounts | reactive metals metals that will rapidly (explosively) react with other chemicals such as acid or water | reactivity of metals a measure of the rate at which a metal will react with other chemicals in a standardised test, producing the reactivity series | sacrificial metal a block of reactive metal that will corrode and is easily replaced with the intention of preventing iron turning to rust | smelting metals heating the metal oxide with carbon so as to extract the metal | sorting metals placing metals into different classes | transition metal an element in the periodic table that is between group 2 and group 3 | unknown metal an element that behaves as a metal, so conducts electricity, but you do not know which one | unreactive metals elements that will conduct electricity, but can safely be left in acid or chlorine because they are inert | uses of metals using the properties of metals (conduct electricity and heat, shiny malleable, ductile) to produce useful objects depending on the metal

metallic having properties, such as being shiny or conducting electricity, that are associated with metals | metallic element an element that will conduct electricity | metallic oxide the compound formed between a metal and oxygen; metallic oxides are basic or alkaline

metallised a thin film of metal layered on to a non-metallic base such as plastic or wood

metalloid elements that show some properties of metals and some properties of non-metals, *eg* carbon will conduct electricity (a characteristic of metals), but produces an oxide that is acidic (a feature of non-metals)

metallurgy the study of the properties of metals

metals a general term meaning any or all of the elements that conduct electricity

metamorphic able to change form, producing a different structure | metamorphic rock the type of rock produced by subjecting existing rocks to high temperature and pressure, *eg* chalk (a sedimentary rock) is turned into marble

metamorphism changing form, usually a rock or some form of life, *eg* from a tadpole into a frog

metamorphosis massive changes that occur in a creature going from a juvenile to an adult, *eg* a caterpillar turns into a butterfly

metatarsals the long bones in the feet

meteor a piece of rock, or sand, that enters the atmosphere from space and glows brightly because of friction with air particles

meteorite a piece of rock from space that survived speeding through the atmosphere and landed on the ground

meteorological involved with weather

meteorology the study of weather and climate

-meter (*Greek* measure)

meter (in UK only, not metre which is a unit of length) an instrument that is used for measuring (in the USA, a unit of length defined by the standard meter in Paris) | meters per second (USA) (mps, m/s) the measure of speed that is used in science | meter rule (USA) / meter ruler (USA) / meter stick (USA) a straight piece of plastic or wood that is 1 meter long and divided into centimeters and millimeters | analog meter / analogue meter (UK) an instrument that shows the output as a needle moving over a dial | digital meter an instrument in which the output is in numbers | electrical meter an instrument that needs electricity for its power source | electricity meter an instrument for measuring the amount of electrical energy that is used, usually in a house | force-meter any instrument that can be used to measure the size of a push, a pull or a weight | lightmeter an instrument for measuring the brightness of light | micrometer (USA) (μm) a millionth part of a meter, a thousand micrometers is a millimeter | micrometer an instrument for accurately measuring very small distances | millimeter (USA) (mm) a thousandth part of a meter | multimeter an instrument that can be used to measure several different electrical functions such as current, voltage and resistance | newton-meter / newtonmeter an instrument, often a calibrated spring, that is used for measuring force | pH meter an instrument that allows

the pH of a solution to be measured using a glass probe | pulse meter an instrument for automatically measuring the heart rate | seismometer equipment for detecting then recording the movement of the crust of the Earth | sound-level meter an instrument for measuring the intensity of sound | speedometer equipment that shows the speed at which the vehicle is travelling | square meter (USA) a unit of area equivalent to a square of side 1 meter

methane [CH_4] natural gas, the hydrocarbon that is used in most gas supplies, boiling point −164°C

methanoic acid [HCOOH] formic acid, the irritant that is in the sting of ants and nettles

methanol [CH_3OH] a fuel, also called wood spirit or meths, that can lead to blindness if drunk

method the way, technique or means for finding out some data | method of investigation the technique that you are using to find out the answer to a problem | method of transmission the way that an organism, such as a parasite or bacterium, moves from one creature to another | accurate method a technique that is capable of giving results that are reliable and repeatable | agricultural method the techniques, chemicals and schedule that are followed for the large-scale production of food | alternative method a second way of finding the information that has some advantage of cost or safety or speed | appropriate method the way to carry out a change that is best for safety or cost or accuracy in a particular experiment | asexual method reproduction of a single cell, to give two offspring that are identical to the parent | compare methods to see which of two or more methods, is likely to be the best in terms of safety, accuracy, speed or some other factor | cooling method the equipment or procedure that is used to remove heat | different methods listing at least two different ways for achieving the same end result | evaluate methods to see if the techniques are suitable or appropriate and to decide any improvements | farming methods means for raising crops that increase profits and yield | indirect methods looking at one indicator that will reflect the change in some other variable, *eg* the number of microbes could identify pollutants | investigative method the way in which you try to find out what is happening | modern methods using theories, equipment and recipes that have been developed over the past two decades | physical methods techniques that cause no permanent change and are reversible, *eg* melting point | safe method a technique that will not cause injury | sampling method the way that a small portion is taken that should represent the whole amount | separation methods ways in which different compounds can be isolated from a mixture | simple method a technique that does not need complicated apparatus, is safe and gives a clear result | suitable method a technique that gives the required accuracy at the right cost

methodology the way that a process is carried out

methyl orange an indicator that is red below pH 3.7 and yellow above pH 3.7

methyl red an indicator that is red below pH 5.1 and yellow above pH 5.1

metre (in the UK – not meter which is an instrument) unit of length defined by the standard metre in Paris (Lavoisier and others in 1789 decided that the distance from Pole to the equator was to be 10 million metres) | metres per second (mps, m/s) the measure of speed that is used in science | metre rule / metre ruler / metre stick a straight piece of plastic or wood that is 1 metre long and divided into centimetres and millimetres | micrometre (not micrometer which is a measuring instrument) (μm) a millionth part of a metre, a thousand micrometres is a millimetre | millimetre (mm) a thousandth part of a metre | square metre a unit of area equivalent to a square of side 1 metre

metric a system of measurement | metric standard the pieces of material (the atomic clocks, the kilogram mass and the 1 metre rule) that have been agreed as fundamental to the SI system of measurement | metric system an agreed scheme of measurement based on the kilogram, metre and second

Mg magnesium, proton number 12, an alkali earth metal

mg [milligram / milligramme] a unit of mass that is a thousandth part of a gram, 1000 mg is 1 gram

mica a form of silicon oxide that is split very easily into thin plates

mice (plural of mouse) small mammals with long tails | field mice a type of small mammal that lives in grassland

micro... / μ... (Greek small) tiny, a millionth part

micro-beast / microbeast any creature that is difficult to see without the aid of a magnifying glass or a microscope

microbe a tiny creature that is not visible to the naked eye, but that can be seen under a microscope, many microbes cause no problems, some are essential for a healthy gut and a few cause diseases | resistant microbe a microbe that is not affected by the presence of a specified antibiotic

microbial concerning microbes, usually bacteria | microbial growth an increase in the number of microbes, colonies of microbes are starting to become visible | microbial infection growth of a microbe, usually a bacterium, but can be a fungus or a virus, that leads to the host organism feeling ill | microbial material any substance that contains, or has been produced by, microbes | anti-microbial a chemical that prevents the growth of micro-organisms

microbiological laboratory the room or area that is specifically designed and built so that microbes can be handled safely

microbiologist a person who studies microbes

micro-circuit a collection of many thousands of electrical components that are made into a tiny package

micro-climate / micro-environment the range of temperature, amount of moisture or light and wind that is found in a very small area, eg under a log

micro-electronics electrical circuits that are too small to be seen and are able to be used as sensors or logic circuits

micrograph a picture taken of the sample on the stage of a microscope

micrometer (UK & USA) (not micrometre which is a tiny distance) an instrument for the accurate measurement of distance

micrometer (USA) μm, a millionth part of a meter, a thousand micrometers is a millimeter

micrometre (UK) (not micrometer which is a measuring instrument) μm, a millionth part (10^{-6}) of a metre, a thousand micrometres is a millimetre

micron μm, a micrometre, a millionth part of a metre

micro-organisms any small creature that can be seen only with the aid of lenses

microphone equipment for turning speech or sound in to electrical signals

micro-projection apparatus / micro-projector equipment that can take the image from a microscope and project it onto a screen

microscope a tube containing two or more lenses that can be used to tiny make items such as bacteria look very much larger | microscope evidence information, pointing to a specific series of events that was obtained by using a microscope | microscope slide a thin, oblong glass sheet, approximately 5 cm x 2 cm, that is used to support a specimen under the lens of a microscope | compound microscope an instrument that has at least two lenses for magnifying tiny objects | electron microscope uses a beam of electrons (rather than light) to look at objects that are much too small to be seen with a light microscope | light microscope an instrument, using two or more lenses, that uses visible light to illuminate the specimen | powerful microscope a microscope that is capable of seeing very tiny objects, *eg* an electron microscope can magnify objects 100,000 times

microscopic tiny, too small to be seen | microscope examination using a microscope in order to look at fibres or dust | microscopic hole a tiny puncture through which air can move, but which is too small for water to pass through | microscopic observations using a microscope to find the features and measurements of tiny objects | microscopic units tiny building blocks

microscopy studying objects by using microscopes to enlarge the image

micro-switch a piece of equipment, usually less than 1 millimetre square, which can be use to turn the current on and off

microvilli (plural of microvillus) tiny folds (approximately 1 micrometre long) in the membrane of most cells that increase the surface area

microwaves electromagnetic waves, similar to light, that have wavelengths of several micrometres | microwave meal a balanced mix of foods that can be heated using microwaves | microwave oven a metal box, inside which microwaves are produced, that can be used for heating water or solutions, but the box prevents the microwaves from escaping

mid-day noon, the time when the Sun is at its highest point for that day

middle centre | Middle Ages the years between the collapse of the Roman Empire in the fifth century and the Renaissance in the fifteenth century, Ibn-al-Nafis is one important scientist during this thousand-year period | middle ear the section of the ear between the ear drum and the cochlea where the ossicles are found | middle-ear infection invasion of the middle ear, where the ossicles are found, by a microbe which reproduces in the warm, moist conditions and leads to ear ache | middle shore the area between sea and land that is expected to be covered at high tide and uncovered at low tide

midnight the dark time of night when the Sun is directly under your feet, 12 o'clock at night

midsummer a period of approximately one month each side of the summer solstice (June 21 in the Northern Hemisphere, December 21 in the Southern Hemisphere) when temperatures are high

midwinter a period of approximately one month each side of the winter solstice (December 21 in the Northern Hemisphere, June 21 in the Southern Hemisphere) when temperatures are low

might (not mite which is a tiny spider) possibly, high strength

migrate to move from one area of the world to a distant place in order to ensure a better chance of survival

migrating animals, often of the same species, all moving in the same general direction, usually for a reason such as seeking water or a place to breed

migration movement of lots of animals in a specific direction in order to improve the probability of survival

mile a distance, originally 1000 paces of a Roman soldier, but now defined as 1760 yards (approximately 1584 metres) | miles per hour (mph) the unit of speed that is used for transport

military concerned with the fighting forces

milk the liquid produced from the breast of any mammal, which is produced for feeding the young; to take milk from a female mammal, especially a cow, which will encourage her to produce more milk | milk cells the cells in the mammary glands that produce the milk | milk float a vehicle, powered by batteries, that is used for transporting containers of milk in large numbers | milk glands the cells or tissues that produce the milk for feeding young offspring | milk of magnesia a suspension of magnesium oxide [MgO] or magnesium hydroxide [$Mg(OH)_2$] in water that is effective in neutralising the acid in the stomach | milk powder an amorphous white solid, or powder, that is produced by removing the water from milk | milk teeth the first set of teeth in humans, milk teeth start to appear soon after birth and all 28 will have been replaced by age 16 | breast milk the liquid produced by the mammary glands that is a perfect nutrient for a human baby

milking cow cattle that are selectively bred so as to give high yields of milk, a dairy cow

milky a white opaque solution

Milky Way the name of the galaxy in which Earth exists, the Milky Way is a disc, approximately 100,000 light-years diameter and comprises approximately 200 million stars

mill a building in which grain is ground to a powder; to grind | millstone a rock containing very hard fragments making it suitable for grinding cereal in a mill | windmill a building in which the grindstones are connected to the vanes that are turned by the wind

millennia (plural of millennium) several thousand years

millennium (plural is millennia) a thousand years

millepede / millipede a long bodied arthropod made from many double segments, each with two pairs of legs

milli... / m... (*Latin* thousand) prefix for a thousandth part of a unit, 10^{-3}

millibar / mb a thousandth part of a bar, used as the common unit when measuring atmospheric pressure, which averages 1013.25 mb at sea level

milligram (UK & USA) **/ milligramme** (UK) **/ mg** a unit of mass, a drop of water has a mass of approximately 330 milligram

millilitre (UK) **/ milliliter** (USA) **/ ml** a unit of volume, a thousandth part of a litre, the same as 1 cm^3

millimetre (UK) **/ millimeter** (USA) **/ mm** a unit of length, a thousandth part of a metre

million lots and lots, one million is 1,000,000 or 10^6 | millions of years a very, very long time | parts per million (ppm) a measure of concentration

millipede / millepede a long bodied arthropod made from many double segments, each with two pairs of legs

mill-stone a shaped piece of millstone grit that is used for grinding corn or wheat

millstone / millstone grit a rock containing very hard fragments

milometer equipment for measuring distance moved

mimic someone who imitates; to change appearance, smell or behaviour so that one organism appears to be another, to copy

Minamata disease an illness that affected the people living on the shores of Minamata Bay, Japan, in the mid-1950s; the disease had symptoms similar to bad 'flu', but with paralysis, and often led to death. The cause was eventually traced to mercury from a nearby factory entering the food chain and leading to death by mercury poisoning

mind (not mined which is extracted from underground) brain-power, the ability to use memory, the working of the brain; to look after, to pay attention | mind map a diagram showing ideas and facts linked by logical statements

mine a personal descriptive, possessive, an explosive, an area of ground from which an ore or a mineral is extracted | copper mine a hole in the ground from which copper ore is obtained

mined (not mind which is brain-power) extracted from rocks, obtained by digging into the ground

miner (not minor which is less important) a person who digs minerals out of the ground

mineral naturally occurring compound that has a crystal structure, the elements that are needed by living organisms (including magnesium for chlorophyll and iron for red blood cells) | mineral acids any acid that does not contain carbon, the common laboratory acids | mineral composition the type and amount of each mineral in a rock or in the water | mineral content the amount of a particular compound in a rock or water | mineral deficiency the diet does not contain an adequate amount of one or more minerals, leading to a disease | mineral grains rock particles, up to a centimetre in diameter, that are found in other rocks | mineral needs the need of all living creatures to absorb minerals such as potassium, iodine, calcium | mineral oil a liquid that looks like oil, but may be manufactured from other chemicals, often used to improve high power lenses in microscopes | mineral requirements the need of any living creature for minerals such as magnesium, iron, sodium, chloride | mineral water water that has been extracted from underground wells and so contains dissolved minerals | mineral wool material that looks like cotton wool, but is made from non-reactive chemicals such as silica | dissolved minerals the ions, or charged particles, that will dissolve in water | platey minerals / platy minerals have a layered structure caused by slow magma flow | range of minerals many different types of crystals or ores | transport minerals to move the minerals from one site to another, either naturally, by rock and ice flow, or by artificial means

mine-shaft experiment a model that demonstrates convection, a box has two chimneys connected by a shaft, a small fire is lit at the bottom of one chimney so hot air rises and pulls cool air down the other chimney and along the shaft

mingle to diffuse, to mix by random motion

mingling mixing slowly and randomly

miniature tiny; a small version of a real object

minimal smallest, hardly noticeable | minimal impact causes almost no change to the surroundings | minimal requirement the least amount of material required

minimise (UK) **/ minimize** (USA) to make as small as possible

minimum lowest point | minimum-and-maximum thermometer an instrument for measuring temperature that has two pointers, one to show the lowest temperature achieved and the other to show the highest temperature reached

mining digging so as to obtain some solid ore or fuel | coal mining digging underground in order to remove the coal

mink a mammal, similar to a weasel, that lives in woodland that is close to river and was bred or killed for its fur

minor (not miner which is a person who digs) little, less important, not significant | minor intrusion a small amount of magma has penetrated the solid rock, then cooled slowly

minuscule tiny

minute extremely small, a unit of time that is 1/1440 of one day (24 hours of 60 minutes each) | light-minute the distance that light travels in one minute in a vacuum (approximately 18 million kilometres)

mirror a surface, either polished metal or a piece of glass, that reflects light | mirror image the way that an object appears in a mirror, usually with lateral (left to right) inversion, but upright | mirrored room a room in which many, or all, of the walls and the ceiling are covered with mirrors | flat mirror / plane mirror a flat reflective surface | paired mirrors using a pair of mirrors to look around a corner, *eg* in a periscope

miscarriage loss of a foetus from a pregnant uterus

miscible liquids that are able to mix

misconception wrong idea, misunderstanding

misleading results the data seem to show one idea or direction, but further information would point to a different interpretation

miss to fail to see an important item, to land wide of the target

missed (not mist which is a fine spray) failed to hit a target

missing data that should be present have not been collected or have not been found

mission a purpose, an objective

mist (not missed which is failed to hit) fine droplets of a liquid, usually water, have condensed into the air

mistake an error, something has gone wrong

mis-use deliberately applying equipment or a method in a way that could cause harm

mite (not might which is strength or a possibility) a tiny spider | dust mite a tiny arthropod that lives by eating dead skin cells

mitochondria (plural of mitochondrion) organelles in each cell where the respiration reaction occurs

mitochondrion (plural is mitochondria) the organelle where respiration occurs

mitosis asexual reproduction, cell division leading to daughter cells with an identical number of chromosomes as the parent cell

mitral valve / bicuspid valve the flaps between the atrium and ventricle on the left hand side of the heart

mix a mixture; to add chemicals together, to stir | cake mix a powder to which egg and milk are added and then cooked to produce an edible cake | re-mix to blend together substances that have separated out

mixer equipment for mechanical stirring of a powder or liquid | food mixer electrical equipment that uses rotating paddles to mix ingredients

mixes the process of adding one chemical another with the intention of having a similar composition throughout

mixing adding one chemical to another, stirring

mixture two or more chemicals that are not bonded together, may be in any proportion, and which retain their own chemical and physical properties | cake mixture a powder to which egg and milk are added and then cooked to produce an edible cake | common mixtures mixture with which you are likely to be familiar, *eg* air, sea water, milk | complex mixture contains very many different molecules | cough mixture a liquid medicine that helps remove a cough | freezing mixture any combination of chemicals that causes a large drop of temperature – adding salt to ice is a freezing mixture that was used for making ice cream | ice/salt mixture adding salt to ice so that the freezing point and the temperature of the mixture are both lowered – can be as low as –20°C | reacting mixture two or more chemicals added to each other start to react – often explosively

ml [milliliter (USA) / millilitre (UK)] a unit of volume, a thousandth part of a litre, the same as 1 cm^3, 1000 ml is 1 litre

mm [millimeter (USA) / millimetre (UK)] a thousandth part of a metre, 1000 mm is 1 metre

MMR / MMR vaccine [mumps, measles, rubella vaccine] a single injection containing all three of these viruses in an inactivated form, in order to provide protection from these infections

Mn manganese, proton number 25, a transition metal

mnemonic a method for remembering facts often by using a sentence, *eg* the colours of the rainbow or spectrum are Richard of York gave battle in vain (red, orange, yellow, green, blue, indigo, violet)

mobile can be moved, a structure, often made from several balanced levers, that moves with the breeze

mode method, most common value

model a structure that reflects the shape and connections of a real construction; to make a structure or produce an idea that reflects real life | model building the assumptions that go into the construction of an idea or a structure | model cells to make a drawing or a structure that shows the position of the different organelles within the cell | model changes to make a structure that will react in a similar way to the real world |

model engine a small version of a full-size engine that shows how the different parts work together, but is not very powerful | model gut using plastic bags and semi-permeable tubing to mimic the chemical changes that occur in the gut | model house a miniature version of a human dwelling place, possibly with decorations and working lamps, but without heating or running water | alternative model the second of two ideas that may be used to explain the same observations | anatomical model a diagram, or an inanimate (usually plastic) representation of a human body, in order to show where all the various organs are to be found | ball-and-spoke model a method for making a model of a molecule using balls which represent each atom and are bonded together with spikes | bell-jar model equipment demonstrating how air enters the lungs, (a balloon is put inside a bell jar, the bottom sealed with a flexible sheet that can be moved up and down, like a diaphragm, causing the balloons to change shape)| domain model explains magnetism in iron by assuming that the metal is made from millions of small areas, or domains, of magnetism | dynamic model an structure in which the various components can change in response to external changes | early model first ideas that have since been modified | flow model using particles to show how a fluid moves through pipes and how an object moves through liquids or gases | geocentric model the idea that the Earth is at the centre of the universe | heliocentric model the idea that the Sun (Helios) is at the centre of the Solar System and that the planets and asteroids are in orbit around the Sun | molecular model a structure, that is often made from balls and sticks, showing the position and bonding of all the atoms in a molecule | particle model the idea that everything in the universe is made from tiny particles that are in constant motion (also called the kinetic theory) | scale model an artificial model of an item in which the size of all components are in the same ratio as in the real article | 3D model / three-dimensional model a structure that shows the position of different components in both the horizontal and vertical planes | water model the idea that the behaviour of electrons in electricity is similar to the movement of water through tubes | working model an idea that may not be perfect, but is adequate to explain most observations

modelled turned an idea into a structure that can be seen to change and used to explain some observations

models structures, which may be constructed or mathematical, that show an idea in a simple form, reflecting behaviour of a real object

moderate not destructive, medium; to oversee

moderately reasonably, medium quality, to some extent

modern recent, up to date | modern disease an illness that has been important only in the past few years | modern idea suggestions and theories that have been put forward in the recent past | modern medicines the drugs and treatments that have become available during the past fifty years | modern methods using theories, equipment and recipes that have been developed over the past two decades | modern plants the crops and garden flowers that have been bred over the past twenty years

modification a small change

modified changed | genetically modified changing one or more of the instructions in the chromosome so as to improve the desirable characteristic

modify to change a small part of an idea or structure

Moissan (Ferdinand 1852–1907) born to a poor family in Paris, he started as an apprentice pharmacist, at age 14, then studied medicine and eventually became a Professor at the Ecole Supérieure in 1886, the same year in which he isolated fluorine.

moist damp, having a thin film of water

moisten to make damp

moisture humidity, water vapour | moisture level the humidity, the amount of water vapour | moisture sensor a probe that is able to respond to the presence of small amounts of water | moisture test a method for finding the presence or amount of water vapour – water vapour will turn blue cobalt chloride paper to pink

moisturiser an emulsion of oil in water that is used to make dry skin feel more supple

molars / molar teeth grinding teeth at the back of the jaw, adult humans should have a total of 12 molar teeth | premolars grinding teeth that are between the molars and the canine teeth

molasses a dark-coloured liquid that is extracted from sugar cane

mold (USA) **/ mould** (UK) a fungus, the kingdom of life that is characterised by a cell wall and no chlorophyll, a cast into which a liquid is poured that then turns solid; to shape | leaf mold the brown remains of dead leaves that line the ground in autumn

moldy (USA) / **mouldy** (UK) areas of fungi are seen | **moldy food** food that is so old that areas of coloured fungi are visible – possibly producing harmful chemicals

mole a mammal that is adapted for digging tunnels and living underground, the formula mass expressed in grammes

molecular mass the mass of one molecule of material relative to the mass of a proton | **molecular models** using balls and rods to make structures that look like the molecule, but is millions of times larger | **molecular structure** the way that the atoms are arranged in molecule

molecule a pure chemical that contains more than one atom, the atoms are present in definite proportion and are joined in specific ways to each other | **diatomic molecule** a compound that is two atoms bonded together | **food molecules** chemicals that are found in food and are capable of being absorbed, possibly after digestion or being broken into simpler molecules | **glucose molecule** a chemical that has the formula $C_6H_{12}O_6$ | **insoluble molecules** material that will not dissolve in that solvent | **large molecule / macromolecule** a compound that contains many hundreds of atoms joined in specific sequence, *eg* proteins often contain more the 10,000 atoms | **long molecule** a compound that is made from many units joined end-to-end and so appears like a piece of string | **neutral molecule** a chemical that has no charge, but does have a definite composition | **simpler molecules** the smaller molecules that are made by breaking down large molecules such as proteins or fats | **small molecule** a molecule that contains only a few atoms bonded together | **smaller molecules** comparing a molecule, such as an amino acid which contains less than a hundred atoms, to a large molecule, *eg* a protein, that contains several thousand atoms | **soluble molecules** material that will dissolve in a stated liquid | **sugar molecule** a carbohydrate which tastes sweet

mollusc an invertebrate animal that has a very hard outer protective shell

molt (USA) / **moult** (UK) to lose the outer skin deliberately

molten a material that is solid at room temperature and has been heated above its melting point | **molten iron** iron that has been heated above its melting point (1535°C) and so will flow | **molten rocks** any rock or soil that is so hot that the rock has melted and is able to flow | **molten sulphur** the temperature of the sulphur is above the melting point (113oC), and so is a liquid, but there is insufficient oxygen for the sulphur to

burn | **molten wax** the temperature is sufficiently high that the wax will flow, but not high enough for combustion

molting (USA) / **moulting** (UK) getting rid of one layer of skin, hair or feathers to be replaced by a new layer

moment a measure of time that is usually short | **moments** turning forces (not to be confused with a force – the force is applied in a straight direction, a moment is the rotating force) | **moment of a force** torque, the turning force produced by applying a force to a specified point turning moment = applied force x distance to pivot (newton-metres)   (newtons)   (metres) | **anti-clockwise moment** a turning force applied in the opposite direction as the clock hands move | **balanced moments** the torque, moment or turning force (= force x distance to pivot) in the clockwise direction is exactly matched by torque or turning force in the anti-clockwise direction | **balancing moments** applying the law of moments so that a lever is exactly level | **clockwise moment** a turning force that tries to push the lever in the same direction as the hands of a clock move | **law of moments / principle of moments** the idea that, at equilibrium, the turning force (moment) in a clockwise direction is exactly balanced by the turning force in the anti-clockwise direction | **turning moment** torque, turning force applied to a lever

turning moment = applied force x distance to pivot (newton-metres)   (newtons)   (metres)

momentum the product of mass and velocity, the total momentum before a collection is identical to the total amount after the collision (momentum does not have a named unit)

momentum   =   mass   x   velocity

monera one of the five kingdoms of life, containing single-celled organisms that do not fit into any of the other four categories

monitor a television screen; to measure, to check | **monitor temperature** measure the temperature at regular intervals to make sure that it stays within limits | **monitor the environment** to check the area, and surrounding water and air, for any changes in the concentration of chemicals or light or temperature | **pH monitor** a glass rod, attached to a meter, that will continually measure the amount of acid or alkali in solution

monitored measured, checked

monitoring measuring the concentration of chemicals at intervals and following the changes | **monitoring data** continually looking for trends and changes in information that is being produced | **environmental monitoring** measuring the concentration of chemicals in the water and the air | local monitoring following changes of specific items in a specified area | national monitoring looking at the trend of different variables over the whole country

mono- (*Greek* one)

monocotyledon a flowering plant that produces a seed from which a single leaf is initially produced

monocycle a transport vehicle with a single wheel

mono-hybrid cross sexual reproduction in which one gene of the offspring is being studied

monomer a single unit, a chemical building block that will be joined to form a polymer

... monoxide containing a single oxygen atom | carbon monoxide [CO] a poisonous gas that binds to the haemoglobin in the red blood cell so the cell can no longer carry oxygen

monsoon extremely heavy rainfall that occurs in the tropics at the same time each year

month a period of approximately 28 days | calendar month one of the 12 divisions of the year that is decided on a social (rather than any observational) basis | lunar month the time taken for the Moon to go from a new moon, through the full moon to the next new moon – a period of 27.3 days

monthly occurs every 28 days | monthly cycle an event, or a series of events, that occurs every 28 days | monthly period the loss of blood that occurs each month from the uterus wall of women

mood a state of mind, a feeling | mood swing the state of mind changes unpredictably between happy and depressed

Moon the natural satellite of the Earth, a rock about 3500 kilometres in diameter and 385,000 kilometres from the Earth | Moon's phases the change of appearance of the Moon throughout the month | crescent moon the Moon appears as part of a circle a few days before and just after a new moon | eclipse of the Moon the Sun, Earth and Moon are in a straight line so the Moon is in the shadow of the Earth | full moon the Moon appears as a bright circle, reflecting the light from the Sun | half moon the Moon appears to be a semi-circle | new moon the appearance of the Moon as a thin crescent on the right hand side | phases of the Moon the appearance of the Moon from the Earth, starting with the thin crescent of a new moon, waxing to a full moon then waning to disappear

moons rocks, or natural satellites, that orbit other planets

moor / moorland exposed areas of hill that are covered with heather and bushes

moraine a deposit of rock from a glacier

moral issue an argument, usually based on opinion, that has no clear answer, but may cause great distress, *eg* is abortion right?

mordant a chemical that causes colours to grip tightly to a fibre or cloth

more (not maw which is a throat) larger, greater | more accurate results that are reliable and repeatable | more dense the mass per centimetre cubed is greater than the density of another item | more quickly faster, with greater speed | more reactive higher in the reactivity series compared to another metal | more rounded looking like a sphere, without hard edges

morning the time of day when the Sun is above the horizon and still climbing

morph- / -morph (*Greek* form)

morphine an opiate drug that relieves pain, and that can be addictive

mort- (*Latin* death)

mortar a heavy dish that is used, with a pestle, to grind powders; the mixture of water, sand and cement that is used to hold bricks in a building

Moseley (Henry Gwyn Jeffreys 1887–1915) graduated in 1910, volunteered for the army in 1914, and was killed by a sniper. In those four years, he discovered the importance of the proton number, predicted the properties of six missing elements and explained the link between the chemical properties of an element and its atomic structure.

mosquito (plural is mosquitoes) a flying insect (there are over 2000 species), several species have parasites in their guts that can be transmitted to people | malarial mosquito the type of mosquito that is able to transmit the malaria parasite from human to human

mosquitoes (plural of mosquito) flying insects, found mainly in tropical countries, four species of which are carriers for different forms of human malaria, another will carry yellow fever and others transmit dengue fever

moss (plural is mosses) a type of plant that has neither roots nor the tissues that allow easy transport of water

most the greatest, the largest | most quickly fastest | most reactive the fastest reacting, the element at the top of the reactivity series

moth a nocturnal flying insect | moth-proof un-affected by the presence of moths, protected

mother the female parent; to raise and nurture offspring

motile the cell is capable of movement

motion movement; to signal by moving hands or arms | Brownian motion random movement of small particles, such as dust or pollen, in gas or water | circular motion moving at a fixed distance around a point | fluid motion movement of part of a liquid or gas through the same liquid or gas; graceful, continuous | laws of motion three laws proposed by Newton

1. Every body continues at constant velocity unless a force is applied
2. The change of velocity is proportional to the force applied
3. Every action has an equal and opposite reaction

| linear motion moving in a straight line | opposes motion a force, usually friction or fluid resistance, that tries to prevent movement | planetary motion movement of the planets, in elliptical orbits, around the Sun | random motion movement of an object in a direction and at a speed that can not be predicted | satellite motion movement of a body around a planet

motor / electric motor a mechanism that turns electrical energy into moving or kinetic energy | motor control the command and movement of muscles | motor-generator equipment that will produce movement if an electric current is applied, but will generate electricity if the centre is rotated | starter motor the electrical equipment that is used to rotate a car engine rapidly | wind-up motor not a true motor, but a spring-driven mechanism that needs putting under tension so as to be able to drive a set of wheels

mottled having blotches, covered with spots of different shades and sizes

mould (UK) **/ mold** (USA) fungi – the kingdom of life that is characterised by a cell wall and no chlorophyll, a cast that can be filled with liquid; to shape | leaf mould the brown remains of dead leaves that line the ground in autumn

mouldy (UK) **/ moldy** (USA) areas where fungi are growing | mouldy food food that is so old that areas of coloured fungi are visible – possibly producing harmful chemicals

moult (UK) **/ molt** (USA) to lose the outer skin deliberately

moulting (UK) **/ molting** (USA) getting rid of one layer of skin, hair or feathers to be replaced by a new layer

mountain change of height of a geographical area that is both large and sudden | mountain face one side of a mountain that appears to be almost uniform | mountain rescue the act of using a group of experienced climbers to find a person who was lost or injured on a mountain and remove them to safety | high mountains any rocks which are large, with steep sides and long drops

mountaineer a person who climbs hills and rock faces for pleasure

mountaineering a sport in which people climb large, high natural features

mounted riding an animal, especially a horse, a specimen that has been prepared, fixed, stained and attached to the slide ready for viewing under a microscope

mouse (plural is mice) a small mammal with a long tail | field mouse (plural is field mice) a type of small mammal that lives in grassland

mouth entrance or aperture at the start of the digestive system | mouth breeder a fish that protects its young in its mouth | mouth-parts the collection of tissues that allow an animal to ingest food | mouthpiece equipment that is used for changing sound energy of speech, into electrical signals

mouth-parts the collection of tissues that allow an animal to ingest food | piercing mouth-parts part of the insect's mouth is a tube that can be used to penetrate through skin

mouthpiece equipment that is used for changing sound energy of speech, into electrical signals

movable able to change position or time | fully movable able to rotate in all directions | slightly movable able to move if a large force is applied, able to move a small distance

move to change position, to create an emotional response | move off to leave a specific place and go to somewhere unknown

moved shifted, changed

movement shifting position, motion | movement energy kinetic energy, the ability to do work, or cause a change, that an object has because it is moving | movement of sediment a change in the position of the layer of mud and silt that has been dropped by a slow moving river | annual movement migration, the journeys that some animals undertake each year in order to get the best chance of finding food and shelter | apparent movement the change that you see from your position, which may be different from what actually happens, eg the Sun appears to rise in the east | controlled movement shifting position by a method that is safe and predictable | heat movement loss or gain of thermal energy causing a change of temperature or change of state | random movement change in the position of particles in all sorts of directions at a range of speeds | regular movement a change that occurs at predictable intervals, a rhythm | repetitive movement a change that keeps occurring at predictable intervals | speed of movement a measure of how fast the object is changing position | tectonic movement the change of position of the massive plates that are the crust of the Earth | wave movement the regular up and down motion of the surface of the sea, which is caused by wind

moves changes position, changes location

moving shifting position relative to another object | moving air wind, the bulk movement of air particles | moving energy the ability to do work, or cause a change, that an object has because it is moving, also called kinetic energy | moving heat the type of energy caused by particles moving rapidly (heat) is transferred to a cooler area by conduction, convection or radiation | moving object any body that is shifting position relative either to another body or to a fixed point | moving off leaving | moving particles the tiny particles are either pushing past each other (a liquid) or moving at high speed and rarely col-liding (in a gas), which is the basis of the kinetic theory | moving surfaces one area is changing position relative to another area | moving water a flow of water, a river, a stream, sea waves | freely moving able to rotate or slide without any friction or air resistance

MP / mp / m.pt. [melting point] the temperature at which a solid turns into a liquid

mph [miles per hour] a measure of speed that is used for transport

mps / m/s [metres per second] the measure of speed that is used in science

MR GRENS a mnemonic for the characteristics of life [move / respire / grow / reproduce / excrete / nutrition / sense]

MRSA [methicillin-resistant *Staphylococcus aureus*] a super-bug that is unaffected by current antibiotics

MRS GREF a mnemonic for the characteristics of life [move / respire / sense / grow / reproduce / excrete / feed]

MRS NERG a mnemonic for the characteristics of life [move / respire / sense / nutrition / excrete / reproduce / grow]

m/s / mps [metres per second] the measure of speed that is used in science

mucous (UK) **/ mucus** (USA) a slimy fluid that is produced over the surfaces of many organs | mucous plug / mucus plug the jelly-like substance in the cervix of a pregnant lady | mucous-producing cells / mucus-producing cells the epithelial cells, lining tubes such as the trachea or the intestine, that produce mucus

mud a mixture of tiny grains of rock and water that is able to flow slowly, the layer of grains that form a sediment at the bottom of lakes and rivers

mud-free lagoon an enclosed section of clear sea water in which there is no sediment of fine clay

mudstone a sedimentary rock with very fine grains that is the precursor of slate

muffle to reduce the loudness of a sound

muffler a tube that reduces the noise made by exhaust gases, an exhaust pipe

mug a cup, a container for drinks

mule the offspring of a female horse and a male donkey that is always sexually sterile (the offspring of a female donkey and a male horse is a hinny or a jennet)

multi- (*Latin* many)

multicellular made from many cells | multicellular organism a living creature that is made from lots and lots (maybe several million, million) of cells, some of which may be specialised, and all of which are co-ordinated

multi-faceted several different features or important sides

multimeter an instrument that can be used to measure several different electrical functions such as current, voltage and resistance

multiple having many parts, numerous | multiple births several offspring or babies are produced at the same time | multiple-choice questions a test in which the questions have a limited number of answers from which to choose

multiplier an item that causes an increase | distance multiplier a machine, lever or pulley, that causes the object to move a greater distance than would normally result from the effort | force multiplier a machine, lever or pulley, that makes the force applied to the object greater than the effort force applied

multiplies becomes larger in population numbers

multiply to give the product of two numbers, to increase the number of cells by reproduction

mumps an illness caused by a virus that causes the salivary glands to become inflamed | mumps, measles, rubella (MMR) a single injection containing an attenuated form of all three of these viruses that should provide protection from a natural infection

muscle (not a mussel which is a mollusc) the tissue that is able to contract and relax leading to move-ment | muscles groups of muscle cells that allow different parts of the body to move in relation to each other; there are approximately 600 muscles in the human body, each of which can only con-tract or relax | muscle cell the individual cells that are found within a muscle, these cells can only contract or relax | muscle control the ability to guide your muscles smoothly and with precision | muscle strength the force produced by a specified muscle | muscle system a group of muscles that work together to cause a change, *eg* walking may involve changes in a dozen muscles in the legs | muscle tissue the collection of muscle cells (but not the tendon) | antagonistic muscles pairs of muscles that pull in opposite directions, *eg* the biceps cause the arm to bend then the triceps cause the arm to straighten | associated muscles the muscles that are involved with a particular movement | cervix muscles the muscles at the junction of the uterus with the vagina, that must dilate to allow birth to occur | ciliary muscle the tiny muscles that control the size of the lens in the eye so the image is focused onto the retina | gut muscles the radial or longitudinal muscles that change the shape of the intestine in order to push food along, the abdominal muscles | hair muscle the tiny muscle at the base of each hair in the skin of a mammal | heart muscle the specialised cells in the heart that are able to contract and relax at a rate of once each second, sometimes for over a century | intercostal muscles the muscles that are found between the ribs and are needed for breathing | leg muscles the muscles that allow the leg, or parts of the leg, to move | rib muscles the muscles attached to the ribs that are used in breathing

muscular lots of strong muscles

museum a building containing a collection of related objects that are displayed and interpreted to the public, named after the *muses*, the goddesses of arts and sciences

mushrooms a group of organisms within the fungus kingdom (and so have no chlorophyll) that produces a large body above the ground; many mushrooms are poisonous to eat

music sound produced by instruments, mixtures of frequencies that produce a pleasant sound | pop music sound and rhythms that are enjoyed by many people, *ie* are popular

musical instruments equipment, made from almost any material, *eg* wood, plastic, metal, that can be used to produce pleasant sounds

musicians people who play instruments in order to produce enjoyable sound

mussel (not a muscle which is the tissue that provides movement in an organism) a sea creature with an external skeleton of two shells, a mollusc

mutation a change in at least one of the bases of DNA so that the instruction is permanently changed.

mycoproteins the proteins (long chains of amino acids) produced by fungi

myriapod an invertebrate with jointed legs, a distinct head with antennae and a segmented body, *eg* a centipede

myth a story that is based on an event that may have taken place a long, long time ago

myxomatosis a virus that is deadly to some species of rabbit

N / newton the unit of force, one newton will change the velocity of a one kilogram mass by 1 metre per second in one second

N nitrogen, proton number 7

N [north] one of the main points on a compass

n… / nano… (*Greek* dwarf) prefix for a thousand, millionth of a unit, 10^{-9}

n^0 [neutron] the particle in the nucleus of an atom the has no charge and a mass of 1 dalton

N_2 nitrogen gas, an unreactive gas that is 80% of the air around you

Na sodium (*Swedish* natrium), proton number 11, an alkali metal

nail a solid cylinder of metal with a point at one end and a flattened head at the other | bed of nails a board, about bed size, through which nails have been hit, some people sleep on all those sharp points | finger nail the plate of horny material found at the end of each digit, each nail grows approximately 1 millimetre per week | iron nails / soft iron nails cylindrical objects with a point that are made from a metal that is easily magnetised

naked bare, uncovered | naked eye without the use of a magnifying instrument | naked flame a flame that is not protected by a shield such as glass or gauze

name the word that is used to identify an item; to give some identifying word | chemical name the word, or words, that will identify a compound | common name the name, description or title that is used in everyday speech | everyday name the term that is used by most people to describe an object | scientific name the word and meaning that has been accepted by scientists as giving a single meaning or item

NAND gate a logic circuit that is OFF only if both inputs are ON

nano… / n… (*Greek* dwarf) prefix for a thousand, millionth part of a unit, 10^{-9}

nanometer [USA] / **nanometre** [UK] [nm] a unit of length, 10^{-9} metres, there are a thousand million nanometres in a metre

nanotechnology the use of incredibly small parts to build tiny structures

naphtha / naptha a mixture of hydrocarbons with boiling points between 100°C and 180°C

narcotic a chemical that both reduces pain and causes drowsiness (sleep)

narrow thin, a gap that is small compared to what went previously; to become smaller

narrows becomes more constricted

NASA [National Aeronautical & Space Administration] the organisation responsible for the American space programme

nasal concerned with the nose | nasal passages the channels in the nose that allow air to be cleaned during breathing

nasty horrible, unpleasant, repulsive, *ugh*!

natal birth | pre-natal / ante-natal any feature that occurs after conception, but before the birth

national relevant to a particular country | National Aeronautical & Space Administration [NASA] the organisation responsible for the American space programme | National Council of Bio-technology Education a committee that seeks to increase the knowledge of issues related to biotechnology, *eg* cloning, genetically modified organisms, enzymes | National Dairy Council a committee that looks after the interests of the people who produce milk and eggs | national data information concerning the people and re-sources in a country, *eg* the average age or height | National Grid the network of pylons, wires and transformers that allows electrical energy to be transmitted from the power station to the homes, shops and factories | national investigation research that involves collecting information from the whole country | national monitoring trying to measure items, and how they change over time, throughout the country | National Park an area that has been set aside for recreation and study and in which building is very restricted

nations countries, people sharing a common identity

native being born and raised in that area | native birds the winged creatures with feathers that are found in that area or were there before humans arrived | native iron a rock that contains iron as the metal not as an iron compound | native metals metals (elements that conduct electricity) that are so unreactive that they are found in the ground in a pure state | native ores tiny pieces of pure metal are mixed in with the soil and sand, *eg* gold ore

natural as found in the wild, absence of inter-ference by humans | natural abundance the numbers that occur in the wild | natural barrier the skin the prevents invasion by microbes, a fence, mountain or an impassable river that prevents mixing of different forms of life | natural defence mechanisms methods by which organ-isms prevent entry of microbes or methods by which the infecting microbe can be destroyed | natural defences items that do not need changing in order to prevent entry of an invading organism | natural disaster a large-scale change in an environment caused by an event that is not caused by people | natural fibers (USA) / natural fibres (UK) filaments that are made from material that is grown, *eg* wool, cotton, silk | **natural gas** methane [CH_4], the gas that is found with crude oil and is now used in most homes in Britain | **natural habitat** the area or environment where an organism is usually found and where the organism can survive without artificial help | **natural immunity** the ability to defend yourself against invasion by a microbe without needing any artificial boost or injection | **natural material** a substances that is obtained from plants or animals, *eg* cotton, wool, leather | **natural processes** methods for producing some item or chemical that does not involve machinery | **natural satellite** any object that orbits a planet and has not been produced by people, *eg* the Moon | **natural selection** survival of the fittest, choosing the genes that are useful for survival | **natural sources** areas where items may be found without any intervention by people | **natural spring** a place where water leaves the ground and forms a stream | **natural string** twine or cord made from animal or plant products, eg cotton, flax or wool

naturalist a person who studies life, a collector of organisms

nature to do with life, the type | **nature center** (USA) / **nature centre** (UK) an area, often indoors, that interprets and gives meaning to the signs, history and life in the immediate area | **nature reserve** an area that is not developed so the native wildlife can continue to live and breed | **seasonal nature** something that will occur only at one time of the year, a combination of temperatures, rainfall and day length that forces an event

navigate to find a way through unknown territory

navigation finding their way to an unseen destination

navigator a person who plans the route or directs the direction of travel

NB [Latin *nota bene*] note well, important point

Ne neon, proton number 10, an inert gas

neap tide the change in height of the seas caused by the Sun and Moon being at opposite sides of the Earth (much smaller than a spring tide)

near close | **near-constant** almost unchanging | **near point** the point closest to the eye that the lens is able to focus on to the retina

nearby close, neighbouring

nearer closer

nearest closest

nebula (plural is nebulae) a large mass of dust that gets in the way of light from more distant stars

nebulae (plural of nebula) vast volumes of dust in the universe that are seen by the light they reflect from nearby stars, but which will obscure any stars beyond them

necessary needed, essential

neck the part of the body between the head and the trunk | **neck vertebrae** the bones at the top of the spinal column that allow the head to rotate and to nod

nectar a sugar solution that flowers produce in order to encourage visits by bees

nectary (plural is nectaries) the area at the inside base of a flower where the sugar solution, nectar, is produced and stored

need (not knead which is pushing and pulling) a requirement that is essential for survival; to want an item that is essential for survival | **recognise a need** (UK) / **recognize a need** (USA) to be able to identify the items (physical, chemical or emotional) that are required | **emotional needs** the love and comfort that are needed for the stable development of an offspring | **mineral needs** the ions that are needed for survival, *eg* iron, calcium, iodine | **physical needs** the conditions of temperature, light and moisture that are needed for survival

needed essential, required, important to possess

needle a long, thin object of metal with an eye at one end and a point at the other | **compass needle** the thin arrow of metal that aligns north–south in a compass | **knitting needle** a long, thin cylinder with a point at one end that is used for producing material from wool | **pine needle** the long, thin leaf of a pine tree | **syringe needle** a thin, steel tube that allows the contents of a syringe to be injected into skin, vein or muscle

needs the resources required to keep an organism alive, necessities

negative less than zero, not positive | **negative charge** one of a pair of characteristics called charge, conventionally the electron is given the negative charge and the proton has a positive charge | **negative effects** a stimulus causing responses that reduce the change | **negative electrode** cathode, the metal that has the excess number of electrons and so has a negative charge | **negative numbers** numbers below zero | **negative terminal** the output of a battery towards which the current flows (although current is the flow of electrons) | **negative values** numbers that have a minus in front

negatively behaving as though it had a minus charge; refusing, acting against

negligible a quantity so small that it can be ignored

neighbor (USA) / **neighbour** (UK) the person who lives very close, but not in the same home, the person in the next seat

neighborhood (USA) / **neighbourhood** (UK) the area surrounding a specified position

neighboring (USA) / **neighbouring** (UK) next door, very close, the nearest item, the closest occurrence of the named object | neighboring atoms (USA) / neighbouring atoms (UK) the atoms that are close to the specified point

neither not one nor the other

nematode / **nematode worm** slender round worms, some are free-living in soils whereas others live as parasites

neomycin sulfate (USA) / **neomycin sulphate** (UK) an antibiotic extracted from a fungus

neon (Ne, proton number 10, boiling point –246°C) a group 0 element, an inert gas that has been used in tubes to give fluorescent lighting

nephron one of thousands of units in the kidney that filter the blood and reabsorb the water

Neptune a gas giant of a planet (diameter of 50,000 kilometres) that is almost the last planet in the Solar System (distance from the Sun is 4500 million kilometres), named after the god of the sea, Neptune was discovered in 1846 (although Galileo, in 1612, had mistaken the planet for a star)

nerve / **nerve cell** any of the many types of cell that detect a change, carry messages to or from the brain or cause changes to other cells | nerve endings the small objects that are at each end of a nerve and transmit the message to the next part | nerve fiber (USA) / nerve fibre (UK) the long part, or axon, of a nerve cell | nerve impulse / nerve signal the message sent to the brain or from the brain | audio nerve / auditory nerve the collection of thousands of nerve cells that carry information from the ear to the brain | effector nerves cells that carry messages from the brain to cause a response in another cell | optic nerve the bundle of thousands of nerve cells that carry information from the eye to the brain | sensory nerve a cell that transmits a signal from receptor to the brain

nervous worried, concerned with the transmitting electrical signals around the body | nervous impulse the message passing along a nerve cell | nervous system the collection of cells that is responsible for detecting a stimulus from the outside world, passing the data to the brain then sending the response commands to the cells that can respond appropriately | nervous tissue a collection of nerve cells

nest place that is safe for an animal to lay their eggs and rear their young (most often applies to birds); to build a safe place for the young

nesting site the particular place or type of area where a nest is found

net (not nett which is overall) a mesh, overall, the amount that is left after removing specific parts: to capture

nett (not net which is a mesh) the overall affect of one item going in one direction minus the item going in the opposite direction

nettles plants that love damp places and have stings in the underside of each leaf | nettle sting the structure under a nettle leaf that is able to inject formic acid [HCHO]; the reaction that has been produced after touching the underside of a nettle and so being injected with formic acid

network a mesh, net or web of lines connecting facts or processors; to interact with lots of people | capillary network the millions of tiny tubes that allow blood to reach individual cells

neuro- (*Greek* a nerve)

neuron (UK & USA) / **neurone** (UK) a nerve cell, a brain cell | sensory neuron the long cell joining the receptor to the spinal cord then to the brain

neutral without charge, in the middle, without bias | neutral buoyancy the object remains suspended at a constant depth of fluid, neither rising nor falling | neutral liquid a solution that has a pH of 7 ie is neither acid nor alkali | neutral molecule a substance that does not have any overall charge | neutral pH pH 7 so the solution is neither acid nor alkali | neutral solution a liquid, containing dissolved chemicals, that has a pH of 7 | neutral wire the cable in a plug or socket through which the current returns to the power station

neutralisation (UK) / **neutralization** (USA) reacting two chemicals, an acid and a base, so the liquid has a pH of 7 | neutralisation reaction any chemical change which causes the reacting solution to go to pH 7

neutralise (UK) / **neutralize** (USA) in chemistry, to take to pH 7, but in general, to remove a threat

neutralising (UK) / **neutralizing** (USA) taking to pH 7, preventing a stimulus from causing a change

neutralization (USA) / **neutralisation** (UK) reacting two chemicals, an acid and a base, so the resulting liquid has a pH of 7 | neutralization reaction any chemical change which causes the reacting solution to go to pH 7

neutralize (USA) / **neutralise** (UK) in chemistry, to take to pH 7 but in general, to remove a threat

neutralizing (USA) / **neutralising** (UK) taking to pH 7, preventing a stimulus from causing a change

neutrons particles found in the nucleus of an atom, each neutron is neutral (has no charge) and has a mass of 1 dalton or 1 atomic mass unit, which is 1.6×10^{-27} kg

never not once, at no time

new (not knew which is to have information) not seen before | newborn an offspring that is so young that the age is measured in hours or days | new cells the offspring, by asexual reproduction, that have identical genes to the parent, but may appear or react in a different way | new compounds chemicals that were not previously available | new evidence observations and data that were not available when the original decision was reached | new ideas bringing together observations and data then providing a simple explanation that no one else had thought of | new materials chemicals that have just been produced either by an industrial company or by a reaction in the living cell | new moon the thin crescent that is seen on the day after the Moon had disappeared from view | new product a material that either has just reached the shops or that you have made from other chemicals | new species organisms that have been discovered in recent times

newborn an offspring that is so young that the age is measured in hours or days | newborn baby a human child that is less than a week old

Newcomen (Thomas 1663–1729) was a Cornish blacksmith who used the idea that 1000 cm^3 of steam will condense to give 1 cm^3 of water to produce a powerful pumping engine. Unfortunately Newcomen had to share all the profits with another inventor who had written a very wide-ranging patent that covered this invention.

Newlands (John Alexander Reina 1837–1898) started to study the chemistry of sugars. In 1864, he proposed his *law of octaves*, which showed that similar properties repeated when the elements were put in order of atomic mass. He claimed the credit when Mendeleef published his ideas for a periodic table in 1869, and was eventually awarded a prestigious medal by the Royal Society.

newly discovered found in the recent past

newspaper large sheets that are published on a regular basis, and often in booklet form, that carry information, results and comments about recent events

newsprint the type of font and ink that is used by newspapers

newt a small amphibian, a creature that lives on land and in water at different stages of its life cycle

Newton (Sir Isaac 1642–1727) one of the three princes that revolutionised the thinking in science (the others are Gauss and Archimedes), Newton was born in Lincolnshire, was a mediocre pupil at school then spent most of his life working at Cambridge University and had the honour of both being knighted and buried at Westminster Abbey. In 1666, the *miraculous year*, he returned to his home at Woolsthorpe in order to avoid the plague, there he developed a field of maths called calculus, he explained colours, he proposed the law of gravity and devised the laws of motion. Later, he made the first reflecting telescope (all major telescopes use this idea). Most of these discoveries were not published until 1685 in a book that has been called the most influential science book ever written – *Principia Mathematica*. Even then, his friend Halley had to pay for the publishing costs. A later book, *Opticks*, published in 1704, gave an organised account and explanation for the behaviour of light. He became Lucasian Professor at Cambridge in 1669, a post he held for 32 years. He was a member of Parliament, but spoke only once in the chamber – to ask for a window to be closed. During the last few years of the seventeenth century, he became Warden of the Royal Mint – a venture which he returned to profitability and for which he was knighted. Newton was President of the Royal Society for last 24 years of his life – turning that Society from a social gathering into a respected organisation for the world's leading scientists.

newton / N the unit of force, one newton will change the velocity of a one kilogram mass by one metre per second each second

force = mass x acceleration
(newton) (kilogram) (metres/sec/sec)

newton balance a spring with a length that is calibrated in newtons and is used for measuring weight

newton-meter (UK) (not newton-metre which is a turning force) the instrument, usually a spring moving against a scale, that is used to measure force

newton-meter (USA) the instrument, usually a spring moving against a scale, that is used to measure force, the turning force or torque

newton-metre / Nm (UK) (not newton-meter which is a measuring instrument) the turning forces torque

Newton's laws of motion three laws proposed by Newton

1. Every body continues at constant velocity unless a force is applied

2. The change of velocity is proportional to the force applied

3. Every action has an equal and opposite reaction

next the subsequent, the one following | next to adjacent, standing as neighbours

Ni nickel, proton number 28, a magnetic metal

nibble to cut out small pieces

NiCad battery / NiCad cell an rechargeable electric cell with one nickel electrode and a cadmium electrode

nichrome an alloy of nickel and chromium that is commonly used to make strong wires

nickel (Ni, proton number 28, melting point 1450°C) an unreactive metal that is attracted by a magnet | nickel-cadmium cell / NiCad cell a rechargeable cell that has nickel as one electrode and cadmium as the other | nickel coins metal currency containing nickel, coins that are not worth a lot of money

nicotine the drug that is found in tobacco plants and finds its way to the brain when you smoke cigarettes

night the time of darkness when the Sun has sunk below the horizon | night blindness an inability to see in low light conditions, often caused by a lack of vitamin A and so cured by eating carrots | night light a candle that is usually short, so will not fall over, but contains sufficient wax to burn all night | night temperature the air temperature after the Sun has set | overnight during the hours of darkness, from the end of one working day to the start of the next

nimbus clouds up to a height of 3 kilometres that produce rain and snow

nit the egg of a head louse

niter (USA) / **nitre** (UK) potassium nitrate [KNO_3], or sodium nitrate [$NaNO_3$]

nitrate / nitrate ion [NO_3^-] the charged particle that is attached to hydrogen in nitric acid [HNO_3] | nitrate fertiliser (UK) / nitrate fertilizer (USA) a mixture of chemicals that contains the nitrates of ammonium and potassium and so is a good source of nitrogen for plants | nitrates / nitrate salts compounds containing a nitrate ion [NO_3^-] bonded to a metal | ammonium nitrate [NH_4NO_3] an important source of nitrogen in fertiliser, but has the disadvantage of being very soluble and so is washed out by the rain | calcium nitrate [$Ca(NO_3)_2$] the soluble salt of calcium that is produced when calcium oxide reacts with nitric acid | copper nitrate [$Cu(NO_3)_2$] a salt prepared by heating copper oxide with nitric acid | iron nitrate [$Fe(NO_3)_2$] a soluble salt of iron | lead nitrate [$PbNO_3$] a soluble salt of lead | potassium nitrate [KNO_3] important as a mineral for plants

(giving N and K in NPK fertiliser), used to make explosives | silver nitrate [$AgNO_3$] produces a characteristic precipitate with halogens and halides, the chemical originally used in photographic films because silver nitrate breaks down when light is present

nitre (UK) / **niter** (USA) potassium nitrate [KNO_3], or sodium nitrate [$NaNO_3$]

nitric acid [HNO_3] a strong acid that produces nitrate salts with bases

nitrifying bacteria microbes that convert ammonium ions [NH_4^+] into nitrates [NO_3^-]

nitrogen (N, proton number 7) an atom that is an important constituent of proteins and nucleic acids; [N_2] an unreactive gas, boiling point −210°C that was isolated in 1772 by Scheele, in Sweden, and by Rutherford, in Scotland | nitrogen atom emphasising that the object is the atom not the gas | nitrogen compound a molecule that contains nitrogen atoms bonded to other atoms | nitrogen cycle the number of atoms in the world is fixed so individual atoms have to move through plants and animals and be reused over and over again | nitrogen dioxide [NO_2] a brown gas that dissolves in water to produce nitric acid [HNO_3] | nitrogen fixation changing nitrogen gas [N_2] into ammonium compounds [NH_4^+] and nitrates [NO_3^-] that can be absorbed by plants | nitrogen-fixing bacteria microbes that convert nitrogen gas [N_2], from the air, into ammonia [NH_3] which then becomes the nitrates [NO_3^-] that can be absorbed by plants | nitrogen gas / nitrogen (g) [N_2] the unreactive molecule that is formed when two nitrogen atoms bond together, air is 80% nitrogen gas, nitrogen was isolated in 1772 by Scheele, in Sweden, and by Rutherford, in Scotland | nitrogen oxides a mixture of the several different compounds that are produced when nitrogen bonds to oxygen | liquid nitrogen the liquid that is formed when nitrogen gas [N_2] is cooled to 196°C or lower | oxides of nitrogen several compounds that can be formed when different proportions of oxygen bond to nitrogen

Nm [newton-meter (USA) / newton-metre (UK)] the unit of turning force or torque

nm [nanometre] a unit of length, there are a thousand million nanometres in a metre, 10^{-9} metres

no (not know which is to understand) denial, a negative answer

Nobel (Alfred Bernhard 1833–1896) was educated by tutors in Russia, including a study of five modern languages! He worked in Paris, America, Russia and Sweden where he started to manufacture high explosives in 1859. Unfortunately, the factory exploded, killing five people, including his younger brother. He developed safer explosives in 1866 (dynamite) and 1875 (gelignite). He held 355 patents, and left his large fortune as a source of income for the Nobel Prizes.

Nobel Prizes awards, of a medal and a large sum of money, that are given each year to up to three people that have made outstanding contributions to specified areas of knowledge, the money results from the will of Nobel

noble inert, unreactive | noble gases group 0 in the periodic table, the elements that have a full outer shell and so will not bond to other atoms and remain gases down to very low temperatures | noble metals any metal (an element that conducts electricity) that is not very reactive, *eg* gold [Au] or platinum [Pt]

noct- (*Latin* night)

nocturnal at night | nocturnal house an animal enclosure that is kept 12 hours out of step with the real world so visitors can see night time animals awake during a daytime visit

nodding ducks / Salter's ducks equipment that uses the changing height of waves to produce electricity

nodules lumps | root nodules small swellings on the roots of plants caused by invasion then growth of nitrogen-fixing bacteria

noise any sound that you do not want to hear | noise levels intensity of unwanted sound | noise pollution sound that prevents you hearing the sounds that you want to hear | loud noise sound at high volume that you do not want to hear | traffic noise the disturbing mixture of sounds produced by engines, tyres and mechanical movement of vehicles on the road | white noise sound in which the mixture of frequencies and their intensities varies randomly

noisy high intensity of sound, usually unwanted, making it difficult to pick out what you are trying to hear

non- (*Latin* not) produces the negative of the word that follows

non-abrasive unable to wear away, will not scratch

non-biodegradable not able to be broken down by any creature's metabolism and so will last a very long time in the environment

non-biological not produced by a living organism, does not contain chemicals that have been produced by an organism

non-colored solutes (USA) / **non-coloured solutes** (UK) chemicals that will dissolve in a liquid without affecting the colour of the solvent

none not any, not one

non-flowering / non-flowering plant an organism that lives by using photosynthesis, but does not produce a flower and so pollination will not involve an insect

non-identical similar, but with important differences | non-identical twins a pair of babies that were born at the same time, but had developed from two fertilised eggs

non-igneous rock any rock that was not produced by cooling of the magma

non-interlocking separate, not fitting into each other | non-interlocking textures the small parts of a rock do not fit into each other

non-linear the path or graph is not a straight line

non-living the object is not capable of growing or reproducing, although it may once have been alive

non-luminous not giving out light | non-luminous object an item that does not produce its own light and so must be seen by reflection

non-magnetic not affected by a magnetic field | non-magnetic material substance that is not affected by a magnetic field and does not change the magnetic field

non-metal an element that will not conduct electricity and will form an oxide that is acid in water | non-metal oxide / oxides of a non-metal compound containing oxygen bonded to a non-metal and so must have a pH below 7 when dissolved in water

non-metallic conductor a type of material that will allow electricity to flow, but is not a metal | non-metallic element an element that does not conduct electricity, characterised by producing oxides that are acidic in water | oxides of non-metals compounds of a non-metal and oxygen, these oxides produce and acid solution in water

non-permeable will not allow a fluid to pass through

non-persistent pesticide a chemical that is intended to kill pests, but will become inactive after a short time

non-porous the solid has no tiny holes and so will keep the fluid in place

non-pregnant there is no embryo or foetus in the uterus

non-renewable can be used once, but this causes a change that can not be reversed | non-renewable energy sources places from which energy can be obtained, but then the source will not be renewed within a lifetime | non-renewable fuels / fossil fuels chemicals that can be burned to give heat and light, but will not be renewed within the next century |

non-renewable resources reserves of useful material, *eg* oil, that can never be replaced

non-reversible unable to go back | non-reversible change a chemical reaction that can not be returned to the original state

non-seed-producing plant a plant (and so capable of photosynthesis) that reproduces by producing spores

non-slip resists movement, not smooth

non-smoker a person who does not smoke tobacco or other drugs that require a cigarette

non-smoking household a group of people living together, none of whom smoke

non-stick friction-free, material will slide over the surface

non-vascular lacking tubes | non-vascular plants producers that do not have specialised tubes for carrying water from the roots

non-windy environment an area that is protected from any violent or sudden movement of air

noon mid-day, the time of day when the Sun is at its highest and the shadows are shortest, 12 o'clock

nor (not gnaw which is to use teeth) and not, neither one nor the other | NOR gate a logic circuit that is ON only if both inputs are OFF

normal usual, average; a line at right angles to a surface | normal air the air that you would expect to find in vast open spaces

normally usually, as expected, at right angles

North (Marianne 1830–1890) botany was the one part of Science that was considered suitable for ladies, and North excelled in scientific knowledge and artistic skill. Prior to the death of her father (in 1869), she travelled through Europe, drawing and painting the plants that she saw. After 1869, she travelled the world, and returned with new species and superb paintings. A special gallery was built at the Royal Botanic Garden to display her art.

north a direction towards which a freely suspended magnet will point – the Pole Star (Polaris) seems to be directly over the geographical North Pole | north magnetic pole an imaginary point on the surface of the Earth, somewhere in northern Canada, that seems to be where all the lines of magnetic force enter the Earth | North Pole a geographic point that is the centre of the Arctic circle and seems to lie directly below the Pole Star | north pole the end of a magnet that will point towards the South Pole | north-seeking pole the end of a magnet that will point towards the north pole of a magnet or the Earth | magnetic north the point, currently in northern Canada, to which compasses point as North – this point is drifting randomly at a speed of approximately 15 kilometres each year | true north an imaginary line that joins your position to the axis of rotation of the Earth

northern a direction that is found by looking for the Pole Star | northern forest the type of woodland that is found near the Arctic circle | Northern Hemisphere the half of the Earth that is north of the equator

nose (not knows which is having information) the sense organ for smell or scent | runny nose a symptom, lots of mucus is produced as a response to the presence of a bacterial or viral infection

nostril one of a pair of tubes inside the nose

not (not knot which is a method for joining string) spelling for a negative | NOT gate turns an ON to an OFF or turns an OFF to an ON | not moving still

notch (plural is notches) a cut in the shape of a deep V; to produce a deep cut | slag notch the hole in a blast furnace through which the slag can be released

note a brief writing that includes the important points; to write down the major points

nothing zero, not there, emptiness

notice an announcement; to see something

noticeably easily seen

notion an idea

noun a word defining an object

nourished given sufficient nutrients and water for good growth | well nourished receiving adequate amounts of food

nourishment the part of the food that is able to be absorbed and used by cells

novel different, unexpected, a written story | novel context a new or different setting

NPK [nitrogen, phosphorus, potassium] fertiliser containing salts that are needed by plants

nuclear concerned with the centre of the atom, the control centre of a cell | nuclear bomb an explosive device where the heat energy arises from the loss of mass that occurs in some nuclear reactions | nuclear energy the heat produced by changes in the nucleus of an atom | nuclear fission breakdown of the nucleus of an atom to produce new elements | nuclear fuels (not a true fuel because a chemical reaction with oxygen is not involved) metals that can be used to give a controlled release of nuclear energy | nuclear fusion two nuclei have joined together to become one nucleus, this could be in sexual reproduction (where the nuclei of two sex cells join together) or the fusion of two atomic nuclei to give a new element and release heat energy |

nuclear membrane the thin layer that controls movement of chemicals into and out of the cell nucleus | nuclear power using changes in the nuclei of atoms to produce a controlled release of heat energy | nuclear radiation the energy that is given out when a nucleus changes structure, the radiation travels in straight lines and may cause damage to cells | nuclear reaction changing the number of protons or neutrons in a nucleus leading to the formation of new elements | nuclear reactor the building in which the heat energy, released from changes in the nucleus of the atom, can be used safely to produce steam that generates electricity | nuclear waste the material from a nuclear power station that is not suitable as a source of energy, but is dangerously radio-active

nuclei (plural of nucleus) the mixture of protons and neutrons at the centre of an atom; the control centre of a living cell | cell nuclei the control centres of cells, which contains the genetic coding for that organism | female nuclei the structure in a cell containing the chromosomes of a female, especially a female sex cell | male nuclei the structure containing the chromosomes of a male – often refers to the male sex cell

nucleic acids large molecules that are acidic and were originally found in the cell nucleus, DNA (deoxyribonucleic acid)

nucleon number the total number of protons and neutrons in the nucleus

nucleotide one of the building blocks of nucleic acids / DNA / RNA, a molecule made from a five-carbon sugar attached to a base (adenine, cytosine, guanine, thymine or uracil) and a phosphate group

nucleus (plural is nuclei) at the centre of the atom, the control centre of the cell | atomic nucleus the tiny particle that is found at the centre of the atom and is made from protons and neutrons | cell nucleus the control centre of the cell that contains the chromosomes (named by Brown)

nugget a nodule, a small block of material

number a total, a tally; to count | number line an axis on which the important numbers (eg, dates, sizes or weights) are arranged in regular order | number of atoms how many atoms have a specific property, eg how many are found in a certain volume or take part in a reaction | number of measurements how many measurements have to be taken so as to ensure that a trend is apparent or that error is minimised | number pyramid a diagram to show that the number of organisms changes going up a food chain | appropriate number how many measurements have to be taken in order to give the accuracy

required for that experiment | atomic number / proton number the number of protons in the nucleus | binary numbers counting that uses two numbers, computers use 1 and 0 only | E-number the number or label that has been given to a food additive so as to avoid naming the chemical | large numbers numbers that are sufficiently large that an exact value is not given; the number of members in a population is sufficiently large that counting is difficult | limited number some restriction means that only a small number of observations is possible or have been taken | mass number atomic mass, relative atomic mass, the total mass of protons and neutrons in an atom | negative number any number that is less than zero | nucleon number the total number of protons and neutrons in the nucleus | pH number a measure of the acid (less than 7) neutral (at pH 7) or alkali (greater than 7) in a solution | proton number the number of protons in the nucleus of an atom | pyramid of numbers the number of each organism that is involved in a food chain | relative numbers giving an idea of the size of two populations with respect to each other, without stating exact numbers | significant number important number; a large proportion | sufficient numbers enough items, animals or people, are involved that random variations are cancelled out

numeral the symbol for a number | Roman numeral a counting system that uses I (for 1), V (for 5), X (for 10), L (for 50), C (for 100), D (for 500) and M (for 1000)

numerical numbers | numerical answers quantitative, the results are measured using a scale | numerical data the information is collected as numbers

nurture to care for, to feed; feeding and up-bringing may be important in some characteristics such as height, weight or even musical ability

nurtured the offspring was brought up in a particular way, especially extra help given during illness

nut a metal hexagon that is screwed onto a bolt, a dry, woody fruit | nut allergy a reaction that some people show when near to a nut – the breathing changes (and may stop) and there is a change in the flow of blood

nutrients chemicals that are needed for health and so are usually small molecules that are easily absorbed, chemicals from the soil that are used by plants | nutrient agar plate a petri dish containing a layer of jelly (agar) in which has been dissolved the chemicals that are essential for the growth of specific microbes |

nutrient broth a liquid containing all the nutrients needed for the growth of microbes | nutrient deficiency the diet is missing one or more of the chemicals that the body needs for healthy growth | absorbing nutrients taking from the environment into the organism the small molecules that are essential for cell growth | essential nutrients chemicals, *eg* vitamins, that are needed for good health and can not be replaced by other chemicals | main nutrients the chemicals that are essential for health that are present in large amounts in specified food | plant nutrient a chemical that is soluble in water and so can be absorbed through the roots of the plant | range of nutrients several of the chemicals that are essential for good health | soil nutrients the salts and minerals that should be in the soil for healthy growth of plants | specific nutrients a stated range or type of chemicals that the body needs for a particular purpose

nutrition the chemicals and foods that an animal eats in order to live and grow

nutritional content the main chemicals that are present in a food | nutritional information a table of the amounts of each of the main food types (carbohydrates, minerals, vitamins, fats) and the amount of energy that are in a food *or* a table that gives data concerning the energy or the composition of many types of food | nutritional information panel the table on the wrapper of a tin or on the container that shows the amount of each nutrient and the energy content of that food | nutritional value the importance of a type of food as a source of particular nutrients, *eg* fresh fruit as a source of vitamin C, the amount of energy in a type of food

nuts fruit with hard shells

O oxygen, proton number 8

O₂ oxygen gas, the gas that comprises almost 20% of the air around you

oak tree starts as an acorn then grows over a period of several hundred years

oar a long pole with a flattened end that is used for moving a boat forward

obelisk a monument, especially a very large rectangular stone

obese overweight to such a large extent that there is a danger to the health

obesity fatness, especially a state of being grossly overweight

object article, item, thing; to protest | luminous object an item that gives out its own light | colored object (USA) / coloured object (UK) an item that reflects or transmits part of the visible spectrum and so appears to be a colour, *ie* neither black nor white | common objects items that are easily obtained | everyday objects items that are likely to be sold in local shops or markets | falling objects items that are approaching the ground | familiar objects items that you are likely to see every few days because they are in your house or school | floating object an item that has no visible support, yet does not fall, especially material on the surface of water | luminous object anything that gives out its own light | metal object an item made from material that is able to conduct electricity | moving object an item that is changing position | non-luminous object an item that does not give out its own light, but is seen by reflected light | pivoted object the article is able to move freely around one axis | raised object any item that is slightly higher than the surrounding material | stationary object an item that is not moving

objection an opposition, a dislike

objective without prejudice, unbiased, a lens in a microscope, a target | objective lens the lens in a microscope that is closest to the object to be observed

objectivity not prejudiced to one side or the other

oboe a musical wind instrument

observable able to be seen | observable change a difference that is able to be seen | observable differences details that are not the same on two similar objects | observable feature an easily seen characteristic that distinguishes a particular object | observable variation differences that can be seen between objects

observation a fact that is able to be seen, a measurement | accurate observations measurements that have been made carefully, in fine detail and are repeatable | appropriate observations measurements and recordings that are important for that part of an experiment | careful observations recording changes in fine detail | close observation looking at the fine detail of an object | detailed observations looking at the fine structure of an object or measurements of tiny changes | empirical observations measurements that do not need a supporting theory, but are able to be used by themselves | explain observations to say why the changes have occurred | first-hand observation you made the measurements and actually saw what was happening | interpret observations to show how the measurements are able to fit into a theory or support an idea | make observations to take measurements and write them down | microscopic observations looking at the behaviour and structure of tiny objects under a microscope, the measurements that are very small | precise observations measurements that are very accurate | qualitative observations making estimates that allow comparisons such as faster or higher | quantitative observation putting numbers and units on to the information | record observations make a permanent record, such as writing down the data | relevant observations measurements that are important for the understanding of that change | repeating observations making the same measurement again, usually to check for error | sufficient observations enough measurements or data collection for that particular task | systematic observations following a plan, so that many accurate measurements are made in a short time

observatories (singular is observatory) buildings that are made to hold and protect telescopes

observe to see, to watch, to record information

observed watched and recorded | observed data changes that you have seen happen, measurements that were made

observer a person who collects information

observing watching, collecting information then recording the data

obsidian an igneous rock that looks like black glass

obstruct to get in the way, to attempt to prevent movement

obtain to gather, to collect | obtain evidence to collect information

obtained collected

occur to happen, to take place

occurrence an event

occurs happens, takes place

oceans the five largest bodies of water that cover the Earth (Pacific, Atlantic, Indian, Southern, Arctic) | ocean ridge any of the large mountain ranges found under the seas | ocean trench a deep trough in the ocean floor

octane [C_8H_{18}] a hydrocarbon that is used as a liquid fuel, petrol, a measure of how easily the fuel will ignite

odd not even, not divisible by two, different, unusual | **odd result** an anomaly, a measurement that does not fit the pattern

odor (USA) / **odour** (UK) a smell | **odor detector** (USA) / **odour detector** (UK) equipment that is able to react to particles in the air

Oersted (Hans Christian 1777–1851) worked all his life at Copenhagen. In 1820, he demonstrated that an electric current produces a magnetic field that will affect a compass.

oesophagus (UK) / **esophagus** (USA) the gullet, a flexible tube that connects the mouth to the stomach

oestrogen (UK) / **estrogen** (USA) a hormone that causes many of the female characteristics

oestrus (UK) / **estrus** (USA) the time when the female is able to conceive | **oestrus cycle** the changes that occur in the female from the production of one egg to the production of the next egg, this period is around 28 days in humans, not switched on, mouldy, no longer fit for consumption

off removed, not switched on, mouldy, not fit for human consumption | **break off** to stop an activity, to remove a portion | **broken off** damaged, destroyed, removed by force | **give off** to produce a gas | **gone off** when some food, *eg* milk or meat, has become contaminated with bacteria and so is no longer suitable for eating | **move off** to leave a specific place and go to somewhere unknown | **moving off** leaving | **run-off** water from the land flows into a stream without absorption occurring | **take off** to remove a layer, to rise

off-peak electricity the electrical energy is being supplied at a time when the majority of the population is not using electrical appliances | **off-peak heating** producing heat at periods when very few people want electricity

offshore wind movement of air away from the shore towards the sea

offspring any new creatures produced by mature adults, *eg* calves (from cows), puppies (from dogs), kittens (from cats) and children from human parents | **identical offspring** twins, two organisms with exactly the same genetic sequence

often many times, frequent

Ohm (Georg Simon 1789–1854) held a series of mundane academic posts in Germany before becoming professor at Munich in 1849. In 1827,

he proposed the simple idea that the current (flow of charge) depends on the potential difference (voltage), but general acceptance took nearly 20 years. Ohm's law is the relationship between the potential difference (V for voltage), current (I for induced) and resistance (R):

potential difference	=	current	×	resistance
(volts)		(amps)		(ohms)
V	=	I	×	R

A second important idea from Ohm, that the ear hears by responding to individual frequencies, was also ignored.

ohm / Ω (not home which is a place to live) the unit of electrical resistance, a potential difference of 1 volt will produce a current of 1 amp through a resistance of 1 ohm

OHP [overhead projector] the instrument, usually with a light in the base, that allows text and pictures to be shown on a large screen

OHT [overhead transparency] the transparent sheet through which light is shone by an overhead projector

oil a liquid that will not mix with water (immiscible) and may be used either for cooking or for separating moving surfaces, thus reducing friction | **oil** can be a container for transporting lubricating oil, a small container, with nozzle and trigger, that allows controlled application of oil | **oil field** the area of land, often vast, below which is found the reservoir of oil | **oil-fired** the fuel that is providing the heat energy is a hydrocarbon | **oil glands** the groups of cells that are found near the base of the hair follicle and produce small volumes of a liquid that is not soluble in water | **oil refinery** a large complex of industrial buildings that are used to separate crude oil into many fractions | **oil refining** distilling crude oil so as to obtain pure hydrocarbon molecules | **oil rig** the structure that surrounds and supports the pipe that is drilling for oil | **oil shale** a type of mud that is silt or clay held together by oil, and from which oil can be obtained by distillation | **oil well** the tube that is drilled in order to obtain the crude oil from underground | **barrel of oil** the standard unit (equal to 159 litres) used to measure crude oil | **bead of oil** a small sphere of oil in either air or water | **castor oil** the liquid obtained from crushing the seeds of an ever-green tree | **cooking oil** an extract produced by crushing some plant storage organs that is suitable for frying food | **corn oil** the liquid produced by crushing the ears of corn | **crude oil** a smelly, brown or black 'treacle' that is the remains of sea creatures after 'cooking' for millions of years at high temperature and pressure | lubricating oil hydrocarbon with a boiling point in the range 250–300°C | mineral oil a chemical that behaves in a similar manner to oil, when used to reduce friction between moving surfaces, but is not made from hydrocarbons | olive oil the liquid produced by crushing the fruit of the olive tree | plant oil the chemical that is used as a store of chemical energy in the seeds of many plants | refining oil using distillation to separate the mixture of hydrocarbons in crude oil into pure molecules or fractions | stored under oil keeping under an oil, so that the material is isolated from the oxygen and moisture in air, especially true of reactive metals

oiling applying a layer of oil

oils a mixture of hydrocarbons; adding oil to separate surfaces

oily feeling slippery; a thin layer of oil

old adult, used, obsolete, earlier | old age the time of life when a person is no longer considered suitable for work

older born earlier | older children offspring of the same parents that were born at an earlier time

olive oil the liquid produced by crushing the fruit of the olive tree

Olympic Games competitions that were originally held between Greek City States then banned in 393 AD, the modern Games were started by Baron de Coubertin in 1896

omega / Ω the last letter of the Greek alphabet

omni- (Latin all) everything

omnivore an animal that will eat both plants and meat

omnivorous will eat any type of food

on above, supported by | on demand provided when requested | rely on to trust, to be dependent on

on-screen information that is shown on a monitor | on-screen graphics pictures or diagrams that are shown on the monitor

once at a specified time; a single event | once-living the species used to exist but now is either extinct or no longer found in that area

one unity; a single item, 1 | one-fourth a quarter, $\frac{1}{4}$

onion / onion bulb a vegetable of the *allium* family, all of which have a pungent smell | onion epidermis the single layer of cells that occurs between the layers of an onion | onion-skin weathering the effect on rocks of alternating high and low temperatures that causes the rock to lose thin layers of material

onwards further, along a path, more far, moving forward

Oort cloud a vast volume of millions of particles, in the size range from dust to planets, that extends to about 1 light-year beyond the orbit of Neptune

ooze a fine mud found on the bed of rivers, lakes and sea

opaque will not let any light through | opaque material the substance will not transmit any light

open to produce a gap | open circuit there is a break in the circuit so no current flows | open habitat the area is not protected from environmental factors such as wind, rain or sun | open water an area of water that is sufficiently large that it is affected by winds

opener a starter, equipment for getting into an area | can opener equipment for opening a sealed cylinder safely

opening a gap, a beginning | stomatal opening the gaps on the underside of leaves, through which gases can enter and leave the leaf

operate to work, to control

operated worked, used | battery-operated power is supplied from a chemical cell | hydraulically operated using a fluid with a piston in a cylinder, to change the direction, position and size of a force | manually operated worked or controlled by hand | pneumatically operated using air pressure to carry out a process, usually opening or closing a valve | spring operated the drive mechanism is powered by a flat coil that requires winding or a spring that needs compressing

operating working, controlling, carrying out a surgical procedure

operation a process, a method, a surgical procedure | manual operation worked by hand | safe operation able to work without damaging anything | scale of operation an approximate measure of the size or danger of a process

opinions a person's ideas or thoughts

opium a mixture of chemicals, including morphine, that are obtained from the unripe seed capsules of the opium poppy

opportunity (plural is opportunities) an occasion, which occurs rarely, but allows progress to be made, a time when something new could happen

opposes tries to slow down movement, pushes against | opposes motion tries to prevent an object from moving

opposing preventing movement, pushing in the other direction, presenting the other side of an argument | opposing pull a tension that is trying to stop movement | opposing push a compression that is preventing a movement

opposite contrasting, very different | opposite charges one charge is positive and the other is negative | opposite directions one object leaves a point then another object leaves the same point along the same line, but in the other direction | opposite poles one magnetic pole is north and the other magnetic pole is south

opposition the other direction, people with different ideas

optic to do with light, concerned with vision | optics the study of light or vision | optic nerve the collection of cells that transmits information from the retina of the eye to the brain | fiber optic (USA) / fibre optic (UK) a thin glass tube in which light is transmitted from one end to the other by internal reflection

optical to do with the eyes | optical fiber (USA) / optical fibre (UK) a thin filament of glass through which light can be passed either to transmit a picture or to convey information | optical illusion a picture, diagram or scene that your eye interprets in one way although the scene is created in a different way

optician person who examines eyes and prescribes lenses to optimise vision

optics the study of light and the eyes

optimise (UK) / **optimize** (USA) to provide conditions in which the work is done best

optimum best | optimum concentration the amount in a fixed volume that will give the best or fastest reaction

optional choice is available, the article may be used or may be ignored

or (not ore which is a metal compound in the ground) present an option

OR gate an electronic component that will switch on if either input is ON

oral (not aural which concerns the ear) concerned with the mouth | oral administration giving a drug by mouth

orally through the mouth, via the mouth

orange a member of the citrus group of fruit | orange juice the liquid produce by squeezing an orange | methyl orange an indicator that is red below pH 3.7 and yellow above pH 3.7

orbit (NOTE electrons around the atomic nucleus are found in ORBITALS) path taken by a satellite around a more massive body; to move in a circle around an object | circular orbit the satellite is moving round a path that is a constant distance from the large body | elliptical orbit the path taken by a satellite is an oval or a circle that is distorted so as to be longer in one direction than in another direction | elongated orbit the path of the satellite is represented by a squashed circle or an oval | equatorial orbit the path followed by the satellite is directly above the equator of the Earth | geostationary orbit the satellite is in an

equatorial orbit with an orbital period of 24 hours around the Earth and so appears to be remaining over the same spot | heliocentric orbit moving around the Sun | low orbit a path around the Earth at a height of less than 1000 kilometres | lunar orbit the path taken by the Moon in moving around the Earth | polar orbit the path taken by a satellite around the Earth passes over each pole

orbital one of the paths taken by electrons in the atom, to do with moving in a circle | orbital period the time taken for a satellite to go once around the more massive body | orbital radius the distance from the centre of the more massive body to the path taken by a satellite | orbital time the period taken for the satellite to complete one orbit | outer orbital the 'track' furthest from the nucleus in which electrons are found

Orbiter a Space Shuttle, any space-craft that is going to circle around the Sun or a planet, eg Viking Orbiter (1975), Mars Orbiter (2005), Solar Orbiter (2013)

orbiting going around a bigger body

order a command, a sequence, a group of related families in the classification of life; to put into a sequence or line | order of magnitude a factor of ten, ten times larger, a tenth the size | order of reactivity a table, or league, showing the metals in order from very reactive, eg potassium, which reacts explosively with water, through the less reactive, eg iron, to the metals that are so un-reactive that they are found as pieces of metal in the ground, eg gold | re-order to ask for a further batch, to request replacements, to re-arrange

ore (not or which is an option) the mixture of minerals, soil and sand from which a material can be extracted | metal ore a mixture of a metal compound (often the oxide) with soil, sand, plants, worms… | native ore tiny pieces of pure metal are mixed in with the soil and sand, eg gold ore

organ a set of tissues that produces a recognisable shape that is able to carry out a large-scale task, eg the stomach | organ rejection the failure of an organ transplant to be accepted by the recipient | organ structure the way different tissues, eg muscle, lining cells or glands, are arranged within an organ | organ system the several organs, or groups of tissues, that allow a function to be carried out, eg digestion requires a mouth, stomach and intestines | body organs any of the visible structures inside the body | important organs the collections of tissues that are essential for the maintenance of life | internal organs the structures, each with a special function, that are hidden inside the body | sense organs the groups of tissues that detect stimuli in the surroundings then send messages to the brain | sex organs the tissues that are essential for the production and fertilisation of an egg by a male gamete, the ovaries or testes of animals, the stamen and carpels of plants | specialised organ (UK) / specialized organ (USA) a well-defined structure of tissues and cells that carries out specific tasks essential for survival | transplanted organ an organ, *eg* liver, heart, lung, that is taken from one person (the donor) and used to replace a diseased organ in another person (the donor is usually dead but a living person can donate organs such as a kidney) | vital organ the tissues and cells that are essential in order for a person to be alive

organelle any structure with special functions that is found inside a cell

organic any chemical that contains carbon (except carbonates and the oxides of carbon), chemicals produced by living organisms | organic content the amount of chemicals that have been produced by animals or plants | organic farm an area that produces crops without the help of manufactured chemicals | organic farming not using any artificial fertiliser, herbicide or pesticide when growing crops | organic food a crop that has been grown without the addition of chemical such as fertilisers, herbicides or insecticides | organic material any substance made by a living creature | organic structure any molecule that contains carbon and more than four atoms | organic system the small parts that make up the system may grow, divide and respond to local conditions so the system is able to survive

organisation (UK) / **organization** (USA) a group of people who are trying to achieve a common goal, ordering or arrangement of information | organisation of tissues the way that groups of similar cells (tissues) are arranged so as to form an organ | conservation organisation people who join together in order to save specific habitats or creatures | Governmental organisations people who are associated with, or employed by, a stated Government | health organisations groups of people that are concerned with ensuring that the local people are able to become, and to remain, healthy | hierarchical organisation a group of people in which there is a definite ladder from the lowest member of the team to the person in charge | World Health Organisation (WHO) an organisation, based in Geneva, but supported worldwide, that co-ordinates and carries out research into diseases that are important to many areas of the world

organise (UK) / **organize** (USA) to put into an order based on a simple idea, *eg* by height, alphabetically | organise content to put the information or data into an order based on a simple idea | organise data to arrange the information into an order based on a simple idea | organise facts / organise ideas / organise information to arrange the observations into an order that brings together similar or related ideas

organised (UK) / **organized** (USA) arranged, ordered

organism any creature (animal, plant, fungus, microbe) that is able to live without artificial help | causal organism the creature that brings about the effect | complex organism living creatures that have many specialised tissues, organs or behavioural patterns | dead organisms creatures that are no longer alive | donor organism the animal that has the organ that is to be transplanted | genetically modified organism (GMO) a living creature that has had the genetic instructions, the DNA, changed by chemical means, usually to allow the organism to be grown more profitably | higher organisms living creatures that have more complex and more specialised organs or behaviour | indicator organisms creatures that will grow under some specific condition, *eg* the type of fungi that is found may be characteistic of the temperature range, the acidity of the rain or the amount of smoke pollution | living organisms emphasising that this type of creature is alive today| micro-organism any small creature that can be seen only with the aid of a lens or microscope | multicellular organism a form of life that is made from millions of cells which work in a co-ordinated manner | named organism stating the type of organism that could live in those conditions | unicellular organism a living creature that is made from one cell only, *eg* bacteria, protoctista

organization (USA) / **organisation** (UK) a group of people who are trying to achieve a common goal; ordering or arrangement of information | organization of tissues the way that groups of similar cells (tissues) are arranged so as to form an organ | conservation organization people who join together in order to save specific habitats or creatures | Governmental organizations people who are associated, or employed by, a stated Government | health organization a group of people who are concerned with ensuring that the local people are able to become, and to remain, healthy | hierarchical organization a group of people in which there is a definite ladder from the lowest member of the team to the person in charge

organize (USA) / **organise** (UK) to put into an order based on a simple idea, *eg* by height, alphabetically | organize content to put the information or data into an order based on a simple idea | organize data to arrange the information into an order based on a simple idea | organize facts / organize ideas / organize information to arrange the observations into an order that brings together similar ideas

organized (USA) / **organised** (UK) arranged, ordered

organs structures that are easily seen and which perform specific overall tasks such as breathing or digestion; organs are made from specialised cells that join to form tissues and several tissues may be present in each organ | associated organs the structures in the body that are functionally linked to another organ, *eg* the windpipe is needed for the lungs to function | delicate organs groups of tissues, organised for a particular function, that are easily damaged | female reproductive organs the ovaries of plants and animals, which produce the ova or female gametes | human organs groups of tissues that carry out specific tasks in humans | internal organs the structures, each with a special function, that are hidden inside the body | male reproductive organs the testes of animals or the stamen of plants, each of which produces male gametes | plant organs groups of tissues that are usually found in plants, *eg* leaves | primary sex organs the groups of tissues that produce the gametes and the hormones that are characteristic of that sex | reproductive organs the groups of tissues that are essential for the reproduction of an organism | sense organs the groups of tissues that detect stimuli in the surroundings then send messages to the brain | sex organs the tissues in which the gametes (sperm, pollen and ova) develop *or* the tissues that are associated with a particular sex, *eg* breasts | specialised organs (UK) / specialized organs (USA) structures in an organism that carry out large scale and easily defined changes *eg* organs for breathing or digestion | transplanted organs organs, *eg* liver, heart, lungs, that are taken from one person (the donor) and used to replace the diseased organs in another person (the donor is usually dead but a living person can donate organs such as a kidney) | vital organs the tissues and cells that are essential in order for a person to be alive

orientation matching the direction of various items

origin the starting point, the beginning

original the first | original sample the amount that was taken at first

originally initially, in the first place

originates starting from

origins starting points

ornithology the study of birds

oscillations vibrations, waves, repetitive movement either up and down or from side to side

oscilloscope / cathode ray oscilloscope (CRO) looks like a small television set but is used to show the signals in an electrical circuit, especially the electrical signals produced from sound waves by a microphone | oscilloscope screen the circle of glass in which the signal shows as moving dot or a line | oscilloscope trace the line that appears on the screen of a cathode ray oscilloscope when a signal is applied

osmosis movement of water from a region of high concentration of water to an area of low concentration, this means that water will try to leave a cell if the external concentration of solute is high (it is usually the concentration of solute that is measured so osmosis is often defined as the movement of water from a region of high concentration of solute to a region of low concentration)

osprey a fish eagle, a bird of prey, similar to an eagle

ossicles the three tiny bones (hammer, anvil and stirrup) connecting the ear drum to the cochlea

osteo- (*Greek* a bone)

osteoporosis thinning and weakening of the bones

otc [over the counter] / **otc medicine** a chemical that could affect the body which can be bought from a pharmacy without prescription

other different, separate, additional

otter a small carnivorous mammal that is adapted to living in rivers, the adaptations include webbed feet, streamlined shape of body

ounce a measure of weight in the imperial system, abbreviated to oz, one ounce is 28.45 grams

our (not hour which is time) belonging to us

out away from, gone away | breathe out to blow air out of the lungs | carry out to perform, to do something | find out to discover, to observe | point out to show, to highlight | push out to get rid of, to change the shape of a container | spread out diffused; to take up a larger area | wipe out to remove entirely, to cause to become extinct

outbreak a sudden increase in the proportion of organisms, including people, catching a disease

outcome a consequence, the result | outcome variable a result, a measurement, the consequence of changing the value of the input variable

outdoors in the open air, outside the house

outer on the outside | **outer core** a layer of molten nickel and iron near the centre of the Earth that extends from the base of the mantle, at 2900 kilometres to the inner core, at 5100 kilometres | **outer ear** the part of the ear that you can see – made from the pinna, the ear canal and the ear drum | **outer electrons** the electrons in the outer shell that are important in bonding | **outer layer** the coating, the surface of a structure | **outer orbital / outer shell** the 'track' furthest from the nucleus in which electrons are found | **outer surface** the part of the object that is affected by the outside world | **outer wall** the skin of a building

outfall the end of the pipe that is taking waste water to the river or the sea

outlet a tube or passage that allows a fluid to flow from a container | **water outlet** the position at which waste water leaves the equipment

outline a brief description that misses out details such as volume or length, a simple drawing; to give brief instructions, to provide the main points of a plan

output the signal, the material that is at the end of a process, the product | **analog output** (USA) / **analogue output** (UK) the signal can take any value | **digital output** the signal is a stream of numbers, often the binary digits of 0 and 1 | **energy output** how much work is actually done by some organism or machine (often compared to the energy input)

outside external, remote, greater than expected | **outside temperature** the temperature outside the box, body or home that is being considered

outward pull the force trying to move objects apart

ov- (Latin egg)

ova (plural of ovum) eggs, the female gametes

oval a squashed circle, an ellipse | **oval window** the part of the cochlea which is in contact with the stirrup of the ossicles in the ear

ovaries more than one ovary

ovary (plural is ovaries) the organ, in animals, in which eggs mature and are then released

oven an insulated box that can be heated from the inside and held at constant temperature, used for cooking food | **oven temperature** the temperature at which food is being cooked in the oven | **microwave oven** a metal box inside which microwaves are produced, which can be used for heating water or solutions or for cooking food, the box prevents the microwaves from escaping

over above, finished | **change over** a sudden transformation of one object or colour into another, distinct object or colour

overall to view the whole picture, taking most of the evidence into one idea, taking account of all available information | **overall consequences** the final or significant outcome

overcome to conquer, to be covered

overcook to leave on the heat for too long, to burn

overdose taking too much of a drug, leading to illness or death

overeating (not over heating which is becoming too hot) taking in more energy than is used in keeping warm or movement so the excess is stored as fat

overflow to add more liquid than can be carried by a vessel

overhead cables / overhead power cables the thick aluminium wires that carry low current / high voltage electricity from generating station to the local neighbourhood | **overhead projector** (OHP) the light source, mirrors and lenses that allow writing to be projected on to a screen | **overhead transparency** (OHT) the piece of clear material that can be written or drawn upon and then the image is projected on to a screen

over heating (not overeating which is taking in too much food) becoming too hot, starting to burn

overlap the area covered by two surfaces; to cover part of one surface with part of another sheet

overload to add sufficient weight that the carrier breaks, to increase the size of an electric current so there is a danger of fire starting

overnight during the hours of darkness, from the end of one working day to the start of the next

overstretch to take a spring or piece of elastic beyond its elastic limit so the item will not return to the original length when the force is removed

over-the-counter (otc) **medicine** a chemical which can be bought from a pharmacy without prescription and that could affect the body

over-the-limit higher than a specified amount – usually refers to the amount of alcohol that is allowed in the blood of drivers

over-weight having more fat than is expected for a healthy person, obese

over-wintering acts or responses that take place in order to allow an organism to survive the cold of winter

oviduct the egg canal, the fallopian tube, the tube that joins the ovary to the uterus | **blocked oviduct** the egg canal has a defect, so the ovum can not reach the uterus

ovist a person who believed that the tiny person (homunculus) was to be found in the egg and needed chemicals from a man in order to develop

ovulate to release an egg or ovum

ovulation release of an egg from the ovary | **ovulation date** the estimated date on which an egg was released from the ovary | **infrequent ovulation** the egg is released at irregular intervals sometimes much longer than every 28 days

ovule the structure in plants where the ova mature then the seeds develop

ovum (plural is ova) egg or female sex cell

owl a nocturnal, carnivorous bird | **owl pellets** the faeces, or excretion products including some undigested material, of owls

owner the person who has paid for the goods | **land owner** the person who has lawful possession of an area of land

ox (plural is oxen) a bull that has had its testicles removed and is used to pull farm machinery

oxidation addition of oxygen to an element or compound, loss of electrons | **oxidation reaction** a chemical change involving the addition of oxygen

oxide any compound containing an element bonded to oxygen | **oxide ion** [$O^=$] the charged particle produced by an oxygen atom gaining electrons | **oxides of nitrogen** any compound containing oxygen and nitrogen only, and may be any or a mixture of nitrous oxide [N_2O],nitric oxide [NO] and nitrogen dioxide [NO_2] | **oxides of non-metals** compounds containing a non-metal bonded to oxygen, these oxides are acid in solution | **oxides of sulfur** (USA) / **oxides of sulphur** (UK) either or both of sulphur dioxide [SO_2] and sulphur trioxide [SO_3] both of which are formed when sulphur burns, and each dissolves in water to give acid solution | **acid oxides / acidic oxides** compounds containing a non-metal bonded to oxygen that produce acids when dissolved in water | **aluminium oxide** (UK) / **aluminum oxide** (USA) [Al_2O_3] a white powder that is also called alumina, bauxite is the ore containing alumina | **basic oxide** a molecule that contains oxygen linked to a metal and so is able to neutralise an acid, basic oxides that dissolve in water are called alkalis | **calcium oxide** [CaO] a white powder that is stable when heated but glows white (limelight) when hot, also called lime; a chemical that is used to improve the drainage of clay soils, to neutralise acid soils, and in the production of cement | **copper oxide** [CuO] a black powder used to prepare copper salts | **excess oxide** the solid that remains when too much of an insoluble metal oxide is added to neutralise an acid | **iron oxide** [FeO] a compound of iron and oxygen | **iron (III) oxide** [Fe_2O_3] a compound of iron and oxygen, also called rust | **magnesium oxide** [MgO] a white powder produced by burning magnesium | **manganese (IV) oxide / manganese dioxide** [MnO_2] the

compound containing manganese bonded to oxygen that increases the rate of decomposition of hydrogen peroxide to produce oxygen and water | **metal oxides / metallic oxides** any compound formed by a metal (conductor of electricity) bonding to oxygen, these oxides can be used to neutralise an acid | **nitrogen oxides** a mixture of the several different compounds that are produced when nitrogen bonds to oxygen | **non-metal oxide** a compound produced when oxygen bonds to a non-metal, non-metal oxides produce acids when dissolved in water | **zinc oxide** [ZnO] a white powder produced by zinc bonding to oxygen that turns yellow when heated

oxidise (UK) / **oxidize** (USA) to add oxygen

oxidising agent (UK) / **oxidizing agent** (USA) a chemical that will readily give oxygen to another chemical

oxidize (USA) / **oxidise** (UK) to add oxygen

oxidizing agent (USA) / **oxidising agent** (UK) a chemical that will readily give oxygen to another chemical

oxygen (O proton number 8) the atom is never found alone, but always combines with other atoms to produce oxides, or with other oxygen atoms to give oxygen gas [O_2] or ozone [O_3]; [O_2] a gas, boiling point −183°C, that is important for the respiration of cells and for the burning of fuels, described by Rutherford (1772), Priestley (1774) and Scheele (1777) | **oxygen availability** the amount of oxygen gas that is present and can be used | **oxygen concentration** the amount of oxygen gas in a specified volume, the concentration of oxygen in air is around 20% | **oxygen gas** [O_2] a molecule (boiling point −183°C) that is important for the respiration of cells and for the burning of fuels, described by Rutherford (1772), Priestley (1774) and Scheele (1777) | **oxygen level** the concentration of oxygen gas in a mixture | **oxygen probe** a glass or metal rod that has a sensor in the tip that can measure the concentration of oxygen | **oxygen production** the release of oxygen from plants during photosynthesis, isolating oxygen from air | **oxygen-rich** contains more than the expected amount of oxygen | **oxygen tent** a sheet is placed over the head of a patient so that an atmosphere with extra oxygen can be breathed | **availability of oxygen** how much oxygen gas there is present that can be used | **dissolved oxygen** the concentration or amount of oxygen that has been dissolved in water and so is available for fish to use | **liquid oxygen** oxygen has been cooled below its boiling point of −183°C and so has turned into a liquid that can be transported in a tank just like any other liquid | test for oxygen a glowing splint will relight if put into oxygen (this test will work only with oxygen)

oxygenate to add oxygen, to bubble oxygen through water, to aerate

oxygenated oxygen has been added to the mixture | oxygenated blood blood that has passed through the lungs so has oxygen bound to the haemoglobin | de-oxygenated the oxygen has been removed from a mixture

oxy-haemoglobin (UK) **/ oxy-hemoglobin** (USA) the molecule produced when oxygen links to haemoglobin in the red blood cell

oz ounce, a unit used for weight, 1 pound is 16 ounces, one ounce is 28.35 grams

ozone [O_3] a poisonous gas made from three oxygen atoms linked together that forms a thin protective layer near the top of the atmosphere | ozone depletion the thinning of the layer of ozone high in the atmosphere, possibly caused by use of CFCs (chloro-fluoro-carbons) and leading to increased risk of skin cancer | ozone layer the part of the atmosphere that is high above the Earth where ozone is produced from oxygen gas, the ozone layer prevents the entry of dangerous ultra-violet (UV) waves from the Sun

P phosphorus, proton number 15

P... / peta... prefix for a thousand, million, million of a unit, 10^{15}

p... / pico... prefix for a million, millionth part of a unit, 10^{-12}

p⁺ [proton] a fundamental particle in the atom with a positive charge and a mass of 1 dalton, 1.66×10^{-27}kg, 1 atomic mass unit

Pa / pascal unit of pressure, one pascal is one newton per square metre (1 N/m^2)

pacemaker a small instrument that is inserted into the chest and is used to ensure that the heart beats continually and regularly

pack a set, a box, a sack; to put items into a container for transport or for safe keeping | fertiliser pack a sack of chemicals that will be spread on the soil so as to encourage plant growth | lab pack an electrical power supply used in a laboratory that provides a variable potential difference (voltage) | power pack a box that uses mains electricity (240 volt, 50 hertz ac in the UK, 110 volt, 60 hertz in the USA) as input, but puts out a lower potential difference (voltage) | variable power pack the potential difference of the output can be changed

packaging the outer covering of a packet or box | food packaging the boxes, cartons and wrapping that is used to keep food looking fresh and free from dirt

packed stored, pushed in | closely packed there is no room for any more, making the best use of space | tightly packed squashed, pushed together

packet a box, a parcel

packing material that surrounds an object so as to prevent damage, putting articles into a case or box for safety or travel

pad a cushion, a block of soft material, the soft part of a dog's foot; to fill with spongy material | brake pads the pieces of material that are heat resistant, but have lots of friction, and are pushed on to a rotating wheel in order to slow it down | horny pad the flat pad that replaces the upper front teeth in some herbivores

paddle wheel wood or iron boards are attached at right angles to the outside of a circle

paid to be given money for a service or goods

pail (not pale which is loss of colour) a bucket

pain (not pane which is a sheet of glass) an ache, a hurt | pain killer a drug or chemical that stops a person from feeling a discomfort | pain sensor a nerve cell that is sensitive to pain

paint a coloured liquid that is used to cover a surface and then allowed to dry to a solid coating; to apply a liquid to a surface | paint brush an instrument, made by attaching fibres to a stick, that is used to apply liquids to a solid surface | spray paint a covering applied as fine jets or as a mist

painting a work of art created using paint, the act of applying paint

pair (not pear which is a fruit) two of a kind | pair of eyes two eyes so the creature is able to estimate of size and distance | antagonistic pair two muscles that move a joint in opposite directions

paired mirrors two parallel mirrors that make a periscope

pairings putting items into groups of two with similar properties

pale (not pail which is a bucket) looking ill, loss of colour

palisade a fence made from tall stakes placed close together | palisade cell a type of cell that is tall and thin, and is found in leaves of plants | palisade mesophyll the layer of tall cells, immediately below the epidermis, where photosynthesis takes place

pamphlet a leaflet, a very thin book

pan a container for cooking; to find gold by swirling the sediment | pan base the bottom of the pot | pan handle the insulating rod or knob that can be used for lifting a pan | pan pipes a set of many hollow tubes, with lengths from 2 centimetres to 30 centimetres, that can be used to produce music by blowing across the tops of the tubes | frying pan a flat, metal pan intended for cooking with fat | weighing pan the container in which material is held for weighting

Panama Canal the waterway connecting the Atlantic Ocean to the Pacific Ocean that is a mixture of canals and lakes and was completed in 1914

pancreas the organ in the body, near the stomach, that produces not only an enzyme for digestion in the gut, but also a hormone, insulin, that controls the concentration of sugar in the blood

pancreatic juice the liquid containing enzymes that is produced by the pancreas

panda a mammal that inhabits the bamboo jungles of China

pandemic an outbreak of a disease over a large area such as a continent

pane (not pain which is a hurt) a sheet | pane of glass a sheet of transparent material | window pane the sheet of glass that is held by the frame of the window

panel a thin layer of stiff material | nutritional information panel the part of the box containing data on the food that is contained in the box | solar panel a water-filled structure, similar to a domestic radiator, that is painted black and is intended to absorb the heat from the Sun

Pangaea / Pangea the super-continent proposed by Wegener

panning extracting gold by swirling the ore in water in a pan

paper thin sheets of material, made from crushed plant stems and used for many purposes (the world uses 200 millions tons of paper each year) | paper clips / paperclips bent pieces of wire that are used to hold papers together | paper cup a waterproof cylindrical container with a volume of approximately 200 cm³ | paper strip a piece of paper that is long and thin | blotting paper paper that is highly absorbent, and so is used for drying ink writing | chromatography paper paper that is used to separate the chemicals in a solution by allowing the solution to migrate up the paper | cobalt chloride paper paper that is blue if the conditions are dry, but turns a very pale pink or white if the air is damp | filter paper paper that has millions of tiny holes so that liquids will soak through, but solid particles are left behind as a residue | greaseproof paper a paper that has a wax-like coating that prevents any grease passing through the paper | litmus paper paper that will turn blue if the liquid is alkaline (pH>7) and will turn red in acid solution (pH<7) | pH paper filter paper that has been dipped into an indicator solution then allowed to dry, the dried paper will then change colour depending on the pH of the test solution | rough paper paper in which the fibres are visible because the surface has not been polished nor covered with a filler | sand paper the paper is coated with a layer of sand and can be used to smooth down surfaces | tissue paper very thin paper | tracing paper translucent paper that is strong enough to be written on without tearing, used to transfer a pattern | universal indicator paper paper that can be used to indicate the pH of a solution | waxy paper the paper has been saturated with an oil then dried and so is water-proof

paper clips / paperclips bent pieces of wire that are used to hold papers together

paprika an annual plant, native to America, that is used as a food flavouring, the spice that is produced by grinding the seeds of a sweet pepper

Paracelsus (Philppus 1493–1541) was born in Switzerland, but did much of his training in mine-technology in Austria. He practised medicine in Sweden, in numerous towns in Germany and while travelling through the Middle East. He had a contempt for the writings of ancients such as Galen, although much of his work was based on magic and superstition. His views on chemistry greatly influenced Boyle.

paracetamol a mild painkiller available without prescription, but that causes liver damage if taken in large quantities

parachute a vast layer of silk that increases air resistance and so slows the speed of descent; to fall safely through the air with the aid of a parachute

parachutist a person who voluntarily jumps out of a plane, but lands safely because they use a parachute

paradox (plural is paradoxes) using logic to move from a real position or idea to an impossible conundrum

paraffin (UK) / **kerosene** (USA) a hydrocarbon fuel that has a higher boiling point than petrol

paragraphs sections of words, that may be one or more sentences, that contain a set of related ideas

parallel lines (such as railway tracks) that remain a constant distance apart | parallel arrangement organising items so that the long axes form a series of lines that do not meet | parallel circuit the components in two or more branches have a common power source so the potential difference is identical, but the current depends on the branch | parallel connections two or more attachments that allow independent movement along each branch | in parallel running next to each other; in electrical circuits, this means there must be a pair of junctions

paralyse (UK) / **paralyze** (USA) to prevent from moving

paralysis inability to move or to control movement

Paramecium an aquatic protozoan that moves by using a coat of cilia

parameter a factor that could change, but will be held constant for that experiment, a variable

parasite an organism that lives inside (or on the outside of) another organism in order to obtain warmth, protection and nutrients without giving anything in return except perhaps to make the host organism feel ill

parasitically existing in a combination that is highly suitable for the parasite but damages the host organism

parcel a package, a bundle that is sealed

parent one of the two organisms that produced an offspring, the mother or father of a child, the dam or sire of a horse | parent cell the cell that started a line of identical cells with features of special interest | parent plant the plant that was used to reproduce and provide the offspring of interest | female parent mother, ewe, hen, cow or dam that provides the nutrient filled egg that is fertilised by the male gamete | **male parent** father, ram, cock, bull or sire that provides the male gamete or sperm that fertilises the egg

parental an attitude of care for a young animal

parenting looking after and protecting offspring and teaching them survival skills

park an area of field, flowers and space that is cultivated for aesthetic enjoyment | car park an area for leaving cars | deer park a large area of woodland and grassland that is a suitable habitat for deer and which is protected from predators | National Park an area that has been set aside for recreation and study and in which building is very restricted | theme park an entertainment area with lots of exciting / thrilling rides

parsec the unit of measurement used by astronomers, 3.26 light-years

part a fragment, a section; to separate | hard parts the parts of an animal that will not rot away easily, eg bones, teeth, nails and claws | male parts the organs that will produce the male sex cell | smallest part a fragment, a tiny fraction of the substance, a tiny section

partial not complete, not full | partial eclipse part of the face of the Sun is covered by the Moon

partially incompletely

participate to take part in

particle a small object, a tiny piece, a grain | particle diagram a drawing that shows the tiny particles in a substance in order to emphasise their behaviour as a gas, liquid or solid | particle explanation explaining all chemical and physical changes as being the result of collisions and change in forces between particles | particle model the theory that a solid comprises particles in fixed position, a liquid comprises particles that are free to move and that particles in a gas are moving rapidly and are widely separated | particle size the dimensions of a small object | particle theory the idea that everything in the world is made from tiny particles that are in constant motion | adjacent particles grains or tiny pieces that are close to each other | air particles the molecules that are found in air, specks of dust that may be found in the atmosphere | alpha particle a helium nucleus (He^{++}) produced by breakdown of a radio-active nucleus | arrangement of particles the pattern formed by tiny particles in a material | atomic particle one of the three tiny bits that are found in the atom, ie neutrons, electrons and protons | charged particles any tiny bit of material, from an atomic particle to a speck of dust, that has a positive or negative charge | cooler particles the molecules

are moving more slowly, the grains are at a lower temperature | dust particles tiny specks of material, often human skin cells, that float in the air and gradually sediment | magnetic particle a tiny piece of iron [Fe], nickel [Ni] or cobalt [Co] that is a permanent magnet, the powdered iron that coats a recording tape | moving particle any tiny object that is changing position, usually travelling in a straight line | scent particles the molecules that evaporate from the liquid and cause reaction in the smell cells of the nose | solid particles grains that are in fixed position so the object keeps its shape | sub-atomic particles the three objects that make up the atom, ie the neutrons and protons in the nucleus and the electrons in their shells | tiny particles very, very small parts, small grains | transfer particles to move tiny parts between places | type of particle grains with common characteristics

particular special, unique | particular characteristics unique features especially those adapted for survival, special marks | particular direction on a known angle of the magnetic compass | particular feature special marks or behaviours that are unique to that organism or species | particular functions the special jobs that are to be carried out | particular habitats places having several features in common | particular soil the type of earth that is most suited to the growth of that form of life

particularly especially, specifically

partly-movable joint / partly-moveable joint the bones have a limited amount of movement, eg the spine

partridge a type of bird that looks like a small, brown pheasant without a tail

parts segments, components, building sections | parts of a cell the several structures that form special areas within a cell, eg the nucleus, chloroplast, mitochondria | parts of a plant the several areas of a plant that have specialised functions and so have different shapes and cells, eg the leaves and roots | parts per million (ppm) a measure of concentration | female parts the reproductive organs in a female animal, especially a woman | male parts the reproductive organs of a male animal | mouth-parts the collection of tissues that allow an animal to ingest food

Pascal (Blaise 1623–1662) was a Frenchman who suffered from headaches and indigestion for his whole life. He was educated at home then managed to prove a major idea in mathematics at the age of 16. The following year, he published a book which proved most of the theories in geometry from a few simple ideas. Two years later, he built his first computer. His interests moved towards physics and he measured pressure at increasing heights, by climbing a mountain with a barometer, then showed that the pressure is the same in all directions in a liquid and invented the syringe. The unit of pressure is named the pascal in his honour. He returned to maths and developed several ideas that are used in working out combinations and probabilities. Following a miraculous escape from death, Pascal devoted the last seven years of his life to religion and went to live with his sister at a religious house.

pascal / Pa the unit of pressure, 1 newton per square metre ($1N/m^2$)

pass a low area between mountains, suitable for travelling across the mountains; to move between, to move an object from one person to another | pass through to cause a gas to bubble through a liquid, to cause a fluid to flow between solid particles

passage a tube, a corridor, a journey, a section of writing | air passage any of the tubes (trachea, bronchi, bronchioles) that are in the lungs | nasal passages the channels in the nose that allow air to be cleaned during breathing

passed (not past which is earlier times) gone through, changed hands, taken place, succeeded at an exam, reached the required standard

passes moves between

passive not being active, resting | passive immunity instant but short-lived protection, produced by injecting the body with antibodies against the particular germ | passive smoking breathing in the fumes and dust from a cigarette that someone else is smoking

past (not passed which is movement or success) earlier times, long ago, historical | past conditions the situation of food, temperature and water that existed some time ago

pasta a paste of flour and water that is made into many different small, thin shapes, allowed to dry then cooked in boiling water

paste a cream, a suspension; to glue | cellulose paste a suspension, produced by boiling plants, that can be used as a glue

Pasteur (Louise 1822–1895) was the son of a local leather worker near the border of France with Switzerland, yet he was given a state funeral when he died – the reason being that not only did Pasteur discover the cure for half a dozen diseases, he also started the whole new branch of science that is called microbiology. His first studies

did not sound very practical – he observed the behaviour of light as it passed through a solution – but this initial pure research with no practical application was to lead to discoveries that placed Pasteur at the pinnacle of science. He became professor of chemistry at Lille in 1854 and directed the department in solving problems of the local industry, especially brewing. He was able to prove that yeast was essential for fermentation, but that other bacteria could ruin the brew, these un-wanted microbes could be killed by heating the solution to a high temperature, a process now called 'pasteurisation'. Pasteur extended these studies of germs to show that many other pro-cesses and illnesses were caused by microbes. Pasteur rescued the silk industry from disaster by isolating the microbe infecting the silkworm, he introduced vaccination to prevent anthrax and developed a vaccine against rabies, the ten year old boy who was the first person to be vaccinated later became the caretaker of the Institut Pasteur. This was a research centre and house in Paris that the French Government gave to Pasteur and where research is still carried out today, the bodies of Pasteur and his wife are buried in the crypt of the house. Pasteur was partially paralysed in 1868, but continued working. He received honours from every country, and turned down many more as being too ostentatious.

pasteur pipettes tubes that are used to transfer small amounts of liquid; there is a teat that can be squeezed at one end and the other end is drawn to a point

pasteurisation (UK) / **pasteurization** (USA) heating a liquid, *eg* milk, to about 65°C so as to destroy the bacteria and prevent the liquid turning sour

pasteurised (UK) / **pasteurized** (USA) a liquid that is sterile after being heated to 65°C

pasture / rough pasture existing grassland that has not been cultivated but is being used for the grazing of cattle or sheep

patch (plural is patches) a small area, a membrane used for repair; to mend by applying a piece of material | eye patch a semi-circle of light-proof material that is placed over the eye

patella the knee cap, the small bone at the front of the knee joint

patent legal protection of a novel idea

path route, line | path of light / light path lines on a diagram to show the expected track of the light beam | footpath a track for use by walkers only | random path the line has no pattern for either length or direction

pathogen a microbe that causes disease

pathogenic able to cause a distressing illness or death | pathogenic bacteria microbes that cause death

patient a person who has a disease and is being treated by a medic, tolerant

pattern a regular change, a repeated motif, a guide, a model | patterns in data a simple relationship, a series of changes that link one variable to another | pattern of development the series of changes that occur at specific times as an organism ages | patterns of evidence finding simple relationships in a vast amount of information | pattern of reproduction the frequency and seasons at which reproduction occurs, the changes that cause or are caused by reproduction | circular field pattern the magnetic field around the current in a single wire is a circle | clear pattern the variables show a clear relationship | common pattern a relationship or series of changes that is often encountered | describe patterns to summarise the changes that occur in the measurements of one variable as another variable is changed | development pattern the massive changes that occur in the structure of an organism, with growth or loss of limbs and a general change in shape, as the organism transforms from a single fertilised cell through adolescence to adulthood | fit into a pattern to show how the measurements match a previously described distribution | general pattern a simple description that is widely applicable | growth pattern the changes that occur in size and shape as an organism grows older | identify patterns to see how the data or information has changed in regular way so that future changes can be predicted | magnetic field pattern the distribution and direction of the lines of magnetic force that are made visible using either a compass or iron filings | regular pattern a repeating behaviour | reproduction pattern / reproductive pattern the way that the structure or behaviour of an organism changes in order to increase the chances that offspring will be produced and will survive | weather patterns regular changes in temperature, wind and amount of rain that occur at a similar time every year

pause (not paws which are feet with claws, nor pores which are small holes, nor pours which is movement of liquid) a short break, an interlude; to have a short rest

pavement a raised path, next to a road, that is intended for walkers to use, a road | limestone pavement a natural formation of rocks and boulders of limestone that are close to each other and have been weathered to the same height

paving slab / paving stone one of many flat pieces of rock that are used to produce a level surface that is long lasting, and is suitable for using as the surface of a path

paw (not pore which is a tiny hole nor pour which is to move liquid) the part of the leg that a dog puts onto the ground; to pull apart by dragging

paws (not pause which is an interlude, nor pores which are tiny holes, nor pours which is movement of liquid) scrapes the ground; the feet of an animal that has claws

Pb (*Latin* plumbous) lead, proton number 82, an unreactive metal that was used for making water pipes

pd [potential difference] the voltage change between two parts of a circuit that drives the current

$$\text{potential difference} = \text{current} \times \text{resistance}$$
$$\text{(volts)} \qquad \text{(amps)} \qquad \text{(ohms)}$$

PE [potential energy] the position of an object means it has the ability to cause a change some time in the future

$$\text{potential energy} = \text{weight} \times \text{height}$$
$$\text{(joules)} \qquad \text{(newtons)} \quad \text{(metres)}$$

pea (plural is peas) the seed, in a pod, of the pea plant which is a legume and so will add nutrients to the soil as the roots are covered with nodules of nitrogen fixing bacteria, used by Mendel to study genetics and variation | pea shooter a tube in which a wad of paper is placed near one end then blown, by mouth, out of the other end | boiled peas the seeds from the pea pod have been boiled so destroying the enzymes, including those needed for respiration | fresh peas the edible seeds produced by splitting open the pod | frozen peas peas that have been taken from the pod and then frozen so as to preserve the colour, texture and flavour | germinating peas the seed is starting to produce a shoot and a root

peace (not piece which is a fragment) calm, quiet, without rancour

peak a high point, the highest position, at the top; to reach the high point

peanuts a plant that is also called groundnuts, because the flower grows downwards after pollination and the fruit (nuts) develop in the soil

pear (not pair which is two of a kind) an edible fruit

pearl a smooth, blue–grey coloured sphere that is produced in some oysters in response to a foreign body such as a grain of sand | pearl bulb a filament lamp in which the glass envelope has a pale grey powder on the inside

peas (plural of pea) seeds of the annual legume plant

peat remains of plants that have decomposed in waterlogged soil in which there is very little oxygen, used both as a fuel in Ireland and Scotland and spread on gardens to give nutrients to the soil | peat bog an area of ground that is waterlogged with some water-plants and small islands of grass

pebble a small rock that has had all sharp edges removed by moving about in water

pectin a group of large molecules that are made from a variety of sugars, but all form gels in water

pectinase an enzyme that dissolves the pectin released from the skins of fruit

pectoral fin the fin on the side of the body of the fish, immediately behind the gill slits

pedal a foot holder at the end of the crank on a cycle; to push a crank around using legs and feet | brake pedal the lever that is pressed by a foot in order to slow the movement of a car

pedalling moving the cranks with the feet

pedigree a family tree, the parents, grandparents and other ancestors are known by name | pedigree animals are born of parents with a known history and will be used in reproduction to give offspring with the same, desirable characteristics

peel the rind, the outer layer of a citrus fruit; to remove the outer layer

peer (not pier which is a long platform) a person of equal status; to stare

pelargonium a type of perennial plant that produces flowers

pellets small balls or spheres | owl pellets the faeces of an owl | slug pellet a tablet that contains chemicals either to kill or to scare off garden slugs and snails

pelvic girdle used to emphasise that the pelvis, that supports the spine and the legs, is circular in shape

pelvis the large structure, made from bone and cartilage, that supports the base of the spine and the top of the legs

pen a writing instrument, an enclosure for sheep; to write | felt tip pens the writing tip is a wick of felt which is in a reservoir of coloured liquid | marker pen a writing instrument that can be used on most surfaces

penalty (plural is penalties) a punishment, a fine

pencil a writing instrument that uses a thin cylinder of graphite in clay to deposit a thin layer of carbon | pencil lead a mixture of powdered graphite (carbon) and clay that is the thin cylinder that will write on paper

pendulum a weight on the end of a line that is allowed to swing freely in a regular arc

penetrate to enter, to break into, often through a small opening

penguin a seabird that has lost the ability to fly through air but is adapted to 'flying' underwater

penicillin the antibiotic discovered by Fleming

Penicillium the type of fungus that produces penicillin

penis the male sex organ that can be used to deliver sperm

penumbra the area that is partially darkened by shadow because the light source is extended

people more than one person | diabetic people humans who are unable either to produce insulin or to respond to insulin and so have difficulty controlling the concentration of sugar in their blood | young people teenagers

pepper a spice; to scatter | Pepper's ghost putting two images on top of each other, *eg* a flame in a jar, by using a sheet of glass at 45° to each object | pepper pot a sealed cylinder with lots of small holes in one end

pepsin an enzyme that breaks proteins down in the acid conditions of the stomach

pepsinogen the protein produced by the stomach that will become pepsin, and start to digest proteins, when a small part of the amino acid chain is removed

peptide a chain of up to twenty amino acids joined together, a very small protein

per for every | per cent / percentage the amount as a proportion of the whole given in parts per hundred

perceptible clear, apparent, able to produce a change in a sense organ

perception the view of the world or of events

perch a fresh-water fish, a pole used by birds; to sit on a pole

percolate to diffuse, to move a fluid downwards through a porous solid

percussion banging, a sudden sound produced by hitting two solid objects together

perennial growing again every year

perfect without fault | perfect environment the temperature, moisture, food and any other variables are just right for rapid growth and reproduction of a specified organism

perform to present, to enact, to carry out a task

performance the achievement, a presentation | performance data information and measurements that are used to see if a target has been achieved | performance enhancing chemicals that improve the speed or endurance of an athlete

perfume a scent, a chemical that is applied to make one sex more attractive to the opposite sex

peri- (*Greek* around) about

peridotite an igneous rock that cooled very slowly and is often associated with the ore of nickel [Ni]

period an interval, a regular term, especially the bleeding that is seen at the start of the menstrual cycle | period of time an interval | fixed period a specified length of time | gestation period the length of time between conception and the birth of the baby, approximately 40 weeks for a human | horizontal period the elements in each row of the periodic table that have the same number of orbitals | incubation period the time taken for symptoms of an infection to become apparent | limited period a stated duration during which time an event can occur | monthly period the loss of blood that occurs each month from the uterus of women | orbital period the time taken for a satellite to return to the same spot in its orbit | rotation period the time taken for a body, such as the Earth, to spin on its own axis and return to same orientation | short period a relative term meaning a time interval that is small in comparison with another duration

periodic occurring regularly or repetitively | periodic changes differences that occur at regular intervals, usually in response to an external stimulus | periodic table an arrangement of the atoms, in order of proton number, such that elements with similar properties are found in vertical columns

periodically at regular intervals

periscope two parallel mirrors, separated and held by a tube, that can be used for seeing round corners, or over heads, or permitting people in a submerged submarine to see what is happening on the surface

peristalsis the regular contraction and relaxation of the muscles of the intestine causing the ball of chewed up food to be moved through the gut

Perkin (Sir William Henry 1838–1907) was fascinated by chemistry after seeing some experiments at age 12. In 1856, he produced the dark purple dye, called mauverine and set up a dye works (truly difficult as he was only 18 and he had to make his own nitric acid and purify the coal tar), which was so profitable that he was able to retire to a life of pure research at age 36. His three sons had equally successful careers in chemistry.

permanent always, everlasting, unchanging | permanent change the reaction that produced the new materials can not be reversed | permanent deafness the damage to the hearing will never be repairable | permanent ice the area is so cold that the water remains frozen throughout the year, permafrost | permanent magnet a piece of nickel, iron or cobalt the has been magnetised and will remain a magnet forever | permanent teeth the teeth that replace the baby teeth and remain through adulthood

permanently forever

permanganate / permanganate ion [MnO_4^-] | potassium permanganate [$KMnO_4$] a purple crystal that is soluble in water, an antiseptic

permeability a measure of the rate at which a gas or liquid moves through a solid

permeable porous, a solid with small holes that will allow slow movement of a fluid | non-permeable will not allow a fluid to pass through | selectively permeable the material will allow certain molecules to pass through, but will prevent the movement of others, often the material is permeable to small molecules, but will not allow large molecules to pass through

permutations the number of ways in which a group of objects can be arranged by selecting different numbers of the group

perpendicular vertical, straight up and down

Perseids' shower the vast number of shooting stars that appear in early August and seem to be arriving from the constellation Perseus

persistent continual, always, will not go away | persistent substance a chemical that can not be removed | persistent toxic material chemicals that are poisonous and will stay unchanged in the environment for a very long time | persistent toxin a poison that is produced by microbes and remains in the body for a long time | persistent waste material for which no use can be found that will remain a hazard for many, many years

person a human being, an individual

personal concerned with one person and should not involve others | personal alarm small equipment that can be easily triggered to give a loud noise if the person is attacked | personal health the fitness and freedom from disease of a person | personal stereo equipment for playing recorded music that uses small ear phones so only that one person can hear the sound

perspective a viewpoint, a way of looking at the information, an overview

Perspex™ a transparent, tough plastic | Perspex block an cube shape made from a transparent plastic

perspiration the salty solution that is produced by the sweat glands of the human skin to help maintain a constant body temperature

perspire to sweat

persuade to encourage a person to agree with your viewpoint

persuasion putting forward an argument to support your point of view

pest any organism that is growing in a place that is likely to cause a problem | pest control reducing the number of unwanted animals or plants | pest species the type of organism that is destroying a crop | crop pest any microbe, insect or bird that destroys the plants that a farmer is raising for profit | insect pest an insect which destroys the farmer's crops

pesticide a chemical that is sprayed in order to kill organisms that reduce the crop yield | non-persistent pesticide a chemical that is intended to kill pests, but will become inactive after a short time

pestle the small club that is used for grinding the material that is held in a tub called a mortar

PET [poly-ethene tetra-phthalate] a type of plastic that is easy to recycle | PET bottle a container, with a screw lid, made from the polymer called PET

pet an animal that is kept in the home for enjoyment of the people; to stroke or pat an animal | pet food a meal that is intended to be eaten by the domestic animal | domestic pet an animal with which you are happy to share your house

peta... / P... prefix for a thousand, million, million, 10^{15}

petals the colourful part of the flower that will both attract insects and provide a landing platform

Petri (Julius Richard 1852–1921) studied medicine and gradually moved up in Society until he was both the Head of a large hospital and an advisor to the Government. He is remembered for the dish that he developed during the two years that he spent as an assistant to Koch from 1877 to 1879

petri dish a pair of cylinders that are low but wide, typically 0.5 centimetre high and 8 centimetres wide, that form a base and top and are superb for growing bacteria or fungi safely (the dishes were designed by Petri)

petro-chemistry the study of the changes involved when producing and using oils and hydrocarbons

petrohol a mixture of petrol and alcohol that can be used as a car fuel

petrol (UK) / **gasoline** (USA) a hydrocarbon liquid fuel that is used in the internal combustion engine | petrol consumption the distance travelled on each litre of petrol over a specified course | petrol engine equipment that uses petrol as fuel and produces kinetic energy of a rotating shaft

petroleum crude oil, the fractions of oil that are liquid at room temperature but are easy to burn | petroleum jelly a hydrocarbon used in medicines

as a lubricant | liquid petroleum gas (LPG / lpg) many hydrocarbons are gases at room temperature, but form liquids when pressure is applied and can then be transported easily in tanks

pewter a grey alloy based on tin

pH (*pondus hydrogenii*, the power of hydrogen) a measure of the acidity in a solution, measured on a scale of 1 to 14, in which pH 7 is neutral | pH chart a card showing the colours that an indicator will produce at each pH | pH indicator a chemical that changes colour depending on the pH, most indicators will have one colour above a known pH and a different colour below that pH | pH meter an instrument that allows the pH of a solution to be measured using a glass probe | pH monitor an instrument for continually measuring the pH of a solution, especially useful when studying water quality | pH number the value of the pH, on a scale of pH 1 to pH 14, for that solution | pH paper filter paper that has been dipped into an indicator solution then allowed to dry and will give a colour that depends on the pH of the test solution | pH probe a rod which is put into a solution and will change electrical properties depending on the pH value | pH range the extent of the pH scale for which a change will happen, from the highest to the lowest pH values that are allowed for that reaction | pH scale the range of values of pH from the strongest acid (pH 1) through to the strongest alkali (pH 14) | pH sensor a glass tube that changes properties at different pH values, attaching the pH sensor to a recording device gives a pH monitor | pH value the pH number of that solution | low pH the amount of acid is sufficient to produce a pH below 3 | neutral pH neither acid nor alkali, but at a pH of 7

phalanges the bones of the fingers and toes

pharmaceuticals legal drugs, chemicals that have a beneficial effect on the body | pharmaceutical industry the people involved in the research, development, testing, manufacturing and selling of chemicals that can affect the body or treat disease

pharmacist a person who has a knowledge of the effects of chemicals on the body, a chemist who will dispense medicines prescribed by a medic

phase an interval, a period, a stage | phases of the Moon / Moon's phases the changes in the shape of the Moon when looked at from the Earth

phenol [C_6H_5OH] carbolic acid, the original antiseptic | phenol red an indicator that is yellow below pH 7.9 and red above pH 7.9 | phenol phthalein an indicator that is colourless below pH 8.2 and pink above pH 8.2

phenomena (plural of phenomenon) events, especially those that are rare or special | everyday phenomena events that occur regularly, but which should still amaze us | physical phenomena events that can be seen, heard or felt

phenomenon (plural is phenomena) a unique object, an observation that can be repeated under specific circumstances

phenotype the visible characteristics of an organism

phenylketonuria (pku) genetic disease in which the person is unable to use phenylalanine

phenyl salycylate /salol a chemical that is stable and has a fixed melting point of approximately 42^0C

Philolaus (of Tarentum or of Croton, maybe 470–385 BC) followed the teachings of Pythagoras and was a successful mathematician, physician and teacher, he probably taught Democritus. He wrote two books, which have since been lost, that had a profound affect on the thinking of the Greeks.

philosopher a thinker, a scientist | philosopher's stone a mythical piece of rock that would magically turn lead into gold

phlegm the sticky jelly or mucus that is produced from the lungs as the trachea in order to remove dust and microbes

phloem the long tubes in plants through which sugars are distributed around the plant from the leaves

phlogiston the material with a negative weight, that was lost when substances burns | phlogiston theory the idea that a substance called phlogiston was lost whenever a substance burned was popularised by Stahl but was disproved by Lavoisier

phon a unit for measuring the intensity of sound that is rarely used

phosphates / phosphate ions [$PO_4^=$] charged particles that are found bonded to a metal, they are essential minerals for growth and are found in DNA | calcium phosphate [$CaPO_4$] a mineral that is important in providing strength to teeth and bones | super-phosphate calcium phosphate [$Ca(HPO_4)_2$], used as a fertiliser

phosphoric acid [H_3PO_4] the strong acid produced when phosphorus pentoxide [P_2O_5] dissolves in water

phosphorus (P, proton number 15, melting point 44°C) an element that is white when pure, but reacts spontaneously and rapidly with air, phosphorus is an essential atom in DNA, discovered by Brand in 1669 and rediscovered by Hooke in 1680 | phosphorus pentoxide [P_2O_5] the powder produced when phosphorus burns

photo- (*Greek* light)

photo-cells thin layers of material that transform light energy into electrical energy

photocopiers machines that make a copy of a document by reflecting visible light

photo-degradable able to be broken down by exposure to sunlight

photo-finish the contestants in a race finished so close together that a photograph needed to be examined to establish who won

photograph a picture or permanent image on a film; to take a picture using visible light | false-colour photographs pictures taken with a camera, but the colour on the picture is different from that which is seen with the human eye

photographic evidence observations and measurements that were taken using a camera and so are permanently available | photographic film the paper sheet that is coated on one side with chemicals that change when exposed to light

photography the process of taking a picture or image on to film | time-lapse photography a series of photographs is taken at widely spaced intervals and then played back in a much shorter time so you can follow a slow-moving event, *eg* a plant growing

photomicrograph a picture taken of the sample on the stage of a microscope

photoreceptors cells that are able to detect and respond to light, especially the rods and cone cells that are found in the retina of the eye

photosensitive able to detect light, changes that occur when light is present

photosynthesis the process that occurs in the palisade cells of green plants in which the light energy from the Sun is turned into chemical energy of sugars | products of photosynthesis the sugar and oxygen that are formed by the action of sunlight on green leaves | rate of photosynthesis the amount of sugar that is produced each second in the leaf of a plant

photosynthesise (UK) / **photosynthesize** (USA) to use sunlight in order to produce sugars in the leaves of plants

photosynthetic able to turn light energy into sugars and oxygen | photosynthetic bacteria microbes that are capable of turning light energy from the Sun into chemical energy | photosynthetic pigment chlorophyll, the chemical that captures the light energy in the cells of producers

phototropism bending or growth of the stem of a plant as the leaves are attracted towards a light

phrase a short sentence; to word an idea carefully | key phrase the important few words

phyla (plural of phylum) the forms of life into which each kingdom may be divided

-phyll (*Greek* a leaf)

phylum (plural is phyla) the next division of the major kingdoms of life, a group of related classes

physical of the body, tangible reversible, observable without causing a permanent change | physical activity speed and duration of movement | physical causes movement of air or water, or changes in temperature, bring about a change | physical change a difference that occurs without any change in the chemicals, *eg* freezing of water, the differences that occur in visible features of a person such as weight, tone of voice or amount of hair | physical damage breakage into smaller pieces without any chemical change | physical digestion the chewing, biting, squashing and squeezing that turns food into a mush | physical disability a change to the nervous system, joints or muscles that causes movement to be restricted | physical factors variables that do not involve chemicals, *eg* temperature, pressure, light intensity | physical features characteristics that can be seen or felt | physical maturation the observable changes that occur during growth, *eg* height, weight | physical means / physical method a technique or procedure that does not change the type of particle, although different particles, may separate | physical needs the environment of temperature, moisture or light that an organism requires | physical phenomena features that can be seen or heard | physical process a change that is reversible, *eg* freezing and thawing, conducting electricity | physical property a characteristic that can be altered and then the process reversed to return to the original state, a feature that can be observed without causing a change | physical protection a method of preventing rusting by using a layer of oil or paint to prevent the moisture or oxygen from reaching the iron | physical state deciding if the material is a solid, liquid or gas, the appearance of a person or an item, how healthy and fit a person is feeling | physical weathering changes in rock structure and the appearance of the landscape caused by wind, rain, freezing of water / thawing of ice and flowing water

physicist a person who studies phenomena that can be described by mathematical equations | astro-physicist a person who studies the formation and evolution of stars

physics the study of phenomena that are usually reversible, leading to equations that make understanding much easier, the study of matter, energy and their interactions, once known as 'natural philosophy' | astro-physics the study of the changes that occur to stars or the behaviour of atoms when they are in the massive gravitational force of a star

physiotherapist a skilled person who helps injured people to regain the use of muscles and joints by judicial use of exercises

pi / π the ratio of the circumference of a circle to the diameter, an irrational number that is approximately 3.14159 or 22/7

piccolo a wind instrument smaller than a flute

pickled food that has been preserved for later use by putting into salt or vinegar

picnic a prepared cold meal that is eaten for pleasure in the great outdoors

pico... / p... prefix for a million, millionth part of a unit, 10^{-12}

pictograph a diagram or symbol that has meaning and information beyond a simple diagram

pictorial giving information by using pictures

picture an illustration, a diagram, a drawing | false-colour pictures photographs in which the colours of each object are not the same as the colours seen by the human eye, the addition of such colours can be used to distinguish features in the image | satellite pictures photographic images taken using a camera that is in space

pie chart a way of showing data in which a circle is divided into segments – just like a pie

piece (not peace which is quiet) a part, a segment | eye-piece the lens at the top of the tube of a microscope at which you put your eye

pier (not peer which is a person or to stare) a platform that extends a long distance, usually over water

pierce to push a pointed tube through a surface

piercing penetrating, pushing a tube through a skin | piercing mouthparts part of the insect's mouth is a tube that can be used to penetrate through skin, *eg* so that a mosquito can access blood

pig a type of animal raised on farms that is sold as pork, bacon or ham, a container for molten iron

pigeon a bird that is found worldwide, pigeons can be trained to return to their own nest-box and were useful in carrying messages

pigment a coloured chemical, especially a chemical that can produce a colour in another material | pigment-producing cells the layer of the skin that is made from cells that produce melanin, a coloured chemical that protects against dangerous ultra-violet light | green pigment chlorophyll, the chemical that is essential for photosynthesis | photosynthetic pigment chlorophyll, the chemical that captures the light energy in the cells of producers

pike a predatory fish, a long pole with an axe head or spear on the end

pile a heap; to form a collection of objects on top of each other

piling producing a tower; a tree trunk that is driven into the ground

pill a tablet containing drugs | contraceptive pill the tablet containing female hormones that is taken to prevent pregnancy | sleeping pill a tablet that is taken to increase the ability to sleep | slimming pill a tablet that should cause you to lose weight without conscious effort or change of life-style

pillar a rod, a girder, a vertical support

pillow soft block used for resting the head during sleep

pin a pointed piece of metal, a fastener; to fasten | pin hole a tiny puncture, a small perforation | drawing pin thumb tack, a small nail with a wide head

pine an evergreen, coniferous tree; to waste away while waiting | pine needle the long, thin leaf of a pine tree

pin hole a tiny puncture, a small perforation | pinhole camera a box with a screen or film at one end and a pin hole at the other, used to show that light travels in straight lines as the image is always upside down and in focus

pink a colour produced by mixing white with red, a type of carnation

pinna the part of the ear of the outside of the head, made from cartilage, may help in making the ear more sensitive to sound

pint unit of volume in the imperial system, approximately 570 cm^3

pipe a tube, the passage through which magma moves inside a volcano | pipeline a very large diameter tube that carries hot oil from the oil-well to the terminal or refinery | copper pipe a tube made from copper [Cu] | exhaust pipe the tube taking the products of burning away from the engine | hosepipe a long plastic tube that can be used for moving large volumes of water in order to water the garden, to put out a fire or to wash the car | light pipe an optical fibre, a thin tube of glass down which light is transmitted from end to end | pan pipes a set of many hollow tubes, with lengths from 2 centimetres to 30 centimetres, that can be used to produce music by blowing across the tops | wind pipe trachea, the tube joining the mouth to the lungs

pipette a hollow tube that is used for transferring liquids | dropping pipette a tube that can hold

liquid and then release the liquid in small drops | pasteur pipette / teat pipette a small tube, approximately 2 cm^3 volume, which has a teat at one end that is squeezed and, upon release, liquid is drawn into the tube and held there until the teat is squeezed again

piranha any of the several types of aggressive flesh-eating fish that are found in the rivers of South America

pistil (not pistol which is a gun) the seed-bearing organ of a flower

pistol (not pistil which is part of a flower) a small gun | starting pistol equipment used to start running races that both produces a bang, so the runners can hear the start, and sends an electronic signal to the timing equipment

piston the smooth rod that moves inside a cylinder and provides a leak-proof seal

pit a hole, a depression for catching animals, a coal mine | arm pit the concave area of skin between arm and the shoulder

pitch (plural is pitches) the frequency of a note, a tar that turns molten when heated, the area on which games are played, the slope of a roof | high pitch the frequency of the sound is high, maybe above 3000 hertz | higher pitch the frequency of that note is higher than others | low pitch the frequency of vibration is low, below approximately 200 hertz | range of pitch the lowest frequency to the highest frequency of sound

pitched produced at a specific level

pitcher a jug | pitcher plant a plant that obtains additional nitrogen by trapping and digesting insects

pitchfork a garden implement with a long handle and several teeth that is used to pick up (pitch) hay

pitted marked with small holes | pitted glass slide / pitted slide a microscope slide with a depression on one surface so a drop of fluid can be examined

pituitary gland a small endocrine gland at the base of the brain that produces chemical messengers that control several of the other hormone-producing glands

pivot an axle, a fulcrum; to move around an axle, to move in a circle | pivot joint a junction of two bones that allows movement in one plane only, eg the knee joint

pivoted able to move around a point | pivoted object the article is able to move freely around one axis | freely pivoted able to move around an axis with no friction between the moving surfaces

pixel one dot on a TV screen, a monitor or a newspaper

place (not plaice which is a flat fish) an area; to put into position | appropriate places suitable positions | cold place an area where the temperature is such that lots of clothing is needed to stay at a temperature that is comfortable | fire place an area in which a fire may be lit safely | work-place the area set aside for a particular task

placebo sugar pill, a pretend treatment | placebo effect the observation that people will get better when given a pill that contains no active ingredient

placenta the organ that is produced to help the foetus obtain nourishment and get rid of waste, the arteries and veins of the placenta are continuous within the umbilical cord, but there is no continuity between the placenta and the uterus

placing putting into order, installing

plague an outbreak of a disease that causes the death of a substantial proportion of the population | plague of locusts millions of locusts descend on any plant, including crops, and will eat everything in their path, leaving behind devastation and starvation | bubonic plague a bacterial disease that causes the skin to form boils or buboes (inflammation of the lymph glands) | Great Plague the Europe-wide outbreak of plague that occurred in 1665 and caused Newton to leave Cambridge

plaice (not place which is an area) a flat fish found in the seas around Europe

plain (not plane which is flat) obvious, a large area of level ground, not fancy or adorned in any way, not beautiful

plan an outline for a course of action; to decide what should be done in order to test an idea | draft plan a preliminary outline, an outline of future actions | group plan the idea that has been discussed and agreed by all members of the group

planaria (plural of planarian) flat-worms that are found in any watery environment

plane (not plain which is land) flat, smooth; an aircraft, a carpenters' tool for smoothing wood; to glide | 'plane an aeroplane, an aircraft | plane mirror a flat reflective surface | plane surface a flat covering | solar plane the imaginary sheet on which all the planets (except Pluto) and the asteroids seem to lie

planet a large body that orbits a star | Blue Planet the Earth | habitable planet a planet (which means any natural satellite of a star) that has an atmosphere, temperature and gravitational acceleration that is similar to those found for Earth | inner planets the four planets nearest to the Sun that are all made from rock, Mercury, Venus, Earth and Mars | Red Planet Mars

plac
↓
plan

planetarium a building with a dark concave ceiling onto which can be projected points that represent stars, a system of lenses and mirrors controlled by a computer allows the viewpoint or the time to be changed

planetary day the length of time that a particular planet takes to turn once on its own axis | planetary motion the movement of a planet around the Sun

planetoids the thousands of pieces of rock that orbit the Sun that are too large to be called asteroids and too small to be called planets

planets the major chunks of material that orbit the Sun, the major planets are Mercury, Venus, Earth, Mars, Jupiter, Saturn, Uranus, Neptune and Pluto

planing (not planning which is preparing) skimming on top, or just above, a surface, making smooth

plankton microscopic life that lives in open water | animal plankton tiny animals that drift in water, some types will develop into larger animals such as star fish or sea urchins | plant plankton tiny plants that drift in the water

planning (not planing which is smoothing) deciding what actions to take, the schedule and which resources should be used | planning an experiment deciding how to carry out the practical part of an investigation

plans decides what needs to be done, what equipment is required and what schedule

plant a form of life that is capable of photosynthesis and has vascular tissue; to bury a seed into the ground | plant biomass the mass of plant that is available as food or fuel | plant breeder a person who specialises in reproducing and growing plants | plant cells the building block of all plants, characterised by having a cell wall composed of cellulose, a very few plant cells will also have chloroplasts | plant characteristics the features that either distinguish plants from other kingdoms of life or allow different plants to be recognised | plant cuttings small pieces of plant that will grow to give new plants that are identical to the original plant | plant disease an infection of a plant that slows the growth or causes death | plant embryo a group of cells within the seed that will produce the plant at germination | plant fertiliser (UK) / plant fertilizer (USA) chemicals, especially NPK (nitrogen, phosphorus and potassium) that are added to the soil or water in order to encourage healthy growth | plant food nutrients that are added to the soil or water in order to encourage plant growth | plant growth the increase in size or mass of a plant over a given period of time | plant kingdom one of the five kingdoms of life (plant / animal / monera /

protoctista / fungi), characterised by the cells having a nucleus and a cell wall of cellulose | **plant life** the vegetation in an area | **plant material** any substance obtained from a plant, especially stems and leaves that are used for fuels and construction | **plant nutrients** chemicals that need to be absorbed by the root hairs so as to allow healthy growth of the plant | **plant oil** a liquid extracted by crushing the seeds of corn, sunflowers or rape that will not mix with water | **plant organs** the parts of a plant that are observably different and have different functions, *eg* roots, flowers | **plant plankton** tiny plants that drift in the water | **plant population** the number of a specified type of plant that is found in a given area | **plant pot** a cylinder or cube shaped container which is filled with soil and used for growing plants | **plant product** any chemical or material that is obtained from a plant and which is useful | **plant remains** dead plants that have been partially decomposed | **plant reproduction** increasing the population of a plant by either asexual or sexual reproduction | **plant respiration** the reaction that occurs in all plant cells between sugars and oxygen, releasing energy | **plant roots** the parts of the plant that extend below ground so as to provide an anchorage and allow water and minerals to be absorbed | **plant species** a defined type of plant | **plant specimens** examples of types of plant | **plant tissue** a set of cells that have a defined function, *eg* anther | **plant variety** a type of a specified plant, *eg* there are lots of varieties of rose or of apple | **aquatic plant** any plant that lives in water | **broad-leaved plant** a flowering plant that has flat leaves | **carnivorous plants** plants that obtain some of their nutrients by trapping insects, digesting the body, then absorbing the chemicals | **chemical plant** a factory for the large-scale production of chemicals | **climbing plant** plants that are able to grip a vertical surface and so grow upwards in order to reach more sunlight | **crop plant** any plant that is grown for profit | **culturing plants** growing plants in special conditions and soils | **desalination plant** a factory for producing fresh drinking water from salty water (saline) | **desert plant** a producer that is adapted to living in a hot region where rain rarely falls | **dwarf plant** a plant that has the genetic instructions to remain low | **extraction plant** one or more industrial buildings that are used to purify a metal from an ore | **floating plant** a plant in which the leaves float on the surface of water with the roots dangling in the water | **flowering plant** a plant that will have a flower, but may not have any at present | **genetically modified plant** a plant in which a piece of DNA has been inserted into the chromosome so as to change the genes or instruction set | **green plant** emphasising the fact that the leaves of the plant must contain chlorophyll | **growing plants** plants that are becoming larger | **healthy plant** a plant that is growing with a strong stem, lots of leaves and adequate roots | **individual plant** a single or specified plant | **industrial plant** machinery that can be used to carry out a large-scale process | **insect-pollinated plant** a plant that produces pollen that sticks to the insect and is knocked off at the stigma of the next flower | **living plant** a plant that is growing and developing | **modern plants** crops and flowers that have been discovered or genetically developed in the past decade | **non-flowering plant** a plant that does not produce a flower and so does not use insect pollination | **non-seed-producing plant** a plant that reproduces by producing spores | **non-vascular plant** plants that do not contain any tubes for the distribution of water, *eg* mosses | **parent plant** the plant that gave rise to those offspring | **parts of a plant** the organs of a plant, *eg* leaves, stem, roots, flowers | **pitcher plant** a plant that obtains additional nitrogen by trapping and digesting insects | **potted plant** a producer that is grown in a container of soil and so can be moved or can be grown indoors | **rooted plants** organisms that are producers, with chlorophyll in the leaves, and a separate root structure connected to the leaves by vascular tissue | **seed-producing plant** any plant that reproduces by forming an embryo surrounded by a food store and a protective coat | **separation plant** the industrial buildings that are used to isolate large quantities of pure chemicals from mixtures such as oil or air | **sewage plant** an area, with building and equipment, that turns the dirty water from the sinks, washing machines and toilets of lots of houses, into water that is clean enough to return to the river | **typical plant** the type of producer organism which is usually found in that environment | **vascular plants** organisms that have chlorophyll for photosynthesis, but also have tubes for the transport of water and sugar solutions | **water plant** a plant that grows either totally under fresh water or the roots and a major part of the stem are under water | **weed plant** any plant growing in an area where it is not wanted | **wild plant** any plant that has arrived by accident and then grows | **wind-pollinated plant** a plant in which the pollen is scattered into the air with the chance that some will be carried by the wind and land on the female part of a similar plant | young plants plants that have developed their first true leaves

plaque the hard residue on teeth produced by allowing bacteria to grow

plasma / blood plasma the liquid part of blood, containing dissolved chemicals, after the cells have been removed by sedimentation (serum is similar to plasma, but the clotting factors have been removed)

plasmid a small piece of DNA, in the form of a circle, that is found in many bacteria | recombinant plasmid a closed circle of DNA in which extra genes have been bonded and is then ready for inserting back into a bacterium

plaster a fine powder that is mixed with water then allowed to dry, a sticky strip that can be used to protect cuts and grazes; to put a layer on to the wall | plaster of Paris calcium sulphate / calcium sulfate [$CaSO_4$], gypsum, a fine powder that is mixed with water to give a suspension that can be poured or shaped, but which dries quickly to leave a white solid

plastic able to be stretched then will retain its stretched form, a non-biodegradable synthetic material | plastic beaker the cup is made from plastic and so can be used for mixing chemicals, but should not be heated | plastic bottle a closable container made from a synthetic material | plastic case a flexible, but strong, container made from a plastic | plastic coat / plastic coating a protective layer of a polymer or a rubber | plastic foam a springy solid that is made from plastic and contains many small bubbles of air | plastic thread a filament made from plastic | clear plastic a polymer that allows all colours to pass through without scattering | foam plastic a hard material that is made from plastic and contains many small bubbles of air | thermoplastic a plastic that can be repeatedly heated, reshaped then cooled | thermosetting plastic synthetic material that starts off soft, but turns permanently hard after heating

Plasticine™ (UK) / **Play-Doh™** (USA) a synthetic material resembling clay that can be used for producing models, but remains soft and can be re-used

plastics solid materials that have been prepared by changing oil chemically

plate a thin solid with a shape that approximates to a circle; to add a thin layer, *eg* of gold | plate tectonics the study of the panels that make up the crust of the Earth | agar plate / nutrient agar plate a layer of agar in a petri dish that is used for growing bacteria | rating plate the sheet on electrical equipment that gives the safe

voltage, current and power | silver plate a thin layer of expensive silver covering a cheap, strong metal | tectonic plates the major pieces of the Earth's crust that are separated by thin regions where volcanic activity and earthquakes occur | tin-plate a thin layer of tin [Sn] is used to cover and protect from corrosion an article that has been made from a cheap but strong metal such as iron

plateau a flat, high area; to reach a flat area that is higher than the surroundings

platelets small cell fragments in the blood that are important in producing a solid plug or clot at the site of an injury

platey minerals / platy minerals rocks that show lots of thin layers, *eg* slate, mica

plating covering with a layer that is thin and tough | tin plating using an electric current to lay down a layer of tin, or chromium, on to the surface of an iron article, so as to prevent corrosion

platinum (Pt, proton number 78, melting point 1772°C) a very unreactive metal that is used as inert electrodes and in expensive jewellery

platy minerals / platey minerals rocks that show lots of thin layers, *eg* slate, mica

Play-Doh™ (USA) / **Plasticine™** (UK) a synthetic material resembling clay that can be used for producing models, but remains soft and can be re-used

playing enjoying a game, performing a drama | playing field an area of grass that is marked out for ball games

pleasant agreeable, pleasing

Pleiades a cluster of stars in the constellation of Taurus that contains up to 250 stars

plentiful ample amount, abundant supply

plenty ample, lots, abundant

pliers equipment, like very wide scissors, that is used for squeezing or cutting wires

Plimsoll line the International Load Line, a line on the hull of every large ship that shows the weight of cargo that can carried safely, introduced by Samuel Plimsoll in 1875

plot a plan, a piece of ground; to plan, to draw the points onto a graph | plot of ground a defined area of land that is to be used

plotting moving information from a table of numbers to a graph or diagram, planning, scheming | plotting compass a small magnetic compass that is used to find the strength and direction of a field around a magnet | plotting graphs putting the data points onto a graph then drawing the best fitting line

Plough a constellation visible from the Northern Hemisphere, also called the Great Bear or the Big Dipper

plough (UK) / **plow** (USA) farm equipment for turning soil over; to use equipment to turn over the soil

ploughing turning the earth over using an instrument, the plough, that is pulled through the soil

plow (USA) / **plough** (UK) farm equipment for turning soil over; to use equipment to turn over the soil

pluck to pull out, to denude a bird's body of feathers

plug a component at the end of a wire that can be easily pushed into a socket so as to give an electrical connection, a stopper that is used in the end of a tube, in a flask or to stop water escaping from a sink; to prevent material escaping by closing a hole | plug hole an exit hole that can be blocked by a plug | ear plugs cylindrical pieces of wax or plastic that are inserted into the ear canals so as to limit the damage caused by loud and continuous noises | electric plug / mains plug the object on the opposite end of a flex or wire to the electrical appliance and which has prongs to fit into a socket | mucous plug (UK) / mucus plug (USA) the jelly-like substance found at the neck of the pregnant uterus | three-pin plug the standard connector that is used to join electrical equipment to mains power in the United Kingdom

plumbing the pipes, taps and basins that allow controlled use of water in the house

plumule the earliest signs of a growing shoot in a germinating seed

plunger a piston, equipment used for clearing drains

Pluto the outermost planet in the Solar System, the orbit is very elongated so the Pluto is currently closer to the Sun than is Neptune

pm [*Latin* post meridian] after noon, evening

PMT [pre-menstrual tension] the changes in mood that occur in some women just before the start of her monthly menstrual bleeding (this may be caused by changes in concentration of hormones)

pneumatic using air | pneumatic system a mechanism that uses compressed air either for operation or for control | pneumatic tire (USA) / pneumatic tyre (UK) an air-filled tube that fits over the circumference of a wheel

pneumatically operated power or control is provided by changing air pressure

pneumatics the study of using air to control systems

pocket small, an enclosed space; to steal | pockets of air volumes of air that have been trapped either accidentally as in a porous rock such as pumice, or intentionally between layers so as to prevent loss of heat

pod- / -pod (*Greek* a foot)

pod / seed pod a capsule, a case for the seeds of legumes such as peas or beans

poem a series of words that provide a description, in addition the order, stress and use of the words gives a rhythm

point a sharp end, a major idea, a position; to show the direction | point out to show, to highlight | boiling point the temperature at which the liquid has to turn to gas, this temperature is a characteristic of the liquid | bullet point one of a series of important ideas | condensation point the temperature at which a gas turns to liquid, this temperature is identical to the boiling point | connection points the spots or positions that allow joints to be made easily | discussion point an important idea that needs to be argued about | far point the furthest point that can be seen clearly | fixed point unchanging position | freezing point the temperature at which a liquid turns to solid, this temperature is characteristic of the liquid | key points the very important ideas | main points important ideas | melting point the temperature at which the solid turns to liquid, the temperature is identical to the freezing point | near point the point closest to the eye that the lens is able to focus onto the retina | significant points the critical ideas | speed at a point the rate at which an object is moving when measured at a specific place

pointed shown by using an out-stretched finger, having a thin sharp end

pointing showing, identifying

poison a chemical that will kill a particular organism, especially a chemical that is eaten or ingested; to use a chemical in order to kill an animal, *eg* a pest such as a rat | cholera poison the chemical that is produced by the cholera bacteria and causes diarrhoea in people and often leads to death by dehydration | rat poison a chemical that is put out with the intention of killing rats

poisoned killed by a chemical

poisoning adding chemicals that will cause death | alcohol poisoning the symptoms produced by drinking so much alcohol that the liver is no longer able to work properly | blood poisoning a disease (that is often fatal) caused by bacteria releasing toxins into the blood stream | food poisoning an illness caused by bacteria in the food excreting chemicals that interfere with the normal working of the digestive system | mercury poisoning breathing in or swallowing compounds containing mercury which leads to paralysis and death

poisonous likely to kill | poisonous chemical a substance that will cause death | poisonous gas a chemical that can diffuse through the air and will kill one or more types of organism, *eg* chlorine gas

poker a card game played for money, a metal rod that is used for rearranging the coal or wood on a solid fuel fire

polar... concerning the area around the magnetic and geographic poles at the extremities in the north and south of the Earth | polar bear a mammal that is big, white and adapted to living on the ice in the Arctic | polar ice cap the layer of frozen water that covers the Arctic sea in the northern hemisphere and the Antarctic land mass in the southern half of the Earth | polar orbit the path taken by a satellite in orbit around the Earth, which passes over each magnetic or geographic pole

Polaris / Pole Star the star in the tail of the Little Bear that appears to be directly over the North Pole and so was used for navigation

polarise to filter of affect a transverse wave so that all the vibrations occur in the same direction

polarity (plural is polarities) (nothing to do with the poles of a magnet) is the charge on an electrode either positive or negative

Pole one of the points on the Earth's surface to which a magnet will point | pole one of the two ends of a magnet, one is north and the other is south, a bar, a stick | Pole Star / Polaris the star in the tail of the Little Bear that appears to be directly over the North Pole | geographic poles the points on the surface of the Earth through which the axis of rotation seems to pass in the north (Arctic) and south (Antarctic) | like poles magnetic poles that are the same, either both are north or both are south | magnetic poles the two ends of a magnet, the points at which the Earth's magnetic field seems to start and finish | North Pole a geographic point that is at the centre of the Arctic circle and seems to lie directly below the Pole Star | north pole the end of a magnet that will point towards the South Pole | north magnetic pole an imaginary point on the surface of the Earth, somewhere in northern Canada, that seems to be where all the lines of magnetic force enter the Earth | north-seeking pole the end of a magnet that will point towards the north pole of a magnet or the Earth | opposite poles one of the poles is north and other is south, so they are attracting each other | similar poles the magnetic poles of the material are both the same | South Pole the point in the centre of the Antarctic continent through which the axis of rotation seems to pass | south pole one of the two ends

of a magnet | south-seeking pole the end of a freely rotating magnet that points south | unlike poles the two magnetic poles are different and so will attract each other

polio / poliomyelitis a disease caused by a virus that produces symptoms similar to 'flu' except in a minority of cases when extensive damage occurs to the nervous system leading to paralysis and loss of muscle control

Polish a person from Poland

polish the suspension which is used for making a surface more reflective; to rub a surface

polished having a smooth, shiny surface | polished metal metal which has been rubbed so to produce a smooth, shiny surface | polished rice the outer husk has been removed from the seed

polishing rubbing a surface, often using wax, to produce a shine

pollen / pollen cell the male sex cell, or gamete, of plants | pollen count the number of pollen grains in one cubic metre of air | pollen grain one item of pollen | pollen tube the pipe or shaft that a pollen extends from the stigma to the ovary so that the male nucleus can fertilise the female cell

pollinate to transfer the pollen from the stamen to the stigma | wind-pollinate to scatter the pollen on to the wind

pollination movement of the male gamete of a flower (pollen) to a female sex cell | cross-pollination the pollen from the flower of one plant fertilises the ova in another plant | insect-pollination the pollen is transported, unknown to the animal, by an insect, so this pollen must be large and be sticky or have hooks | selective pollination isolating flowers or animals so that the breeder can decide which specific organisms should be the parents | self-pollination the pollen from one flower is used to fertilise the ova of that same flower | wind pollination the pollen is transported by the air currents and so this pollen must be small and light

pollutant a material or energy that changes the habitat in such a way that the environment no longer suits the existing organisms | pollutant gases the gases that change the composition of the atmosphere in a specified area, especially the oxides of sulphur, phosphorus and nitrogen (gases that cause acid rain) or carbon dioxide (the greenhouse effect)

polluted dirty, containing chemicals that are new to the population of several species so causing a change as a result of their presence | polluted river a flow of water that contains dissolved poisonous material so is unlikely to support life

pollution introducing a chemical or energy into an environment, leading to an undesirable change of habitat | pollution indicator an organism whose presence or absence reflects the conditions in that environment, *eg* many lichen are sensitive to sulphur dioxide in the atmosphere | air pollution / atmospheric pollution changing the proportion of gases in the air, *eg* increasing carbon dioxide levels, increasing CFC concentrations | industrial pollution the waste chemicals or energy that are introduced into the environment in sufficient amounts to cause a change in the local habitat | noise pollution an unacceptable increase in the amount of unwanted sound | water pollution adding chemicals to rivers and lakes causing a change in the environment and the populations of aquatic life

poly- (*Greek* many)

poly-ester a polymer, a synthetic fibre used to make material that has a high strength and is chemically inert

poly-ethene tetra-phthalate (PET) a polymer that is used for making most drinks bottles

polymer a large molecule made from many monomers or building units

polypeptide / polypeptide chain a string of amino acids, a very small protein

polystyrene a solid made by linking many molecules of styrene [$CH_5.CH:CH_2$] | polystyrene ball a sphere made from expanded polystyrene so the ball has a low density and is an electrical insulator | polystyrene chips random shapes of polystyrene foam with lengths up to 3 centimetres | polystyrene cup a drinking vessel without a handle, made from a solid white foam so the heat is not conducted to the outside | polystyrene glue an adhesive, usually polystyrene dissolved in an organic solvent, that is used to join polystyrene pieces together | expanded polystyrene a very low-density material that is useful as an insulator, made by introducing bubbles of air as styrene [$C_6H_5.CH:CH_2$] is turned into polystyrene

polythene a plastic made by linking millions of molecules of ethene [$CH_2:CH_2$] | polythene sheet a thin layer of polythene

p.o.m. [prescription only medicine] drugs that can be obtained only with a prescription from a medical practitioner

pond a small lake, a volume of water | pond community the animals, plants and microbes that live together in a small lake and are interdependent | pond life the types of organism that are found in a small lake | pond skater an insect, about 2 centimetres long, that lives on the surface of static water | pond water the static water that remains in a freshwater pond | pond weed *Elodea*, a plant that grows naturally in a pond | dew pond a collection of stones in a depression that always remain cool so dew forms and the water can be collected | evaporating pond a small lake of salt water that is being left to evaporate so as to obtain the salt

pool a puddle, liquid on the floor; to bring together | pool results to collect the measurement and observations from several groups or experiments and then treat the data as one set of results | swimming pool a volume of water in which humans can move about for recreation or competitive sport

poor not good, sub-optimal | poor conductors materials that will allow the flow of heat or electricity, but the resistance is high | poor hearing the ear is not very sensitive to low intensity sounds | poor insulators substances that could be used to slow down the flow of heat or electricity, but are not a good choice | poor sight unable to see well because the light is too dim, the points are too close together or the eye is damaged | poor thermal conductors material that can be used as heat insulators because the substance does not allow the movement of heat

poorer having less money or resources | poorer countries areas of the world in which the majority of inhabitants have very little money

pooter a small cylindrical container with a tube leading to a mouthpiece that is used for the safe collection of insects

pop music sound and rhythms that are enjoyed by many people

pop! a sudden loud noise or squeak | *pop!* test the test for hydrogen – a lighted splint in hydrogen goes *pop!*

population the number of that species in a specified area | population change the difference in the numbers of a species in an area between surveys taken at different times | population crash a sudden drop in the numbers of a specified animal in a stated location | population explosion a rapid rise in the number of that species in that area | population size the number of a particular type of organism that is found in an area | animal population the number of animals that are found in an area, usually ignoring the small animals, such as insects and spiders | bird population the number of birds that are found in a given area | heron population the number of herons in that habitat | local population the number of the stated species that will be found within a short distance of a specified point | plant population the total number of green plants that are found in an area | sample population the number of examples of a particular organism that is taken for further study | sampling populations taking a small number of individuals in order to examine them in detail | size of population the number of that species found in the specified area | stable population the number of a specified species remains constant in the area, an unchanging number of a stated type of life | vulnerable population the particular part or number of that species that would be affected by the change of circumstance, such as the arrival of a virus

porcelain hard, translucent material made by heating special clays to high temperature

porcupine a rodent in which many hairs have become modified to form sharp spines

pore (not paw which is the foot of an animal, nor pour which is to empty) a tiny hole, the opening of a gland on to the surface, *eg* the sweat glands on the skin | pore space the ratio of air volume to total volume in a porous solid

pores (not pause which is a short break, nor paws which are feet with claws, nor pours which is movement of liquid) tiny holes, the opening of glands on to the surface

pork the meat obtained from a pig

porosity a measure of how easily a fluid will move through a solid, *eg* water through soil under gravity

porous a material that is sufficiently solid as to support a weight, but has tiny holes that allow water to move through | porous ground land into which water is absorbed | highly porous a solid that allows fluid through at high speed | non-porous the material will not allow any fluid to diffuse out as there are no tiny holes or pores

porpoise a species of mammal, related to the whales and dolphins, that is adapted to living in the sea

portable easily moved or carried

portion a part, a slice, an allocation | standard portion the size of meal that would be served to the average person

pose a way of positioning yourself and your body parts; to show yourself in a specific way, to put forward a question

position place, location, viewpoint; to put into place | fixed position a specified place that should not move | relative positions the distance and direction between the given objects without referring to any other outside events or places | rest position the place to which an object returns if the force is removed, the position taken by an animal during sleep | shady position an area which should receive lots of sunlight, but is below

some solid object such as leaves or a rock | sunny position an area that receives a lots of light and heat from the Sun

positional energy the ability to do work because of the place that the object occupies

positioning placing into a particular spot and pointing in the correct direction

positive certain, one of the two types of charge | positive charge the property that makes a proton attractive to an electron, the state that results when electrons are removed from a neutral substance | positive electrode the metal that is dipping into the solution and which has too few electrons | positive results the measurements support the idea | positive terminal the electrical connection which has too few electrons

positively absolutely, without doubt

possess to have, to own

possibility a chance, an option, the probability that an event may happen

possible maybe, likely, potentially | possible approach a method of investigation that could answer the question | possible causes several different reasons that could explain why an action had happened | possible cures different methods for restoring an ill person to good health | possible sources various starting points that could lead to a better understanding

post- (*Latin* late) after

post box a container with a long narrow opening near the top that will allow envelopes and small packages to await collection

poster a large sheet of paper that is hung on a wall either for decoration or to provide information

post-meridian pm, after noon, evening

post-mortem a study carried out after death usually to find why the person died

posy a bunch of flowers

pot a container for growing plants, baked clay; to transfer a plant into a container | pot holes caves, underground passages, unevenness in a road | pepper pot a sealed cylinder with lots of small holes in one end | plant pot a cylinder or cube which is filled with soil and used for growing plants

potable water that is suitable for drinking

potash potassium oxide [K_2O] | caustic potash a solution of potassium oxide in water, potassium hydroxide [KOH]

potassium (K because called kalium in Swedish, proton number 19, melting point 64°C) a very reactive silver-coloured metal, a group 1 element, an alkali metal | potassium aluminium sulphate [$K_2SO_4.Al_2(SO_4)_3$] alum, crystals formed from a solution containing dissolved potassium sulphate and aluminium sulphate | **potassium bromide** [KBr] a white crystalline chemical similar to common salt (which is sodium chloride [NaCl]) | potassium chlorate (V) [KClO$_3$] weed killer, a strong oxidising agent, a component of explosive powder | potassium chloride [KCl] a white crystalline solid similar to sodium chloride [NaCl] and which is used to replace common salt in some diets | potassium fluoride [KF] a white crystalline solid that looks like common salt | potassium hydroxide [KOH] a white, waxy looking solid that dissolves in water to give a solution that is strongly alkaline ie pH well above 12 | potassium iodide [KI] white crystals that look and taste similar to salt | potassium manganate (VII) / potassium permanganate [KMnO$_4$] a purple crystal that is soluble in water, an antiseptic | potassium nitrate [KNO$_3$] saltpetre, nitre, one of the ores of potassium that was used in early forms of gunpowder, but is now more important as a very soluble fertiliser | potassium permanganate / potassium manganate (VII) [KMnO$_4$] a purple crystal that is soluble in water, an antiseptic

potato (plural is potatoes) the familiar spheroid shaped vegetable with a brown coating are the swollen roots of a potato plant | potato blight a fungus that attacks potatoe plants, often the first signs are seen when it is already too late to save the crop | potato scrapings thin slices of potato

potatoes (plural of potato) the swollen roots of the potato plant, used as a vegetable

potential capable, possibly acting in the future | potential difference (pd) the voltage change between two parts of a circuit that drives the current

$$\text{potential difference} = \underset{\text{(amps)}}{\text{current}} \times \underset{\text{(ohms)}}{\text{resistance}}$$
(volts)

| potential effects changes that may occur as a result of some change | potential energy stored energy, gravitational potential energy is the work done in lifting a weight through a height, measured in joules if the weight is in newtons and the height is in metres

potential energy (J) = weight (N) × height (m) = mass × acceleration due to gravity × height | elastic potential the ability to cause a change because the material is either being compressed or being stretched | gravitational potential the object is above the surroundings and so may cause a change by falling

potentially harmful may cause damage unless specific precautions are taken

pot holes caves, underground passages, unevenness in the road surface

potted plant a producer that is grown in a container of soil and so can be moved, or grown indoors

poultry hens and turkeys that are kept for eggs and meat

pound a unit of mass in the imperial system abbreviated as lb (453.6 gram), an area for keeping animals, a unit of money (£) in the UK; to hit repeatedly

pour (not paw, which is the foot of an animal, nor pore, which is a space) to empty, to move liquid from one container to another using gravity

poured a fluid is transferred from one container to another by using gravity

pours (not pause, which is an interlude, nor paws, which are feet with claws, nor pores, which are tiny holes) empties, moves liquid from one container to another using gravity

powder pieces of a solid that are just visible to the eye, a solid that has been ground into small pieces; to turn a solid into fine grains | baking powder a mixture of sodium carbonate [Na$_2$CO$_3$] and tartaric acid [(CHOHCOOH)$_2$] that produces bubbles of carbon dioxide [CO$_2$] when dissolved in water [H$_2$O] | biological washing powder a grated solid that contains both a soap, to dissolve fats, and an enzyme, to break down proteins | copper powder fine particles of copper [Cu] | gun powder the mixture of chemicals that will burn rapidly, thereby producing an explosion | milk powder a fine solid that remains when the water is evaporated from milk using a vacuum | silica powder quartz that has been ground to dust | washing powder a soap that has been grated | whey powder the solid produced when the suspension from sour milk is dried completely

powdered ground into tiny fragments, a surface that has been covered in a fine solid

powdery behaves like lots of tiny particles, settles with lots of air gaps

power the rate at which energy is being transferred, the amount of work done each second

$$\text{power (watts)} = \frac{\text{work done (joules)}}{\text{time (seconds)}}$$

| power cables thick wires, made from copper or aluminium, that are used to transfer large quantities of power | power level the amount of energy that is being used or produced each second | power lines the overhead aluminium cables that carry large amounts of electrical energy around the country | power pack equipment that is connected to the mains electricity supply (240 volt, 50 hertz ac in the UK, 110 volt, 60 hertz in the USA) and produces a potential difference that is low and safe, typically up to

24 volts | power rating the amount of electrical power that can be used safely with that equipment | power socket an electrical connection that provides a high current | power source the type of energy that is used to cause the required change | power station a building in which kinetic energy is converted to electrical energy, which is then transferred around the country | power supplies /power supply the equipment that is the source of electrical energy at a low voltage and so is safe | power tool equipment, using electricity as the energy input, for carrying out a specific task | combining power the number of arms or valency of an atom | electrical power doing work by using an electrical current | geothermal power obtaining heat from rocks | high power a relative term that indicates the amount of power is high for that process or usage | hydro-electric power (HEP) using the potential energy of water stored in a dam or reservoir to force water through a turbine which turns a generator producing electricity, a renewable source of electrical energy, but at the cost of flooding a valley | low power the potential difference, or voltage, is sufficiently low that no damage would result to a person touching the terminals | magnifying power the number of times that a magnifying glass or microscope increases the apparent size of an object | mains power the electrical power supplied by using household electricity at 240 volts (UK) or 110 volts (USA) | nuclear power using the heat produced by the breakdown of the nuclei of some atoms | solar power using the heat or light from the Sun in order to produce electricity | tidal power using the change in height of the sea to produce electricity | water power turning a turbine, to produce electricity, using any type of moving water, eg waves, tides, rivers | wave power the rhythmical movement of the surface of the sea is used to turn a turbine | wind power using moving air to turn the vanes that are used either in a mill or to turn a turbine

powered moved by a stated source of energy | human powered the muscle movements of a person provides that energy that moves the equipment or turns the generator | solar powered the energy for the equipment is either the light or the heat form the Sun

powerful forceful, strong | powerful microscope a microscope that is capable of seeing very tiny objects, eg an electron microscope could magnify an object 100,000 times

power pack equipment that is a safe source of potential difference, usually with simple terminals | variable power pack equipment that is usually connected to mains electricity, the potential difference of the output can be varied

ppb [parts per billion] a measure of concentration (using a billion as a thousand million)

ppm [parts per million] a measure of concentration

practicable possible, usable, able to be carried out

practical involving manual work, achievable, physically possible, changing | practical activities / practical activity work that involves equipment or physical change | practical applications techniques or equipment which are usable and result from an idea or theory | practical approach how the problem can be solved using the equipment that is available | practical conclusion an outcome that has some working application or use | practical implications an outcome that changes the way that experiments can be carried out | practical technique a method of analysis or working that leads to useful results or outcome | practical work experiments involving work at the laboratory bench

practice / practise (use is confusing! In America, practice is a verb and practise is the noun but in Britain practice is the noun and practise is a verb) a habit, a rehersal; to carry out many times, to have a profession

prawn / shrimp (usage depends on local area) a small aquatic crustacean

pray (not prey which is animal to be eaten) to ask for help from a deity

pre- (Latin before)

precautions taking steps to minimise the possibility of an accident | safety precautions steps that are taken so as to minimise the cance that anyone is injured by the work or the experiment

precious important, rare, expensive, valuable | precious metals the unreactive metals that cost a lot to buy, usually because they are rare, eg gold, silver

precipitate a sediment, a powder that has fallen to the base; to sediment, to fall down as a powder

precipitation falling from a fluid, water that falls from the sky in any form, eg rain, sleet, snow, fog | precipitation reaction a chemical change in which one of the products is insoluble and forms a cloud | chemical precipitation a reaction produces a powder that forms a cloud of very fine powder | smoke precipitation removing smoke from the products of burning fuel by using special equipment at the top of a chimney

precipitators equipment that is used to cause fine particles to settle out as a powder | electrostatic precipitators equipment that uses electric charge to attract the particles onto the dust pile | sulfur precipitators (USA) / sulphur precipitators (UK) equipment used in the oil industry to remove the sulfur / sulphur from fuel

precise exact, accurate, careful | precise measurements the measurements, *eg* of length, time or mass, are made very accurately | precise observations the examination is accurate in every detail

precisely exactly, accurately, with care

precision accuracy, reliability | adequate precision the measurements are made to an accuracy that is suitable for that experiment | appropriate precision the accuracy that is acceptable will depend on the other measurements in the experiment | degree of precision stating how small is the error in the measurement

predation living by eating other animals

predator an animal that hunts, kills and eats other animals | predator–prey graph a diagram with time along the bottom axis and individual lines for the number or predators and prey in a given area

predatory awaiting opportunity, taking more than a fair share, destructive | predatory animals will hunt and eat other animals

predict to state what is likely to happen

predictable likely to happen on the basis of past events

predicting stating what will happen in an experiment if the idea is correct

prediction a statement as to what should occur if the theory is correct, a description of an event that will occur in the future | firm prediction foretelling exactly what will happen and when | make predictions to write or say what you think will happen on the basis of previous work | support a prediction to have agreement between the results that were predicted and the measurements that were taken | test predictions to carry out experiments to see if the predictions are true

predominant strongest, most important

predominate majority, most

pre-existing already present before the event | pre-existing rocks the rocks and material that existed in that area before a specific event

prefer to choose one thing over another

prefix (plural is prefixes) letters that go in front of a word so as to change the meaning

pregnancy the time between conception and the birth of the baby | unwanted pregnancy intercourse has taken place, but the fertilisation was not intended

pregnant an embryo or foetus is in the womb (or uterus) of the woman | pregnant uterus there is an embryo in the womb and a placenta has developed | pregnant women a female who has a foetus developing in her womb | non-pregnant there is no foetus in the uterus

pre-historic the long period when people existed, but there are no written records

preliminary early, starting | preliminary findings measurements that are taken near the start of the project | preliminary test the first experiment that is carried out to check for safety and speed of reaction | preliminary work experiments that are carried out to check the accuracy and reliability of a method

premature earlier than expected | premature baby a child born after a period of pregnancy (gestation) that was less than 35 weeks (the full term is 40 weeks), so the baby is likely to be low birth-weight and have difficulty breathing | premature birth the baby is born less than 35 weeks after conception

pre-menstrual tension (PMT) the changes in mood that occur in some women just before the start of her monthly menstrual bleeding

premolars grinding teeth that are between the molars and the canine teeth

prenatal any feature that occurs after conception but before the birth | prenatal development the changes that occur to a fertilised egg in the nine months of gestation | prenatal scanning antenatal screening, examining the uterus, placenta and foetus by analysing the echoes of an ultrasound beam

pre-pack to prepare food and put portions into small, sealed containers

preparation planning, the starting activities, a particular or specified mixture of chemicals or drugs that will be used later | medical preparations chemicals that are used by health workers

prepare to get ready, to make something

prepared drawings diagrams that are printed but need finishing off, *eg* by adding labels | prepared slides slides, for use with a microscope, that have been made by an expert and can be looked at in order to learn

preparing getting ready, making a chemical by using a reaction | preparing a salt making a salt, often by reaction of the acid with a metal carbonate or a metal oxide | preparing material getting a substance ready for an experiment

prescribe to give permission for specific drugs to be used, to give advice, to plan in detail

prescription permission or order to obtain a drug, a recipe, a method | prescription drugs chemicals that affect the body but need special permission from a medic | prescription only medicine (p.o.m.) chemicals that are considered to have such a powerful affect on the body that only a medical practitioner can give permission for their use

presence attendance, appearance

present today, now; to exhibit, to display | present data to show your information to other people | present day this decade, contemporary, modern | present measurements to show the data to others | present results to display your information and observations, usually with an interpretation as to their significance

presentation an award for good work, a talk about your ideas which is open to the public | appropriate presentation method of showing data that keeps everything simple but gives sufficient detail

presented gave, introduced, made public

presenting giving, discussing

preservation keeping from change, maintaining at the current value or level, taking measures to reduce further decay | food preservation treating food in a such a way that it will remain edible for a long time

preservative a chemical that slows the loss of texture, chemicals and taste in food

preserve to keep, to maintain

preserved kept unchanged | preserved material any substance that was useful in the past but is now kept in a state that is unchanging | preserved specimens animals and plants that have been put into a liquid, often alcohol [C_2H_5OH] or formaldehyde [$HCHO$], that keeps the structure for a very long time

preserving keeping, retaining, maintaining | preserving food treating food, with salt, sugar or high temperatures, so that the material lasts for longer and is not broken down by microbes, pasteurising

press the newspapers, equipment used for squeezing items; to force downwards

pressure the amount of force on an area

$$\text{pressure (pascals)} = \frac{\text{force (newtons)}}{\text{area (square metres)}}$$

| pressure change the pressure is different at other points or times, leading to effects such as winds | pressure cooker a closed vessel with a safety valve so that food can be cooked at up to 120°C | pressure gauge equipment for measuring the pressure (force per unit area) | pressure head the pressure caused by a height of liquid | pressure switch a component that keeps an electrical circuit open until a specified force is exceeded then the circuit is completed | pressure tubing thick-walled rubber tube that will not change diameter if a high pressure is applied | air pressure / atmospheric pressure the pressure in the air at a particular height above sea level, the force per metre square (pressure) that is caused by

that 20 kilometres deep layer of air pushing down on to you and on to everything around you, the effect of the heat from the Sun changes the atmospheric pressure and causes the weather | blood pressure the pressure in the blood vessels caused by the heart pushing blood against the resistance of the tiny vessels in muscles and organs, usually measured at the upper arm | external pressure the pressure that is outside the container or vessel | gas pressure the pressure exerted by the gas usually because there is a pump increasing the pressure so as to cause the gas to move | high blood pressure the pressure in the blood vessels caused by the resistance in muscles, is higher than would be expected and could indicate an illness or lead to the heart not been able to work properly | high pressure the pressure in that area is higher either than normal or the surrounding area | hydrostatic pressure the pressure produced by the weight of water above that point | large pressure the force per unit area is so high that special precautions are needed | low pressure the pressure is less than that in the surrounding area | underwater pressure the pressure that is produced by the weight of water above that point | units of pressure should be in pascals (newtons per square metre), which are rarely used, the units often follow those of force and area, *eg* newtons per square centimetre (N/cm²), meteorologists use a millibar, blood pressure is measured in millimetres of mercury | water pressure the pressure that is found at that position in the water, usually caused by the height (head) of water that is above the point

pressurised to be subject to increased pressure | pressurised container a vessel in which the pressure has been increased

prevent to stop an event by taking some action | prevent growth to stop the increase in the number of microbes | prevent heat loss to use an insulation method to reduce movement of heat

preventative measures the steps taken to stop an event taking place

preventing stopping from occurring

prevention the stopping of an event by using an active method | disease prevention to stop an illness by taking such steps as vaccination of the population or isolation of individuals | fire prevention to take steps that will reduce the risk of a fire starting or spreading

previous earlier, pre-existing | previous experiments / previous research procedures or tests that were carried out earlier | previous work experiments that were made earlier

previously earlier, the time before

pre-warm to heat an item to a higher temperature before it is used

prey (not pray which is to ask) animals that are chased or captured by other animals then eaten | birds of prey feathered animals that feed on other animals

preyed hunted particular animals, lived by eating another type of animal

prickles spikes on leaves and stems that are intended to make the plant unpleasant for eating

Priestley (Joseph 1733–1804) had a difficult childhood, he was often ill and was orphaned young, he then had a troubled life. He was a preacher and a teacher who became so unpopular that a mob burned down his house and Priestley had to flee to America in 1794. He was exceptionally charming, wrote widely on religion, history, chemistry and physics and could speak at least nine languages. He was probably the greatest experimental scientist of the eighteenth century, but he had great problems in providing simple theories to explain his observations, perhaps because he believed in the phlogiston theory for combustion. His meeting with Franklin in 1766 led to Priestley writing a book on *The History of Electricity* twenty years before Galvani and Volta had developed reliable methods for producing electricity! In 1767, there were only three gases known, air, fixed air (carbon dioxide) and hydrogen (studied by Cavendish) but, in the next 23 years, Priestley discovered twenty more (including oxygen, which he tested by breathing it). He also studied the density and thermal and electrical conductivity of gases.

primary first, major, early | primary colors (USA) / primary colours (UK) the three colours from which all other colours can be made, the eye is sensitive to red, green and blue (RGB), so these are the primary colours used in science, artists use reflected light so their primary colours are cyan (blue), magenta (red) and yellow, together with black (CMYK) | primary consumer the animal that eats the producer or plant | primary sex organs the organs that produce the sex hormones and are essential for reproduction such as the testes, ovaries and uterus | primary sources the books or text that contains descriptions of experiments and observations that were carried out by the authors | primary teeth milk teeth, baby teeth | primary waves the fast moving waves that result from an earthquake, pusher waves, longitudinal waves

primates mammals that are able to walk on legs and use their hands for grasping, these include humans and their near relatives such as apes, gibbons and monkeys

primitive early, using few styles or tools

primrose *Primula*, a perennial plant that is found in the hedges and woods of Europe and North Africa, and is grown in gardens for its flowers

principal (not principle which is a rule) major, main, a leader

principle (not principal which is main) a rule, a proposal | principle of moments the idea that a lever is balanced if the sum of the turning forces in the clockwise direction is exactly equal to the sum of the turning forces in the anti-clockwise direction | principles of digestion the ideas that explain how the food that goes into the mouth is moved through the gut and is broken into small molecules that can be absorbed | key principles ideas or laws that must be followed and should never be broken

print a mark; to push marks onto paper | fingerprints the marks left by the raised lines on the ends of your fingers | footprint the mark left by standing, the area needed for an activity

prior work experiments that were carried out earlier

prism an object that has three rectangular sides and a triangular cross-section | glass prism a prism that is made from glass and can be used to produce the colours of the rainbow | hexagonal prism a solid transparent object that has faces made from six rectangles of equal size

prize an award; to value | Nobel Prizes awards, of a medal and a large sum of money, that are given each year to people who have made outstanding contributions to specified areas of knowledge, the money results from the will of Nobel

probability the likelihood that an event will occur expressed as a number, one represents certainty and zero is impossible

probable likely, possible, may happen

probe a sensor, a small stick, a satellite used for obtaining information; to try to find information | environmental probe an instrument or organism that is able to give information about the conditions in a specified area | glass probe a tube with a tip of thin glass that responds to the surroundings | light probe an electrical component with a resistance that depends on the intensity of light | oxygen probe a membrane on the end of a rod that can be used to measure the concentration of oxygen | pH probe a thin tube of glass that can be used to measure accurately the strength of acid or alkali in a solution | satellite probe / space probe an unmanned space craft containing many information-gathering instruments | temperature probe a temperature sensor on the end of a rod that is usually connected to a computer

probing trying to obtain information

problem a question, a complication that prevents the smooth running of an event, a puzzle requiring resolution | circulatory problem a disease of the arteries, heart or veins that means the blood is more difficult to move around the body | environmental problems changes to the weather conditions or chemicals in an area that will affect many species | growth problems a slower than expected rate of growth either by the foetus in the womb or by a child | measuring problems difficulties in providing numerical values for the variables of interest | social problem trouble caused by different people having different needs and talents

procedure a method, a recipe, a plan | appropriate procedure a suitable method, a plan that is safe and gives results to an acceptable accuracy | safe procedure a method that can be used with almost no risk | safety procedure a plan that ensures that the method is safe

process (plural is processes) a method, an action; to change | process of formation the method by which new materials or organisms are produced | biological process the changes in the environment that are produced by living organisms, chemical reactions in plants or animals | bio-technological process a method that uses the cutting, manipulation and insertion of nucleic acids into a microbe | chemical process a change in which the starting material produces new substances | complex process a method that has many stages, especially where one change could influence many steps | continuous process a change that occurs all the time, a production method that does not stop | electrolytic process the manufacturing method used electricity to bring about the required chemical change | geological processes changes the occur in rocks, changes caused by rocks, movement of rocks from the mantle and in the crust | key process the main method for changing from one position or chemical to another | life processes / living processes the changes that are associated with life, *ie* moving, respiring, growing, reproducing, excreting, eating and sensing the surroundings | manufacturing process the method used for large-scale production | natural processes changes that occur without the influence of people | physical processes changes that are reversible, *eg* melting, freezing | rock-forming processes the several methods for producing the

solid rocks that make up the crust of the Earth | separation process the method used to isolate pure components from a mixture | thermit process / thermite process the reaction of aluminium with iron oxide to produces a temperature sufficiently high that the iron will melt | weathering processes changes to solid objects that occur over a long period and are caused by the wind, moving water, living organism or changes in temperatures

processes (plural of process) methods, actions

processing changing, making ready meals from raw materials | processing data changing information from the raw input to an output that can be interpreted | processing materials changing objects or compounds into new substances | food processing changing food on a large scale, so that the food is either easier to prepare or to eat

processor equipment for changing material, the part of a computer that carries out the calculations

produce a farm crop; to make, to form, to change | produce a graph to draw a graph from a set of numerical results | produce sound to turn some form of energy into sound energy | produce young to give birth | dairy produce any food made from milk (usually from a cow)

produced made, formed

producers plants, organisms that turn light energy from the Sun into sugars by photosynthesis

producing making, changing, forming | cone-producing a large group of trees that produce their seeds in cones

product a new chemical that is formed in a reaction | dairy products any food made from milk (usually from a cow) | new product a material that either has just reached the shops or that you have made from other chemicals | usable products / useable products useful chemicals that have been produced as a result of either a chemical reaction or a separation procedure

production manufacture, making in large quantity | production costs the amount of money needed to make a specified amount of that substance or instrument | ammonia production the large-scale manufacture of ammonia [NH_3] from nitrogen [N_2] and hydrogen [H_2] by the Haber process | annual production the amount of material or crop that is made each year | crop production the growing of large numbers of plants that are that then sold for profit | food production growing crops, raising animals, the large-scale manufacture of material that is suitable for eating | heat production the energy that is released from a chemical reaction provides an increase in temperature | oxygen production the release of oxygen from plants during photosynthesis, isolating oxygen from air | soil production the changing of rocks, silts and dead material into material that is suitable for the growth of plants

productivity the amount of material produced in a particular time interval

products chemicals produced in a reaction | products of digestion the simple chemicals that are produced when food is broken down, *eg* sugars, amino acids | products of photosynthesis the glucose / sugars and oxygen that are produced by reactions facilitated by chlorophyll that fix the light energy from the Sun | dairy products milk and the substances that are made from milk (usually from a cow), *eg* butter, cheese, yoghurt | excretion products chemicals that are produced within a cell and are then pushed out in order to prevent poisoning of the cell (egestion describes the loss of material that has not been absorbed in the intestine) | food products any material or substance that is bought in a shop with the intention of eating | household products chemicals that are likely to be found in most households, *eg* washing-up liquid | new product a material that either has just reached the shops or that you have made from other chemicals | plant products materials produced from plants | useful products substances that are made by an organism for one purpose, but can also be used by people | waste products chemicals that the organism gets rid of in order to avoid poisoning

professional competent, trained, qualified, a person in a vocational position | health professional a person who looks after the physical or mental wellbeing of people

profile an outline, a side-view, an outline of a vertical section; to produce a diagram of a vertical section | energy profile the total energy in the bonds of the reactants, the separated atoms and the bonds of the products are shown as horizontal lines | soil profile a diagram showing the layers of different soil in a vertical section

profound important, far reaching, a deep thought

profoundly deeply | profoundly deaf never had any ability to hear, totally insensitive to sound

program (USA) / **programme** (UK) an outline of events, an agenda | Apollo program the series of NASA missions that was intended to put a man on the Moon by the end of the 1960s. Apollo 11, commanded by Neil Armstrong, landed on the Moon on 20 July 1969 and the last mission (Apollo 17) left the Moon in December 1972 | breeding program (USA) / breeding

programme (UK) achieving some specific characteristics in an organism by choosing the parents and then deciding which of offspring should be used as new parents | fitness program (USA) / fitness programme (UK) the prescribed exercises used in order to reduce the heart rate and blood pressure and increase your stamina

progress to move towards an objective, to change for the better

progresses moves towards stated goals

progressive changing with time | progressive depletion the gradual and continuing loss of number of species and populations

project a plan, an intention; to shine out | Human Genome Project a worldwide collaborative task to find the position of every atom in the DNA of all 46 chromosomes of the human cell

projection moving forward a line or an image, a part of something jutting out, extrapolation, passing of light through a film on to a screen

projector equipment using light for showing a picture on to a large screen | micro-projector equipment that can project the image from a microscope on to a screen | overhead projector (OHP) the light source, mirrors and lenses that enable writing to be projected on to a screen

prokaryote a cell that has chromosomes, but has no nucleus, a bacterial cell

promote to increase awareness, to publicise, to put forward

prompt immediate, on time; to remind, to help

prongs the spikes that extend from a cross piece, like a fork

proof cannot be penetrated, evidence showing an idea is correct | child-proof a simple lock prevents entry by a child, but allows access by an adult | final proof the evidence that confirms a prediction, thus showing the idea must true | fire-proof / flame-proof will not burn; to treat a material so it will not catch fire | light-proof no light is able to pass through the material | moth-proof unaffected by the presence of moths | water-proof a layer that prevents the entry of water | wind-proof material through which the moving air is unable to penetrate

proofing treating a material with a chemical so that a specified liquid will not pass through the fabric | sound proofing adding absorbent material so the vibrations are absorbed and so can neither be transmitted nor reflected

propagation division of one plant to give many identical offspring

propane [C_3H_8] a hydrocarbon fuel that turns to liquid when pressurised and so can be transported easily

propanone [$(CH_3)_2CO$)] acetone, a liquid with a boiling point of 62°C that is used as nail varnish remover

propel to push along

propellant a substance that causes other materials, such as a rocket or the liquid in an aerosol, to move rapidly | chemical propellant the rocket fuel that is burned in order to provide thrust

properly correctly, skilfully, in the right way

properties (plural of property) characteristics, ways of reacting to other chemicals or stimuli | chemical properties the predictable way in which the material will react when other chemicals are added | common properties the features that are shown by all the materials | distinct properties the features that are unique to that type of material | elastic properties the ability to be compressed or stretched then return to the original length when the force is removed | magnetic properties the ability to react to the presence of other magnets or to cause other magnets to change | physical properties characteristics that can be tested without any permanent change to the material

property (plural is properties) a characteristic, a predictable way of reacting, a possession

proportion (plural is proportions) a ratio, a comparison, a part | appropriate proportion the ratio of the several components is suitable for that purpose | fixed proportion the ratio of one item to another remains constant, even though the absolute amounts have changed | greatest proportion largest fraction, highest ratio, the majority | inverse proportion increasing one variable by a given number causes the other variable to be reduced by the same fraction

proportional the two variables are related so that changing one variable would cause the other variable to change by the same fraction

proportionality related by a definite ratio or number

proportions ratios, comparing the properties of one object with the similar properties of another object

proposal an idea, a suggestion, a hypothesis

propose to put forward an idea

proposed produced, an idea that has been put forward | proposed approach the way of investigating, a method that could work

prose written work that is not intended to have any rhythm

prospector a person who searches for a mineral, gold or oil

prostate gland the small sac near the base of the bladder that adds liquid to the sperm to produce semen

protease / protease enzyme proteins that cause the breakdown of other proteins into the individual amino acids

protect to prevent damage, to keep safe

protected safe from damage or misuse

protecting providing a safe environment, supplying a wall or barrier

protection preventing damage, a cover | protection circuit a part of the circuit that can be ignored in normal use, but which opens the main circuit, therefore preventing any flow of current, if the current becomes too high | chemical protection the use of a sacrificial, reactive metal, *eg* magnesium or zinc, to prevent rusting of iron | environmental protection taking steps and procedures to try to ensure that the conditions within an area do not change | eye protection goggles or a visor that prevents damaging particles from entering the eye | hearing protection using muffs or pads to cover the ears and prevent damage from loud sounds | physical protection a method of preventing rusting by using a layer of oil or paint to prevent the moisture or oxygen from reaching the iron

protective giving safety | protective cells the tough layer of cells that protect the underlying cells | protective cover a layer that is fitted in order to prevent damage | protective gear clothing that is worn so as to provide safety and avoid injury | protective layer a blanket, cover or stratum that prevents entry by a damaging object | protective mask a thin gauze worn over the mouth and nose to prevent entry of pollutant gases

protectors equipment for preventing damage | ear protectors covers that fit the ears so as to reduce the intensity of sound reaching the ear-drum | hearing protectors pads that fit over each ear so as to prevent any damage that could be caused by a loud sound

protects prevents damage, keeps safe

protein a large chemical made from amino acids joined together in a long line or chain | protein breakdown to break the bonds, or links, between some of the amino acids to give smaller molecules | protein coat the outer layer of a virus that provides the shape and protects the nucleic acid | protein deficiency symptoms that appear when there is not sufficient protein or amino acids in the diet | animal protein the type of protein (a long chain of amino acids) that is found principally, or only, in animals | meat protein the types of protein (a long chain of amino acids) that are found in the muscles of animals | mycoproteins the proteins (long chains of amino acids) produced by fungi | test for protein is that any protein should turn blue biuret solution to purple or mauve | **textured vegetable protein** the powder or paste that results when protein is extracted from plants

protista / protoctista single-celled organisms that have a nucleus

proto- (*Greek* first)

protoctista / protista single-celled organisms that have a nucleus, some have chlorophyll and so can photosynthesise whereas others need to absorb food

proton (p+) the subatomic particle with a positive charge that is found in the nucleus, has a mass of 1 dalton (1 Da) or 1 atomic mass unit (1 amu) or 1.66×10^{-27} kg | **proton number / atomic number** the number of protons in the nucleus, this number defines the atom and can not be changed

protozoa (plural of protozoan [USA] / protozoon [UK]) single-celled organisms

protozoan (USA) **/ protozoon** (UK) (plural is protozoa) a single-celled organism that has the characteristics of life, but can not be classified as animal or plant

protractor a semi-circle that is calibrated so it can be used for measuring angles

prove to show to be true

provide to give, to produce | **provide evidence** produce observations that support the idea

provided given, produced

proving showing to be correct, using evidence to support an idea

provision requirement, preparation, allowing for, food

provoke to cause a change in behaviour, to annoy

proximity near, close

pseudo- (*Greek* false)

pseudopodia (plural of pseudopodium) the change in shape of part of the cell membrane and cytoplasm of some cells that allow them to move

pseudopodium (plural is pseudopodia) a change of shape used by some single-celled organisms in order to move (pseudo–podium translates as *false foot*)

psychological concerned with the brain, relating to the mind

psychologically dependent a person has developed that habit of carrying out certain actions and is unable to stop repeating the action

Pt platinum, proton number 78, a very expensive, unreactive metal that is used in jewellery

Pterodactyl / Pterosaur a group of flying reptiles, with wingspans from 10 centimetres to 15 metres, that became extinct 65 million years ago

PTO [please turn over] a request to continue reading on the next side of the paper

Ptolemy (of Alexandria 90–170) is famous for the four books summarising the astronomical knowledge of the ancient world. The distances to the Sun and to the Moon were accurate, his description of the world as a sphere encouraged Columbus to sail west and find America by accident. However, Ptolemy's idea that the Earth was the centre of the universe caused major problems for over a thousand years.

puberty the time of changing from a child to the mature adult

pubic hair the hair that grows around the pubic region, which is near the primary sex organs

public health the measurement of illnesses and prevention of diseases to everyone living in a particular area | **public health issue** a discussion related to the prevention or spread of a disease to the general public

public transport vehicles that should follow regular routes and timetables so that they may be used by anyone paying the required fare

publication dissemination of information; a newsletter, a magazine, an article in a journal

publish to present written material in a neat form so anyone can examine the work

puck a small cylinder used in ice hockey or air hockey

puffin a sea bird with a multi-coloured beak

pull a force that tries to bring an object closer to the person that is pulling; to bring an object closer by applying a force | **pull apart** to use force to separate two items | **gravitational pull** the force that causes every object to be attracted to every other object, but becomes important only when one of them has a very large mass | **opposing pull** a force that is applied in the opposite direction to a pulling force | **outward pull** the force trying to move objects apart

pulled applied a force to try to bring an article nearer

pulley one or more cylinders, that are able to rotate freely on an axle, around which is wound a rope | **frictionless pulley** there is very little force resisting the rotation of the wheels of the pulley, da Vinci invented a frictionless pulley in about 1500

pulling applying a force in the same direction as the person applying the force

pulls (not pulse which is a heart beat) applies a force in the direction of the machine or person pulling

pulmonary concerned with the lungs | **pulmonary artery** the main blood vessel carrying deoxygenated blood from the heart to the lungs |

pulmonary vein the vessel (tube) that carries the oxygenated blood from the lungs to the heart

pulp the inside material of a tooth, a mush of material especially of paper or wood with water; to mash material into a suspension; to produce a mash | pulp cavity the space inside the dentine of the tooth in which are found the nerves and blood vessels

pulse (not pulls which is a force) the rhythmic expansion and contraction of arteries, caused by the pumping of the heart, that can be felt at the wrist and neck, a type of pea or bean | pulse meter an instrument for measuring the heart rate | pulse rate the number of times each minute that you feel the artery expand and relax

pulses beans, peas

pumice an igneous rock with a low density because cooling had been so extremely rapid that the gas bubbles inside did not have time to escape

pump equipment that can be used to move or apply pressure to a fluid; to increase the pressure | pump handle the long bar that is moved up and down in order to deliver water from a lower reservoir | air pump equipment that is used for moving air, usually used to remove the air from an item, but can also be used to inflate balloons | balloon pump a piston in a cylinder that is used to put air into balloons | bicycle pump a piston in a cylinder that is used to put air into cycle tyres | double pump used to describe the heart which in worms is two separate pumps, but in many animals the two pumps are found in a single organ | vacuum pump equipment that is used to remove air so as to produce a vacuum | water pump equipment that is used for moving water, equipment for removing air that is powered by the flow of water

pumping action using regular application of pressure to move a liquid | pumping station a building containing the equipment that shifts water or sewage through pipes from one place to another

pumpkin a plant that is native to America, this plant produces an enormous fruit that is used either as food or to produce a candle holder at halloween

pumps moves a liquid by applying a pressure

punnet square a diagram showing the genetic possibilities when the genes from one parent are crossed with genes from the other parent

pupa (plural is pupae) a stage in the life of an insect when the young offspring disappears into a chrysalis and later re-appears as a mature adult

pupae (plural of pupa) more than one of the cocoons that is part of the life cycle of an insect

pupil a student, a learner, the dark centre of the iris through which light enters the eye

puppy a young dog

pure 100%, a single material, unpolluted, un-spoiled | pure bred a single strain, an animal with known parents and grandparents | pure chemical / pure compound the substance is made from only one type of molecule | pure element the material is made from one type of atom | pure liquid a liquid that is made from only one type of chemical, and so has a sharp freezing point and a single boiling point | pure orange juice the liquid that is obtained by squeezing oranges without the addition of any other chemical | pure salt sodium chloride [NaCl] crystals without any other chemicals | pure solvent a liquid, in which other chemicals will be dissolved, but the liquid is made from one type of chemical | pure substance the material contains only one type of chemical, the material has a sharp melting point and a sharp freezing point | pure water a liquid that should contain only water with no dissolved solids or gases, distilled water

purification the process by which a desired chemical is extracted from any other material that is not required

purified any chemicals that are not the specified material have been removed

purifying removing the required chmical from other materials

purity the mass of the required chemical as a fraction of the total mass

purple the colour produced by mixing red and blue | purple crystals tiny shiny objects that reflect violet light, solid potassium permanganate [$KMnO_4$]

purpose a role, the use to which an object should be put, a reason | medical purpose the intention is to cure an illness or to alleviate the symptoms | specific purpose the precise intention

pus (not puss which is a cat) the remains of white blood cells that have died in an attempt to prevent invasion of the body by a microbe

push a force that causes compression and the object to move away from the force; to apply a force to try to move an object | push down to apply a force in the same direction as the attraction by gravity | push out to get rid of, to change the shape of a container | push switch an electrical component that can open or close a circuit by pressing on to a button | opposing push a compression that is preventing a movement

pushed a force is applied

pusher waves longitudinal waves, the fast moving waves produced by earthquakes

pushes tries to move away from the person applying the force

pushing the act of trying to move an object by applying a force in the same direction as the movement | **pushing force** an effort that tries to move an object away from the force

puss (not pus which is dead white cells) a cat (slang)

putrefaction the process of decaying or rotting in the absence of oxygen

putrefying bacteria microbes that break down other cells in the absence of oxygen

PVC [poly vinyl chloride] a plastic made from vinyl chloride [CH_2:CHCl]

pylon a tower especially a tall structure for holding high-voltage wires

pyramid four identical triangles are set onto a square base and meet at the tip | **pyramid of biomass / pyramid of mass** a triangle in which the bottom area represents the mass of producer that is neededto support the mass of primary consumer leading to the mass of secondary and tertiary consumers at the top | **pyramid of numbers** a diagram in which each rectangle represents the number of organisms, the bottom rectangle shows the numbers of producers, above this is the number of primary consumers, then the number of secondary and tertiary consumers | **food pyramid** a diagram showing the large mass of the producers at the bottom, through the smaller mass of consumers to the tiny mass of the top consumer | **number pyramid** a diagram to show that the number of organisms changes going up a food chain

Pyramids a set of stone pyramids (building with a square base and four triangular sides) that were built near Cairo almost 4000 years ago as burial mounds for the pharaohs, but there are almost another hundred pyramids in Egypt and even more in Sudan

pyrethroid a name given to a group of over a thousand related chemicals, most are used at very low doses (less than 1 milligram per square metre) to kill insects

pyrogallate / pyrogallol a solution that is used to absorb oxygen

pyrotechnic a firework, a controlled explosion

Pythagoras (of Samos 582–500 BC) was taught by Thales. Pythagoras moved to southern Italy to start a school of philosophy (a word invented by Pythagoras to mean 'love of wisdom') for the study of astronomy and mathematics, the rules were similar to a monastery, advocating obedience, silence and a vegetarian diet. He emphasised that an understanding of mathematics would give an explanation of the universe. Pythagoras taught that the Earth was a sphere orbiting the Sun – unfortunately this idea was lost somewhere between Pythagoras teaching Plato and Plato founding his own academy at which Aristotle was a pupil and teacher.

quad- (*Latin* square) four

quadrat a grid of wires that is usually of 0.5 metre each side | quadrat sample the information obtained by throwing a square frame on to an area of land | quadrat sampling to throw a quadrat over a piece of ground so as to see what (and how many) organisms lie within a specific area chosen at random

quagga an extinct animal that showed some of the features of a horse and some of the features of a zebra

quake a shake; to shake repeatedly, to shiver | earthquake movement of some area of the Earth's crust

qualitative involving comparisons, such as larger, hotter, higher, but no numbers | qualitative data information that compares items, but does not use any recognised scale of measurement | qualitative observations looking and recording features that can not be given a numerical value | qualitative results measurements and data that allow a rank order to be produced, but without using a numerical scale

qualitatively making observations that allow comparisons, but without any scale of measurement

quality (plural is qualities) a feature, condition, grade, characteristic | quality of life a measure of a person's impression of fulfilment with their way of living | quality of sound / sound quality how pleasant a vibration sounds to a person, the similarity between the sound signal that is recorded or generated and the sound that is produced | air quality a measure of the amount and number of pollutants and irritants that are in the atmosphere | high quality an item that is likely to last for a long time without failing | meat quality the appearance, smell and suitability for eating of a piece of meat | water quality the amount and number of chemicals in a sample of water, the suitability of the water for a purpose such as drinking or swimming

quantify to put numerical values onto observations

quantifying turning observations into measurements, giving numbers to descriptions, measuring

quantitative having numerical values, using a recognised and measurable scale | quantitative data information that is expressed in numbers and units | quantitative observation information that can be related to a general scale | quantitative relationship giving precise positions and rankings

quantitatively carrying out observations that give numerical answers, concerned with amounts that can be measured against a standard

quantities (plural of quantity) more than one amount or number

quantity (plural is quantities) amount, mass, number | quantity of energy amount of energy either released by a change or needed for that work to be done, measured in joules | appropriate quantity using an amount that is safe and sufficient, but not so much as to make the method dangerous or too expensive | increasing quantity a larger amount | small quantity a low mass, not very much

quarry a large hole in the ground from which ores and rocks are extracted; to remove large amounts of ore or rock from the ground

quarter a fourth part, one of four identical portions that comprise the whole, 25%

quartz a form of silicon dioxide [SiO_2] that produces crystals, also called rock salt, introduction of coloured impurities produces amethyst

quartzite an metamorphic rock made from grains of quartz or recrystallised silicon dioxide [SiO_2] (sand)

quenching putting out a fire, reducing a thirst

question an enquiry, a discussion; to ask, to examine, to dispute | appropriate questions ask questions that can be answered with the knowledge, time and equipment that is available | challenging questions producing problems to which there are no easy answers | empirical question a problem that can be answered by observation without the need for a theory | ethical question discussion concerning behaviour of people, based on moral values or acceptance by society but cannot be answered by experiment | frame a question to ask a question in a way that points towards the method of examination | key questions the very few queries that must be answered in order to prove or disprove the solution to a problem | raise questions to ask for explanations | relevant questions asking a question that could help to explain the evidence or could produce new observations | scientific question a problem that can be solved using a combination of direct observation and established theories | simple question a inquiry that can be answered by a *yes* or *no* | suitable question a problem that can be answered using the equipment available

questioning asking, arguing, enquiring, curious

quick rapid, fast, speedy | quick lime calcium oxide [CaO], another name for lime

quicker faster or more rapid than a comparable item

quickest fastest, most rapid

quick lime calcium oxide [CaO], another name for lime

quickly rapidly, in a short time | most quickly fastest

quiet low noise, almost silent

quieter producing less sound

quietest / quietist making the least amount of sound

quit to stop, to leave, to resign, to give up

quiz a test of knowledge; to ask many questions | quiz board a sheet with questions and answers randomly arranged on one side, but correctly connected by electrical wires on the hidden side | quiz sheet a paper with lots of questions relevant to a specified topic

Quorn™ a protein made from soya bean that is used as a meat substitute

quota a limited number, a proportion, an allowance

R [resistance] the ability of a wire to reduce the current, measured in ohms (Ω)

r [radius] the distance from the centre to the circumference of a circle

rabbits herbivorous furry mammals with long ears that live communally underground in burrows in a warren

rabid suffering an infection of rabies, extreme, violent

rabies a virus infection, also called hydrophobia, that affects dogs, cats, foxes and bats; it can be transmitted to humans by a bite and is fatal un-less given an immediate vaccination. Pasteur developed the first vaccine against rabies.

race a group of people with related and distinct characteristics or appearance and originating from the same geographic area, a competition involving speed; to run a distance to establish who is quickest

rack a storage unit | test tube rack a block or piece of folded metal in which test tubes can be stored vertically

radar RAdio Detection And Ranging, using the echo of radio waves in order to find the distance and direction of an object | radar gun the tube and meter that give the speed when pointed at a moving vehicle

radiant energy infra-red or heat energy that is being transferred between surfaces as electro-magnetic waves | radiant heater equipment that uses a current to heat a coil of resistance wire to several hundred degrees Celsius or red heat

radiate to give out energy from a surface, to draw lines leaving a point in all directions

radiated energy energy that has been lost as electromagnet waves from a surface

radiates gives out energy from the surface

radiation heat and light from a surface such as the Sun, any loss of heat as electromagnetic waves from a surface, the radioactivity produced by break-down of some types of atomic nuclei | radiation energy the intensity, or brightness, of the infra-red waves that are given off by a hot surface | alpha radiation the stream of helium nuclei (He^{++}) that is ejected from the nuclei of some atoms | background radiation the amount of radio-active radiation that is found everywhere because of the breakdown of atoms in rocks such as granite, and the radiation produced by nuclear fusion in all stars | beta radiation electrons (e$^-$) from the nuclei of some atoms | gamma radiation the high frequency electromagnetic radiation that is produced when radio-active nuclei break down | heat radiation / infra-red radiation the electromagnetic waves, with a wavelength of

0.7–1 micrometres, that is produced by a surface that is hotter than the surroundings | ionising radiation (UK) / ionizing radiation (USA) rays produced by the breakdown of the nucleus of an atom that may cause a molecule to lose or gain electrons, *ie* to form ions | nuclear radiation the energy that is given out when a nucleus changes structure, the radiation travels in straight lines and may cause damage to cells | thermal radiation loss of heat from a surface by giving out infra-red rays with a wavelength of between 0.7 micro-metres and 1 micrometre | ultra-violet radiation the wavelength of the light is below that of visible light

radiator any body that loses heat from the surface by giving out infra-red radiation, household equipment that is part of the hot-water system and helps spread the heat – but the transfer of heat is by convection not radiation! | radiator reflector a sheet of shiny foil that is placed on the wall behind a radiator in order to reflect heat | car radiator the black-painted tubes through which hot water from the engine is passed in order to lose heat and keep the engine cool

radical (not radicle which is a plant root) an ion, a group of atoms that join together and have a charge

radicle (not radical which is a charged particle) the early sign of a root in a germinating seed

radio concerned with the electromagnetic spectrum above 1 millimetre, equipment for receiving electromagnetic waves | radio-activity radiation produced by breakdown of the nucleus | radio telescope equipment for receiving and analysing long-wave electromagnetic radiation | radio waves the part of the electromagnetic spectrum that has wavelength greater than 1 millimetre | wind-up radio a radio receiver that is powered by turning a key so as to increase the tension in a spring

radio-active producing radiation by the break-down of atomic nuclei | radio-active atom an atom with an unstable nucleus | radio-active element a substance that is made from only one type of atom, but the nuclei of those atoms are unstable and will break down, at random intervals, to produce radiation and new elements | radio-active emission the radiation produced by breakdown of a nucleus | radio-active isotope an atom that is one of a family of elements with identical proton numbers, but different mass numbers, and whose nucleus will change so as to produce alpha-, beta- or gamma-radiation | radio-active source material that produces radiation from the nucleus, but is packed so it can be handled safely | radio-active waste material that is produced as a by-product of making and using nuclear fuel, which is of no further use, but is dangerous because it is giving off radiation

radio-activity the causes and effects of the nucleus of an atom breaking down to give radiation and produce new elements

radio-telescope equipment, in the shape of a radio aerial or a curved dish for receiving radio and television channels, that studies the universe by analysing the radio wave part of the spectrum

radio wave the part of the electromagnetic spectrum that has a wavelength longer than 1 millimetre, *ie* longer than microwaves

radish a small vegetable with a dark-red skin that is eaten raw in salad

radius the distance from the centre of a circle to the circumference, the bone in the lower arm that is nearer to the thumb | orbital radius the distance from the centre of the planet or star to the object that is circling in an orbit around the planet or star

radon (Rn, proton number 86, melting point −71°C) an inert gas that is radio-active

rage anger, a torrent, a storm; to express anger

ragworm a carnivorous worm that swims close to the sea-bed

rail (not real which is actual) a track used for guiding movement, a bar from which items are suspended

railings a fence | metal railings a fence made from vertical and horizontal metal rods

rails parallel tracks on which trains are able to run

railway lines the parallel bars of steel along which railway vehicles can travel

railways transport systems that use vehicles with rimmed wheels that run on fixed tracks

rain (not reign which is the job of a king or queen, nor rein which is a control strip) the water that falls when condensation of water vapour is too much to remain suspended in the clouds; to fall as water from clouds | rainbow the colourful semi-circle in the sky that shows all the colours of the visible spectrum (ROYGBIV – red, orange, yellow, green, indigo, violet) caused by raindrops reflecting and refracting light | rain drop a single splash of the water in rain | rainfall the amount of rain that has fallen in that area in a stated period | rainforest the types of trees and other plants that are associated with areas with lots of rain | rain gauge an instrument for measuring the depth of water that has fallen as rain | rain shadow land that is dry because the nearby mountains receive all the rainfall | rainwater / rain water the water that falls as rain and can be

collected, could cause the landscape to change or cause flooding | acid rain the water that falls as rain which has a very low pH because the water has absorbed the oxides of sulphur, of nitrogen and of phosphorus, forming a mixture of sulphuric acid, nitric acid and phosphoric acid | falling rain emphasising that the water is dropping from the sky onto the ground | heavy rain a large amount of water falling in a very short time

rainbow the colourful semi-circle in the sky that shows all the colours of the visible spectrum (ROYGBIV – red, orange, yellow, green, indigo, violet) caused by raindrops reflecting and refracting light | rainbow experiment mix universal indicator with sodium hydrogen carbonate in a tube then gently add hydrochloric acid and watch a rainbow of colours

rainforest the types of trees and other plants that are associated with areas with lots of rain | tropical rainforest the habitat, with large, tall trees that shade the undergrowth, that is found in areas of the world near to the equator and that receives high volumes of rain

raining droplets of water are falling from the clouds

raise (not rays which are thin beams of light) to go higher, to rise, to build, to increase | raise questions to ask for explanations, to introduce a new query

raised moved to a higher level, lifted up | raised object an object that either protrudes above the surface or has been lifted up

raising moving upwards

ram [relative atomic mass] atomic mass, the mass number, the total mass of the atom, the number of neutrons and protons in the nucleus,

ram a male sheep; to hit hard

ramp a slope, a plank that is used to produce a sloping runway; to increase

Ramsay (Sir William 1852–1916) is the only person to have discovered and isolated a complete periodic group of elements *viz* the noble gases. He initially worked with Bunsen in Heidelberg, then moved to Bristol, where he measured accurately the density of air. He eventually settled in London, where he removed all the known gases from air and was still left with 1%, a gas he called argon. He then discovered helium in rocks, a gas which Bunsen had previously inferred was in the Sun. With the discovery of methods for cooling air, Ramsay then discovered three other inert gases (krypton, xenon and neon).

random in no order, with no discernable pattern, unable to predict the future from the past |

random motion / random movement movement of particles in all sorts of directions at a range of speeds | random path a route that shows no predictable direction | random sample a small amount taken so as to be representative of the whole bulk | random sampling taking small amounts from different places or at different times which are not predefined

range a difference, the amount between limits, an area of rolling countryside used as a farm, a cooking oven, a series of mountain peaks; to move freely over a large area | range of activities a group of many different movements, or performances or experiments | range of cases several examples of a similar investigation with different approaches, equipment and measurements | range of devices a variety of instruments using different methods to achieve the same result | range of evidence the variety of indications and observations that are used to support an idea | range of fuels the many different materials that can be used to produce heat by reaction with oxygen | range of habitats a variety of areas, with different conditions of moisture, wind, light and availability of nutrients | range of hearing the frequencies of sound, from the lowest to the highest, to which an animal will respond | range of human hearing the frequencies of sound which a person is able to hear, from 20 hertz to 25 kilohertz in a young person, reducing to 40 hertz to 16 kilohertz in elderly people | range of illnesses many different types of disease | range of materials a variety of substances | range of measurements several sets of data that are used to support an idea, the differences between measurements obtained from different people carrying out the same experiment | range of minerals the variety of metal and non-metal ions that are needed by the body, the many different types of rock that are found in an area | range of nutrients the variety of different molecules that are required by the body for healthy growth | range of pitch the difference between the highest and lowest frequencies that the organism is capable of hearing or of producing| range of resources the equipment, expertise, books and money that are available for solving the problem | range of results the measurements that were obtained independently by different people carrying out the same experiment, different sets of information and observations that are used to support an idea | range of situations several different circumstances or conditions | range of sounds the many different patterns that may be distinguished within a source of sound |

range of sources several different books, experiments and discussions were used to obtain the information | range of techniques a variety of different methods and measurements will be used | range of temperatures the difference between the highest and lowest temperatures that are used | appropriate range the upper and lower limits are suitable for that experiment with those measurements | audible range the set of frequencies, between the lowest and the highest, over which a person can hear clearly and is able to distinguish patterns | hearing range the frequencies, from lowest to highest, for which that organism is able to hear | pH range the limits between which the pH is measured or likely to be found | temperature range the difference between the highest and lowest temperatures found in a particular area or a particular experiment | tidal range the difference in sea level, at the time of the highest and lowest tides, varies from 30 centimetres in the Mediterranean to 16 metres off the Atlantic coast of Canada | wide range the upper and lower points are widely spaced in the units that are being used

ranging occurring, the limits between which measurements are made | wide ranging over a large number of different topics

rank an ordering, a league, a line, a status; to put into an order or a line

rap (not wrap which is to cover) popular poetry set to a rhythm; to hit repeatedly and rapidly

rapid fast, hasty | rapid cooling the temperature drops very quickly | rapid growth the size increases much more than would normally be expected in a given time

rapidly quickly, swiftly, speedily

rapped (not rapt which is absorbed, nor wrapped which is covered) hitting a solid object with a hard ruler or hammer, an abrupt blow was struck

rapt (not rapped which is absorbed, nor wrapped which is covered) absorbed in an act, carried away on dreams, totally focused

rare unusual, not found very often, not cooked thoroughly | rare breed the species or strain of a farm animal that is not best suited to the market conditions of today and so is no longer common on farms and may be on the verge of dying out | rare breed center (USA) / rare breed centre (UK) a zoo or farm that deliberately breeds and uses animals that were found on farms in past times, but are not suitable for today's conditions

rarefaction an area of low pressure in the air caused by a sound wave moving the particles

rarity scarcity, not many available

rash thoughtless, reckless, an area of skin that has changed colour or texture and may exhibit spots

rasher a thin slice of bacon

rat a small mammal, similar to a large mouse, that is found everywhere that people live | rat poison a chemical that is used to kill rats

rate the amount of change in a specified period of time | rate of cooling the decrease of temperature per second or per minute, more rapid cooling leads to tiny crystals | rate of photosynthesis the amount of sugar that is produced, or the amount of carbon dioxide that is used, in each minute or each hour | rate of reaction the speed with which a chemical change occurs | application rate the amount of that substance which is spread over a specified area of skin or ground | birth rate the number of offspring born per thousand of population | breathing rate the number of breaths, inhaling and exhaling, that occurs each minute | cooling rate the decrease in temperature each second | death rate the number of people who die during a given period or from a particular disease compared to the size of population | different rates the speed with which a change occurs will vary depending on conditions | flow rate the amount of fluid passing a given point each second | heart rate the number of times each minute that the heart contracts and relaxes | pulse rate the number of heart beats per second, as measured by feeling the pressure pulses in the arteries at the wrist or neck | recovery rate the time taken for the heart to return to its resting rate after vigorous exercise | survival rate how many creatures were left alive at the end of the time period compared to the population size

rating a limit, a ranking | rating plate the sheet on electrical equipment that gives the safe voltage, current and power | current rating the highest current that can safely be passed through that cable | power rating the amount of electrical power that can safely pass through the equipment, the power output of an electrical machine | voltage rating the size of the potential difference that is best suited for use with that component

ratio proportion, comparative amounts

rationale the reasoning, the logic behind an assumption, the thought processes

rattle a baby's toy; to push repeatedly and rapidly, to produce a noise when moved

raw (not roar which is a sound) uncooked, figures that have not been used in mathematical processing | raw material the ore, oil or chemicals that are used to produce other materials | raw meat the flesh that is to be eaten has not been cooked | raw sewage the excrement and organic waste have not been treated in any way

ray a very thin beam (usually of light), a line drawn to show the path that a light beam would follow | ray box a lamp holder with a flat base and a slit or slits from which a thin beam of light can emerge | ray diagram a drawing that shows the path taken by a ray of light | ray of light a very thin beam of visible radiation, the path followed by the edge of a light beam | cosmic rays any part of the electromagnetic spectrum that originates from outside the Solar System | emergent ray the visible path of the light that is leaving a surface | gamma ray an electromagnetic wave, with a frequency and energy that is higher than an X-ray, which is produced by breakdown of the atomic nucleus | incident ray the beam of light that is directed towards a mirror | light ray a very thin beam of light, used in diagrams, to show the path that the light beam will take | reflected ray the beam that bounces off a mirror | refracted ray a beam of light that has changed direction at a boundary because the speed of the wave has changed | transmitted ray the line showing where the light beam has continued after passing through a transparent block | ultra-violet rays electromagnetic waves with wavelengths lower than that of visible light | X-ray part of the electromagnetic spectrum that is more energetic or higher frequency than ultra-violet light, a shadow photograph taken using X-rays

rays (not raise which is to increase) thin lines that shows the path that a beam of light would follow

Rb rubidium, proton number 37, a very reactive alkali metal

rbc [red blood cells] (erythrocytes) the cells in the blood that contain haemoglobin, a chemical that turns brilliant red when combined with oxygen

Rd radon, proton number 86, an inert gas

rda [recommended daily allowance] the amount of a nutrient that you need each day

re- (*Latin* again) to repeat

re-absorbed taken back into the starting place without any obvious change

reach to achieve, to stretch towards

react to change in response to a stimulus, to form new chemicals | react chemically to start with one set of chemicals and end with another set | react completely all the reactant is used up

reactants the chemicals that are present at the start of the reaction, the reactants always go on the left-hand side of a chemical equation (with the products on the right-hand side)

reacted changed, produced new substances

reacting mixture the chemicals that will react are all mixed together

reaction a permanent change, a response, a force that resists movement | reaction force the push in the opposite direction to the applied force that opposes any movement | reaction time the interval between seeing an event occurring and making a move to show a reponse | allergic reaction a change to the body chemistry as a result of a particular chemical being present in the environment | chain reaction a continually increasing change as one breakdown causes several more changes, each of which then causes more breakdowns | chemical reaction a permanent change in which the reactants become products | combustion reaction a chemical change that occurs in the presence of oxygen that releases heat energy | decomposition reaction one chemical changes to produce simpler substances | displacement reaction a chemical change in which a more reactive metal pushes out a less reactive metal from a salt | endothermic reaction a chemical change in which energy is taken in, *eg* photosynthesis | exothermic reaction a permanent change in which energy is given out, *eg* burning of a fuel | hazardous reaction a chemical change which is so rapid that special precautions are needed | neutralisation reaction (UK) / neutralization reaction (USA) a chemical change in which the pH is taken to 7 | nuclear reaction the formation of new elements either by the nuclei of two atoms fusing together or a nucleus breaking apart | oxidation reaction a chemical change that involves adding oxygen to one of the reactants | precipitation reaction a chemical change in which one of the products is insoluble and forms a cloud | rate of reaction the speed with which a chemical change occurs | redox reaction a chemical change in which one reactant loses oxygen (reduction) and the other reactant gains oxygen (oxidation) | reduction reaction removal of oxygen from a compound, an element gains electrons | reversible reaction a chemical reaction that reaches an equilibrium because the products can react to form the reactants, *eg* producing ammonia from nitrogen and hydrogen | similar reactions grouping chemical changes together so as to highlight common features | test-tube reaction a chemical reaction that may be carried out safely in a small tube | thermit reaction / thermite reaction a violent reaction in which aluminium displaces iron from iron oxide, producing temperatures above 1600°C, so the iron melts | vigorous reaction the chemical change produces large amounts of heat or

bubbles in a short time | violent reaction a chemical reaction that is rapid, gives out lots of heat and may be explosive

reactive able to take part in a reaction, not inert | reactive metals the metals (elements that conduct electricity) that will react with acids or with water | highly reactive any reactions by this substance will give out lots of heat and may be explosive | less reactive lower down the reactivity series than another metal or halogen | more reactive this metal will react faster, and give out more heat, than the other metal | most reactive the fastest reacting, the element at the top of the reactivity series

reactivity a measure of how readily a metal or a non-metal will take part in a reaction | reactivity of metals how readily the metals will take place in a reaction such as producing an oxide when placed in oxygen or releasing hydrogen from an acid | reactivity series a league of metals with the most reactive at the top (caesium or potassium) then, in order, down to the inert or non-reactive metals of gold and platinum, the metals always keep this order whenever any reaction is considered | higher reactivity the element is higher in the reactivity series and so will react faster | lower reactivity reaction of that metal with acid, water or oxygen will be much slower than the first metal | order of reactivity the arrangement of metals with the most reactive at the top, then in order, down to the least reactive | relative reactivity comparing the position of two metals in the reactivity series

reactor equipment in which a change can occur | nuclear reactor the building in which the heat energy, released from changes in the nucleus of the atom, can be used safely to produce steam in order to generates electricity

reacts changes, responds, opposes

read (not red which is a colour) having looked at words to decode their meaning

read (not reed which is a water plant) to find meaning in written words, to decipher a message

reader equipment for obtaining data from print, diagrams or visible markings | bar code reader a mechanism, based on the reflection of laser beam, for decoding the information that is in the form of bars of different thickness and spacing

readily smoothly, easily, willingly

reading a measurement, deciphering text | reading strategy a plan for being able to understand a text | current reading the measurement that is shown at the present time, the current that is flowing through an ammeter | lip reading understanding what someone says by watching

reac
↓
read

the movement of their lips | repeat readings to take the measurements again to check for accuracy

reagent a chemical that is used in a reaction | chemical reagent a substance or material that is used in a reaction that results in a permanent change

real (not rail which is a track) actually exists, tangible, can be touched | real image the image can be projected onto a screen

real-time display a dial or number that shows what is occurring at the same time as the event is happening

realise to understand, to recognise, to achieve, to bring about

rearrangement a changing of the order

rearranging putting into a different order

reason the aim, an explanation, the rationale; to debate, to analyse | environmental reason a justification that is based on the effects on the wildlife

reasoned explained by showing the steps | reasoned argument an explanation that is based on observation, but uses logical connections

reasoning arguing, persuading, using logic

reasons the explanations, the rationalisations

re-assemble to put back together again, to re-build

rebound to bounce back again, to be reflected, to return

recall to remember, to use again

recent / recently in the near past

receptacle the part of the stem from which the flower emerges, a container

receptors / receptor cells cells that are able to detect a specific stimulus and respond by sending a message to the brain | light receptors / photo-receptors the cells (cones and rods) at the back of the eye that are able to respond to light | sensory receptor a cell that sends a signal to the brain if a specific event is detected | touch receptors the cells in the skin that respond to a pressure

recessive the gene that is not expressed | recessive characteristic a feature that is coded in the genes that is expressed only if the gene for a dominant characteristic is not present | recessive allele the form of the gene that is not expressed unless both alleles are recessive

recharge to add more energy

rechargeable able to put an electric current in the reverse direction, causing a reversible chemical reaction | rechargeable battery a series of electrical cells that provide a current in one direction, but can be recharged by passing a current in the opposite direction | rechargeable cell an electrical cell that provides a current in one direction

and can be recharged by passing a current through it in the opposite direction

reckless ignoring warnings, disregarding safety

reclassify to move an article from one category to another

recognise (UK) / **recognize** (USA) to see, to distinguish from others, to note features, to realise the truth | recognise a need to think about a change that would fulfil a requirement | recognise hazards to be able to see actions or objects that could cause injury

recognised (UK) / **recognized** (USA) seen, observed, distinguished

recognition identification, acknowledgement of a personal achievement

recognize (USA) / **recognise** (UK) to see, to distinguish from others, to note features, to realise the truth | recognize a need to think about a change that would fulfil a requirement | recognize hazards to be able to see actions or objects that could cause injury

recognized (USA) / **recognised** (UK) seen, observed, distinguished

recombinant plasmid a closed circle of DNA in which extra genes have been bonded, and is then ready for inserting back into a bacterium

recombine to cause to be reconnected

recombined joined together again

recommend to suggest a course of action, to report favourably

recommendation a proposal that the material or equipment is the most suitable for the purpose

recommended approved, promoted | recommended daily allowance (rda) the amount of a vitamin or mineral that is needed each day in order to maintain good health

reconcile to bring very different ideas together, to reach an agreement

reconsider to think again

record a data entry, a document, a best attempt ever, an index; to make a permanent entry into a database or table | record attempts to write down or film the details of an experiment, to try to break a record | record changes to write down the differences | record data to put the information into a database or table, to write down | record observations to write down all the details of the changes and differences that are seen, heard, smelled or tasted | record results to put the output variable of an experiment into permanent form | land speed record the fastest that any person has travelled in that type of vehicle on land | medical record information concerning any previous diseases or medicines used | speed records the fastest speed achieve

recorded measured, written as a permanent form

recorder a musical wind instrument

recording a permanent statement of the process and the measurements | recording head the part of a tape player that transfers the electric signal to the magnetic domains of the tape | recording studio a sound-proof room in which a permanent record of music or speech can be made | sensor recording an electronic recording of the information provided by the probe

records details of an experiment

recount to tell a story

re-count to count again, to add up again

recover to get better from an illness, to isolate a chemical from a mixture

recovered now in better health, a chemical that has been isolated

recovery returning to full health | recovery rate the time taken for the heart to return to its resting rate after vigorous exercise

recreational leisure activities done for pleasure | recreational drugs chemicals that are taken voluntarily, and usually for pleasure, which cause dramatic changes to the brain

recrystallisation (UK) / **recrystallization** (USA) a method of purification in which the impure crystals are dissolved in a solvent, then allowed to reform crystals

rectangular a shape made from four lines where each pair meet at right angles | rectangular block a piece of material, often transparent, in which all sides are parallel and the sides always meet at an angle of 90°

rectifier valve a diode, a glass valve for ensuring that a current can flow in one direction only

rectum the last part of the digestive canal, after the large intestine, where the faeces collect

re-cycle to use an object again, either for the same purpose or as a source of raw material

re-cycling finishing with an item then using the item for another purpose or in another form

red (not read which is looking at words) the part of the visible spectrum above orange or yellow, visible light with a wavelength of greater than 600 nanometres | red blood cells (erythrocytes) the doughnut shaped cells in the blood that appear red from the haemoglobin that they contain, each cell has a lifetime of between 100 and 120 days | red cabbage a vegetable of the *Brassica* or cabbage family, the colour can be extracted in water and will turn red in acid and green in alkali | red cells the disc shaped cells in the blood that are red from the haemoglobin that they contain | red deer a hoofed mammal with horns that has a coat that turns from light brown

in summer to dark brown in winter | red filter a piece of glass, Perspex or other transparent material, that has a coating or contains chemicals so that only red light is able to pass through | red giant a star that has a diameter greater than the orbit of the Earth and the surface temperature is approximately 2000°C and so glows red | red heat at a temperature sufficiently high (above 600°C) that red light is given off | red-hot the material is at a temperature above 600°C | red liquid a red dye has been added to make the liquid easier to see | Red Planet Mars | Red Sea the long, thin extension of the Indian Ocean that separates Asia from Africa | red shift the change in the spectrum of a star because the star is moving away from us | brick red the dull red colour of many types of building brick | infra-red the part of the spectrum that has a longer wavelength than red (about 600 nanometres) and so is not visible to the human eye | methyl red an indicator that is red below pH 5.1, and yellow above pH 5.1 | phenol red an indicator that is yellow below pH 7.9, and red above pH 7.9

redden to increase the amount of red in the colour

redox REDuction and OXidation occur at the same time | redox reaction a chemical reaction in which one reactant is reduced, *ie* loses oxygen, causing another reactant to be oxidised

Red Sea the long, thin extension of the Indian Ocean that separates Asia from Africa (the sea is not red, but a common, local seaweed is that colour)

reduce to make less, to lower, to remove oxygen | reduce heat loss to improve insulation, to take steps to ensure that less heat energy is dissipated

reduced lessened, lowered, oxygen has been removed | reduced resistance the force that was trying to slow the speed has been decreased

reduces becomes smaller, gets less, removes oxygen

reducing getting less, becoming smaller | reducing acidity adding a base so as to increase the pH towards pH 7 | reducing agent a chemical that removes oxygen from another substance | reducing alkalinity adding an acid in order to decrease the pH to nearer pH 7 | reducing friction increasing the ease with which two surfaces will move across each other, *eg* by using a lubricant | reducing heat loss taking steps so as to maintain the temperature difference between two objects | reducing sugars carbohydrates, of the general formula $C_nH_{2n}O_n$ which will cause Benedict's solution to turn red

reduction getting smaller or less, removing oxygen, adding hydrogen, the gain of electrons |

reduction reaction a chemical change usually involving loss of oxygen from an oxide

reed (not read which is a to interpret text) a tall water plant that has roots in the bed of the river or lake | reed bed an area of the river or lake where tall water plants grow in large numbers | reed switch a very small switch that is encased in plastic and can be controlled by a current

re-establish to form new connections, to put back in place, to re-start

re-evaluate to look at the observations and conclusions in the light of new evidence

reef a line of rocks or coral in the sea

reference a mention, showing the source of the information | reference book printed literature that is an authority on the subject | reference material a substance of known composition or size | reference source material that has a measured composition, an agreed standard | reference sources the sites, people or books from which information or guidance is obtained | reference to using a particular example or specific circumstance

refine to make clear, to separate into pure parts | refine ideas to improve a theory both by making the idea simpler and by including more data

refinery (plural is refineries) / **oil refinery** a vast area covered with large buildings that are used to separate crude oil into useful substances

refining making more pure, simplifying | refining ideas improving a theory | refining oil separating the many different molecules in crude oil by using fractional distillation

reflect to bounce back from a surface, to think deeply

reflectance the bouncing back of waves, especially light, at a surface | diffuse reflectance the surface roughness causes the incident beam to be reflected in many different directions

reflected returned, bounced from a surface | reflected beam the rays or shaft of light that has been bounced from a surface | reflected image the picture that is produced by light from an object being reflected at a smooth surface | reflected light the light that has bounced off a surface | reflected rays the tracks taken by a very thin beams of light after reflection at a surface | reflected sunlight the light from the Sun has been reflected from one or several surfaces

reflecting bouncing, returning | reflecting light changing the direction of light by bouncing the light from a reflective surface

reflection the image in a mirror or on water | angle of reflection the angle between the ray that has bounced of the surface and the normal at

that point | diffuse reflection light is reflected in all directions from a surface | internal reflection the light bounces off an inside surface | law of reflection the angle of incidence equals the angle of reflection | total internal reflection (TIR) the reflection of all the light at a boundary between two transparent media, the behaviour of a beam of a light when moving from to a medium of lower density and meeting the surface at an angle above the critical angle

reflective able to bounce back, returning, thinking about past events | reflective clothing material that is worn with the intention of bouncing back any incident light and so is very easily seen | reflective strip a band that is highly visible when illuminated by a light | reflective surface a boundary that causes a wave to bounce back

reflector a surface that is intended to return light along exactly the same path along which the light arrived, often found on moving vehicles | radiator reflector a sheet of shiny foil that is placed on the wall behind a radiator to reflect heat away from the wall

reflex (plural is reflexes) / **reflex action** a rapid and involuntary response that does not require involvement of the brain and so can not be controlled

refract to bend at a boundary

refracted changed direction because of a change of speed | refracted beam / refracted ray the path of the light after the beam has changed speed

refraction the bending of a wave at a boundary caused by a change of speed | angle of refraction the angle between the normal and the path of the ray after leaving the boundary | law of refraction the direction of movement of a wave bends towards the normal if the speed slows down, and bends away from the normal if the speed increases

refrigerated cooled by using the compression and expansion of gases to move the heat to another place

refrigerator a box or cupboard, the inside of which can be cooled, that is used in the house for storing food for several days | refrigerator temperature the temperature inside the refrigerator after the door has been closed, should be 4°C

refutes opposes an idea, shows to be wrong, denies

regions areas, defined areas of a country, fields | volcanic regions areas of the world where volcanoes are active: producing smoke and ash, and occasionally erupting

register an official record; to cause a visible change or movement, to align, to recognise

regular at predictable and similar intervals | regular exercise carrying out some task, that is physically demanding, several times a week in order to keep fit | **regular movement** a change that occurs at predictable intervals, a rhythm | **regular pattern** behaviour that repeats itself many times | **regular sequences** an arrangement of numbers or parts of DNA that keeps repeating in the same order | **regular supply** materials, such as food or water, are provided at fixed intervals

regularly at predictable intervals

regulate to control, to manage, to apply rules

regulations rules, controls | **safety regulations** the guidelines which outline the steps that should be taken in order to prevent accidents | **water regulation** the processes by which the amount of water is controlled

rehydrate to replace the water

reign (not rain which is drops of water nor rein which is a strip) the time for which a person is monarch; to be the king or queen

rein (not rain which is drops of water nor reign which is the job of a monarch) a leather strip for guiding a horse

reinforce to make stronger, to strengthen

reinforcement strengthening material

re-introduce to replace, to put an object or organism back into an area from which it had disappeared

reject an item that is not required; to put in the waste bin, to get rid of

rejection failure to be accepted | **organ rejection** the failure of an organ transplant to be accepted by the recipient

relate to report, to connect, to compare, to empathise | **relate ideas** to connect different theories so as to explain the observations, to tell your theory to other people | **relate results** to show how your measurements either support the theory or prove that the idea is wrong

related connected | **related ideas** theories that are similar | **related terms** words that describe the same observations or ideas

relates tells another, empathises

relating comparing, telling

relationship a connection, an equation relating changes in one variable to the effect on other variables | **ecological relationship** the way that different organisms are affected by other living things in the environment | **feeding relationship** the connection between one or more animals and their food and any predators | **genetic relationship** the genes encoded in the DNA of one set of chromosomes, compared to the genes in other cells or organisms | **quantitative relationship** the equation that shows how changing the value of one variable will affect the value of another

variable | **simple relationship** changing the value of one variable will have an immediate and predictable effect on another variable | **symbiotic relationship** two or more creatures that live in close proximity and help each other to survive, each providing something that the other needs

relative comparative, comparison of two or more items, another member of a family | **relative accuracy** finding which method gives the result that most closely represents the correct answer | **relative atomic mass** the mass of one atom of an element compared to the mass of a proton | **relative changes** a qualitative description as to which item is more affected by an event | **relative density** comparing the mass in one centimetre cubed of one substance to the mass of a single centimetre cubed of another material | **relative distances** comparing two displacements | **relative molecular mass** the formula mass, the total mass of all the atoms in the molecule (measured in atomic mass units or daltons) | **relative numbers** relating the count of items in one set to the count of items in another set | **relative positions** giving an idea of where two or more items are to be found in relationship to each other | **relative reactivity** comparing the position of two metals in the reactivity series | **relative sizes** comparing the shape, dimension or mass of different objects | **relative strength** comparing the ability of different structure to cause movement or withstand a force

relatively comparatively, qualitatively, comparing without numbers

relatives organisms that are related by sharing common parents or ancestors

relax to slacken, to stop working

relaxation resting, playing

relaxing lowering the tension, taking life easy

relay a component used as a switch; to carry in small stages | **relay switch** a component that allows a small current in one circuit to control a high voltage in a separate circuit

release to give out, to let go | **release energy** to change one form of stored energy into some type of work done | **energy release** changing energy from one form into a form that is more useful

releasing energy converting one form of energy into useful work

relevance the connection between observations or results, the importance of an observation

relevant appropriate, pertinent | **relevant adaptions** changes in structure or behaviour that can be shown to be related to a specific need | **relevant devices** equipment that could be used for that task | **relevant evidence** the information that is important in explaining the event or supporting a conclusion | **relevant factors** the variables that are likely to be important to the outcome of an experiment | **relevant information** facts, figures, observations and data that could help lead to a valid conclusion | **relevant observations** measurements and changes that are important to that experiment and to that conclusion | **relevant questions** asking a question that could help to explain the evidence or could produce new observations | **relevant variables** any item or factor that, if changed, would probably lead to different results

reliability the confidence with which you can put into the outcome when you start some equipment or an experiment | **reliability of results** a measure of whether the same results will be obtained in repeat experiments

reliable can be trusted, repeatable | **reliable conclusions** the summary or theory is based on evidence that is shown to be accurate and valid | **reliable data** the measurements are able to be repeated | **reliable evidence** the observations are able to be repeated | **reliable information / reliable results** the measurements and data are trustworthy and repeatable

relied on depended on, trusted

relies on depends on

relieve to remove a pain, to take away | **relieve symptoms** to reduce the intensity of such physical manifestations as pain or a rash

re-light to ignite the flame again

religion a belief, a system of understanding the world through faith

religious beliefs ideas that are held by faith rather than being proven by experiment

rely / rely on to trust, to depend on

remain to stay, to wait

remaining the amount or number that are left

remains residue, that material that is left at the end of the process | **plant remains** dead plants that have been partially decomposed

remedies (plural of remedy) chemicals or treatments that can relieve a pain or help a person recover from an illness

remedy (plural is remedies) a cure; to put right | **indigestion remedy** a tablet or liquid, often containing magnesium hydroxide, that should cure a stomach ache

rememberies (plural of remembery) simple forms of important ideas

remembery (plural is rememberies) a fact that should be known but has been forgotten

remind to give information a second or third time

remix to blend together substances that have separated out

remote no direct physical connection, a far distant place | **remote controls** boxes that allow an item to be switched between different states without any physical connection, the message is encoded onto an infra-red or radio beam | **remote data** information that is collected at a distance from the area being examined | **remote data collection** obtaining measurements from a far distant place often involving the use of satellites to take measurements of areas of the Earth | **remote sensing** obtaining information without any direct contact

removal extraction, elimination

remove to take away

removing taking away

renal concerned with the kidney | **renal artery** the thick-walled vessel that carries blood from the heart to the kidney | **renal vein** the vessel that returns blood from the kidney to the heart

rename to give a new identifier

renewable able to be replaced, can grow again (NB this is not the same as reusable!) | **renewable energy / renewables** energy that will be replaced in the near future, *eg* energy from the wind, waves, tides or sunlight | **renewable fuels** materials that can react with oxygen to release energy and are able to grow again, *eg* trees, grass, straw | **renewable source** the material from that origin will never run out | **non-renewable** can be used once, but this causes a change that can not be reversed

rennet the liquid from the stomach of a calf or ` lamb that contains rennin

rennin an enzyme from the stomach of a calf or a lamb that causes milk to form a hard clot that is the basis of many cheeses

re-order to ask for a further batch, to buy replacements, to put into a new ranking

repair a reconstruction, a correction; to remove a defect, to mend, to make as good as new

repeat a duplicate; to do again | **repeat measurements** to do the same experiment again, without any changes | **repeat readings** to take the measurements again to check for accuracy

repeatedly repetitively, doing many times

repeating duplicating, carrying out the experiment again | **repeating measurements / repeating observations** collecting a second set of data using exactly the same experimental details

repel to push away

repelling pushing away

repetitive occurring again and again and . . . | **repetitive movement** a change that keeps occurring at predictable intervals

replace to substitute, to take away one item and to fill the gap with another

replacement a substitute | replacement joint to remove a joint, such as knee, that is not working properly and replace it with a new joint made from metal and plastic | hip replacement to remove the top of the thigh bone, or femur, and replace with a metal rod with a ball on the end

replicate to try to follow precisely the actions of another, to reproduce asexually so the offspring are identical to the parents

report an account, a description of actions and results; to tell other people | media reports accounts or summaries that appear in newspapers or on radio or television

represent to show in a different, usually simpler, way, to act in place of another person or organisation | represent data to show the information as a diagram or a cartoon figure

representation a diagram, a picture

representative a sample taken at random from a whole set, a person who speaks on behalf of one or several others

representing using one item as a symbol for another object

reprocess to take waste material and turn into a useful substance

reproduce to make copies that are almost identical, to make more of the same species

reproduction making more of the same cell or organism; a copy | reproduction pattern the regular changes that occurs in the life cycle of an organism leading to more of the same species | asexual reproduction one cell or organism producing more of the same cell or organism without the involvement of a partner | human reproduction the pattern and methods for the production of children | mammalian reproduction the methods and times at which animals who have hair and produce milk to nourish their young (mammals) are able to produce offspring | patterns of reproduction common features in the organs, rituals or timing of reproduction of many different species | plant reproduction a description of the organs and events that are associated with the reproduction of plants | sexual reproduction production of an offspring from two parents in which each parent contributes half the genetic material | spore-bearing reproduction the method of producing offspring that depends on the formation and spreading of spores | vegetative reproduction asexual reproduction in plants from bulbs, rhizomes or runners

reproductive concerned with making more of the same | reproductive cells the special cells, or gametes, that are used in sexual reproduction and contain half the usual number of chromosomes | reproductive organs the distinct structures that are essential for the production of new cells that lead to offspring | reproductive pattern the regular changes in behaviour and appearance that go with one organism trying to become two or more | reproductive structures the forms, shapes and collections of cells that are found to be essential for the organism to reproduce | reproductive system the collection of organs and tissues that are needed for reproduction to occur

reproductive cells the special cells, or gametes, that are used in sexual reproduction and contain half the usual number of chromosomes | female reproductive cell ovum, the reproductive cell that is filled with nutrients and does not move | male reproductive cell sperm in animals, pollen in plants – the motile gamete

reproductive organs the distinct structures that are essential for the production of new cells that lead to offspring | female reproductive organs the ovaries, fallopian tube and uterus of mammals, the carpel, style and stigma of plants | male reproductive organs testes in animals, stamen in plants

reptile a cold-blooded vertebrate with dry skin that uses lungs for breathing, they usually lay eggs but some give birth to live young

repulsion pushing away | magnetic repulsion the observation that similar magnetic poles will push each other away

require to need something in order to work properly

requirements the needs, the necessities | mineral requirements the metals and ions that are needed by living organisms for healthy growth | minimal requirements the least amount of material needed

re-radiate to absorb light and then radiate the light back again

rescue a move to safety; to move someone to safety | mountain rescue the act of using a group of experienced climbers to find a person who was lost, then guiding them to safety

research collecting evidence to find the answers to simple questions by using experiments that should be controlled and easily repeated | independent research working by yourself, not dependent on a sponsor for money | previous research experiments carried out and reported earlier

resemble to look like

reservation a booking, an area in North America where indigenous people continue to live, a doubt

reserve material that is not used being used and so is put into store; to keep aside | reserve battery / reserve cell an emergency source of electricity that is activated by adding sea water | food reserves the amounts of food that are stored for future use | nature reserve an area that has been set aside from development because it contains wildlife that is not available elsewhere

reservoir a vast volume of liquid, often in a large lake, the volume of liquid at the base of a thermometer

re-set switch a button that allows a system to be returned to its starting state

resettable able to be returned to a zero point or the original, working state

resident an animal that normally lives in that area all the year around

residue the material left behind, the solid that remains in a filter paper

resin the fluid that some trees leak out, which may eventually form amber

resist to try to prevent movement, to oppose a change

resistance preventing movement, able to withstand attack by microbes and viruses, affecting the current in a circuit | resistance to cold able to survive at temperatures well below the freezing point of water | resistance to disease will not be affected by the microbe that, in other animals or plants of the same species, could cause symptoms or death | air resistance the force caused by the air particles that increases as the speed of the object increases until terminal velocity is reached | antibiotic resistance a bacterium is not affected by a chemical that will kill other microbes | disease resistance the ability of an organism to resist infection by a microbe | drug resistance the microbe is not affected by that chemical, development of new strains of bacteria which are not affected by the chemical | electrical resistance the effect of atoms in the wire trying to prevent the flow of electrons that is the electrical current | fluid resistance the force that opposes the movement in a liquid, gas or powder | frictional resistance the slowing force caused when a moving surface comes into contact with another surface that is moving more slowly or is stationary | reduced resistance the size of the opposing force is lowered | tear resistance the ability of the material to stop a cut or rip from spreading though the cloth | water resistance the particles of water get in the way of a moving object and try to slow the movement, the low ability of water to pass an electric current | wear resistance the ability of a surface to withstand continual usage

resistant able to prevent change | resistant microbe a microbe that is not affected by the presence of a specified antibiotic | resistant to disease will not be affected by the microbe that could cause symptoms or death in other organisms or plants of the same species | corrosion-resistant the metal is not affected by the usual chemicals of water and oxygen that will change the properties of many metals | disease-resistant able to withstand infection by a microbe that causes an illness | water-resistant not affected by water | weather-resistant will not change, despite changes in temperature, wind or light conditions

resisted prevented change

resistive force the force that opposes your attempts at changing speed, *eg* friction, air resistance

resistor an electrical component which functions to reduce the current | light-dependent resistor (LDR) a component with a resistance that decreases as the brightness of light shining increases | variable resistor / rheostat a piece of electrical equipment, with a slider or rotary control, that can be moved so as to change the resistance of the component

resonance an oscillation, or vibration, of high amplitude that occurs at a specific frequency as a result of using a small amount of energy

resorb to change some cells or tissues of your own body so that the material can be re-used for new cells

resource a store of material, money, time or energy that is available to be used | resource materials the substances that may be available for that experiment | alternative energy resources / alternative resources places where energy can be found that do not depend on burning fossil fuels | appropriate resources using the substances or equipment that will allow an accurate answer in a short time | energy resources the places or changes that can be used for obtaining energy | food resources the type of animal, plants and fungi that are available for eating and can be used for obtaining nutrients | non-renewable resources reserves of useful material, *eg* oil, that can never be replaced | range of resources / variety of resources many different sources that supply the material or energy | water resources the area from which water, which is suitable for a specified purpose, can be removed and used

respectively in the same order

respiration a process that occurs in every cell in which glucose, which may react with oxygen, is changed into new chemicals and releases energy |

aerobic respiration the reaction of glucose and oxygen that occurs in many cells and produces carbon dioxide and water and releases lots of energy | anaerobic respiration the cells are changing glucose into new chemicals, usually including carbon dioxide and water, in the absence of oxygen, anaerobic respiration in yeast is called fermentation and produces alcohol | artificial respiration helping a person who is not breathing to get air in and out of the lungs either by pressing on the chest or by breathing directly into the mouth | plant respiration the reaction of glucose with oxygen that occurs in every plant cell so that the energy released can be used to make new chemicals

respiratory concerned with getting air in and out of the lungs | respiratory disease any illness that affects the lungs so that breathing becomes difficult | respiratory system the several tissues and organs that are needed for exchange of gases to occur, including the lungs, the trachea and bronchi

respire to change sugar into carbon dioxide and other chemicals in the cell so as to release energy, to breathe, to inhale and exhale air

respiring cells the cells that are chemically changing sugars so as to release carbon dioxide, other chemicals and energy

respirometer equipment that is used to measure the volume of air that is entering the lungs, the speed of flow and the amount of oxygen used in each breath

respond to give a reply, to answer

response the return, the reply | voluntary response changing position as a result of thinking about the action

responsive able to react quickly and predictably

re-spray to sprinkle another layer, eg of paint

rest the ones that remain, the excess, the sleep, a period of inactivity; to become less active, to stop for a while | rest position the place to which an object returns if the force is removed, the position taken by an animal during sleep | at rest remaining in one position, not moving

restaurant a café, a place that serves meals and drinks

resting using minimum exertion | resting level the concentration, number or pressure of some variable when the component or organism is doing the least amount of work

restless Earth a picture of the crust of the Earth as moving up and down and from side to side over long periods

restore to return to the original condition, to repair damage

restrict to introduce a boundary, to set a limit

restricted limited, available only under certain circumstances

restricting keeping within specified boundaries, preventing free movement

result outcome, measurement, data | odd result an anomaly, an unexpected measurement, a reading that does not fit the pattern

resultant the overall force and direction after applying more than one force | resultant effect the outcome related to a specific variable or input | resultant force the overall or net force that occurs when more than one force is applied

results measurements, data, observations | results sheet paper on which is written a table of the outcome of a game or experiment | results table a method of presenting measurements using columns and rows | anomalous results measurements that do not fit the curve, even allowing for error or lack of accuracy | combine results to join the measurements from more than one experiment | compare results to see if the measurements that were obtained in two or more experiments are similar or different | display results to show your data, especially in a poster | distribution of results the curve that results when the data are plotted out, the spread of the data | experimental results the measurements and observations that are found by practical work | misleading results some measurements or observations point to an idea that is later found to be wrong | pool results to collect the measurements and observations from several groups or experiments and then treat the combined data as one set of results | positive results the measurements support your idea, the test confirmed the condition | present results to show your results, to display the data | qualitative results the observations allow comparisons to be made, eg lower, darker, hotter | range of results data from several experiments, the spread of measurements from smallest to largest | record results to put the measurements of an experiment into permanent form | relate results to find a pattern that joins the observations to a theory | reliability of results a measure of whether the same results will be obtained in repeat experiments | reliable results observations that are accurate and should be obtained again if the experiment were repeated | set of results several measurements or observations that indicate a trend or direction | spread of results the range of the data, the extent of the measurement from smallest to largest | table of results putting the data into columns, with title and units, and aligning rows of related measurements | validity of results the measurements are accurate and the instruments are precise

retailer a seller, a shop | food retailer a person or a shop that sells food

retain to keep

retaining keeping, not allowing to escape

retard to slow down | retarding force the force that tries to slow the object, *eg* brakes

retina the layer of 120 million cells, at the back of the eye, that is sensitive to light

retire to leave the game, to stop working, to go to bed

retort a round bottomed flask in which the neck turns into a long side-arm, a large vessel used for distillation, a reply | retort stand the base and rod that is also called a clamp stand

retreating returning to the area from which they started, going back

return to go back to the same place | return spring a coil, or springy strip, of metal that causes some item to return to its original position when the force is removed

re-usable (UK & USA) / **re-useable** (USA) has been used previously, but is still suitable for further use

re-use to use the item again for the same purpose

reveal to show, to bring into the open

reverse the opposite; to go backwards | reverse thrusters the tubes that eject hot gases in order to decrease the speed of a rocket

reversed moving in the opposite direction to that undertaken before

reversible able to go in both directions | reversible change a difference that can be taken back to the starting point, *eg* water can be frozen to ice and then thawed to give the original water | reversible reaction a chemical reaction that reaches an equilibrium because the products can react to form the reactants, *eg*

$$\text{ammonia} \rightleftharpoons \text{nitrogen} + \text{hydrogen}$$
$$2\ NH_3 \qquad N_2 \quad + \quad 3\ H_2$$

review to look over, to examine the whole set of experiments, results and conclusions | review ideas to go over the conclusions to see if other ideas could be used

reviewing looking over the data or the conclusion

revise to learn, to change, to reconsider

revolution a rotation, a complete turn through 360°, a sudden change of Government or of ideas | Industrial Revolution a period when many manual tasks start to be taken over by machines, the Industrial Revolution in Europe started approximately 1775 with the mechanisation of the cotton and woollen industries

revolve to spin, to turn around an axis

revolving turning about an axis | revolving doors three or four doors revolve around the central axis of a cylinder so that there is minimal exchange of air from inside and outside the building

RGB / rgb [red, green, blue] the three colours to which the human eye is sensitive

rheostat a variable resistor, an electrical component that can be used to change a resistance, *eg* in volume controls

rhesus a type of monkey | rhesus factor one of the characteristics of blood that is either present (rhesus positive Rh^+) or is missing (rhesus negative Rh^-)

rhizome a thick horizontal stem that sends out shoots and roots along its length

rhododendrums / rhododendrons an evergreen shrub that produces many flowers and prefers acid soil

rhubarb an annual plant in which the stalks are edible | rhubarb leaves the large leaves of the rhubarb plant that contain poisonous oxalic acid

rhythm a throb, a regular beat, a cycle | diurnal rhythm follows a 24-hour cycle, often with distinct differences between night and day

rhythmical contractions squeezing that occurs at regular intervals

rib one of the thin curved bones joining the spine to the sternum in the centre of the chest | rib cage the spine and sternum are attached to each end of the ribs, forming a cylindrical structure | rib muscle a muscle that helps move the ribs up so as to expand the chest cavity so that air enters the lungs, a thoracic muscle

ribbon a tape, a strip of material, a thin band | magnesium ribbon a thin tape of magnesium, which is convenient for cutting off small amounts

riboflavin (UK & USA) / **riboflavine** (UK) vitamin B2, found in most green plants and in milk, deficiency leads to cracked skin

ribonucleic acid / RNA a long chain of nucleotides in which the sugar is ribose

ribs the long thin curved bones that are attached to the sternum and spine so as to form the chest cavity in mammals

rice a cereal crop that is the staple source of carbohydrate for half the population of the world | polished rice the outer husk has been removed from the seed

rich containing a lot, without specifying exactly how high is the proportion | rich in trace elements the material contains many of the metals, such as zinc [Zn] or magnesium [Mg], that are essential for life, but are needed only in minute or trace amounts | rich supply lots | carbonate-rich a rock or liquid containing a high concentration of a carbonate salt [CO$_3$=] | colostrum-rich milk that also contains many of the chemicals found in colostrum | iron-rich rocks that contain sufficient iron, usually as iron oxide, as to make extraction of the metal a profitable task | oxygen-rich an atmosphere that contains a high proportion of oxygen | silica-rich rocks that contain a large proportion of sand-like material

Richter (Charles Francis 1900–1985) studied earthquakes in his home country of America. In 1935, he developed a method for comparing the strength and destructive force of earthquakes, using a scale in which an increase of one unit means the effects are ten times greater.

rickets symptoms of a deficiency disease, caused by lack of vitamin D, in which the bones are soft and so the victim becomes bow legged, cured by eating fish or liver or by sun bathing

rid removed, discarded

ride a time spent in one of the exciting roller coasters or spinning machines in a theme park; to be transported, to travel mounted on a horse or cycle | balloon ride travelling in the gondola of a helium or a hot-air balloon

ridge a long and narrow path with a steep slope dropping from either side | ocean ridge a large mountain range found under the seas

rift a tear, a divide | Rift Valley a wide trough in the Earth's surface in the Highlands of Kenya

rig equipment for investigating and drilling the ground; to fix, to fit in a rush | oil rig the structure that surrounds and supports the pipe that is drilling for oil

right (not rite which is a form of worship, nor wright which is a workman, nor write which is to put pen to paper) correct, accurate, the opposite to left, justice; to bring upright, to correct a wrong | right angle a change in direction of exactly 90°, the corner of a rectangle | right-handed being stronger and more skilful with the right hand than with the left (90% of the population is right handed)

rigid fixed, unmoving, solid

rigorous precise, logical, exacting

rind the stiff outer covering of many fruits or of cheese

ring a circle; to telephone | ring circuit / ring main the way that cables are arranged through the house in the distribution of the mains electricity, the wires within the cable start at the distribution box, are laid around the house and then returned to the starting point | ring of fire the edges of the Pacific ocean, which are the sites

of many active volcanoes | ringworm a fungal infection of the skin that starts at one point then spreads outwards as a red ring | ball-and-ring / ball-in-a-ring a method for showing expansion using a ball that will fit through the ring when both are cold, but heating the ball causes expansion so the hot ball can not pass through the ring | ear-ring an ornament that is attached to the lobe of the ear

rip to tear, to pull violently

ripe ready, finished, mature | ripe apple the fruit is ready to eat

ripen to mature, to change and become ready for the next stage

ripening fruit the change that occurs in colour, texture and chemicals inside a fruit between initial formation and when the fruit is ready for dispersal | ripening time the period taken to go from the immature egg or fruit to the final form

ripple a wave, with a maximum height of 10 centimetres, moving across the surface of water; to produce a small wave

rise an increase; to lift up, to increase | rise in temperature / temperature rise the material becomes hotter

rising increasing, becoming higher | rising damp moisture is rising up the walls of a building because of capillary action in the bricks and cement

risk a hazard, a danger; to take a chance | risk assessment / assess risk deciding the level of danger, thinking about the probability that an accident will occur and what would be the consequences of such an accident

rite (not right which is correct, nor wright which is a workman, nor write which is to put pen to paper) a ceremony, an act of worship, a ritual

river the water that collected in the high ground flows down to the sea in streams that become wider, deeper and more slow flowing, a body of water that is moving because of the gravity of the Earth | river bank the area of land immediately next to and above the river | river bed the layer of stone, sand or silt that is at the bottom of the water flow | river delta a wide area of low lying land at the mouth of a river, in the shape of a triangle, caused by precipitation of the silt as the river meets the sea | river estuary the area of water where the river meets the sea | river water the water of the river, which contains dissolved substances and suspended material | polluted river a flow of water that contains dissolved poisonous material, so is unlikely to support life | tidal river the river near the sea, where the height changes twice a day as the level of the sea water changes with each tide |

underground river the water is flowing through caves and natural tunnels in the rock

rivet a pin used for joining sheets of metal; to join metals together using pins

RNA /ribonucleic acid a long chain of nucleotides in which the sugar is ribose | messenger RNA / mRNA the long chain of nucleotides (with ribose as the sugar) that carries the instructions from the DNA molecule of the chromosome to the cytoplasm

road (not rode which is to sit on a bicycle or horse) a pathway or wide track that is tough enough to take wheeled vehicles | road accident a crash involving at least one vehicle that was moving on the highway | road bridge a structure that supports a road over an obstacle such as a river or a valley | road safety behaving in such a way that you, and other travellers, can arrive safely | road sign a banner or indicator that warns of some hazard or instruction or danger in the near distance | road surface the hard material that is used as the top layer of a path, track or road | road transport the lorries and cars that run on public highways in order to move goods and people

roam to wander, to walk over a large area, to walk in a random direction with no particular destination

roar (not raw which is uncooked) a noise which is long lasting, low frequency and loud, often used by large animals to indicate their presence

roasting very hot, cooking in the oven

robin a small brown bird with a red breast

robot equipment that will carry out a repetitive task accurately (not to be confused with androids, which are automatons that look like people)

rock any sort of material found on the Earth, ranging in size from microscopic clay to the giant mountains of granite and limestone; to move gently and rhythmically from side to side | rock band a layer of rock that differs from adjacent strata in colour or texture, a group of musicians that play loud music | rock cycle the movement of material through the various processes from molten rock in the mantle, being changed into igneous rock at the surface, then becoming sedimentary and metamorphic rock before melting back into the mantle | rock deformation changing the shape of a rock, caused by pressure | rock fall an area of lumps of rock produced by the main area of rock being broken down by weathering | rock formation a defined area of land that shows a distinct structure, the process by which rocks are produced | rock-forming producing rocks from material such as magma, sand or shells | rock-forming processes the several

methods for producing the solid rocks that make up the crust of the Earth | rock fragment a small part that has broken off a larger rock | rock fragmentation breaking of rocks into many smaller pieces, often caused by water freezing in cracks and then thawing | rock layers the strata caused by changing geological conditions leading to the sedimentation of different types of rock on top of each other | rock materials any substance that is found on the Earth and is not growing nor made by humans | rock salt an evaporite (a sedimentary rock) of crystals of sodium chloride [NaCl] mixed in with sand and clay | rock samples small pieces of rock that are taken from an area for further analysis and investigation | rock sequence the different layers of rock are named in sequence, either going across the land or forming a vertical section | rock specimen a typical piece of rock that shows the characteristics of that type of material | rock strata layers of different types of rock | rock surface the part of the stone that is affected by the surrounding material, the visible part of a boulder | rock texture how a rock looks, describing the grains and bands that are seen | rock types a method of classifying the thousands of different rocks, could be by appearance, crystal structure of the chemicals that are found in that rock | band of rock a stratum, a distinct layer of a particular type of rock | bed rock a solid layer of rock | breakthrough rock a sudden change in the type of rock, a sharp turn in the slope of a rock layer | cap rock an impermeable layer of rock that prevents loss of gas | carbonate-containing rock / carbonate rock geological material that contains the $CO_3^=$ ion, usually as calcium carbonate (chalk, limestone, marble), copper carbonate (malachite) or magnesium carbonate | carboniferous rock material formed between 360 million and 290 million years ago when the carbon dioxide concentration was high and plants grew fast and tall | color of rock (USA) / colour of rock (UK) a feature that is used to identify different types of rock and where they came from | crystalline rock a rock containing many small crystals | deformation of rock the changing of the shape of rock layers, or strata, as the Earth's crust moves over a long period of time | deposition of rock dropping or sedimentation of geological material to form layers | existing rocks the silt, boulders and mountains that were present before the change occurred | exposed rock material that can be seen on the surface of the Earth | extrusive rock the magma (molten rock below the crust) penetrates through the crust and cools rapidly on the surface | **folded rock** the layer of rock has buckled and bent by the movement of the surrounding strata| **fragmental rock** any geological material that contains small parts of other rocks | **gabbroic rock** gabbro, a rock with crystals larger than 0.5 millimetre diameter and mainly magnesium [Mg] or iron [Fe] | **igneous rock** any rock that has formed as a result of magma (molten rock below the crust) reaching and penetrating the crust, then cooling to a solid | **intrusive rock** igneous rock that formed by the molten magma cooling beneath the top surface of the Earth's crust | **limestone rock** any material that is mainly calcium carbonate [$CaCO_3$] in the form of hard crystals | **liquid rock** magma, rock that is flowing because the temperature is sufficiently high as to cause melting | **magnetic rocks** stones that are naturally magnetic and will point towards the Earth's magnetic poles, lodestones | **metamorphic rock** existing rock that has been changed as a result of high temperature and high pressure applied over a long period of time | **molten rock** geological material that is so hot that the rock is a viscous liquid and can flow | **non-igneous rock** any rock produced by deposition or changing existing rocks | **pre-existing rocks** the rocks and material that existed in that area before a specific event | **sedimentary rock** rock that has formed as a result of material dropping through a liquid, *eg* chalk from the shells of shell fish, sandstone, clay and salt plains | **softer rocks** material that is able to be scratched by harder rocks | **solid rock** the material will keep its shape and is difficult to break or chip | **tiny rocks** very small pieces of material on the Earth's crust | **type of rock** parts of the Earth's surface that have origins or properties in common | **volcanic rock** material that is now on the surface of the Earth but originated in the mantle | **weathered rock** any rock that has broken off or changed shape as a result of physical weathering (wind, freeze–thaw, moving water), chemical weathering (acid rain) or biological weathering (growing roots, moving animals)

rocket a vehicle in which a jet of hot gases escaping from one end forces the machine forwards, a plant used in salad | **rocket fuel** the chemical that is to burned in the rocket's engines in order to produce the thrust | **water rocket** a lemonade bottle is half filled with water, a valve arrangement allows both air to be pumped in and the valve connection to break so the force of the water pushes the bottle skywards

rockfall a pile of rock near the base of cliffs formed by material being eroded from the rock face

rocky shore the land near the sea is filled with boulders and pebbles

rpc
↓
roo

rod a stick, a rule, a long, thin stick | **rod cells** are found in the retina, at the back of the eye, and are very sensitive to light, but give no information about colour | **glass rod** a cylindrical bar of glass that is used for stirring liquids (the glass is unreactive and will not conduct heat or electricity) | **metal rod** a long, thin object made from material that will conduct electricity and may bend | **steel rod** a thin bar of steel

rode (not road which is a pathway) was on, or riding, a horse or bicycle

rodent a small, furry mammal such as a rat or a mouse, with front teeth that grow continually, and that carry diseases and are pests in houses or farms

roe (not row which is an argument or to move a boat) fish ovaries, containing eggs | **roe deer** the smallest of the deer (approximate height of 75 cm), lives near the edge of woodland

Roemer (Ole Christiansen 1644–1710) made many exceedingly careful measurement of the positions and movement of the moons of Jupiter, and interpreted them as showing that light must travel at approximately 225,000 km / sec – which is almost the value accepted today (300,000 km / sec). He was elected Mayor of Copenhagen in 1705.

role (not roll which is small bread or to tumble) the use of an object, the reason for an object to exist, a part to be played

roll (not role which is an actor's part) a small loaf of bread; to move in a circle

roller a cylinder that reduces friction, which may be used for movement or, in pairs, for squeezing objects | **roller blades** in-line skates with wheels | **garden roller** a heavy cylinder that is used to flatten and compact soil

rolling moving by revolving a wheel or cylinder over the ground | **tongue rolling** the ability to turn the tongue into a U shape, pointing outof the mouth, which is controlled by a single gene

Roman numeral a counting system that uses I (for 1), V (for 5), X (for 10), L (for 50), C (for 100), D (for 500) and M (for 1000)

roof the top part of the house that is exposed to the clouds | **roof insulation** layers of fibre glass or expanded polystyrene that are laid in the loft in order to prevent loss of heat through the roof | **copper roof** the top part of the building is made waterproof by laying sheets of copper, the colour starts off orange but, rapidly turns to green

room space, a box for living in, an area into which organisms can expand | **room temperature (rt)** how hot is that particular area or room |

darkened room a chamber in which the light intensity is just adequate for seeing outlines | mirrored room a room in which many, or all, of the walls and ceiling are covered with mirrors

roost a nest, a resting place; to sleep, to perch

root (not route which is a path, nor rout, which is to defeat) the underground part of a plant which anchors the plant into the ground and absorbs any water, the part of the tooth that is held firmly by bone; to dig around trying to find lost material | root hair a very thin, hair-like, extension from the surface of each strand of the root | root hair cells the long cells with thin membranes through which the root absorbs water | root squash a thin piece of root has been pressed on to a slide for examination under a microscope | root system the structure of the underground part of the plant, the path that the roots take | embryo root the start of the root in the seed | plant roots the parts of a plant that are underground and are used both for absorbing water and minerals and for providing stability

rooted plants organisms that are producers, with chlorophyll in the leaves, and a separate root structure connected to the leaves by vascular tissue

roots the parts of a green plant that are underground, used for anchoring and absorbing water

rope a piece of thick string; to tie together

rose bush a small tree, up to 2 metres tall, that usually has thorns and produces bright flowers

rosette a circle of leaves around a stem

Ross (Sir Ronald 1857–1932) was a perfect candidate for the Anglo-Indian Army Medical Service as he had been born in India and graduated in medicine from London. While serving with the Service in Africa, he decided that mosquitoes must be transmitting malaria (the word means bad air) and so studied them under his microscope – he needed to examine over 100 different species in minute detail before he found that only *Anopheles* could be responsible. He was elected to the Royal Society in 1901, given the Nobel Prize in 1902 and became Director of the Ross Institute in London in 1914. He had a lifelong love of poetry, fiction and mathematics and published in all three, as well as his writings in medicine.

rot to break down, to decompose | dry rot timber decay caused by infection with a fungus

rotate to move around a point, to spin

rotating moving around an axis | freely rotating moving around an axis with very little resistance so the speed is constant

rotation movement around an axis | rotation of the Earth the spinning of the Earth around an axis that is about 22° from a line through the Poles

and will take 24 hours to complete one rotation | rotation period / rotation time the time taken for a body, especially a planet, to turn once around its own axis | axis of rotation a line around which an object seems to rotate | crop rotation putting different types of crop into three or four fields then changing the crop for the next year, so that pests can not build up and nutrients are not lost

rotted has been broken down over time, has become easy to tear

rotten broken down, filled with dead cells and microbes | rotten eggs the contents of the egg have changed chemically so they have the horrible smell of hydrogen sulphide [H_2S]

rotting breaking down, decomposing

rough not smooth, lots of ups and downs | rough paper paper in which the fibres are visible because the surface has not been polished nor covered with a filler | rough pasture grassland that has not been cultivated, but is being used for the grazing of cattle or sheep | rough surface a face or covering that is not smooth and so slows down any movement

roughage material that is taken into the mouth and is egested (given out) at the other end without any change in structure, some roughage is essential for good health

round circular, curved; to turn, to change direction | round-bottom flask / round-bottomed flask / round flask glassware that is spherical, but with a wide glass tube attached at right angles | round worms earth worms, animals without backbones that are long and resemble a tube

rounded curved, without sharp edges | more rounded looking like a sphere, without hard edges

rout (not root which is part of a plant, nor route which is the pathway) a crowd, a noisy group, a fight; to defeat, to send away

route (not root which anchors a plant to the ground, nor rout, which is a defeat) a path taken, a road, a way of getting to a specific destination

routine regular, everyday, the standard method | routine immunisation (UK) / routine immunization (USA) the vaccination that is given at specified ages to every child

routinely the way that a process is always carried out, a regular basis

row (not roe which are fish ovaries) a line, data in a horizontal line, an argument; to use an oar to move a boat | horizontal row the elements in a line running across the periodic table

rt [room temperature] how hot is that particular area or room, normally between 15°C and 25°C

rub to move one surface over another

rubber starts as liquid that drips from a cut in the bark of a rubber tree and then turns solid with elastic properties | rubber band a loop of material that can be stretched by a force then returns to its original shape when the force is removed | rubber bung a slightly flexible stopper for a bottle | rubber sheet a thin covering or film made from a very flexible material | rubber tube / rubber tubing lengths of flexible rubber with a circular cross-section and a hole down the middle

rubbing moving one surface over another

rubbish material that is of no further use

rubella German measles, a disease that is caused by a virus and has little permanent affect on children or adults, but may cause damage to a foetus, so women are vaccinated | rubella vaccine the liquid that is injected in order to help the body to reject any infection by the rubella virus – usually given only to young women

rubidium Rb proton number 37, a group 1, or alkali metal, that is more reactive than potassium and so is not safe to be kept in a school laboratory

ruby a precious stone that is coloured deep crimson to red

rudder a wooden board hung over the stern that can be used to steer a boat

rudimentary undeveloped, a stunted form

rule a length of wood, plastic or steel that can be used to draw straight lines or to measure their length, a law or directive; to tell people what to do, to draw a line | displacement rule a more reactive metal will displace a less reactive metal from a salt in solution, a more reactive halogen will push out a less reactive halogen | meter rule (USA) / metre rule (UK) a stick or bar that is 1 metre long and is often calibrated into milli-metres and centimetres | two-second rule the recommendation of the Highway Code that you should be at least a two second gap between the car in front passing a point and your car reaching the same point NB it takes about two seconds to say "only a fool breaks the two-second rule"

ruler a person who tells the rest of a country how to behave, a king, a leader, a measuring stick with straight edges | meter ruler (USA) /metre ruler (UK) a cuboid piece of wood that is exactly one metre long and divided into millimetres and centimetres

rum an alcoholic drink made by fermentation of sugar solution followed by distillation

run an experiment, a continuous series; to move rapidly | run-off to remove water from the land into a stream without absorption occurring | trial run the initial experiment that leads some variables to be defined more precisely

runner a person who travels rapidly using two legs, a shoot from a strawberry plant that produces roots and a new plant when it touches the ground | marathon runner a person who takes place in races covering a distance of 42,195 metres (26.2 miles)

running moving fast, operating, working | running costs the amount of money that is needed in order to sustain the specified activity | running water drinking water that can be obtained by the turn of a tap, water that is flowing downhill

runny easily poured, a liquid with a low viscosity | runny nose a symptom of an infection in which lots of mucus is produced from the nose

runway a flat piece of ground sufficiently long for 'planes to land, a plank

rupture a tear, a split; to split open

rural in the country, away from urban areas

rush a sudden surge; to move rapidly | Gold Rush any of the several times between 1849 and 1896 when vast numbers of people settled in a small area where gold (and so a financial fortune) was thought to be lying in rivers and underground

rust hydrated iron oxide [$Fe_2O_3.nH_2O$ where n varies] formed by the reaction of oxygen with damp iron (the reaction is much faster if salt is present), a fungus that attacks wheat

rusting the changes that occur in the chemical and physical properties as iron [Fe] turns to iron oxide [Fe_2O_3]

rusty appearance, red and powdery, of iron that has oxidised to rust

Rutherford (Daniel 1749–1819) studied medicine under Black at Edinburgh. In 1772, he carried out experiments similar to those done by Priestley on oxygen, then he isolated nitrogen at almost the same time as Scheele. He became Keeper of the Edinburgh Royal Botanic Garden in 1786

Rutherford (Sir Ernest 1871–1937) was born and educated in New Zealand, he developed a radio-wave detector in 1893 – only six years after Hertz had discovered the waves. He moved to Cambridge, then to Montreal, where his leadership led to the discovery that there are three types of radio-activity. He returned to England, showed that every atom must have a tiny nucleus with a positive charge and was awarded the Nobel prize. After the Great War, Rutherford moved back to Cambridge and found that some nuclei could be caused to break apart, this discovery allowed other workers to produce nuclear reactors and nuclear bombs

rutile an ore of titanium

S sulfur / sulphur, proton number 16, a yellow powder

s / second the unit of time (there are 60 seconds in a minute)

s distance moved

(s) (solid) the state of the chemical is a solid

sac (not a sack which is any bag) cells arranged so as to form a bag in an organism | air sac an alveolus, the tiny endings of the bronchioles of the lungs | amniotic sac a bag formed in the womb, in which the foetus develops | scrotal sac the scrotum, the bag of skin that encloses the testes

sack (a pouch in an animal or plant is a sac) a large, oblong bag

sacrificial metal a block of reactive metal that will corrode and then be easily replaced, thereby preventing the corrosion of a structure made from a less-reactive metal

saddle the seat of a bicycle, a leather seat used for riding a horse, an area near the front of an earthworm

safe will not cause harm, no hazard is anticipated | safe disposal getting rid of material in a way that will cause no damage to the environment | safe dose the quantity of a substance that can be taken each day without causing ill effects | safe flame a highly visible, yellow flame produced by closing the air hole of a bunsen burner | safe method an experiment or procedure that is without any hazard | safe operation using equipment in a way that makes accidents and damage unlikely | safe procedure / safe technique a method that can be used and is not likely to cause harm or damage | safe sex having intercourse while using a condom | safe test a method of identifying chemicals that is unlikely to lead to damage | safe working carrying out a procedure in a thoughtful way so that accidents are unlikely to happen

safely without causing any danger | work safely / working safely the behaviour is thoughtful and does not lead to hazards

safety avoiding damage, ensuring that accidents should not occur | safety clothing garments that prevent the results of accidents causing damage to the person | safety features the characteristics that reduce the chances of an accident occurring, the components that reduce the damage from an accident | safety goggles eye protectors | safety mat a layer of material that prevents damage to the surface | safety precautions taking steps that will reduce the damage if an accident should occur | safety procedures carrying out an experiment in such a way that hazards are reduced | safety regulations the rules that outline the steps that should be taken in order to prevent accidents | safety screen a clear shield that is placed between the experiment and other people | safety valve equipment that opens when the pressure exceeds a given value so that gases can escape and the pressure be reduced | food safety the rules that should be followed in order to ensure that food is not contaminated by undesirable microbes | road safety behaving in such a way that you, and other travellers, can arrive safely

sag to sink in the middle, to bend

Sahara / Sahara Desert the largest area of hot, arid land in the world with an area of 7.7 million square kilometres, covering most of North Africa, contains areas of drift sand, rock and pebbles and has a climate so dry that very little will grow or survive

sail (not sale which is exchanging goods for money) a large sheet that is used to allow the wind to change the speed of a boat; to travel in a boat

sailor a member of the crew who helps the safe movement of ships

salad a mixture based on uncooked vegetables, especially lettuce, tomato and cucumber

salary the amount of money paid each month for the work that has been done in accordance with an agreed contract

sale (not sail which is part of a boat) an exchange of goods for money | jumble sale an event where people give what they consider to be useless items, which other people are prepared to buy

salicin the name for the drug that was extracted from willow trees and helped relieve headaches, now known as acetylsalicylic acid or aspirin

saline any solution of sodium chloride [NaCl] in water | saline drip the sterile fluid, that is mainly a dilute sodium chloride solution, that medics flow into the patient's vein in order to replace lost body fluids

salinity a measure of the concentration of sodium chloride [NaCl] in a solution

saliva the liquid produced in the mouth to help movement of food and also contains amylase, an enzyme that breaks down starch

salivary glands small sacs in the lower jaw that produce the water in your mouth

Salk (Jonas Edward 1914 –1995) born and educated in the USA, he started work on the influenza virus in 1942 (influenza had killed several million after the Great War). In 1953, Salk developed an inactivated virus to be used as a vaccine against poliomyelitis (this disease should be eradicated by 2010). He founded the Salk Institute, in California, in 1975.

Salmonella / *Salmonella* **bacterium** a type of microbe that causes food poisoning

salol (phenyl salycylate) a chemical that is stable and has a melting point of 42°C

salon a shop, a hairdressers, a reception room

salt any compound formed by replacing the hydrogen of an acid with a metal, *eg* sodium chloride [NaCl] | salt crystals the shiny white cubes produced by evaporating the water from a solution of sodium chloride | saltpeter (USA) / saltpetre (UK) potassium nitrate, [KNO₃], nitre, an ore of potassium that was mixed with charcoal and sulphur to produce the first types of gunpowder, and is now used as a very soluble fertiliser | salt solution a mixture of sodium chloride [NaCl] dissolved in water, any salt dissolved in water | salt water saline, a solution of sodium chloride [NaCl] in water | bath salts a mixture of different crystals with soaps and scents | chloride salts the group of chemicals in which a metal is bonded to a chloride ion | colored salt (USA) / coloured salt (UK) the crystal and the solution of the salt in water are coloured, a characteristic of the transition metals, *eg* copper sulphate is bright blue | common salt [NaCl] sodium chloride, the white residue that is left when water is evaporated from sea water | dissolved salts the chemicals have been dissolved in water | Epsom salts magnesium sulphate [MgSO4], originally prepared from a mineral spring in Epsom, Surrey | metal salt any salt, but emphasising that the first chemical is always a metal | preparing a salt carrying out a chemical reaction in which a salt is produced | pure salt the crystals contain sodium and chloride ions only | rock salt material in which crystals of sodium chloride are mixed with sand and soil | table salt the finely ground sodium chloride [NaCl] that is used to flavour food

salted food that has been preserved by storing in salt

Salter's ducks / **nodding ducks** equipment for using the energy from waves to produce electricity, developed by Professor Stephen Salter (born 1938) in 1976 but dismissed by a biased report in 1980

saltpeter (USA) / **saltpetre** (UK) [KNO₃] potassium nitrate, nitre, an ore of potassium that was mixed with charcoal and sulphur to produce the first types of gunpowder, but is now used as a very soluble fertiliser

salty tasting similar to sodium chloride | salty water brine, sea water, water containing lots of sodium chloride [NaCl]

same identical, exactly alike, not different

sample small part that should be representative of the whole, a low number; to take a small amount | sample data the information obtained from a small number that should be capable of extrapolation to the whole population | sample population the number of that organism that is taken for further study | sample size the number of objects or organisms in the small part that is taken | appropriate sample taking a suitable number that can be shown to be representative of the total | food sample a small quantity of the meal has been taken for examination | fresh samples small amounts that have been taken directly from the bulk material | kick sample the number and types of organisms obtained by disturbing the river bed by kicking into the sediment | original sample the small part that was taken before carrying out any changes to the members | quadrat sample the species and population in the small part of the field that lies within a square that measures 0.5 metres on each side | random sample a small quantity that should be representative of the whole material | rock sample a piece of the Earth's crust that has been removed for further study | small sample the number or weight is low in comparison to the size of the population | weighing sample the weight of part of the sample is measured

sample size the number of members or the volume or the mass in a small part taken from the whole | appropriate sample size the number of members in the sample is just right for that purpose | sufficient sample size the amount taken was adequate to be representative of the whole batch

sampling taking small amounts | sampling method the means by which the small amount is taken so as to be representative of the whole | sampling populations taking a small number of individuals in order to examine in detail | sampling technique the means by which the small amount is taken so as to be representative of the whole | quadrat sampling throwing a square wire grid, usually with sides of 0.5 metres, to find a random area to examine in detail | random sampling taking small parts from different parts of the whole at undefined times

sanctuary a place of safety | bird sanctuary an area where the environment is managed in order to encourage birds to live and breed | wild-life sanctuary an area where people are not allowed to interfere with the lives of the animals

sand giant molecular structures made from millions of units of silicon dioxide [SiO₂] covalently bonded together using single bonds | sand bar a ridge of sand, that may be above water at high tide, but there is always sea water between the ridge and the land | sand-blasting removing a surface layer by aiming a jet of fast air containing sand crystals | sand dunes banks, mounds or ridges of loose sand | sand eel a fish that is long and thin, like a snake, and lives in the sand | sand grains the tiny individual pieces of sand | sand-paper flexible sheets, with a layer of sand or glass glued firmly to one side, that are used for smoothing surfaces | sandstone a sedimentary rock made from grains of sand cemented together by silica or limestone | sandwich food made from two layers of bread surrounding a filling | damp sand just sufficient water is present in the sand to allow the grains to be held together | grains of sand the individual pieces of sand | tar-sand sedimentary rock containing hydrocarbons with high melting points | wet sand a mixture of sand and water from which the water can be extracted

sandstone a sedimentary rock made from grains of sand cemented together by silica or limestone

sandwich food made from two layers of bread surrounding a filling

sank fell through the water in an uncontrolled manner

Sankey diagram arrows that show the flow of energy through a system

Santorio (Santorius1561–1636) an Italian who became medical advisor to the King of Poland for 14 years. He returned to the Italian city of Padua, where he probably became a friend of Galileo, because his medical research included measuring the pulse rate, and inventing a clinical thermometer. He tried to apply Galileo's method of always measuring and experimenting in order to examine diet and disease in animals

sap liquid containing sugar that is produced by plants; to diminish | cell sap the liquid that is found in the cytoplasm of a cell

sapr- (*Greek* rotten)

SARS [severe acute respiratory syndrome] an emerging disease similar to 'flu'

satellite any object that is in orbit (*i.e.* following a closed path such as a circle, oval or ellipse) around a larger body | satellite dish a reflecting structure in the shape of a parabola that is used for collecting weak radio signals from a wide area | satellite motion the path taken by the satellite as it orbits around a larger body | satellite pictures photographs obtained from a camera in space | satellite probes equipment that is launched into space in order to observe and to transmit information, but is not meant to return

to Earth | satellite TV television information that was received from a satellite in geo-stationary orbit | artificial satellite any object in orbit that was put in place by a rocket | communications satellite a satellite containing equipment specifically to allow people to transfer information to other parts of the world | geo-stationary satellite / geosynchronous satellite an object that is orbiting the Earth at such a height (39,000 kilometres) that the orbital period matches the rotation period of the Earth | natural satellite any object in orbit that does not depend on the intervention of people, *eg* planets, moons | spy satellite a satellite that is trying to discover facts about a country and its people that the government of that country would prefer not to be known | weather satellite equipment in orbit around the Earth, which measures the temperature, air pressure, moisture and the directions of wind and sea currents

saturated a fluid that already contains so much solute that it is unable to dissolve any more of that chemical | saturated fat the bonds of the fatty acid are all single, animal fat | saturated salt solution a mixture of water and sodium chloride [NaCl] in which no more of the salt will dissolve at that temperature | saturated solution a mixture of a solvent and a solute in which no more solute will dissolve at that temperature

saturation – drying cycle production of layers of sedimentary rock by material dissolving in water and the water evaporating so the dissolved material falls out of solution

Saturn the sixth planet form the Sun, a gas giant with rings and a dozen large moons, named after one of the sons of Uranus

sauce (not source which is an origin) a liquid used to flavour food

saucepan a cooking implement | saucepan base the metal at the bottom of the pan through which heat is conducted | saucepan lid a cover for a pan that prevents evaporation

saucer a flattened dish

saw (not sore which is damaged skin) past participle of 'to see', a ribbon with teeth along one edge that is used for cutting material

sawn cut using a saw

scab the solid plug protecting a wound, formed by dried blood

scaffold to provide support, to build a framework

scaffolding an open structure of tubes that are joined together so builders can work safely

scalar a measurement that has size only (a vector also has direction)

scald damage to tissue caused by very hot liquid; to damage skin by spilling very hot water, to place items into boiling water for a short period

scalding hot enough to cause damage to skin

scale one of many tiny plates that cover the surface of fish, a characteristic of fish, a balance for measuring weights, a method of comparing sizes; to climb | scale bud a plate-like growth that will develop into a shoot or root | scale diagram / scale drawing a simple picture that shows all the components in the correct proportions | scale division one of several marks that divides a length into pieces of identical size | scale factor the ratio that is used to allow several objects to be drawn to the same scale | scale leaf a small dry or hard leaf | scale model an artificial model of an item in which the size of all components are in the same ratio as in the real article | scale of operation the size of the experiment | scale-up to make larger, to increase greatly the amount of reactant and product | analog scale (USA) / analogue scale (UK) a continuous line divided into sections and crossed by a pointer | appropriate scale suitable size | arbitrary scale there is no valid scientific reason why the scale should have the fixed points or range that are being used | bathroom scales equipment for measuring the weight of a person | Celsius scale / centigrade scale a line showing hotness that has fixed points at 0°C, the temperature of melting ice, and 100°C, the temperature of the steam above boiling water | continuous scale a measure of size that may take any value, an analogue scale | decibel scale the agreed series of steps that allow the loudness of a sound to be compared by different people | Fahrenheit scale the temperature line developed by Fahrenheit in which 0°F is the lowest temperature of an ice–salt mix and 100°F is the temperature of the human body | fish scales thin plates that cover the outside of fish | graph scales the choice of range and division of the lengths of each axis | kelvin scale a measure of temperature that has the same divisions as the Celsius scale, but the start is an absolute zero of 0K with the freezing point of ice at 273.2K and the boiling point of water at 373.2K | large-scale big compared to the usual size of operation | pH scale a method for showing the concentration of hydrogen ions, *ie* the amount of acid or alkali in a solution, which has a range of pH 1 to pH 14 | small-scale the mass of material is low in comparison with the usual process | spring scales equipment for measuring weight, which depends on calibrating the extension of a coil or spring | temperature scale any method

for comparing hotness | time-scale duration, length of time given to a task | weighing scales equipment for measuring the weight of an object | zero a scale to move a pointer to the zero mark at the start of a measurement

scaling-down making smaller while keeping the proportions the same

scaling-up making larger but keeping the proportions identical

scalpel a sharp knife used for cutting into bodies

scaly having the appearance of being covered in scales, feeling like a layer of overlapping tiles

scan the picture produced using magnetic imaging; to skim, to examine | ultrasonic scan / ultrasound scan a non-invasive method of investigating the inside of a body, or a pipe, by examining the reflection of sound that has a frequency above the range of human hearing

scanning searching for a particular piece of information, looking for details in the wider picture | pre-natal scanning ante-natal screening, examining the uterus, placenta and foetus by analysing the echoes of an ultra-sound beam

scapula the shoulder blade, a pair of flat bones giving structure to the shoulders

scar a mark left after a wound has healed; to make a permanent mark on the skin

scarce rare, uncommon, not many, in short supply

scared (not scarred which is marked) frightened, panicked, alarmed, in great fear

scarred (not scared which is frightened) marked by a cut or by a burn, damage to the skin

scatter to spread, to throw, to disperse | scatter graph a diagram with axes and each point is shown as a cross, a method of presenting information that was developed by Descartes

scattered spread, dispersed | scattered light the single beam has been reflected in all directions

scattering spreading, distributing | light scattering reflecting light in all directions | seed scattering spreading the seeds over a wide area

scavenger an animal that eats all the dead bits left by other creatures

scene (not seen which is the past of to see) an act, a setting, a part of a drama

scenery parts and screens used on stage so as to give the illusion of a place suitable for the story, the view, the landscape

scent (not sent which is posted) the smell, the odour, the perfume; to smell a chemical, to pick up the trail | scent gland the group of cells that release a chemical into the air with the intention of announcing your presence to other members of the same species | scent particles the molecules that evaporate from the liquid and cause reaction in the smell cells of the nose

Scheele (Karl Wilhelm 1742–1786) was born in Germany and moved to Sweden, when he was 14, to become a trainee pharmacist. He gained a reputation as an outstanding experimental chemist, publishing his only book, in 1777, describing the properties of oxygen (which he had isolated two years prior to Priestley) and nitrogen (isolated at the same time as Rutherford). He also discovered chlorine, thirty years before Davy and described the effects of light on silver salts.

scheme a plan, a representative diagram, an idea, a programme; to put a plan together

schist a metamorphic rock containing layers of minerals

Schleiden (Jakob Mathias 1804–1881) studied and practised law in his native Germany before turning to botany. In 1838, he proposed that all plant structures were made from cells, an idea that led his friend Schwann to suggest that all life is composed of cells.

school a building in which learning and teaching occurs, a group of people with common aims, collective name for a group of fish; to teach, to discipline | school grounds the fields belonging to a school | school laboratory a room suitable for lots of people that is equipped with gas taps, sinks and, possibly a fume cupboard, that allows lessons to be learned by practical means

Schwann (Theodor 1810–1882) graduated in medicine from Berlin then spent the most productive four years of his life. He was the first to isolate an enzyme from an animal (other enzymes had been obtained from yeast). Schwann's major impact was showing that every animal must be made from simple cells – an idea that is still taught and used today. Before he was 30, and a decade before Pasteur, Schwann had shown that fermentation could occur only if microbes were present. This work led to such vicious attacks that Schwann emigrated to Belgium and did no more work in science.

science a volume of knowledge concerning the world and ourselves | science fiction stories that are set in the future, a tale containing one idea that is currently considered to be impossible | science of hearing studying how organisms are able to detect the vibrations of sound and then to make sense of the many frequencies | areas of science fields of knowledge, division of learning into the disciplines of physics, biology, chemistry, astronomy, geology | environmental science studying the way in which creatures are affected by the habitat and local weather conditions | food science the investigation of the changes that occur when food is prepared, cooked and stored | forensic science using equipment and knowledge to find clues about a crime and then interpret their importance in solving the crime | language of science the special and specific words that allow people to describe and explain their experiments

scientific investigating phenomena that can be measured, carrying out experiments to compare the results with a control procedure | scientific advances increases in our knowledge about the way that the world functions | scientific classification dividing objects into sets on the basis of observable features | scientific conclusion the theory is based on logical analysis of experimental information, which allows predictions to be made | scientific developments changes in the knowledge and equipment leading to shifts in interpretation | scientific enquiry asking question that can be answered by the results of simple experiments | scientific explanation a description that explains the current observations in agreement with previous knowledge and suggests further experiments | scientific ideas theories or hypotheses that are able to explain many different observations | scientific information observations, measurements and theories that are supported by reliable and repeatable experiments | scientific investigation solving a problem by considering different ideas then carrying out simple experiments which allow each idea to be tested | scientific issue a problem that can be solved by suitable questions, observations and measurements | scientific knowledge having some learning and understanding concerning the theories, hypotheses, observations and measurements of other scientists | scientific language the words, phrases, terms and equations that are used as a shorthand between scientists | scientific name the word that has been accepted by scientists as giving a single meaning or item | scientific questions problems that can be asked in a simple way and solved by observing variables that can be measured | scientific terminology / scientific terms the words that are used as a shorthand and are understood by others in the same area of science | scientific theory a simple idea that is able to explain many sets of observations and predict the outcome of further experiments | scientific understanding being aware of the evidence that can be measured correctly and how these measurements can be integrated with previous knowledge | **scientific vocabulary** the specialised words that are used by scientists

scientist a person who is trying to find out about the world and try to explain everything in it | **environmental scientist** a person who tries to find how the habitat and the weather conditions affect all the creatures and plants living in an area | **food scientist** a person who studies the effects of different foods or the methods for preparing and storing food | **materials scientist** a person who studies the uses and properties of useful substances

sci-fi science fiction writing, a fictional story in which there is at least one scientifically impossible event

scissors equipment for cutting paper or string

scoop a spoon with a short handle; to pick up rapidly, to use a short spoon, to empty by hand

-scope (*Greek* a watcher)

'scope / cathode ray oscilloscope / CRO equipment with a small screen that shows a spot moving in response to the electrical signals that are put into the instrument

scrap a small part, something that is no longer needed; to throw away | **scrap iron** objects made from iron that were useful but now need melting back into liquid iron before using in a new form | **scrap-yard** a business that separates the metals in old cars for recycling

scrape a gash, a loss of an outer layer; to remove the very outer layer

scrapings shavings, gratings, thin layers | **potato scrapings** thin layers taken from a the storage organ of the potato plant

scratch (plural is scratches) a long, thin, shallow cut; to produce a long shallow cut, to ease an itch

scree rock fragments that gather on the sides of hills and the bottom of mountains | **scree slope** a hillside covered with loose plates of rock

screen a barrier, a partition, a flat surface used for showing an image; to cover; to check for the presence of a specified marker | **filter screen** a mesh that prevents large material entering the tunnels that carry water | **on-screen** information that is shown on a monitor | **oscilloscope screen** the circle of glass in which the signal shows as a moving dot or a line | **safety screen** a transparent barrier that is placed between the experiment and the person | **Stevenson screen** the slotted panel on the front of a weather station

screw a cylinder or cone with a helical thread on the outside; to join objects using screws | **screwdriver** equipment for turning a screw

script writing, a written conversation, a completed examination paper; to write a play | **subscript** numbers or writing below the main writing line | **superscript** letters and numbers above the main writing

scrotal sac the scrotum, the bag of skin that encloses the testes

scrotum the sac containing the testes

scrubber a porous solid or a liquid which is used to remove undesirable material from a gas

scum a foam of rubbish that rises to the top of a liquid

scurvy a disease in which loss of teeth is accompanied by total tiredness and then death, caused by vitamin C deficiency

scythe a long, curved blade at the end of a handle that is used to cut grass; to cut down large numbers

sea (not see which is to look) an ocean, vast volumes of water containing approximately 40 grams of dissolved salts per litre of liquid | **sea anemone** a group of cylindrical marine animals that anchor one end of the body to a rock and have a mouth at the other end | **seabed** the landscape that is at the bottom of the sea | **sea creatures** the animals that live in the salty oceans | **sea level** the starting position for measuring heights of land, an average of the height of the sea at high tide and at low tide | **sea shells** the remains of the external skeleton of shellfish | **sea shore** the area where the ocean meets the land, which may be dry or wet, depending on the height of the tide | **sea water** the water containing salts and dissolved solids (average of 4% sodium chloride [NaCl]) that covers two-thirds of the Earth's surface | **sea wave** the regular up and down movement of the sea's surface caused by the wind | **seaweed** marine algae, producers that live in the salty waters of the oceans | **sea worms** invertebrate animals that have long, cylindrical bodies and live on the sea bed | **Dead Sea** a lake of water to the east of the Mediterranean that has a high concentration of salt (370 grams per litre) | **Red Sea** the long, thin extension of the Indian Ocean that separates Asia from Africa (the sea is not red, but a common, local seaweed is that colour)

seal a mammal that lives in the sea, a closure, a stamp; to close tight | **crabeater seal** a marine mammal that is found in the Southern Hemisphere and lives mainly by filter feeding on krill (despite its name) | **leopard seal** a marine mammal that lives in the Antarctic and feeds mainly on penguins

sealed closed, fastened | **sealed container** a box or canister that is closed and is difficult to open

sealing (not ceiling which is a roof) closing so the item is air-tight, gluing

seam (not seem which is to appear as) a junction, a layer | coal seam a layer of rock that is principally coal

search an organised party with the aim of finding something or someone; to seek, to look for a specified object, to try to find | data search looking through a collection of information in order to find a particular item

searching looking, trying to find

season a period of the year that is characterised by particular weather conditions | growing season the time between the sowing of the seed and the picking of the crop

seasonal an event that happens at certain times of the year only | seasonal changes differences in appearance, growth or temperature that always occur at a known time of the year | seasonal nature something that will occur only at one time of the year, a combination of temperatures, rainfall and day length that forces an event | seasonal variation changes that occur to a feature, *eg* coat colour, because of the time of year

sebaceous gland a group of cells at the base of the hair follicle that produces a grease

sebum the grease that is produced by some cells in the hair follicle

sec / s shortened form of second, a period of time

second a short period of time, arriving after the first | light-second the distance that light travels in one second in a vacuum, approximately 300,000 kilometres | meters per second (USA) / metres per second (UK) (mps, m/s) the measure of speed, which is used in science

secondary following on, arising as a result of other events | secondary colors (USA) / secondary colours (UK) the three colours produced by mixing pairs of the primary colours, CMY, *ie* cyan from green and blue, magenta from red and blue, yellow from red and green | secondary consumer an animal that eats the primary consumer | secondary data information that was obtained from other people or from a published source | secondary sex characteristics / secondary sexual characteristics the features that are associated with sexual maturity, but are not essential for reproduction, *eg* breasts in women | secondary source using information from a book or the internet | secondary wave the transverse wave that results from an earthquake and moves slowly through the Earth

second-hand data information that has been obtained from other people

secrete to produce a fluid

secreted produced, given out, hidden away

secretion a liquid produced by a cell or tissue

section a segment, a part, a cut; to cut into parts | control section the component that co-ordinates the activities of other parts | cross-section the picture produced when an object is cut across without any of the internal parts changing shape or position | geological section a diagram showing a cross-section of the crust between specified points, and including the identity of the different strata | transverse section making a cut at right angles to the longest axis

sectioned cut across, cut into slices, placed apart

sediment a layer at the bottom, the mud, a deposit; to fall, to settle | sediment grains small fragments of rock, rock particles that have become cemented into other rocks | layers of sediment strata, well defined sheets of rock | movement of sediment a change in the position of the layer of mud and silt that has been dropped by a slow-moving river

sedimentary concerned with falling through a fluid, deposited | sedimentary layers sheets of rock that lie on top of each other, but are easily distinguished | sedimentary rocks geological features that have been produced either by material being transported by wind or rivers then falling out of the fluid, *eg* sand, or by shellfish dying and forming vast layers of chalk at the bottom of the sea | sedimentary strata visible layers of rock that were produced by material falling from air or water

sedimentation the occurrence of fragments falling

Sedna an object made from rock and ice that is smaller than the Moon and is orbiting the Sun at a distance of 9000 million kilometres, the first of many objects that were discovered from 2004 onwards, each of which is larger than our Moon and moves around the Sun in an elliptical orbit at a vast distance from the Sun and at an angle to the solar plane

see (not sea which is a vast volume of salty water) to observe, to use the eyes to detect difference in colour and light intensity, to notice

seed a food store surrounding a fertilised egg from a plant, an item that will germinate to produce a plant; to provide small amounts | seed-bearing producing seeds | seed coat the thin outer layer of a mature seed | seed dispersal scattering of seeds by wind, water or animals | seed formation production of a seed after fertilisation of the ovum by a nucleus from pollen | seed pod the long, thin container in which the seeds of a leguminous plant develop | seed-producing plant any plant that reproduces by forming an embryo surrounded by a food store and a protective coat |

seed scattering throwing seeds from the flower, dispersing seeds | **seed trays** boxes which can filled with suitable soil so the seeds can germinate in the best conditions | **germinating seeds** the changes that occur when a dormant seed starts to produce a shoot and a root

seeding planting of seeds | **cloud seeding** spraying a chemical into clouds in order to encourage the falling of rain

seedless the fruit have not been fertilised, so no seeds can be produced | **seedless grape** the fruit from a vine with flowers that have not been fertilised

seedling the plant that forms after germination begins, but before the appearance of true leaves | **grass seedlings** the grass seeds have produced the shoot and roots

seeing looking at, making a connection, understanding, observing, noticing

seek to look for an object, to try to find, to search

seeking looking for, trying to find, searching | **north-seeking** turning in the direction of the North Pole | **south-seeking** rotating so as to try to point in the direction of the South Pole

seem (not seam which is a layer) to appear to be

seen (not scene which is an act) visible, conspicuous | **easily seen** obvious, stands out

seeps slow movement of a liquid through tiny holes in a solid

see-saw a plank that is pivoted in the middle and allows people to sit at each end in order to move up and down

segment a portion, a section; to cut into sections

segmented divided into several parts of similar size | **segmented body** the part of the animal containing lungs and gut looks to be divided into rings | **segmented worm** an invertebrate animal with a long body that is divided into distinct circles or segments

seismic concerned with movements within the Earth, earthquake | **seismic shock** sudden, unexpected movements of the ground | **seismic survey** a study of the distribution of underground rocks by listening to the echoes of controlled explosions | **seismic wave** the propagation or movement of a vibration through the Earth

seismograph the line that shows the movement of the Earth's crust as detected by a seismometer

seismology the study of earthquakes, which leads to an understanding of the structure of the Earth, geology

seismometer equipment for detecting then recording the movement of the crust of the Earth

select the choice, the best; to choose, to pick out | select characteristics to use selective breeding to develop organisms that have the specified characteristics | select information to choose the data, to pick out knowledge

selected preferred, chosen | **selected sources** the information or materials were chosen from a larger group | **selected strains** the type of named organism was chosen

selection the choosing, the mixture | **artificial selection** choosing to breed only from animals or plants that have the characteristics that you think are desirable | **natural selection** the organisms that survived were those best suited to the local environment and conditions

selective careful, particular, notable | **selective breeding** choosing the parents with the desired features in the hope that the offspring will have improved characteristics | **selective pollination** using a paintbrush to move the pollen between selected flowers | **selective weed-killers** chemicals that will kill some weeds, but allow other plants to grow

selectively permeable the material will allow certain molecules to pass through, but will prevent the movement of others, often the material is permeable to small molecules, but will not allow large molecules to pass through

self-discipline the ability to control your own moods and application to work

self-fertilisation (UK) / **self-fertilization** (USA) the male and female gametes are supplied by the same parent

self-pollination the pollen is moved from the stamen to the stigma of the same flower

sell (not cell which is a source of electricity or the building block of living organisms) to exchange goods for money | **sell by the date** by which the shop should have sold the goods

semen the liquid that contains sperm and is ejaculated from the penis

semi- (*Latin* half)

semi-circle half a circle

semi-circular in the shape of a half circle | **semi-circular block** a piece of flat material that has been cut to the shape of a half circle | **semi-circular canals** the three tubes in each ear that are responsible for sensing the position and movement of the head | **semi-circular lens** a length of transparent material of which one side is flat and the other is a half circle

semi-conductor material that will allow a current to flow under certain circumstances

semi-digested food that has been broken into smaller pieces, but is not sufficiently small to be absorbed

semi-lunar valve the flaps of material between each ventricle and the respective artery that prevents the blood from flowing back into the heart

sensation a feeling, a perception | burning sensation feeling as though your skin is on fire

sense an organ for detecting some stimulus; to detect, to notice a change | sense organs the parts of the body that respond to information from the world around us, *eg* nose (smell), eyes (sight), ears (sound and balance), tongue (taste), skin (touch and temperature) | make sense to find a pattern, to relate to previous knowledge

sensible safe, following good practice

sensing detecting, feeling, measuring, being aware | remote sensing detecting information from a long distance away, especially using satellites in orbit to detect what is happening on the Earth

sensitise (UK) / **sensitize** (USA) to increase the response, which is mild with the first stimulus and becomes faster and stronger upon further challenge

sensitive able to respond to a stimulus, painful, tender | environmentally sensitive a bad reaction, *eg* death or lack of growth, caused by a slight change in local conditions | highly sensitive a very slight change will cause a reaction | light-sensitive / photo-sensitive the object will react to the presence of light

sensitively with a thought for the reaction of other people

sensitivity some measure of the lowest level of stimulus that will cause a response | caffeine sensitivity the cell or organ will respond to a low concentration of caffeine | hearing sensitivity the minimum power that is necessary at each frequency in order to provoke a response in the ear

sensitize (USA) / **sensitise** (UK) to increase the response, which is mild with the first stimulus and becomes faster and stronger upon further challenge

sensor probe for detecting a specified stimulus | sensor recording an electronic recording of the information provided by the probe | environmental sensors probes that will measure the strength or concentration of many of the factors that define an environment, *eg* pH, humidity, temperature | heat sensor a temperature probe that responds to the heat radiating from a surface, equipment used to detect temperature | light sensor equipment that will measure the light intensity, equipment that will change state when the light intensity reaches a specified limit | moisture sensor a probe that is able to respond to the presence of small amounts of water | pain sensor a nerve cell that is sensitive to pain | pH sensor a hollow glass rod that changes an electrical property dependent on the pH of the solution | sound sensor equipment for measuring the intensity of sound at a specified frequency | temperature sensor a probe for measuring the temperature of an item or place

sensory concerned with obtaining information and deciding a reaction | sensory nerve / sensory neuron the long cell joining the receptor to the spinal cord and then to the brain | sensory receptor a cell that sends a signal to the brain if a specific event is detected

sent (not scent which is a smell) posted, despatched

sentence a set of words that make sense, a time to be spent in prison as a punishment

sepal the sheet of dead cells at the base of the flower that were originally used to cover the bud

separate independent, distinct, detached; to move apart, to disconnect

separated moved apart, isolated, removed from a mixture

separating dividing into distinct parts | separating funnel a glass cylinder with a stop-cock at the bottom

separation a cut, a division | separation of air using very low temperatures to isolate oxygen, nitrogen, carbon dioxide and the noble gases | separation methods procedures that can be used to isolate specific chemicals from a mixture | separation plant the industrial buildings that are used to isolate large quantities of pure chemicals from mixtures such as oil or air | separation process the method used to isolate pure components from a mixture | separation techniques procedures that can be used to isolate specific chemicals from a mixture

septic a localised collection of dead white blood cells in response to an infection

sequence order, a succession of episodes, a set of successive events, a series of similar chemicals joined together, eg DNA or protein, to put in order | sequence of cell division the order of the changes that occur when a cell divides to form two daughter cells | sequence of diagrams a series of drawings | sequence of events the actions shown in the order in which they occurred | animated sequence a series of similar pictures that give the impression of movement when run through rapidly in order | appropriate sequence arranging the events into the best possible order | base sequence the exact order the building blocks (the bases adenine, cytosine, guanine and thymine) are found in a strand of DNA |

correct sequence the order of events that is known to lead to success | gene sequence the order of the bases in the DNA | regular sequence a pattern of events that is repeated | rock sequence the different layers of rock are named in sequence, either going across the land or forming a vertical section | time-lapse sequence taking a series of photographs of an event at long intervals, so the playback can be much more rapid

series a sequence, a set of successive numbers, a set | series circuit the components occur one after another, the same current flows through all components | activity series a list of metals in the order of the speed with which they react | electrochemical series the metals arranged in the order that they are discharged at the cathode | in series the electrical components occur one after another | reactivity series the metals arranged in the order of the rate at which they react

serum the liquid part left after blood has had the cells removed by sedimentation and then allowed to clot (plasma is similar to serum but the clotting factors have not been removed)

Servetus (Miguel 1511–1553) debated on the nature of God. Servetus was a strong believer in astrology, his views on religion led to his exile to France, where he studied medicine and became a country doctor – including working in Lyon while the plague was raging. His major breakthrough in science was the explanation for the circulation of the blood through the heart, published in his book *The Restoration of Christianity*. He could not prevent himself becoming embroiled in further religious arguments, which were silenced when he was burned at the stake in 1553.

service a support system; to maintain | emergency services the skilled people who help others in a crisis (ambulance / fire / police / mountain rescue / cave rescue / lifeboat) | health services systems for providing the public with the individuals and buildings that can help to monitor public health

set a group, a class; to turn from liquid to solid | set of instructions a series of directions | set of measurements a group of numbers or sizes that refer to the same experiment | set of results a group of measurements, a table of numbers obtained in one experiment | set up to prepare, to assemble | class set sufficient equipment for each pupil to carry out some part of an experiment | data set the information obtained from an experiment | instruction set the directions that should be followed | subset a smaller class within a larger group

SETI [Search for Extra-Terrestrial Intelligence] a US-funded astronomical programme

setting becoming hard | setting Sun the end of the day, the Sun is disappearing below the western horizon | setting superglue the joining material is turning hard

settle to remain, to sediment

settlement tank a large box in a sewage plant that allows suspended material to sediment

seven number between six and eight

sever (not severe which is extreme) to break, to cut through

several many, a few, more than three

severe (not sever which is to break) extreme, harsh | severe acute respiratory syndrome (SARS) a lung infection that originated in the Far East at the start of the 21st century

sewage / sewerage the excrement of animals suspended in water, a mixture of faeces and urine in water | sewage plant an area containing the equipment that changes sewage into clean water | sewage treatment the steps taken to treat sewage, using physical, chemical and biological methods, to produce water that is safe to put into a river | raw sewage / untreated sewage the excrement and organic waste have not been treated in any way

sewerage / sewage the excrement of animals suspended in water, a mixture of faeces and urine in water

sex (plural is sexes) gender, male or female | sex cell a gamete, the cells used in fertilisation, special cells that have half the usual number of chromosomes | sex characteristics features that are always found in one gender, but never in the other gender | sex chromosomes the pair of chromosomes that define whether a cell is male or female, a human male has an X chromosome and a Y chromosome, the human female has two X chromosomes | sex hormones the chemicals produced by the ovaries or testes that lead to the development of the secondary sex characteristics | sex organs the tissues that are essential for the fertilisation of an egg by a male gamete, the ovaries or testes of animals, the stamen and carpels of plants | unprotected sex having intercourse without wearing a condom

sex cell a gamete, a cell containing half the usual number of chromosomes | female sex cell the gamete that is enlarged with a food reserve and so is unable to move, an ovum | male sex cell the gamete that is able to move, sperm or pollen

sexual concerned with the sex, associated with gender | sexual characteristics the features that are associated with gender | sexual intercourse the actions necessary for depositing sperm in the vagina | sexual reproduction the offspring is started by the fertilisation of the ovum by the male gamete, having two parents

sexually concerned with the use of the reproductive organs | sexually transmitted disease (std) an illness that is moved from person to person during sexual intercourse

shade a dark area, a region which is protected from sunlight, an umbrella, the darkness of a specific colour; to provide protection from light, to darken a picture

shaded habitat an area where the intensity of sunlight has been reduced by layers of leaves

shading darkening, adding a diagonal fill to a diagram

shadow a dark area surrounded by light, a ghost | shadow formation production of a dark area by placing an object between the lamp and the screen | rain shadow land that is dry because the nearby mountains receive all the rainfall

shady in the shadow, obscured from light | shady position a place that will not receive direct sunlight

shake to shiver, to tremor uncontrollably

shaker wave the transverse wave that results from an earthquake and moves slowly through the Earth

shaking trembling, shuddering, shivering

shale a fine-grained sedimentary rock formed from silt or clay | oil shale a type of mud that is silt or clay held together by oil, and from which oil can be obtained by distillation

shallow not deep, having little depth

shallower less deep than another area

shampoo a soap with the correct pH and properties for washing hair; to use a special soap for washing hair

shape an outline, an arrangement; to place into an arrangement | beak shape the outline of the beak of a bird, the different shapes indicate the type of diet of the bird | body shape an outline of the organism | grain shape the appearance of the small particles that are in rocks | specific shape a particular arrangement, a type of outline, a form that reflects the environment | streamlined shape a silhouette that is pointed at the front and so moves easily through fluids

share a part, a portion; to divide into parts and distribute

shark a carnivorous sea creature that has a skeleton made from cartilage, but does not have a swim bladder

Sharman (Helen born 1963) *'The girl from Mars'* became the first British astronaut in 1991. Dr Sharman was working for Mars Confectionery when she answered an advertisement for potential astronauts.

sharp pointed, biting, painful, acute | sharp boundary a sudden change, an obvious border | sharp claws talons, the toes can rip and grip | sharp edge a sudden change, a border that is distinctly different | sharp taste tart, without any taste of sugar or salt | sharp teeth the teeth are able to pierce flesh

sharper able to cut more easily

shatter to break into many pieces

shaving foam a soap that prepares the skin for cutting of hair growth

sheath a protective covering, a layer surrounding the axon

shed a hut; to get rid of, to throw off

shedding removing, getting rid of | leaf shedding the dropping of leaves from deciduous tress during autumn

sheep a farm animal reared for meat, skin and wool

sheet a thin covering, a piece of paper | fact sheet a collection of related measurements that are useful for a specific application | identification sheet a display that highlights the characteristics of several organisms | information sheet paper containing notes, data or instructions | polythene sheet a thin material made from a polymer of ethene [CH_2:CH_2] | quiz sheet a series of questions written on paper | results sheet paper on which is written a table of the outcome of an exam, a game or an experiment | rubber sheet a membrane or thin covering made from rubber | spread sheet a series of boxes or cells in which formulae and data can be placed | summary sheet paper on which the main ideas are written

shelf (plural is shelves) a horizontal board, a projecting layer of rock, a sandbank | shelf-life the specified period of time for which material can be safely used | bee hive shelf a short, cylindrical pot with a semi-circular entrance in one side | continental shelf the underwater area extending from the land to the sudden drop of the deep oceans

shell a crust, a hard outer covering, an orbital of an atom, the path of an electron in an atom; to remove the hard outer covering | shellfish sea creatures that have an external skeleton, *eg* mussels, prawns, crabs or lobsters | shell size an agreed method for measuring the length or diameter of the hard outer covering of a shell fish | egg shell the hard, strong protective coat around the egg | outer shell the orbital furthest from the nucleus that has electrons | sea shells the remains of the external skeleton of shellfish

shelly material thin plates, usually of rock

shelter an area that provides protection from the weather; to remain in a protected area

sheltered in a safe area, covered, protected | sheltered shore an area where the sea meets land, and which is protected by islands or hills

shelve to slope gradually

shelves (plural of shelf) horizontal boards, projecting layers of rock

shield a defence; to provide a defensive cover | heat shield the material on the base of space capsules and the Shuttle that protects the craft from the heat generated by moving rapidly through air

shielding a protective layer, a covering intended to prevent harm | magnetic shielding an iron or steel mesh that should stop the effects of a magnetic field

shift a small movement, a length of working time; to move | red shift the change in the appearance of the light from a star caused by the star moving away from us

shifted moved, changed position

shin the front part of the leg between the knee cap and the ankle | shin bone the tibia, the thick bone joining the knee to the ankle

shine to use light to illuminate a surface | sunshine the light that is produced by the Sun and allows us to see during daytime, and permits plants to photosynthesise

shingle small rounded rocks

shingles a painful infection in adults caused by reactivation of the of chicken pox virus

shining giving out light

shiny highly reflective | shiny foil a thin metal sheet that will reflect light and heat | shiny surface the covering is reflective, the exterior of an object reflects light

ship a vessel for transporting goods and people across water; to transport | space ship a vessel that can be used by astronauts to explore the Solar System | wooden ship a large boat in which most structural components are made from wood, usually powered by sails

shiver involuntary rapid movement of muscles in an attempt to keep warm, to tremble, to shake

shoal a large group of any one type of fish

shock a sudden change, a blow, an unwelcome surprise; to startle, to cause a sudden change | shock absorber equipment that reduces the impact of a sudden change by using material that will compress over a time period | electric shock momentary contraction of muscles when a current passes through the body | seismic shock a movement of part of the Earth's crust

shoe a covering that provides protection for the foot; to provide protection for the feet of animals | shoe box a disposable carton in which shoes are stored while awaiting sale | shoe lace string that is used to hold a covering tightly to the foot | brake shoes heat-resistant plates that are pressed against a wheel in order to slow the rotation | snow shoes wide plates that are attached to the bottom of the feet so as to increase the surface area and therefore reduce the pressure to enable walking on snow

shone past of 'to shine'

shook past of 'to shake'

shoot (not chute which is a slide) a stem, a young branch, a water slide; to move swiftly, to eject, to aim with a bullet or an arrow | embryo shoot the initial stages of development of the plant shoot

shooting stars meteors, grains of sand from space that enter the atmosphere at high speed, then glow white-hot because of frictional heating

shop window a large pane of glass that allows you to see the goods that the shop is selling

shore (not sure which is certain) the flat area where a large body of water meets the land | exposed shore an area between land and sea that often experiences high winds | lower shore the land next to the sea that is covered and uncovered at almost every tide | middle shore the area between sea and land that is expected to be covered and uncovered during most tides | rocky shore the area between sea and land is made from groups of rocks | sea shore the area between the high and low tides where the sea meets the land | sheltered shore the area between water and land is surrounded by cliffs and islands so that wind speeds are low on the shore | upper shore the land next to the sea that is covered with sea water only when the tide is very high

short not long, below average height, brief, little | short-circuit a wire accidentally connects two parts of the circuit that should be separated leading to a high current and increased amount of heat | short-lived exists for a short period of time, then undergoes a substantial change | short period a time interval that is not long | short-sight / short-sighted myopic, able to see items that are close but cannot focus on objects that are far away | short-term near future, not covering a long period of time

shortage insufficient, not enough

shortcomings faults, failures

shorten to make less long

shortest briefest, smallest

shorthand a brief form, contracted, using symbols | **shorthand equation** a relationship that uses formulae instead of words in either a mathematical relationship or a chemical reaction | **chemical shorthand** the formula of the chemical showing the symbol and number of each atom

shot putter an athlete who follows special rules in putting, not throwing, an iron ball

should ought, past of 'shall'

shoulder a small ledge, the area between the upper arm and the body | **shoulder blade** the scapula, a flat bone strengthening the shoulders | **shoulder joint** a ball-and-socket joint between the upper arm and the body

shout a sudden, loud utterance; to speak in a very loud voice

show a drama; to point out, to explain

shower a brief downpour of rain, a spray of water: to spray with water | **Perseids' shower** the vast number of shooting stars that appear in early-August and appear to be arriving from the constellation Perseus

showing explaining, helping someone to understand, displaying

shown demonstrated, highlighted, established

shrimp / prawn (usage depends on local area) a small aquatic crustacean | **brine shrimp** a delicate, microscopic animal that lives in salty water, the eggs can be stored dry and remain viable for long periods

shrink to become smaller, to lose weight

shrubby lichen a composite organism, comprising a fungus and an alga living together, that looks like a very small bush

shuffle a slow walk without lifting the feet; to walk slowly without lifting the feet, to mix up playing cards into random order

shutter a thin plate that, in one position, prevents the entry of light, but in a second position, allows light to pass

Shuttle / Space Shuttle a space craft designed to return to the Earth and be re-used again, first flew on 12 April 1981

shuttle a frequent move between positions; to move between two positions

Si silicon, proton number 14

SI system / SI units [Système International d'Unités] a range of accepted measurements, based on standards that are kept in France, including length, mass and time

siblings offspring of the same parents, brothers or sisters

sickle cell anaemia (UK) / **sickle cell anemia** (USA) a disease in which the red blood cells have the shape of a half-moon, and are less effective at carrying oxygen compared to the normal (circular) cells

sickness illness, disease | **altitude sickness** the symptoms of headache, disorientation and nausea produced by moving from close to sea level to several thousand feet above sea level in a short time | **sleeping sickness** a disease of humans caused by infection with trypanasomes, a parasite that has been passed on by insect bites

side-arm a small tube leading from the neck of a flask or the side of a boiling tube | **side-arm flask** a conical flask with an open glass tube welded to the neck | **side-arm tube** a boiling tube with a short delivery tube welded about 1 centimetre from the top

side-effects unwanted changes that result from a treatment

side-tube a small tube leading from the neck of a flask or the side of a boiling tube

sideways moving at right angles to the direction that your head and body are facing | **sideways growth** parts of the root are growing horizontally so as to increase the volume of soil from which nutrients are available

SIDOT [Speed Is Distance Over Time] the speed equation

$$\text{speed} = \frac{\text{distance (metres)}}{\text{time (seconds)}}$$
(metres per second)

sieve a bowl with holes in, a net, a mesh; to separate into different sizes

sieving separating powders or grits into particles of different sizes, using a mesh

sight (not site which is a place) / **eye sight** vision, the use of eyes to see details, the ability to distinguish colours and to separate close objects by using the eyes | **poor sight** the eyes are able to see but can not pick out details

sighted able to see, having been seen | **long-sighted** able to see distant objects, but need converging lenses to focus near articles | **short-sighted** able to see objects that are close, but need concave glasses to focus objects that are far away

sign a mark, a symbol, a signal, a movement, a language using movements of the hands | **early signs** the small, almost insignificant, changes that occur near the start of an event | **hazard sign / hazard warning sign** a visible notice that warns of possible danger | **road sign** a board giving information or instructions to drivers | **warning sign** a notice showing hazards, a diagram indicating possible risk

signal a sign, an event starting change; to give a sign | **signal generator** equipment that will produce a voltage that changes in a regular way | electric signal a change in voltage that causes a reaction | nerve signal the message that is sent along a nerve either to inform the brain or to cause an action | visual signal a sign that can be seen

significance importance, meaning | environmental significance the substantial difference that an event could have on the environment

significant important, vital | significant differences important distinctions, the difference between numbers is large enough to be meaningful | significant number a large proportion | significant points important details, vital differences or similarities

silence a request for noise to stop, a lack of sound | complete silence no noise at all

silencer a tube that is used to reduce the noise of an engine or a gun, a muffler

silent without sound, quiet

silica quartz, sand, silicon dioxide [SiO_2], the main constituent of the Earth's crust | silica powder quartz that has been ground to dust | silica-rich rocks that contain lots of silica

silicate / silicate ion [$SiO_3^=$] a group of silicon and oxygen atoms that do not exist alone, but are found combined to metals | silicates rocks that have a high concentration of the silicate ion | calcium silicate [$CaSiO_3$] a salt that forms very large chains and sheets, that is found in many types of rock, eg asbestos, mica, talc | sodium silicate [Na_2SiO_3] a chemical that is used in solution to prepare crystals and to preserve eggs

silicon (Si, proton number 14, melting point 1410°C) (not silicone which is a plastic) a grey solid that makes up a quarter of all the atoms on Earth, occurs mainly as sand or silicon dioxide [SiO_2] | silicon chips a slice of silicon on which has been etched millions of electronic components | silicon dioxide [SiO_2] sand, silica, the common ore of silicon

silicone (not silicon which is an element) a plastic that contains silicon and several types of organic groups

silk a flexible, strong filament produced by some larvae, and which is used to make a cloth

silken very smooth, material that is soft but very strong – just like silk | silken thread a soft, strong, glossy fibre

sill a hard block at the base of a door or window, a large plate of rock, an igneous intrusion | window sill a decorative slab at the base of a window

silt a sediment of tiny particles of rock, a suspension of fine material

silver (Ag, proton number 47, melting point 961°C) the most reactive of the precious metals, often found uncombined in rocks | silver nitrate [$AgNO_3$] a soluble salt that forms a clear solution that turns white if mixed with a halide, *eg* chloride | silver plate a thin layer of expensive silver covering a cheap, strong metal | silver tree the result of bending a copper wire to the shape of a tree and then placing into silver nitrate solution | quicksilver mercury [Hg]

similar almost the same, not quite identical, in like manner | similar poles the two ends are either both north or both south | similar reactions adding each object to another chemical will cause the same change | similar size the mass, lengths, heights or widths of the objects have almost the same values | similar to emphasising the features that two objects have in common

similarities (plural of similarity) several features possessed by each object look to be almost the same | identify similarities to see which characteristics are shared by several objects

similarity (plural is similarities) the objects each have one feature that looks the same

simple a few parts, a few instructions, not complicated | simple activities experiments that require very little action by the observer | simple arch in fingerprints, the ridges form a bridge-like structure | simple diagrams drawings that show only the essential parts | simple distillation the vapour produced by boiling a liquid in a flask is led directly to a cool tube where condensation occurs | simple generator there is a single coil of wire rotating between opposite poles of a magnet | simple method a technique that does not need complicated apparatus, is safe and gives a clear result | simple molecules the molecule has less than a hundred atoms, the formula mass is below 300 daltons | simple question a problem posed in such a way that the required answer is only yes or no | simple relationship changing one variable will change the other variable in a well-defined manner

simpler not as difficult, easier, less complicated

simplification making less complicated

simplified made easier, details and complexities are missing | simplified diagram a drawing that shows the essential parts only | simplified version a description or diagram that shows the main features, but misses out the details and possible drawbacks

simplify to make less complicated

simulate to pretend, to carry out an experiment using a computer, to copy

simulations carrying out virtual experiments, using computer-generated graphics to reflect a real situation | simulation software the code that allows real situations to be reproduced by a computer

simultaneously at the same time

single one, by itself, alone | single-celled a creature that is made form one cell | single glazing the windows have one layer of glass

sink a basin for water, a reservoir; to fall through a fluid

sinking falling through a fluid

siphon a tube in which one end is in a reservoir of liquid and the other end is at a lower level; to remove liquid by using a tube with the outlet end lower than the end in the reservoir of liquid

Sirius the brightest star in the sky after the Sun, approximately 9 light-years from Earth

sisters girls with the same parents

sitar a stringed musical instrument from India

site (not sight which is the ability to see) the place where an event occurs; to place an item | landfill site the place where the hole that is being filled is to be found | nesting site the particular place or type of area where a nest is found | tipping site an area reserved for the collection of waste and materials for recycling

SI system / SI units [Système International d'Unités] the agreed units for the measurement of mass, length and time that was developed by the French in 1805, and accepted worldwide in 1960

situation condition, position, job, a description of the environment | common situations conditions that occur many times | everyday situations events that you are likely to come across regularly | familiar situations events that you have met many times | range of situations the environment may take wide values of temperature, wind speed, moisture and organisms involved

SI units / SI system [Système International d'Unités] the agreed units for the measurement of mass, length and time that was developed by the French in 1805, and accepted worldwide in 1960

six number between five and seven

size the amount, the length, the mass, the volume; to measure | size of grain the length of the fragments | size of population the number of that type of organism in that area | adequate size sufficiently large | adequate sample size enough members were in the sample so as to give results that are representative for the whole population | appropriate size the length or volume is suitable for that purpose | bed size the length and width of a bed for sleeping, the area of garden used for growing a particular plant | body size the height, the width or the mass of an organism or object |

cell size the length or diameter of that type of cell | crystal size the length of each giant regular structure | estimate size to make a guess of length or mass that is based on previous information | grain size the length of the specks | initial size the mass or volume at the start of the experiment | leaf size the surface area of the plant leaf | particle size the diameter of each of the tiny specks in a chemical | population size the number of that species in the specified area | relative sizes comparing two or more similar objects and putting them in order of mass, volume or height | sample size the number of members or the volume or the mass in a small part taken from the whole | shell size the diameter or length of the exoskeleton of some aquatic creatures | similar sizes comparison of two or more objects shows they have almost the same mass, volume of length | sufficient size the object is large enough for the purpose

skate board two pairs of wheels joined by a plank on which a person may stand and push themselves along

skater a person who glides along a surface using wheels or melted ice to reduce friction

skating moving rapidly over a thin layer of lubricant | ice skating moving over ice by wearing special shoes with thin metal bars that produce a high pressure so the ice melts

skeletal outline, concerned with bones | skeletal system the bones and the way they are organised

skeleton the bones of the body, the hard structure that retains the shapes and holds the softer organs, an outline | endo-skeleton the structural bones are on the inside of the body | exo-skeleton / external skeleton the hard shell of shell fish and insects that provides support and protection for the soft body | human skeleton the underlying shape, number and structure of the bones that are found in a person

sketch a simple diagram, a short performance | sketch a graph to draw the shape of the curve with labelled axes but not necessarily including numbers

skewer a needle, a spear; to push a needle

ski a narrow piece of wood that is used in pairs for moving rapidly over snow; to use skis with skill

skid to carry on moving in a straight line when you intended to stop or change direction, usually on a slippery surface

ski-lift equipment for taking skiers up a slope

skills expertise, abilities obtained by training, talents, occupation | investigative skills the ability to carry out a fair test with sufficient observations and to reach a conclusion | key skills the expertise needed in order to survive in the work place, *eg* the abilities to read, use mathematics and use a computer | manipulative skills the expertise to move items into the required place or to change their shape

skim to remove a thin layer, to read rapidly, to throw a flat stone, on to water, so that it bounces off the surface several times

skimmed removed from the surface, bounced along a surface

skimming removing a thin layer from the top, reading a text quickly so as to find the major ideas

skin the outer layer (an average human has over 2 kilogram of skin, covering an area of 2 square metres, making it the largest organ of the human body); to remove the outer layer | skin cancer uncontrolled growth of cells of the skin | skin capillaries the very tiny blood vessels in the skin that can change diameter and so allow control of heat loss from the body | skin care using ointments that will ensure a healthy skin | skin cells the flattened cells that form a protective layer around vertebrate animals | skin color (USA) / skin colour (UK) the colour of the skin, which reflects both the racial background and previous experiences | skin-diver a scuba diver, a person who swims under water with a tank of air on their back | skin temperature the temperature measured at the skin, this temperature is usually lower than the temperature of the body because heat is lost from the skin | drum skin the material, usually an animal skin or plastic, that is stretched tightly over a circular frame | dry skin cracking and flaking of skin | wrinkled skin one sign of ageing is that the skin is less flexible and forms many ridges

skinny not fat, thin, outline of ribs is visible, undernourished

skis long pieces of material on which you can stand and move rapidly over snow

skull cranium, the major bone in the head that provides protection for the brain and for the sense organs of sight, hearing and smell

sky the atmosphere, the area above our heads | sky-divers parachutists who fall for most of the distance without opening their parachutes and will often perform manoeuvres in the air | sky-scraper a very tall building, a building with over twenty floors | Sky TV a provider of television programmes that distributes the signal using satellites

slab a cuboid piece of rock that is much thinner than the width or height | paving slab a flat piece of rock or concrete that is suitable for using as the surface of a path

slag the molten mixture of silicates, sand and lime that is produced when iron ore reacts in a blast furnace | slag notch the hole in a blast furnace through which the slag can be released

slaked lime [Ca(OH)$_2$] calcium oxide that has been mixed with water

slate a hard metamorphic rock (originally clay) that is easily separated into thin sheets, and used as roofing material

slaughter the killing of large numbers of animals or people; to kill a vast number of people or animals

sledge a vehicle for transport that uses two long runners in contact with the ground

sleep a period of voluntary unconsciousness that is needed on a daily basis by most animals

sleeping partaking in a period of voluntary unconsciousness that most animals require | sleeping bag a sack made from insulating layers that should keep you warm when sleeping in a tent or the open air | sleeping pill a tablet that is taken to increase the amount of sleep | sleeping sickness a disease caused by infection with trypanasomes that have been passed on by insect bites

sleet a mixture of rain and snow, often in high winds

slice a piece that is wide and thin; to cut into pieces

slide a glass plate on which are placed the specimens for microscopic examination, a playground item; to move rapidly over a slippery surface | cavity slide / dimple slide a piece of glass, approximately 5 cm x 2 cm, which has a dip in the centre allowing the examination of microscopic creatures in water | landslide a rapid, downhill movement of a large area of earth or mud | microscope slides the thin glass plates on which are placed the samples that are to be examined using a microscope | pitted glass slide a microscope slide with a depression on one side so a drop of fluid can be examined | prepared slides microscope slides that have the sample to be examined already fixed, stained, mounted and covered

slider an item that is intended to be pushed or pulled along an horizontal track

sliding moving one surface over another with very little frictional resistance | sliding friction the slowing force when a body is moving across a surface

slightly small, unimportant, partly | slightly movable the object could move a small distance if a large force were applied

slim not fat; to become thinner, to lose weight

slime wet material that is slippery and soft | slime trail the track of mucus that is left by a moving snail or slug

slimming trying to become thinner | slimming pill a tablet that should assist you to lose weight

slimy covered with damp, microbial growth | slimy body the outside of the organism is slippery

Slinky™ a metal or plastic spring, about 5 cm diameter, that is used to show wave forms

slip a fall, something small or thin; to fall because of lack of friction | cover slip a thin glass shield that is placed over the sample on a microscope slide | non-slip resists movement

slipped disc a common term to explain back pain, more properly should be said that a disc between adjacent vertebrae has become weakened

slippery there is very little friction between the surface and any object placed on it

slipping one surface is moving over another with little friction

slit a long, thin opening; to make a thin cut | gill slits the perforations on the sides of a fish that allow water to pass over the gills so the fish can obtain oxygen

slope gradient | continental slope the underwater area extending from the land to the sudden drop of the deep oceans | scree slope the side of a hill is covered in thin plates of rock

slot a piece with straight edges has been removed; to push a solid into a gap

slow not fast, unhurried; to obstruct, to reduce speed | slow cooling the temperature takes a long time to reduce speed and so any crystals formed tend to be large | slow down to reduce speed

slowed reduced speed

slower moving a lower speed than another

slowest with least speed, the last person to finish

slowing obstructing, reducing | slowing down reducing speed

slowly without haste, over a longer period of time period of time than might be expected

slows / slows down reduces speed

sludge an ooze, mud, a slimy mixture

slug an invertebrate animal, a small amount, a pellet for a gun | slug pellet a tablet that contains chemicals either to kill or to scare off garden slugs and snails | slug treatment a chemical that will either kill slugs or repel them

slur a comment that humiliates the attempt; to denigrate an action or event, to speak unclearly

small not big, tiny, dwarf, unimportant | small animal a creature that is less than 10 cm long and so is difficult to see | small bowel the small intestine where food is digested and the nutrients absorbed | small creatures animals that can be are less than 10 cm long | small crystal a small, shiny solid that is less than 1 millimetre across | small intestine the tube connecting the stomach

to the large intestine in which breakdown of food continues and the small molecules are absorbed through the villi in the wall of the intestine | small molecule a structure formed by bonding less than 50 atoms together, a structure that can be absorbed across the wall of the intestine | smallpox an infectious disease caused by a virus that was eradicated by 1979, due to the efforts of the World Health Organisation | small quantity a tiny amount | small sample a tiny amount with a composition that should represent the bulk | small-scale not having a large affect, changing a small area or volume, not noticeable

smaller less large, not as big | smaller molecules the products of breaking down a large molecule

smallest tiniest, least large | smallest part a fragment, a tiny fraction of the substance

smash (plural is smashes) a crash; to break into small pieces, to crush, to exceed a record

smell a scent, an odour, a sense for detecting aromas; to detect a scent, to produce an odour | smell cells the sensory cells in the nose of an animal or the antenna of an insect that are able to detect specific scents, odours and chemicals

smelled / smelt detected an odour

smells detects a scent, produces an odour | cooking smells the odours and scents produced when food is being heated

smelly producing an unpleasant odour

smelt to extract a metal from an ore by heating with charcoal or coke, to reduce with carbon

smelt / smelled detected an odour

smelting / smelting metals heating a metal oxide with carbon or coke so as to extract the metal

Smith (William 1769–1839) was a surveyor, for the builders of canals, who developed the first geological maps. He proposed that strata at the bottom were laid down first and the most recent layer would be at the top.

smog a wide-spread fog that occurs in the air of some cities, with a yellow or brown colour caused by the many different molecules that are suspended in the atmosphere

smoke particles of carbon produced during incomplete combustion | smoke alarm equipment that detects when smoke is present and then sounds a warning | smoke control taking steps to reduce the amount of carbon particles that are produced, eg by prohibiting the burning of coal in household fires | smoke detector equipment that sounds a loud alarm if smoke particles are detected | smoke precipitation using methods such as electrostatic plates in chimneys that will cause the tiny carbon particles of smoke to fall into a collector | cigarette smoke the visible fumes that are produced when a cigarette is burned

smokeless fuel that burns without producing any carbon particles | smokeless fuel material that burns without producing carbon particles, solid smokeless fuel is achieved by heating coal or wood in the absence of air so the material is a porous solid of dry carbon | smokeless zone an area of buildings in which any fuel should burn without producing carbon particles

smoker a person who needs to inhale smoke from burning tobacco, a vent of a volcano | non-smoker a person who does not smoke tobacco

smoking giving off particles of carbon indicating incomplete combustion, inhaling the products of burning tobacco, preserving meat by cooking in hot smoke | smoking components the chemicals that are produced when a cigarette is burned | smoking experiment dragging air from a smouldering cigarette through clean cotton wool then through universal indicator so as to show that tars and acids are produced | smoking habit the routine use of cigarettes at regular times | smoking household a home in which many members of the family smoke cigarettes | smoking machine equipment that allows a cigarette to be burned and the chemical products collected | smoking-related illnesses the diseases that are more common among people who smoke and become more probable as the number of cigarettes smoked increases, eg emphysema, lung cancer | effects of smoking the changes that occur as a result of smoking cigarettes | passive smoking breathing in the smoke from the cigarettes of other people in the room so that some of the tars and poisons from the cigarette will go into your lungs

smoky the air is dark with carbon particles

smolder (USA) / smoulder (UK) to burn very slowly and without any flames

smooth flat, calm, polished, steady; to make even | smooth curve a continuous line | smooth ice frozen water that has a polished surface | smooth material the surface of the material has no visible imperfections | smooth surface a polished covering, a shiny face

smoother less rough

smoothly calmly, without jarring, steadily

smother to cover so that air cannot enter, to suffocate

smoulder (UK) / smolder (USA) to burn very slowly and without any flames

Sn tin (stannous), proton number 50, a metal

snack foods edible materials that need no further preparation other than some, such as pizza, need heating

snag a problem, an unforeseen obstacle; to catch on a small spike

snail a mollusc, an invertebrate animal with a single large shell | snail-trail the track of mucus that is left by a moving snail or slug | snail treatment chemicals that are put in the garden with the intention of killing snails and slugs

snake a cold-blooded carnivorous vertebrate that is long and thin

snap to break suddenly

sneeze a sudden blast of air through the nose; to produce a blast of air from the nose

snooker a game played on a flat table with the object of placing coloured balls into holes using a white ball and a cue

Snow (John 1813–1858) was a London medical practitioner who is remembered for two events that occurred when he was just turned 40 and both were based on years spent observing and experimenting. While training as a doctor, Snow had been unable to help the victims of a cholera outbreak but he developed the idea of water-borne diseases. In the 1854 cholera epidemic in London, Snow persuaded the council to close the water pump in the area with the highest incidence of disease, and immediately saw a reduction in the number of cases. This persuasion was based on the fame that he had gathered in 1853 when he applied his expert knowledge of anaesthetics to give chloroform to help Queen Victoria with the birth of her seventh child.

snow flat flakes of frozen water | snowball a sphere formed by using pressure to melt some of the snow | snowboard a thin plank to which boots are attached and which is used for moving rapidly downhill on snow | snow-buggy a small vehicle that will slide across snow or ice, and may be powered by an engine or by the wind | snowflake a single piece of snow that looks like a circle of six flat fronds | snow line the height above which snow is formed | snow shoes a circular frame connected by cross strings that is worn under a shoe so as to spread the weight when walking on snow

soak to saturate with liquid, to drench

soap a chemical produced by heating fat with sodium hydroxide, a chemical that allows fats to be suspended in water; to wash, to lather

soapy feeling like soap, slippery

social friendly, pleasant, concerned with society | social change a difference that has occurred to the way that people live, work, interact or travel | social issue any problem that arises from the way that people live and interact with each other |

social problem trouble caused by different people having different needs and talents

socially with friendship, for leisure

socket a hollow fitting, a connection | ball and socket a joint between two bones, the rounded end of one bone fits into the hollow of the other bone | electric socket / electrical socket a standard fitting into which the plug from the equipment can be inserted | eye socket the area of the skull into which the eye fits | power socket / wall socket a connection that is mounted on a wall and into which an electrical plug will fit

soda a mixture of sodium carbonate [Na_2CO_3] and sodium hydrogen carbonate [$NaHCO_3$] that is important in making glass | soda lake a body of water that is corrosive because the solution is rich in sodium carbonate [Na_2CO_3], resulting in a very high pH | soda lime [Na_2O] sodium oxide, a white solid that is used to absorb carbon dioxide [CO_2] | baking soda [$NaHCO_3$] sodium hydrogen carbonate | bicarbonate of soda [$NaHCO_3$] sodium hydrogen carbonate, baking soda | caustic soda [NaOH] sodium hydroxide | washing soda [Na_2CO_3] sodium carbonate

sodium (Na, proton number 11, melting point 98°C) an alkali metal also called natrium, a group 1 element, soft, low-density, reacts violently with water | sodium bicarbonate [$NaHCO_3$] sodium hydrogen carbonate, baking soda | sodium carbonate [Na_2CO_3] washing soda | sodium chloride [NaCl] salt, common salt, table salt | sodium hydrogen carbonate [$NaHCO_3$] sodium bicarbonate, baking soda | sodium hydroxide [NaOH] a strong alkali, corrosive, produced by dropping sodium on to water | sodium silicate [Na_2SiO_3] used in solution to prepare crystal gardens and to preserve eggs | sodium stearate a compound commonly used in soap | sodium streetlamp a method of lighting large areas in which production of sodium ions [Na^+] causes an orange glow | sodium sulfate (US) / sodium sulphate (UK) [Na_2SO_4] a salt produced by neutralising sodium hydroxide [NaOH] with sulphuric acid [H_2SO_4]

soft easily changes shape, not hard | soft drink a liquid containing no alcohol, which is suitable for reducing thirst | soft iron iron that is not easily shattered, iron with most of the carbon removed and metals added | soft iron nails thin pointed cylinders made from iron that may bend, but will not shatter | soft magnetic material a metal that will become magnetic when surrounded by a current in a coil, but loses its magnetic field when the current is switched off | soft sound low amplitude, quiet, piano | soft tissue groups of cells that can be easily damaged by squashing | software the programme that controls a computer system | soft water water that easily forms permanent bubbles with soap, because it does not contain salts of either calcium or magnesium | magnetically soft the metal is easy to turn into a magnet, but rapidly loses its magnetism

softer / softer material not as hard, changes shape more easily | softer rock the material in this boulder would be scratched by the other stone

soft material rocks that crumble easily, cloth that is smooth a silk, clay that changes shape easily

software instructions, programmes | simulation software instructions that allow a computer version of a real event

soggy soaked with water, saturated and dripping

soil the very top layer of the Earth's crust, earth, the tiny fragments of disintegrated rock in which plants can put down roots; to make dirty | soil animals consumers that obtain nutrients from the organic matter in the earth, eg earthworms, insects | soil community the many types of animals, plants, microbes and fungi that live together in an area of land | soil erosion the removal of fertile soil by wind and rivers | soil formation / soil production the method by which large rocks are changed over a long time into a bed for plants | soil nutrients the salts and minerals that should be in the soil for healthy growth of plants | soil profile a diagram showing the layers of different soil in a vertical section | soil testing measuring the pH and for the presence of specified minerals in soil | soil-testing kit a set of equipment and chemicals that can be used to measure the pH, drainage time and other characteristics of soil | soil treatment adding a chemical to soil so that conditions change and different organisms will grow | soil type a description of the main kinds of material in the soil | acid soil the top layer of earth that has a pH below 7 | alkaline soil the top layer of earth that has a pH above 7 | different soils classifying soils by using observable or measurable features | garden soil the mixture of sand, clay and rocks that is likely to be found in land that has been used for growing flowers | liming soil adding calcium oxide [CaO] to soil so as to raise the pH and so to improve drainage | local soil the earth that is close to a given position | particular soil specifying the place of origin or the characteristics of a soil | top soil the layer of earth that has been turned over by worms and so is most suitable for growing plants | water-logged soil earth in which all the air pockets have been filled with water

Sol the Latin name for the Sun, the star at the centre of the Solar System

sol- (*Latin* Sun)

solar concerned with the Sun | solar cells devices that convert sunlight directly into electricity | solar collector equipment for concentrating into a small area the energy from the Sun that has fallen over a wide area | solar cooker an inverted umbrella made of aluminium foil reflects and focuses the Sun's heat onto a kettle | solar eclipse the darkening of the sky caused by the Moon passing between the Sun and the Earth | solar energy any heat, light or other radiation that arrives from the Sun | solar heating using the heat from the Sun to warm a house or to heat water | solar panel equipment for collecting the heat from the Sun and warming water, the panels look like black radiators, NB the "wings" on satellites are large panels of solar cells | solar plane the imaginary sheet on which the eight major planets and the asteroids seem to lie | solar power / solar powered using the radiation from the Sun as a source of energy | solar solstice the dates when the Sun appears at an extreme position, in June the Sun is at its highest, and in December the noon Sun is at its lowest position | Solar System the collection of eight major planets and their 61 known satellites, the dozens of dwarf planets, the 5000 asteroids, the many comets and the tonnes of dust that orbit around the Sun

solder a mixture of tin and lead that has a low melting point and is used to join wires together

solenoid /solenoid coil a long, thin coil of wire surrounding a movable iron core

solid having a definite shape, certain, not flexible | solid food the material to be eaten will require crunching, chewing and moistening before it can be swallowed | solid fuel a chemical that can be burned and has a definite shape, *eg* coal, wood | solid ice emphasising that ice has a fixed shape and is often associated with temperatures below 0°C so no melting could occur | solid particles grains, specks that are visible in a fluid | solid rock the material will keep its shape and is difficult to break or chip | solid state electronic equipment in which all the components are cut into a slice of silicon | solid waste faeces, discarded material that retains its shape | dissolved solids material that was solid, and will be recovered if the liquid is evaporated, but is now in solution | insoluble solid material that will not dissolve in a specified solvent | waxy solid material that is shiny, flakes easily and has low friction

solidification the process of turning from a liquid to a solid

solidified turned from liquid to solid

solidify to turn from liquid to solid

solidifying turning into a solid

solstice / solar solstice the time of year when the mid-day Sun is at its highest (June) or its lowest point (December) in the sky | summer solstice midsummer day, the date in June when the noon Sun is at its highest point in the sky of the Northern Hemisphere | winter solstice the date, a few days before Christmas, when the mid-day Sun is at its lowest point in the sky

solubility a measure of how much of a solid will dissolve in a liquid at a given temperature | solubility curve the graph depicting the maximum amount of a material that will dissolve at each temperature against the temperature (on the horizontal axis)

soluble able to dissolve in a specified solvent | soluble molecules material that will dissolve into a stated liquid | soluble substance a chemical that is able to dissolve in a liquid | fat-soluble a chemical that will dissolve in fat or oil | water-soluble large amounts of the substance will dissolve in water

solute a solid that will dissolve in a liquid | non-coloured solute a solid that does not have a colour, but is able to dissolve in a liquid

solution a liquid containing a mixture of molecules, a discovery that solves a problem, the self-consistent answer to a mathematical problem | acidic solution a liquid with a pH below 7, a liquid that turns litmus to red | alkaline solution a liquid with a pH above 7, a liquid that turns litmus to blue or purple | ammonia solution / ammonium solution ammonia [NH_3] dissolved in water, a liquid containing ammonium ions [NH_4^+] | aqueous solution a mixture of any substance dissolved in water | Benedict's solution a mixture of copper sulphate and sodium hydroxide that starts blue but turns to green and then red if sugars are present | chlorine solution a liquid for sterilising or bleaching made by dissolving chlorine in water | concentrated solution a large mass of solid has dissolved into a small volume of solvent | copper sulfate solution (USA) / copper sulphate solution (UK) a blue liquid produced by dissolving copper sulphate in water | dilute solution the concentration of the solute is low, there is a small mass of solid in a large volume of liquid | glucose solution a liquid made by dissolving glucose [$C_6H_{12}O_6$] in water | indicator solution a liquid that changes colour in response to a specific stimulus, eg universal indicator solution is red in acid but blue in alkali | iodine solution a mixture of iodine and potassium iodide in water that is often used to test for starch | litmus solution an indicator solution made by crushing certain lichen with alcohol and filtering | neutral solution a water-based liquid that has a pH of 7 so is neither acid nor alkali | salt solution a mixture of sodium chloride [NaCl] dissolved in water, a solution containing any salt in water | saturated solution a solution in which a solid dissolves in a solvent, but there is more of the same solid remaining which will not dissolve | sterilising solution (UK) / sterilizing solution (USA) a liquid which, when applied to a surface, will kill all microbes present | sugar solution a liquid comprising sugar dissolved in water | technological solution the application of science to solve a problem | universal indicator solution a mixture of three different coloured chemicals in alcohol that gives several different colours, depending on the pH | unknown solution the liquid can be seen, but the identity of the solvent and any solutes remains to be discovered | unsaturated solution a solvent has dissolved some solid, but more of the same solid can be added and will dissolve

solve to explain, to account for all the evidence in one simple explanation, to provide the answer to a problem

solvent a liquid in which the specified solid or gas will dissolve | solvent abuse sniffing some liquids that produce a vapour that can be absorbed by the blood, reach the brain and then affect the nervous system | solvent front the moving line that shows the movement of the solvent on a chromatography paper | pure solvent the liquid contains one type of molecule only and will dissolve the specified material

somatotrophin growth hormone, the chemical produced by the pituitary gland that stimulates growth of the body

some (not sum which is to add up) a few, several, a part of the whole

sometimes occasionally, at intervals, not always

somewhere an unknown place, an unspecified area

sonar (SOund Navigation And Ranging) the method used for estimating distance by measuring the time taken for a pulse of high frequency sound to be returned

sonic boom the loud bang that occurs when an aeroplane breaks through the sound barrier, *ie* travels faster than the speed of sound

sonorous sounding like a bell

soot the fine particles of carbon that are produced when combustion is incomplete and are seen as smoke

sooty covered with a fine black powder

sophisticated complicated, capable of many different operations

sorbent tube an open glass tube packed with a powder that easily absorbs any gases that are passed through the tube

sorbic acid [C_5H_7COOH] an organic acid that is used as a food preservative because it inhibits the growth of microbes, but can be used by animal cells

sore (not saw which is seen or a cutting tool) painful, injured | sore throat the back of the mouth is painful so swallowing is difficult | cold sore an eruption on the lips caused by herpes virus

Sörenson (Sören 1868–1939) was the Director of the Carlsberg Laboratory in Copenhagen working on proteins and enzymes. In 1909, he proposed the use of the pH scale to measure the acidity of solutions.

sort the group, the type; to place in order, to arrange into categories

sorted the items have been placed into groups

sorting classifying, categorising | sorting metals placing metals into different classes

sound a vibration, a noise, a periodic disturbance, a longitudinal wave; to produce a vibration | sound card computing equipment that decodes bits into sound | sound energy the energy associated with that sound wave | sound insulation material, often springy and with air pockets, that does not transmit sound | sound intensity the loudness of sound, the amplitude of the wave | sound level the average amount of sound that is either perceived or measured | sound-level meter equipment for measuring the intensity of sound either over all frequencies or at a specified range of wavelengths | sound-power level the intensity or energy of sound that is produced per second | sound proofing adding absorbent material so the vibrations are absorbed and therefore can neither be transmitted nor reflected | sound quality an estimate of the similarity between the original music and the sound that is heard | sound sensor equipment for detecting and responding to any sound above a pre-set amplitude | sound source the area from which the vibrations originate | sound wave a diagram to show how the pressure varies with distance and with time | common sounds the types of sound that are caused by vibrations of everyday objects | frequency of sound the pitch or note of a vibration in the air (sound), the number of vibrations each second | generate sound to produce a wave using electronic components as the source of vibration | loud sounds any vibration which may cause temporary or permanent damage to your hearing | produce sound to cause to vibrate | quality of sound an estimate of the similarity between the original music and the sound that is heard | range of sounds vibrations that have many different frequencies and amplitudes | soft sound a vibration with a low amplitude, quiet | speed of sound the distance travelled by a sound wave in one second in that environment | stereo sound two or more loudspeakers are driven by different waveforms, so the resultant sound appears to originate from different places | ultrasound vibrations that are above the range of human hearing, sound with a frequency above 30 kilohertz

sounding a measurement, measuring depth | echo sounding calculating depth or distance by measuring the time taken for an echo to return

sound level the average amount of sound that is either perceived or measured | sound-level meter equipment for measuring the intensity of sound either over all frequencies or at a specified range of wavelengths

soup a mixture of fine material and larger particles suspended in water, a liquid food

sour a sharp taste, bitter, not sweet

source (not sauce which is a sprinkled on food) starting place, origin | source of energy the place where the energy originated | source of information the place or person from which the data were first obtained | alternative source / different source a second starting point, the item arrived from another place | concentrated source a resource in which there is a large amount of usable energy | energy source the place where energy is produced | food source the place from which you obtain the items that you are going to eat | heat source an item that increases the temperature of the surroundings | information source the place or person that produced the data | light source the item that is producing the light | natural source an origin that occurs without interference by people | possible source one of several places that could be the origin | power source the place or equipment providing the energy that is used to cause the required change | primary source the major origin, the person who carried out the experiments | radio-active source material that produces radiation from the nucleus, but is packed so it can be handled safely | range of sources the several different places which contributed to the final item | reference source material that has a measured composition, an agreed standard | reference sources the sites,

people or books from which information or guidance is obtained | renewable source the origin of the material will be able to produce more of the substance | secondary source the item or information was received from an intermediate, not directly from the origin | selected sources you specify the origins that are to be used | sound source the area from which the vibrations originate | ultimate source the one place from which all the material or energy started, ie the Sun | variety of sources several different origins were used | vibrating source an item is moving rhythmically and causing sound elsewhere | voltage source equipment with terminals that have a potential difference | weak source the number of radio-active counts is low

south a direction opposite to north | south magnetic pole / south pole one of the two ends of a magnet | South Pole a point close to the centre of the Antarctic continent | south-seeking pole the end of a freely rotating magnet that points south

southern anything in the direction of the noon sun in the Northern Hemisphere, any area below the equator | Southern Hemisphere the half of the Earth that is below the equator

soy bean / soya bean the edible seed of a plant that has been cultivated for centuries in Asia and is now used as a source of meat-free protein

space an area, anything beyond the atmosphere of the Earth, a gap, a vacuum | space capsule the container, that is just large enough for the astronauts in their space suits, in which early astronauts travelled as far as the Moon and were returned to Earth | spacecraft a vessel designed either to move objects from the Earth's surface to beyond the atmosphere or to allow objects to be transported in space | space exploration using people and machines to try to find what is beyond the Earth's atmosphere | space probe an unmanned space-craft containing many information gathering instruments | space ship a vessel that can be used by astronauts to explore the Solar System | Space Shuttle a re-usable vessel that flies people from Earth to space, the first American Space Shuttle flew on 12 April 1981 | space station a building suspended in space that allows people to live and move without using protective clothing | spacesuit the several layers of protective clothing and breathing equipment that allow an astronaut to move safely in space | space travel moving people and goods between satellites, planets and stars | air space the gap between particles, the hollow at the end of a hen's egg | deep space the part of the universe that is outside our cluster of galaxies | empty space the universe is a vast volume of vacuum with tiny amounts of solid material | pore space the gap between particles in a porous rock, the gap between cells in a leaf, the volume of gaps in a rock compared to the volume of the rock

spade a shovel, a digging tool, a garden implement

Spallanzani (Lazzaro 1727–1799) was an Italian lawyer who became a priest then a professor of natural history. He showed that the stomach produces chemicals, later called enzymes, that could digest food. He completed the flow of blood in the arteries to the flow in veins that had been started by Harvey and he showed that blinded bats could still find food – an observation that was not explained until two centuries later.

span a gap, a period of time, the distance between two major points; to place a bridge | arm-span the distance between finger tips when the arms are stretched out, almost the same distance as your height | hand-span the distance between the little finger and the thumb when the hand is spread flat | life-span the period of time that a particular type of animal could be expected to live

spanner a tool for increasing the turning force applied to a nut

spark a tiny fragment of red-hot material; to produce a sudden flash

sparrow a small, brown garden bird | sparrow hawk a predatory bird that is at the top of the food chain

spatula a metal rod with flattened ends that is used as a 'spoon' in science

speaker / loudspeaker a cone that converts electrical signals into vibrations and is used to produce sound for music or announcements

spear a strong rod with pointed ends, used for hunting animals or fish

special distinct, unusual, unique, particular | special diet the nutritional requirements mean that the person has to eat specified amounts of certain foods or to ensure that some substances are absent | special job a task that can only be carried out by an operator with unusual talents

specialisation (UK) / **specialization** (USA) a highly developed skill, the feature that allows survival in that habitat

specialised (UK) / **specialized** (USA) modified so as to be outstandingly good at one job | specialised cells the building blocks of life have become modified so that each can carry out a particular function or job | specialised features characteristics that help the creature survive | specialised function the method has been

developed to achieve a specific purpose | specialised organs well-defined structures of tissues and cells that carry out specific tasks | specialised structure equipment that has a single, important function

specialism the area of knowledge that a person knows in detail

specialized (USA) / **specialised** (UK) modified so as to be outstandingly good at one job | specialized cells the building blocks of life have become modified so that each can carry out a particular function or job | specialized features characteristics that help the creature survive | specialized function the method has been developed to achieve a specific purpose | specialized organs well-defined structures of tissues and cells that carry out specific tasks essential for survival | specialized structure equipment that is fixed, but has a single, important function

specially adapted changed so as to be of use in a few particular circumstances

species (plural is also species) a grouping of organisms that are able to reproduce with each other, but are not able to breed with other species | animal species a group of animals with common features | endangered species groups of organisms that are in danger of becoming extinct | new species a type of organism that has not previously been described | pest species any group of organisms that make life difficult for people or for farmers | plant species a group of producers that has the ability to cross-pollinate

specific precise, definite, particular, distinctive, special | specific bacteria the stated strains of microbes | specific cause the single reason that brought about a particular incident | specific cells particular cells, parts of tissue with distinctive properties | specific damage the area of breakage, the particular type of injury | specific disease the stated illness | specific effects the particular changes | specific function the precise purpose of that article, a particular use | specific gravity the ratio of the density of the liquid to the density of pure water at the same temperature | specific illness a distinctive disease associated with some event | specific issue the particular problem, the precise question | specific job the stated types of work | specific measurements the length, weight or voltage at that particular place | specific nutrients the particular chemicals in food that will cure a deficiency or cause a reaction | specific purpose the precise intention | specific shape a distinctive form | specific thermal capacity the amount of heat energy that is needed to increase the temperature of one kilogram of the material by 1°C | specific times regular intervals that are known in advance of the event

specification a detailed description of an object or process, a required standard

specified stated, agreed

specify to state exactly

specimen an example, a sample, a piece of organic material, a biopsy, an illustration | specimen tube a small cylinder with a screw cap | fossil specimen an example of a particular type of fossil | plant specimen an object that shows the important features of that type of plant | preserved specimens dead organisms that have been kept in such a way that they have not rotted away | rock specimen an object that illustrates the characteristics of that type of rock

speck a spot, a very small part

speckled has small spots or stains

spectacle a display, a demonstration, an exhibit, a show | spectacles glasses for the eyes that help the wearer see more clearly

spectra (plural of spectrum) graphs showing the distribution of intensities at a range of wavelengths or frequencies, the different colours that are found in various light sources

spectrometer equipment for measuring the light absorbance at different wavelengths

spectrum (plural is spectra) a graph showing the distribution of intensities at different frequencies or wavelengths, the colours of the rainbow (red, orange, yellow, green, blue, indigo, violet) | electro-magnetic spectrum / em spectrum the transverse waves that can travel through a vacuum at the speed of light; these include gamma waves, X-ray, ultra-violet, visible light, infra-red, microwaves and radio waves | visible spectrum the frequencies of electromagnetic radiation to which the human eye is sensitive

speculate to dream, to have an idea, to produce a theory

speed the rate at which a specified distance is covered, the distance moved in a measured time interval; to move rapidly

$$\text{speed (metres per second)} = \frac{\text{distance (metres)}}{\text{time (seconds)}}$$

| speed at a point the rate at which an object is moving when measured at a specific place | speed camera a device that measures the speed of a car and, if the speed limit is being exceeded, will take a picture for identification of the number plate | speed of cooling the rate at which the temperature changes, the number of degrees Celsius lost each minute | speed data information concerning the rate at which an object is covering

a distance | speed equation (SIDOT) the formula relating speed to distance and time

$$\text{speed (metres per second)} = \frac{\text{distance (metres)}}{\text{time (seconds)}}$$

| speed limit the maximum speed that a vehicle is legally allowed to travel on a particular road | speed of light the distance covered by light each second, a speed of 300,000 kilometres per second in a vacuum | speedometer equipment that shows the speed at which the vehicle is travelling | speed of movement the speed associated with an object changing position | speed record the fastest that any person or object has travelled using the specified method of transport | speed of sound the speed at which a sound wave moves through a medium | speed–time graph a diagram showing time along the horizontal axis and speed up the vertical axis so the acceleration is represented by the slope of the graph, and distance can be calculated from the area under the graph | speed up to increase the rate at which distance is covered each second, to accelerate | speed of vibration frequency, the number of times the object changes direction in each second | average speed the total distance covered, divided by the total amount of time from start to finish | change of speed a shift in the rate at which distance is covered | constant speed the distance covered each second remains the same | everyday speed the speeds that would be expected to be encountered at some time during the day | finite speed the speed is not infinite, and so a measurable time is required for the object to move from one position to another | high speed covering distance in a short period of time | increasing speed the distance moved each second is getting greater | instantaneous speed the speed measured at a single position, the speed with which you are moving | light speed the limit to the rate at which distance can be covered, the speed of light in that material | maximum speed top speed, the fastest speed of which that type of transport is capable | steady speed coveringa given distance in time periods that do not change | terminal speed the fastest speed that is achieved because the thrust or weight is exactly matched by the drag or fluid resistance | top speed maximum speed, the fastest speed of which that type of transport is capable | uniform speed constant speed, the distance covered each second remains the same | wind speed the speed with which the wind is moving over the ground

speedometer equipment that shows the speed at which the vehicle is travelling

spell a short period of time, a magic wish; to convert a word into its letters | dry spell a period when there is no rain

spelled / spelt formed a word by saying each letter

-sperm (*Latin & Greek* to sow)

sperm (plural is sperm) the male reproductive cells in animals, male gametes | sperm cell a single male gamete | sperm count the number of sperm ejaculated in each cubic centimetre of semen | sperm duct / sperm tube the canal joining the testis to the base of the penis

sperm count the number of sperm in 1 cubic centimetre of semen | human sperm the male gamete has been produced by a man | low sperm count the number of sperm in the semen is sufficiently low that pregnancy is unlikely

spermatozoa (plural of spermatozoon) sperm, male gametes

spermatozoon (plural is spermatozoa) sperm, the male gamete

spermist a person who believed that the tiny person (*homunculus*) was to be found in the sperm, but needed the womb in order to develop

sphere a ball, a three-dimensional object that always looks like a circle | atmosphere the layer of gas that surrounds any planet, often refers to the 20 kilometre-deep layer of air that surrounds the Earth | biosphere / ecosphere the Earth's ecosystem, consisting of all the organisms that live on land, in the air or under water, a variety of animals and plants that are in dynamic equilibrium in a sealed container | ionosphere the part of the atmosphere between a height of 50 kilometres and 1000 kilometres, where most particles are ions | lithosphere the crust and outer mantle of the Earth | stratosphere the zone that is between 20 kilometres and 50 kilometres above the surface of the Earth

spherical like a ball | spherical Earth the model in which the Earth is shown as a ball

sphincter the muscles that control the opening and closing of a tube such as the stomach or anus

spices tasty vegetables that have been dried and ground to a powder to be used to add flavour while cooking

spider a predatory arthropod with eight legs, which is able to spin a strong thread | spider diagram a web of lines connecting many different ideas | spider's web the flat net that a spider can produce in order to catch food, such as flies

spike a sharp stick, a point; to impale on the end of a sharp rod

spiky the pointed growth from a surface

spill a thin piece of paper used to light a flame, a splint, an accidental loss of fluid; to overflow, to flow accidentally over an edge

spillage liquid that has accidentally fallen to the ground whilst being moved between containers

spilled / spilt liquid has accidentally fallen out of a container

spin to turn rapidly in a circle, to rotate | axis of spin the imaginary line around which a body rotates

spina bifida a defect in foetal development in which some of the vertebrae are incomplete so the spinal cord may become damaged

spinal concerned with the backbone, referring to the vertebrae | spinal column the set of bones from the tail to the neck through which the nerves pass | spinal cord the thick group of nerves carrying messages to and from the brain that is protected by the vertebrae

spindly a long, thin structure that appears weak

spine the backbone, a sharp, hard hair | spine bone the backbone, the vertebrae, the casing that protects the spinal cord

spinneret the tubes near the mouth of a spider from which emerges the silk threads that are used to form a web

spinning rotating, moving around a fixed point

spiral a path that goes around a central column like the thread of a screw; to follow a curve with a fixed centre, but increasing radius | spiral canal the cochlea, a tube that has been turned around a cone | spiral galaxy a collection of millions of stars that looks like a whirlpool or a Catherine wheel

Spirillum bacteria that have the shape of a spiral or helix

spirit alcohol, strength; a ghost | spirit burner a small stove that uses a wick dipped into a container of alcohol

Spirogyra freshwater algae that look like thin green filaments

splash a small volume of liquid; to drop liquid onto material

splashed covered with scattered drops of water

spleen the small organ, next to the stomach, that both destroys aged red blood cells and helps the immune system

splint a thin piece of wood, metal or paper | glowing splint a thin length of wood with a hot tip because the flame that was alight has been extinguished | lighted splint a thin piece of wood that is burning at one end | wooden splint a thin piece of wood that is used to carry a flame for a short distance

splinter a sliver, a thin piece; to break so the ends have many points

split a crack, a break along the direction of the grain; to separate, to divide

spoil the rubbish that is left after an ore has been removed; to ruin, to damage, to render useless

spoiled / spoilt became uneatable, became less useful, decayed, ruined, marred

sponge a marine animal, the skeleton of the marine animal, a type of cake, material that is able to absorb water; to remove water by absorption

spongy porous; an elastic object, a solid object filled with air pockets that that can be compressed, but will return to its original shape | spongy cells / spongy layer / spongy mesophyll the cells near the bottom of a leaf that are separated by gaps so gases can diffuse through the layer

spontaneous without thought, without previous planning, immediate | spontaneous generation production of a living organism from a mixture of chemicals

spoon concave device for transferring powders | combustion spoon / deflagrating spoon a small stage or bowl at right angles and on the end of a long rod. The spoon allows small quantities of chemicals to be burned safely within a jar of oxygen | tea spoon an implement with a long handle that is used for moving approximately 5 millilitres / 5 cubic centimetres of liquid | wooden spoon a stirring rod with a flattened end that is made from wood and is used when cooking

spore a reproductive structure similar to a seed but without an embryo plant, the fertilised reproductive cell of a fungus

spore-bearing an organism that can reproduce by spreading spores | spore-bearing reproduction the method of producing offspring that depends on the formation and spreading of spores

sports competitions, shows, exhibition of athletic skills | sports injury / sports-related injury damage to a tissue or organ caused by taking part in a competition | sports wear clothing suitable for exercise

spot a position, a small amount; to see, to find | spotlight a high intensity beam of light | blind spot the area with no light-sensory nerve endings at the back of the eye where the optical nerves move through the retina | eyespot an area of skin that is sensitive to light | light-sensitive spot / light spot an area on the head of worms or protozoa that is able to detect light | Sun spots dark patches that are seen in the image of the Sun | tar spot a drop of tar, a stain produced by contact with tar

spotlight a high intensity beam of light | spotlight bulb the half of the bulb envelope that is nearest

to the connector is covered with reflective material

spotting tile a dimple tray, a rectangle with concave indents for holding small volumes of liquid

sprain to damage a ligament

spray a bunch of flowers, a fine jet; to spread a liquid as fine jets | spray drier / spray dryer equipment that injects a fine mist of liquid into a vacuum chamber, so the solvent evaporates and the solute falls as a dry powder | spray drying removing water from droplets of water at very low temperature | spray paint a covering applied to a surface as fine jets or as a mist

sprayed covered with a fine mist, produced as a jet of tiny droplets

spraying spreading as a fine mist

spread the extent, a feast; to take up a larger area | spread of results the range between smallest and largest | spread out thinned, taking up a larger area | spread sheet a series of boxes or cells in which formulae and data can be placed

spreading moving away from a point, dispersing

spring the season from March to June, a coil of material that will change length when a force is applied, but will return to the original length when the force is removed, a jump, a source of water; to jump | spring balance a weighing machine in which the change of length of a spring has been calibrated with known weights | spring energy the amount of work that is stored in the spring because of the change in length caused by a force | spring-operated a flat coil of wire is used to store energy and then release the energy to cause a change elsewhere | springscales a weighing machine that has a coil whose length has been calibrated against weight applied | spring tide the highest tide of the month when the Moon and Sun are in line | compressed spring a pushing force has been applied so the coil has become shorter | natural spring a place where water leaves the ground and forms a stream | return spring a coil, or springy strip, of metal that causes some item to return to its original position when the force is removed | steel spring a thin strip that has been coiled under tension, a coil of wire that can be compressed or stretched then will return to its original length | stretched spring a pulling force has increased the length of the spring | strong spring a large force is needed to change the length of the coil

springy able to vibrate easily

sprinkle to spray liquid as fine drops

sprinkler equipment for producing a spray of liquid

sprinter a person who can run a short distance rapidly, often without breathing

spun turned around its own axis

spurt a sudden increase; to flow rapidly | growth spurt a time period in the early teens when the change of height becomes more rapid

spy satellite an object that is sent into orbit with the intention of finding information that others would rather be kept secret

square a shape with four sides of equal length that join at right angles | square metre a unit of area equivalent to a square of side 1 metre | punnet square a diagram showing the genetic possibilities when the genes for one parent are crossed with genes from the other parent

squash a fruit drink, a slide prepared by pressing down on cells; to press down and cause damage | fruit squash a concentrated form of fruit juice that must be diluted with water before drinking | root squash a microscope slide of root cells

squashed flattened, damaged by pressure

squeak a high-pitched note; to produce a short burst of a high-pitched note

squeaky bursts of sound with a pitch of several thousand hertz | squeaky *pop* test! the effect of hydrogen on a lighted splint is to go *squeak*!

squeeze to press the sides together

squeezing squashing, pushing inwards

squid a carnivorous marine animal with eight arms and two tentacles

squirrel a herbivorous, agile and bushy-tailed rodent that lives chiefly in trees

stability a measure of the force needed to cause a change

stable unchanging, not moving, a home for horses | stable atom an atom in which the nucleus is stable so the proton number will not change and radio-activity is not produced | stable ecosystem the number of each species remains approximately constant | **s**table equilibrium will not change unless a very big force is applied | stable population the number of a specified species remains constant in the area, an unchanging number of a stated type of life forms

stacking lead a connecting wire that has a terminal that can both be plugged into a connector and have another connector plugged into it

stage the part of a microscope on which the slide is placed, a part, *eg* of a life cycle, a period of time, a section of a rocket, a portion of journey; to show, to display | booster stage the part of a rocket that is needed to give additional force and is then discarded | key stage an important part of the whole journey

stagnant / stagnant water water that does not flow and has low concentration of dissolved oxygen, but lots of bacteria

stagnate to remain undisturbed, to go bad, to lack vitality

Stahl (George Ernst 1660–1734) was a physician who taught medicine and chemistry at Jena in Germany. He popularised the theory that a substance burned because it was losing *phlogiston*, the gain in weight following combustion was due to phlogiston having a negative weight. The theory was disproved when Lavoisier showed that oxygen was essential for combustion.

stain a chemical that is used to produce colours in the different structures of a cell, an unintentional mark on material; to change colour accidentally | Gram stain a mixture of chemicals that will colour the cell membrane of Gram-positive bacteria, but will not affect Gram-negative bacteria

stained coloured, specific cell structures have been made visible by using coloured chemicals | stained teeth the natural whiteness of the teeth has been lost due either to diet or to smoking

stainless steel an alloy of iron and other metals, *eg* chromium and nickel, that will never go rusty

staircase a set of horizontal planks or steps that connect two floors of different heights

stairs (not stares which is looking at) a series of steps joining floors at different levels

stake (not steak which is a slice of beef) a long wooden pole with a sharp end

stalactites thin columns of rock that hang from the ceilings of caves, formed by evaporation of drops of water containing dissolved solids

stalagmites columns of rock that seem to grow from the ground in caves

stalk (not stork which is a bird) a stem; to follow prey silently | leaf stalk the thin tube, containing cells for the movement of liquid, joining the leaf to the plant

stalked eye the organ of sight is at the end of a stem

stamen the male reproductive organ of a flower, an anther at the top of a filament

stamina strength to keep going over long distances or for a long period of time

stand an upright, a vertical support; to become upright | clamp stand the vertical rod that screws into a heavy base and is used to support movable fingers | retort stand the old-fashioned name for a clamp stand

standard the accepted measurement, the single piece of material against which other measurements of the same quantity can be compared, the level of competence, the expected level of behaviour | standard form representing a number as a digit between 1 and 10 multiplied by a power of 10 | **standard portion** the size of meal that would be served to the average person | **metric standard** the pieces of material (the atomic clocks, the kilogram mass and the 1 metre rule) that have been agreed as fundamental to the SI system of measurement

standardise (UK) / **standardize** (USA) to take to the same starting point so as to allow comparisons

standing charge the fixed amount charged by gas, electricity and telephone companies for providing a service

standpoint the way that observations are interpreted

stapes (the stirrup bone) one of the ossicles in the ear, the tiny bone connecting the anvil to the oval window of the cochlea

star an astronomical body that shines by its own light, volumes of nuclear fusion in the universe | **starlight** the visible energy produced by a star | **giant stars** objects that are very, very big and that turn nuclear energy into heat and light | **Pole Star** (Polaris) the star that appears to be directly over the North Pole and so never appears to move | **shooting star** grains of sand that enter the atmosphere and glow white hot by frictional heating with air molecules | **visible stars** objects that are not only close enough, but also produce sufficient light so that they can be seen by the unaided eye

starch a polymer of glucose, millions of glucose molecules joined together, the storage molecule for many plants; to make stiff | **starch distribution** the concentration of starch at different positions in the plant | **starch grains** collections of starch molecules that are visible under a microscope | **starch stores** specific areas of a plant where starch is deposited as grains | **starch test / test for starch** yellow iodine solution will turn black if starch is present

stares (not stairs which are steps) focuses all the attention on one point, gazes fixedly

starfish marine animal (an echinoderm) comprising a flattened body with five or more radiating arms

starlings omnivorous songbirds that gather in huge flocks

started begun, set out, a process or journey is under way

starter motor the electrical equipment that is used to rotate a car engine rapidly

starter's gun the equipment used by the person starting the race that not only gives an audible bang, but also produces an electrical signal that is used to start the electronic timer

starting beginning, commencing | **starting materials** the substances that are needed for the reaction to take place | **starting pistol** equipment used to start running races that both produces a bang, so the runners can hear the start, and sends an electronic signal to the timing equipment | **starting temperature** how hot or cold is the material at the beginning of the experiment

startled surprised, frightened, shocked, alarmed

starts begins, causes to begin, jumps because of a sudden noise

starve to stop eating, to deprive the body of food, to become undernourished

starving feeling very hungry, being deprived of food

state a condition, one of gas, liquid or solid, a country, a situation; to tell | **state conclusions** to tell others the meaning and importance of your investigation | **states of matter** the three possible ways that particles are arranged so as to produce a gas, a liquid or a solid | **state symbols** the letters *g*, *l*, *s* or *aq* that indicate if the material is a gas, liquid, solid or dissolved in water | **change of state / change state** the movement from a gas, liquid or solid into one of the other two states | **changing state** moving from one state (gas, liquid or solid) to one of the other states | **inert state** the object is showing no signs of activity, but is likely to become active | **mental state** a description of how close the behaviour is to the expected reaction | **physical state** how well a person is feeling, the appearance of an object | **solid state** the electronic components have been etched onto a solid slice of silicon and so the circuit is one chip | **uncorroded state** the metal surface remains bright and shiny

statement an announcement, a formal summary

states the arrangement, separation and speed of movements of particles in a substance, could be as a gas, a liquid or a solid

static unchanging, remaining still, not moving | **static charge** the area of negative charge (excess electrons) or positive charge (a deficit of electrons) that does not move | **static electricity** the area where there is a charge, the effects seen when there is an area with an unmoving charge | **static friction** the reaction force produced between two surfaces that are not moving that prevents the object from starting to move | **static structure** an arrangement that does not move, an arrangement that does not change

station a place, a position, an office | **generating station / power station** a building where an electrical current is produced, the place where chemical energy (from fuel) or kinetic energy (from moving water) is turned into electrical energy | **pumping station** a building containing the equipment that shifts water or sewage through pipes from one place to another | space station a large craft that has been constructed outside the atmosphere of the Earth and in which people are able to live, *eg* Mir | weather station a place where the weather conditions can be monitored and recorded

stationary (not stationery which is envelopes) remaining still, not moving | stationary object the article remains still | geostationary appearing to remain still when viewed from the Earth

stationery (not stationary which is static) envelopes, papers, any material used when writing

statistical variation small differences that occur whenever the same measurements are carried out several times

statistics the part of maths that studies numerical data to see if differences are important or due to random events

statue a sculpture, often about life size, of an animal or person

stature height, size, importance

stay to remain, to wait

std [sexually transmitted disease] any illness that is produced by microbes that are transmitted from one person to another during sexual intercourse

std an abbreviation for standard

steady stable, unchanging, safe | steady speed a constant speed that is suitable for that occasion

steak (not stake which is a sharp pole) a thick slice of beef that is to be cooked and eaten

steal (not steel which is an alloy of iron) to take without permission from the owner

stealth shadowy, silent, secretive

steam tiny droplets of water that form when water vapour cools down | steam bath a container that is used for heating objects using hot water vapour | steam engine any of several different designs of equipment in which steam is introduced into a cylinder and causes the piston to move | steam turbine several sets of vanes enclosed by a cylinder and which are turned when hot water vapour is introduced at one end and moves rapidly to the other before condensing to water

stearic acid [$C_{17}H_{35}COOH$] the most common acid produced by heating animal fats with caustic soda, used in making candles and soap, melting point 55°C, boiling point 360°C

steel (not steal which is to take without permission) an alloy in which metals are dissolved in molten iron and the liquid allowed to turn solid | steel bar a rod or beam made from steel | steel cable many strands of wire that are wound around each other to give a long structure that is strong under tension | steel can a closed cylinder made from steel that is used for storing food and

drink | steel rod a thin bar of steel, often with ends that are turned up, that is embedded in concrete to give more strength | steel wool a sponge made from long, thin pieces of steel tape | steelyard a type of balance used for measuring heavy weights by using movable weights, usually one arm is much longer than the other | steel yard a scrap yard, an area for collecting iron-containing materials | galvanised steel (UK) / galvanized steel (USA) the alloy of iron and other metals has been covered with a layer of zinc | stainless steel an alloy of iron and other metals, *eg* chromium and nickel, that will never go rusty

steep at a large angle, a severe slope

steepness a measure of the gradient, the slope

steer cattle; to control that direction of a vehicle

stem the part of the plant that joins the roots to the branches and leaves, the thin tube used in a liquid thermometer, the structural part of a microscope that connects the tube to the stage | stem cells the cells from an embryo that have not yet become specialised | hollow stem a tube, a rod, a shoot with a hole down the centre | swollen stem the cells of the stalk have become larger because they contain a store of food | thermometer stem the thin hollow tube into which the liquid can expand | underground stem a rhizome, a method of plant growth in which the stem grows horizontally and puts out leaves and roots at intervals

step a pace, a stride, a level that is higher; to walk | door step the block of flat, hard stone at the base of a door in the outer wall of a building

Stephenson (George 1781–1848) was a self-educated engineer who developed the idea of mounting a steam engine on to specially made wheels which could be used to pull other carriages. His first engine, the *Active* was built in 1825 and had a top speed of 24 kilometres per hour, five years later and the *Rocket* reached 58 kilometres per hour and the railway revolution had begun.

stereo- (*Greek* solid) producing a signal from two or more sources | stereo-sound adjusting the signal to two or more loudspeakers so that the apparent position of the source changes | personal stereo equipment, usually battery powered, that is used to play recorded music into earphones

stereoscopic vision having two eyes so that distances can be judged

sterile clean, no bacteria, unable to reproduce | sterile water water that has been treated so as to remove or kill all microbes

sterilisation (UK) / **sterilization** (USA) having surgery so as to prevent the possibility of fertilisation, making an area completely clean

sterilise (UK) / **sterilize** (USA) to cut either the sperm tube or the oviduct, to clean thoroughly to remove all microbes

sterilising (UK) / **sterilizing** (USA) removing all traces of microscopic life | sterilising solution a chemical that kills microbes

sterilization (USA) / **sterilisation** (UK) having surgery so as to prevent the possibility of fertilisation, making an area completely clean

sterilize (USA) / **sterilise** (UK) to cut either the sperm tube or the oviduct, to clean thoroughly

sterilizing (USA) / **sterilising** (UK) removing all traces of life | sterilizing solution a chemical that kills microbes

stern the back part of a ship or boat, strict, severe

sternum the breastbone, the strong bone between the left and right ribs

stethoscope equipment connecting the ears of the medic to the patient so that internal sounds, *eg* heartbeat or breathing, can be heard

Stevenson screen a panel, made from strips of wood at 45°, that allows air to reach the instruments in a weather station without exposing them to the heat from the Sun

stick a branch, a piece of wood; to glue, to attach | celery stick one of the branches of a celery head | meter stick (USA) / metre stick (UK) a 1 metre length of straight wood that is calibrated for distance | non-stick friction-free, material that will slide over the surface

sticky not easily removed, will not fall off, behaving like glue | sticky tape very long, thin material that has an adhesive on one side

stiff inflexible, not moving, very viscous | stiff material a substance that flows slowly, material that is able to keep its shape

stiffness a measure of how much force is needed to cause the material to bend

stigma the sticky part at the top of the female reproductive organ in flowers, feeling a permanent humiliation

stiletto a knife with a very thin blade | stiletto heels long, thin blocks that are the heels of some ladies' shoes

still unmoving, without motion, remaining, even now, continuing; equipment used for the distillation of fermented material so as to give pure alcohol

stillbirth a sad event when the foetus is dead before birth

stimulant a chemical that causes changes to the brain so you feel more alert, *eg* amphetamines and caffeine, but not alcohol

stimulate to cause an action, to increase the speed of response, to excite a reaction

stimuli (plural of stimulus) actions that cause other organisms or organs to respond

stimulus (plural is stimuli) an action or energy that causes other changes | stimulus material text, video films or music that is intended to provoke a response

sting a tiny weapon used by organisms in order to inject an irritant under the skin of another organism | bee sting the defence used by bees – they use a thin probe to inject an acid that is irritating to the skin | nettle sting the structure under a nettle leaf that is able to inject formic acid [HCOOH]; the reaction that has been produced after touching the underside of a nettle and so being injected with formic acid | wasp sting the alkaline irritant that is injected by an attacking wasp

stinging cells specialised cells that have either static barbs or small harpoons in order to deliver an unpleasant chemical beneath the skin of a consumer

stink a horrible smell, an offensive odour | stink bomb a container of two chemicals that release hydrogen sulphide when mixed

stir to move in a circular motion

stirred mixed by moving in a circle

stirrer equipment used for producing circular motion in a fluid in order to mix the contents

stirring mixing, moving round a circle

stirrup one of the tiny bones, or ossicles, in the ear, foot rests that are used when riding a horse | stirrup bone (stapes) the smallest of the ossicles

stoat a mammal that looks like a thin mouse, but is 20 centimetres long and has different coats in summer and in winter

stock a reservoir, a supply, a herd of cattle or horses, a soup, the shoulder part of a rifle, the standard, the root on to which a trunk is grafted; to keep for sale | stock management looking after animals in order to increase wealth | existing stock the amount of material or the number of animals that you know about | fish stock the population of each species of fish in the specified area | livestock the cattle, sheep or pigs that a farmer will raise in order to sell at market

Stokes (Sir George Gabriel 1819–1903) followed in the footsteps of Newton, both by being appointed Lucasian Professor of mathematics at Cambridge, in 1849, and in working in most areas of physics. His fame rests on the equations that he developed to explain the behaviour of a sphere moving through water.

stoma (plural is stomata) a tiny opening on the underside of a leaf

stomach the bag near the start of the digestive canal in which food is squished and squeezed for several hours and where some digestion takes place | stomach acid the hydrochloric acid produced in the stomach in order to allow the digestive enzymes to function and to cause the breakdown of some foods

stomata (plural of stoma) the openings or pores on the undersides of leaves through which carbon dioxide can enter without loss of water

stomatal opening the gaps on the underside of leaves, through which gases can enter and leave the leaf

stone a rock, a jewel, an imperial weight of 14 pounds (6.35 kilogram) | Stone Age the earliest Age of man, before the discovery of bronze, ended between 3000 BC and 1500 BC depending on the area | stonework the walls, foundations and decoration that are made by carving rocks | building stone large rocks that are shaped and joined to produce houses or roads | hailstones / hail stones spheres of frozen rain | ironstone a sedimentary rock that contains iron compounds and has lots of what look like tiny eggs | limestone a metamorphic rock, made entirely of calcium carbonate [CaCO$_3$], which is a harder form of chalk | lodestone a rock that is naturally magnetic and can be used as a compass | millstone a rock containing very hard fragments making it suitable for grinding cereal in a mill | mudstone a sedimentary rock with very fine grains | paving stones slabs of thin rock that are flat so can be walked on | philosopher's stone a mythical piece of rock that was thought to be able to magically turn lead into gold | sandstone a sedimentary rock made from grains of sand cemented together by silica or limestone

Stonehenge a world-heritage site near Salisbury, England, which comprises a series of massive stone blocks that were assembled between 3000 BC and 2000 BC

stood (not stud which is a button or a horse) remained upright, stopped moving

stool a seat without a backs | stools faeces, excreta that should be solid

stop to halt, to block, to end | stop clock / stopwatch a time piece or clock that has an output that can be frozen or reset to zero

stopped ended, prevented, no longer moving

stopper a plug, a push-in top for a bottle | glass stopper a block of glass that appears almost cylindrical, but is part of a cone that is used to seal bottles

stoppered a bottle in which the plug has been replaced

stopping reducing speed, coming to a halt, preventing | stopping distance the length between the event being seen and the speed being reduced to zero, the sum of the thinking distance and the braking distance for a moving vehicle | stopping force the effort that is applied in order to reduce the speed (energy is force x distance)

stops knobs that prevent further movement, halts

stopwatch a time piece or clock that has an output that can be frozen or reset to zero

storage the keeping of items in special places especially for a long time | storage tank a large container in which liquid can remain before being treated further | food storage keeping food at a cool temperature and for a limited length of time to prevent the growth of microbes | information storage keeping data for later use

store a shop, a reservoir; to keep in a safe place | store data to keep the information in a permanent form | store water to keep a supply of water in conditions that allow the water to be used safely for a specific purpose | energy store chemicals that are retained in the body for later use eg fat in animals and oils in plants | fat store tissue made from cells that contain fat | food store a cache of edible plants that has been retained in a specific place, eg nuts for squirrels | starch store the insoluble carbohydrate, starch, is retained in parts of the plants for conversion to soluble sugars when needed

stored retained, put away safely | stored data information that have been retained permanently | stored energy a state in which work can be done immediately, eg by releasing a spring, producing electricity from a battery or letting water escape from a reservoir | stored under oil a method of preventing oxygen and water reaching the item, especially the alkali metals and iron

stork (not stalk which is a stem) a wading bird with long legs and a long neck

storm a continuing and violent movement of air and rain; to rush and destroy

stove an oven, heating equipment | camping stove lightweight equipment used for heating liquids and cooking simple meals outdoors

stp [standard temperature and pressure] temperature of 0°C and pressure of 760 millimetres of mercury

straight level, without changing direction | straight coil the structure produced by carefully wrapping an insulated wire around a pencil | straight line shortest distance between two points

straighten to remove any kinks or curves

straightening removing bends, making straight

strain often means a pulling force, but should refer to the change of length per unit length, the variety of a species; to damage a muscle | strain energy the amount of work that is stored in a stretched spring | selected strains the members of a species that have the required characteristics | weakened strain the microbe that shows the important features of a particular species, but are less damaging and more easily killed

strainer a sieve, a filter used to remove large objects

strand a filament, a thread, a line | DNA strand a long string of nucleotides, one of the two filaments that wind around each other in the chromosome

strange different, unusual, peculiar

strata (plural of stratum) layers | deep strata layers of rock that are covered in hundreds of metres of other rocks | rock strata layers of rock | sedimentary strata visible layers of rock that were produced by material falling from air or water

strategy (plural is strategies) a plan, a method for achieving an aim | appropriate strategy a method that reaches a goal by using available equipment and knowledge | reading strategy a method for decoding the letters on a page

stratum (plural is strata) a layer of rocks

stratus / stratus cloud the lowest layer of clouds, up to about 500 metres above ground level

straw the thin stalks that support the seeds of corn or wheat, a thin hollow tube used for drinking

streak an irregular line

stream a flow, a small river; to move rapidly in one direction | air stream the continual movement of large volumes of air in one direction for long periods of time | blood stream the movement of blood around the body | down-stream the river and the river banks that are closer to the sea than the stated area | transpiration stream the movement of water through the stem and leaves caused by the leaf losing water through the stomata

streaming moving like a small river of water | streaming lava molten rock that looks like rivers as it flows down the side of the volcano

streamlined a smooth surface, a pointed shape | streamlined shape having a form that moves easily through fluids, a shape that minimises air or water resistance

streamlining producing a shape that has the least amount of fluid resistance

streetlamp / streetlight a source of illumination that lets you see where you are walking at night | street lighting lamps that are placed at intervals

and have a brightness that allow safe passage through a street in the dark | sodium street-lamp a method of lighting large areas in which production of sodium ions causes an orange glow

strength the intensity, an estimate of the force needed to cause a change, a concentration of active material in a solution | strength of evidence examining the balance as to whether the facts support the conclusion | field strength the size of the force around an item | gravitational field strength the size of the attraction of a mass at a specified distance from the centre of mass | impact strength the pressure at a surface when it stops a moving object | magnetic strength / magnetic field strength the size of the force produced by a magnet at a stated distance and known direction from the magnet | muscle strength the size of the force that a muscle can produce when it contracts | relative strength putting into an order based on either the force or chemical concentration | tensile strength the force that is attempting either to pull or to push (but not a bending or rotating force)

strengthen to make stronger, to add to

strengthened made stronger, less easily bent

Streptococcus (plural is *Streptococci*) any of the several species of spherical bacteria that form chains

streptomycin an antibiotic discovered in 1944, that was very effective against the bacterium that causes tuberculosis

stress (plural is stresses) apprehension; often used to mean a force applied to a solid, but should refer to the force / cross-sectional area of the solid; to emphasise, to exert a force | climatic stress the effect of long-term changes in weather has meant that organisms, such as animals or plants, find survival more difficult

stressed changed shape because a force has been applied

stretch to pull to a longer length, to extend

stretchability the amount by which a material can increase in length when pulled and yet return to its original length when the pull is removed

stretched tight, pulled between two adjustable holders, longer than at rest | stretched spring a coil that has had a force applied and so become longer

stretching becoming longer

strike a hit; to hit hard

striking hitting, distinctive, particularly attractive appearance

string a thread, a line; to add a thread | string instrument a musical instrument in which the sound is produced by vibration of a stretched string, *eg* guitar, violin | string telephone a communications tool in which two thin cylinders, *eg* yoghurt pots, are connected by a stretched piece of twine | drill string the long tube (up to 5000 metres!) that connects the drilling rig to the cutting drill bit | heart strings threads in the heart that prevent the valves turning inside out | natural string twine or cord made from animal or plant products such as cotton, flax or wool

strip a ribbon, a flat rod; to remove the outer coating | strip-light / strip-lighting a lamp in which the glass envelope is a cylinder | strip thermometer a tape, containing temperature-sensitive crystals, that shows the temperature of a surface | bimetal strip / bimetallic strip two bands of metal that are strongly bonded to each other so the strip will bend when heated | iron strip a ribbon made from iron [Fe] | magnesium strip a ribbon of magnesium metal | magnetic strip a length of steel that is a weak, permanent magnet | paper strip a piece of paper that is long and thin | reflective strip a band that is highly visible when illuminated by a light

striped (not stripped which is removed) having thick lines of alternating colours

stripped (not striped which is having lines) the outer covering has been removed

stroke the sudden stoppage of blood flow to some part of the brain often resulting in death of some brain cells; to move a hand gently over a surface

stroking moving in lines from one end to the other | stroking technique causing an iron rod to become magnetic by repeatedly moving a magnet along the rod in one direction

strong powerful, extreme | strong acid a liquid having a pH below 3 | strong alkali a solution having a pH above 10 | strong heating using a high temperature by mixing an excess of oxygen with the fuel | strong spring a coil that needs a high force to change shape

stronger more difficult to bend or break

strongest the item that is most difficult to break

strongly at the extreme | strongly acidic having a pH less than 3 | strongly alkaline having a pH value above 10 | heat strongly to use a source of heat energy that gives a high temperature

struck hit, a blow was delivered

structure a shape, an arrangement, an organisation, a building | structure of living things the arrangement of the cells within an organism, the organisation of the cell | basic structure the arrangement of the essential parts | cell structure / cellular structure the shape of the cell and the way that the parts inside a cell are arranged | common structure an arrange-ment which shows a pattern that is repeated in many places, often referring to atoms or to cells | complex structure an arrangement that is not easy to describe, an organisation that has many connecting paths | crystal structure a description of the repeating pattern of ions in a solid | dormant structure an organ that appears to be asleep or passive, but can be easily brought back into use | fibrous structure an arrangement of different materials that contains long threads | fine structure small, delicate parts that require detailed examination and understanding | flower structure the way that the different part of the plant reproductive organs are arranged | giant structure chemicals that contain millions of atoms joined together either covalently, *eg* sand, diamond, or ionically, *eg* salt crystals | internal structure the arrangement of the parts enclosed by a skin or membrane | ionic structure the solid comprise ions joined together by attraction between opposite charges, and so has a regular shape and a high melting point | layered structure the object shows planes of different materials | leaf structure the arrangement of cells within the photosynthetic organ of a plant | lung structure the organisation of tubes and vessels in the breathing organ of vertebrates | molecular structure the arrangement of atoms and bonds within a molecule | organ structure the arrangement of cells and tissues within the organ that has been specified | organic structure the arrangement of atoms in a molecule that contains carbon atoms covalently bonded to other carbon atoms | reproductive structures the arrangement of tissues that allows the organism to reproduce | specialised structure (UK) **/** specialized structure (USA) an item that is needed for a specific purpose and is arranged in a way that is suitable mainly for that purpose | static structure a framework that is intended to remain in one place

struggle a fight, a contest; to make efforts to overcome a problem

stud (not stood which is remaining upright) a type of fastening, a breeding horse

studied analysed with attention to detail, exam-ined, dissected, explored

studies (plural of study) investigations

studio a work place, especially for creating art | dance studio an area for practising movement | recording studio a sound-proof room in which a permanent record of music or speech can be made

study (plural is studies) an experiment, a set of observations, an office; to investigate, to examine in detail | biological study an experiment involving organisms, an investigation into the organisms in an area | case study using an investigation into a single event, eg the disease in one person, as an indicator of what happens in general | long-term study an investigation that takes place over a very long period of time | systematic study to decide at the start all the variables and what information needs to be collected then to ensure that all the data are obtained

stuff any substance; to fill all spaces | foodstuff any material that goes into making a meal

stuffed filled, compressed

stump the small remainder after most of the column or tooth or tree has been broken off, the upright parts of a cricket wicket

stung to have been injected accidentally with irritating chemicals from a plant or an animal

stunt a dangerous manoeuvre; to prevent growth

style the part of the female reproductive organ of a flower connecting the stigma to the ovary, type, approach | life style an approach to living

sub- (Latin under) a part of, below

subatomic smaller than an atom | subatomic particle any of the three tiny particles that are in every atom – the proton, with a positive charge, and the neutral neutron are in the nucleus, which is surrounded by a cloud of negatively charged electrons

subdivide to cut into smaller parts

subdivision a smaller part, the act of subdividing

subgroup a section of the whole group

subject a person, a topic for discussion or learning | human subject a person on whom the experiment is to be carried out

sublimation the process of turning from solid direct to gas because there has been an increase in the amount of heat

sublime to turn directly from solid to gas without producing a liquid, eg carbon dioxide

submarine below the water in an ocean, a boat suitable for descending below the ocean waves | submarine canyon a deep gorge, with steep sides, in the floor of an ocean

submerge to place under water

submersible any type of vessel that is capable of providing a working environment under water

subscript letters and numbers that are written below the main line of text

subset a smaller class within a larger group

substance a material, a chemical | addictive substance a chemical upon which the body becomes dependent | caustic substance any chemical that irritates the skin or causes paint to peel | colored substance [USA] / coloured substance [UK] material, usually a solid, that has

a discernible color | corrosive substance a chemical that is able to cause the loss of desirable properties of another material | harmful substance / hazardous substance a chemical that could damage the health, material that needs to be handled in a special way so as to avoid accidents | persistent substance a chemical that remains in one place because it does not change, or it is not excreted, or it is not degraded | pure substance material that contains a single chemical | soluble substance a chemical that will dissolve in the solvent | useful substance the material is valuable because it has a set of properties that match a need

substation / electricity substation an area containing transformers that change the very high voltage electricity to 240 volts for local distribution

substitute to replace one item with another, eg in solving equations where the numbers replace the letters

substitution the removing of one object and replacement with a similar, but different, object

substrate a chemical that is changed by an enzyme, the material at the start of a procedure

subtract to take away, to remove, to make less

suburban areas housing areas beyond the immediate work area of the city

sub-zero / sub-zero temperatures below the freezing point of water, any temperature at which water will turn to ice

successful achieving the aim, getting a good result

succinct short, concise, using few words

succumb to give in, to surrender

suck to reduce the air pressure thereby causing the movement of air or a liquid

sucked pulled by low pressure | sucked in changed shape or structure because the inside is at low pressure

sucker a stem that runs underground before emerging and eventually forming an independent plant, an organ adapted for creating a vacuum so allowing attachment to a surface

suckle to feed new born offspring at the breast

sucrose [$C_{12}H_{22}O_{11}$] a sugar extracted from sugar cane that is broken down in the gut to give fructose [$C_6H_{12}O_6$] and glucose [$C_6H_{12}O_6$]

sudden sharp, abrupt, without warning | sudden change an abrupt shift | sudden drop a decrease that is both unexpected and substantial

suffer to have a pain, to put up with an inconvenience

sufferer a person who has an injury or disease

sufficient enough, adequate | sufficient amount a quantity that is adequate for that purpose |

sufficient data a large enough number of measurements have been taken | **sufficient light** the amount of energy present in the visible light is enough for the purpose | **sufficient measurements** the numerical data is adequate to show an effect | **sufficient number** an adequate number | **sufficient observations** an adequate number of observations were made | **sufficient sample size** the amount taken was adequate to be representative of the whole batch | **sufficient size** the object is large enough for the purpose

sufficiently enough, adequately | **sufficiently wide range** the difference between the highest value and the lowest value is adequate to show the effect

suffix (plural is suffixes) letters that are put at the end of a word in order to change the meaning

suffocate to prevent air entering the lungs

sugar a chemical that tastes sweet, a simple carbohydrate, *eg* glucose [$C_6H_{12}O_6$], sucrose [$C_{12}H_{22}O_{11}$] | **sugar beet** a plant with a large swollen root from which sugar can be extracted | **sugar cane** a plant with very tall stems which contain a sugar solution, and which resembles bamboo in appearance | **sugar concentration** the amount of sugar dissolved in a given volume of a solvent such as of water or blood | **sugar lumps** cubes made by compressing small crystals of sugar | **sugar molecule** emphasising that the importance of the structure of individual sugar molecules in the chemical reactions | **sugar solution** nectar, a mixture of glucose dissolved in water | **caster sugar / castor sugar** very small crystals of sugar | **icing sugar** a finely ground sugar that mixes with water, then sets hard | **reducing sugar** any sugar capable of turning Benedict's solution to red | **test for sugar** heating a sugar with Benedict's solution will turn the solution from blue to green, then red or brown

sugars a series of organic chemicals with the general formula $C_mH_{2n}O_n$

sugary tasting sweet, sticky white crystals | **sugary texture** feels like granulated sugar with crystals that stick together | **sugary water** a solution of glucose or sucrose in water

suggest to put forward an idea, to discuss | **suggest characteristics** to decide the features that can be used for producing a key or are useful for survival

suggestions ideas, directions, hypotheses

suit matching or coordinating items of outer clothing, such as a jacket with trousers or skirt; to match the object to the purpose | **spacesuit** the several layers of protective clothing that allow astronauts to move safely in space, where the

atmospheric conditions would not support life | **wetsuit** a close fitting garment made from neoprene that is able to minimise heat loss by trapping bubbles of water close to the body

suitability fitness, appropriateness

suitable appropriate, correct, acceptable | **suitable approach** a plan that can be carried out with the equipment and knowledge available | **suitable data** measurements that allow a question to be answered | **suitable format** a presentation that shows the information clearly and appropriately | **suitable location** an area that is correct or adequate for the purpose | **suitable method** a technique that can be used to provide the information required | **suitable question** an inquiry that should be answered by developing a simple plan

suited matched, agreed with, best fitted

sulfate ion (USA) / **sulphate ion** (UK) [$SO_4^=$] the ion, or charged particle, produced when sulfuric acid reacts | **ammonium sulfate** [$(NH_4)_2SO_4$] a fertiliser used as a source of nitrogen. but it will dissolve more slowly than ammonium nitrate | **barium sulfate** [$BaSO_4$] an insoluble compound of barium that is opaque to X-rays | **calcium sulfate** [$CaSO_4$] gypsum, plaster of Paris, a white powder that can be suspended in water, poured like a liquid then turns solid when dry | **copper sulfate** an anhydrous white powder [$CuSO_4$], or beautiful blue salt crystals [$CuSO_4.5H_2O$], produced when copper oxide or copper carbonate reacts with sulfuric acid, and which can be used to kill algae in water | **iron sulfate** [$FeSO_4$] a pale green powder or crystal | **magnesium sulfate** [$MgSO_4$] a white powder | **neomycin sulfate** an antibiotic produced by a fungus | **sodium sulfate** [Na_2SO_4] the salt produced when sodium hydroxide is neutralised by sulfuric acid | **zinc sulfate** [$ZnSO_4$] a soluble, colourless salt produced by heating zinc in sulfuric acid

sulfide (USA) / **sulphide** (UK) [$S^=$] the charged particle produced when sulfur gains two electrons and forms ionic bonds | **hydrogen sulfide** [H_2S] a poisonous gas with the smell of bad eggs | **iron sulfide** [FeS] fools' gold, a compound of iron and sulfur that produces brilliant golden crystals

sulfur (USA) / **sulphur** (USA) (S, proton number 16, melting point 113°C) a non-metallic element that is usually found as a yellow powder, but can also produce a red gum or yellow crystals | **sulfur dioxide** [SO_2] a poisonous gas produced by burning sulfur or by the breakdown of sodium thiosulfate [$Na_2S_2O_3$] | **sulfur precipitator** equipment that is added to oil extracting equipment so as to remove the sulfur | **sulfur trioxide** [SO_3] the main gas produced when sulfur burns | molten sulfur the temperature of the sulfur is above the melting point (113°C), and so is a liquid, but there is insufficient oxygen for the sulfur to burn | oxides of sulfur either or both of sulfur dioxide [SO_2] and sulfur trioxide [SO_3], both of which are formed when sulfur burns, and each dissolves in water to give acid solution

sulfuric acid (USA) / **sulphuric acid** (UK) [H_2SO_4] a strong acid that always produces sulfates / sulphates [$SO_4^=$] in reaction with a metal or a base

sulfurous (USA) / **sulphurous** (UK) smelling of sulfur compounds, such as sulfur dioxide [SO_2] or hydrogen sulfide [H_2S], an unpleasant smell

sulphate (UK) / **sulfate** (USA) [$SO_4^=$] the ion, or charged particle, produced when sulphuric acid reacts | ammonium sulphate [$(NH_4)_2SO_4$] a fertiliser used as a source of nitrogen but it will dissolve more slowly than ammonium nitrate | barium sulphate [$BaSO_4$] an insoluble compound of barium that is opaque to X-rays | calcium sulphate [$CaSO_4$] gypsum, plaster of Paris, a white powder that can be suspended in water then poured like a liquid, and turns into solid when dry | copper sulphate an anydrous white powder [$CuSO_4$] or brilliant blue crystals [$CuSO_4.5H_2O$], the solution produced when copper oxide or copper carbonate reacts with sulphuric acid, which can be used to kill algae in water | iron sulphate [$FeSO_4$] a pale green powder or crystal | magnesium sulphate [$MgSO_4$] a white powder | neomycin sulphate an antibiotic produced by a fungus | sodium sulphate [Na_2SO_4] the salt produced when sodium hydroxide is neutralised by sulphuric acid | zinc sulphate [$ZnSO_4$] a soluble, colourless salt produced by heating zinc in sulphuric acid

sulphide (UK) / **sulfide** (USA) [$S^=$] the charged particle produced when sulphur gains two electrons and forms ionic bonds | hydrogen sulphide [H_2S] a poisonous gas with the smell of bad eggs | iron sulphide [FeS] fools' gold, a compound of iron and sulphur that produces brilliant golden crystals

sulphur (UK) / **sulfur** (USA) (S, proton number 16, melting point 113°C) a non-metallic element that is usually found as a yellow powder, but can also produce a red gum or yellow crystals | sulphur dioxide [SO_2] a poisonous gas produced by burning sulphur or by breakdown of sodium thiosulphate [$Na_2S_2O_3$] | sulphur precipitator equipment that is added to oil extracting equipment so as to remove the sulphur | sulphur trioxide [SO_3] the main gas produced when sulphur burns | molten sulphur the temperature of the sulphur is above the melting point (113°C), and so is a

liquid, but there is insufficient oxygen for the sulphur to burn | oxides of sulphur the mixture of sulphur dioxide and sulphur trioxide in any proportion that is produced when sulphur burns, this leads to acid rain

sulphuric acid (UK) / **sulfuric acid** (USA) [H_2SO_4] a strong acid that always produces sulphate ions [$SO_4^=$]

sulphurous (UK) / **sulfurous** (USA) smelling of sulphur compounds such as sulphur dioxide [SO_2] or hydrogen sulphide [H_2S], an unpleasant smell

sum (not some which is a few) a mathematical operation involving numbers, adding numbers together; to add, to form a total, to take all components into account

summaries (plural of summary) more than one outline

summarise (UK) / **summarize** (USA) to reduce a text to the main points

summary (plural is summaries) an outline of the theory, measurements or information | summary sheet a single page document that outlines the major ideas

summer the season when the days are longer than the nights – from May to August in the Northern Hemisphere and from November to February in the Southern Hemisphere | summer coat the fur that some animals develop in summer that is less dense and darker coloured than their winter coat | summer solstice midsummer day, the date near to June 21st when the noon Sun is at its highest point in the sky of the Northern Hemisphere | midsummer a period of approximately one month each side of the summer solstice (June 21 in the Northern Hemisphere, December 21 in the Southern Hemisphere) when temperatures are high

Sun the star that is nearest to Earth, being 8 light-minutes or 150 million kilometres away, and provides all the energy for this planet | sunburn damage to the cells of the skin caused by exposure to the heat of the Sun | sunlight / sunshine the light that is produced by the Sun and allows us to see during daytime | sun spots dark circles at the surface of the Sun | eclipse of the Sun a loss of light caused by the Moon moving between the Sun and the Earth | setting Sun the end of the day, the sun is disappearing below the western horizon

sundial a clock that uses the shadow of an upright (the gnomon) to show the time and date

sunlight the visible light energy that arrives from the Sun | reflected sunlight the light from the Sun has been reflected from several surfaces

sun-lit illuminated by light from the Sun

sunny bright, warm and dry | sunny position an area that is open to the heat and light from the Sun

sunrise the time when the night sky turns pale as the Sun starts to appear above the horizon

sunset the time when the Sun is about to disappear below the horizon

super- (*Latin* over) above

superglue a bonding agent, made by mixing two liquids, that turns solid and will stick to most surfaces

super-phosphate calcium phosphate [Ca(HPO4)2], used as a fertiliser

superscript letters and numbers that are written above the main line of text

supersonic moving faster than the speed of sound

supper the last meal of the day, a meal taken in the early evening

supple flexible, able to bend, easily bent

supplement an addition, an extra; to add to, to make additions

suppleness amount of bend, flexibility

supplied produced, made available

supplies produces, provides, reserves, food stores

supply a substance that is needed, a food store, a reservoir; to provide, to give | blood supply how effectively the blood, with its oxygen and nutrients, reaches each cell | continuous supply the material is being produced all the time | electrical supply the source of the electrical energy, could be a mains socket, power pack or cell | energy supply the material that will react and provide useful energy, *eg* food, chemicals in a battery | food supply the amount of organic material that is available to be eaten | inadequate supply insufficient amount | low-voltage supply an electrical source with a potential difference that is too low to cause permanent damage | mains supply mains voltage, electricity at the domestic potential difference [240V, 50Hz ac (UK); 110V, 60Hz ac (USA) | power supply a source of electrical current | regular supply essential materials, such as food or water, are provided at fixed intervals | rich supply lots | water supply a reservoir of water of a suitable quality and quantity

supplying providing, giving, producing

support aid, assistance, help; to hold up, to provide help | support a conclusion the summary is based on the measurements | support a prediction to have agreement between the results that were predicted and the measurements that were taken | technological support the equipment that makes the work easier

supporting helping, adding more, holding up, taking the strain | supporting material

observations that provide additional evidence for an idea

suppress to put down, to withhold, to remove electrical signals, to stop the growth, to hold back

sure (not shore which is where sea meets land) certain, confident

surface the external part that has length and width, a covering, the part that is seen; to appear above water | surface area the size of the section that is on the outside | surface membrane the thin layer on the outside of the cell | surface temperature how hot is the area on the outside | surface tension a force at the surface of a liquid that causes bubbles to form in soaps and causes the meniscus of water to be concave | surface water the rain that is not absorbed into the ground and flows off the surface into streams | black surface a covering that not only will absorb any light or heat energy, but is also very good at radiating energy | cold surface the area is at a lower temperature than the surroundings | dull surface a covering that does not reflect light | Earth's surface the area on the outside of the Earth that we are able to see and examine easily | frictionless surface a plane that other objects can slide over without slowing down | leaf surface the cuticle, the part a leaf which is wide and long | lower surface the underside, the area that is below the main structure | moving surfaces one of the two parallel planes is shifting position relative to the second | outer surface the part of the object that is affected by the outside world | plane surface a flat side | reflective surface a surface that does not absorb light, a shiny area | road surface the part of the highway that is in contact with the wheels | rock surface the outside apart of a rock that is exposed to the radiation from the Sun and the effects of wind and waves | rough surface an area that is not smooth, a plane with lots of bumps | shiny surface an area that reflects light | smooth surface an area that has no bumps or ridges, a plane that can be easily moved over | upper surface the area which is higher | white surface the outside of the material will reflect all wavelengths of light, but there will be scattering

surfactant a soap, a chemical that allows oils to be suspended as droplets in water

surge a sudden increase, a large wave; to swell, to push forward

surgeon a person who is trained to perform operations that involve opening the body of a living person or an animal

surgery (plural is surgeries) a building for medics, treating an illness by cutting into a person in order to reach internal organs

surgical extremely clean, cut with a very sharp blade | surgical gloves the protective gloves that are worn by most medical personnel in order to prevent infection when examining a patient | surgical gloves the protective gloves that are worn by most medical personnel in order to prevent infection when examining a patient | surgical instruments equipment that is used for cutting into the body of a living person

surround to enclose, to cover the whole surface

surroundings environment, the local area

Surtsey a volcanic island formed in 1963 off the south coast of Iceland

surveillance keeping a close watch, monitoring the activity

survey a general view, an overview; to look over, to examine an object or an area | survey data the information obtained by examining an area of land | geological survey examining rocks on the surface and underground so as to derive the three-dimensional arrangement of the rock | seismic survey a study of the distribution of underground rocks by listening to the echoes of controlled explosions

survival the act of continuing to live | survival of the fittest the idea that when organisms compete, then the individuals that are best suited to the habitat will survive and breed, this idea was proposed by Darwin in 1858 | survival rates the number of organisms that remain alive at the end of the period, compared to the number at the start

survive to be alive, to live through, to continue living

surviving living, lasting

suspect an idea without data to prove it, a person who is believed to have carried out a crime; to imagine something is amiss

suspend to float, to hang up, to stop

suspended left hanging on a rope, caused to be floating in air or water, but will fall to the bottom when the support is removed

suspension a mist, a very fine precipitate, anticipating an outcome, hanging from a thread | suspension mechanism the method by which an object is prevented from falling | suspension technique the means by which the objects are kept from falling

sustainable able to continue, a plan that can be maintained over time | sustainable developments changes that will continue when the external agent or money has been removed | sustainable forest new trees are planted to replace the trees that have been cut down

swallow a bird; to pass food from the mouth into the tube leading to the stomach

swallowing causing food to leave the back of the mouth and go down the oesophagus into the stomach

swamp an area of shallow water in which mud banks often appear above the surface; to add more water so the vessel sinks

swap / swop to exchange one item for another, to substitute

sweat perspiration, the water secreted on to skin in order to cool; to work hard, to produce liquid from the glands in the skin | sweat glands the tiny sacs in the skin that produce the liquid called sweat

sweating producing water from the skin in order to keep the body cool by evaporation

sweep a curving motion; to look rapidly across an area, to brush, to collect together

sweet the taste of sugar, pleasant to taste

sweetener a chemical that is added to food to make it taste sweeter, but is not necessarily sugar

sweetness a measure of how sweet a dish tastes

swelled/ swollen became bigger, increased in size

swelling becoming bigger; a bulge, an increase in volume

swerve to change direction suddenly and unexpectedly

swim to move deliberately through the water

swimmer an organism that moves itself through the water

swimming moving through water | swimming baths a building containing both a large pool of clean water, in which to immerse and exercise, and the facilities for changing | swimming pool a volume of water suitable for people to enjoy moving about

swing playground equipment; to move regularly from one side to the other like a pendulum | mood swing the state of mind changes unpredictably between happy and depressed

swinging moving like a pendulum, rhythmic movement of an object suspended by a thread

swirl to move in a circle, to whirl

swirling moving in a circle

switch (plural is switches) an item for turning lamps on and off, a controller, equipment for moving a train on to a different track; to turn on or off, to move, to exchange | switch contact the piece of metal that actually completes the circuit when the switch is closed | dimmer switch a rotating button that changes the power supplied to a lamp | electromagnetic switch a relay, a switch that is controlled by an electric current | microswitch a tiny controller | pressure switch a component that keeps the circuit open until a specified force is exceeded then the circuit is completed | push switch a controller that is turned off by pushing and then is turned on by pushing again | reed switch the position of a thin rod (a reed) is moved by changing the current in a surrounding coil | relay switch a component that allows a small current in one circuit to control a high voltage in a separate circuit | re-set switch a button that allows a system to be returned to its starting state | tilt switch uses a pool of mercury that completes a circuit when the component reaches a critical angle | trip switch a circuit breaker, a re-settable switch that turns from on to off when an event occurs, *eg* the current becomes too high | two-way switch one of a pair of switches that allows one lamp to be controlled from two distant places

switches (plural of switch) equipment that can be used to turn equipment on or off, machinery for switching train tracks

switching changing, moving states

swollen / swelled became bigger, increased in size, has greater volume, made larger, inflated | swollen stem the cells of the stalk have become larger because they contain store of food

swoop to descend suddenly on a prey

swop / swap to exchange one item for another

sycamore a large (height up to 35 metres) deciduous tree that has a leaf with five points and produces seeds with wings that are joined in pairs

syenite a group of rocks containing feldspar [$KAlSi_3O_8$] that formed from rocks deep in the magma and cooled very slowly

symbiosis two or more creatures that live in close proximity, each providing something that the other needs

symbiotic relationship two or more creatures that live in close proximity and help each other to survive, each providing something that the other needs

symbol a sign that represents an idea, a shorthand, a diagram providing information | symbol equations the reactants and products of a chemical reaction are shown using their chemical formulae | chemical symbols the shorthand for the specified chemical | circuit symbols the diagrams that are used to show electrical components (*see* inside back cover) | conventional symbols the diagrams that have been agreed to represent information or actions | hazard symbols / hazchem symbols diagrams that are used on bottles and transporters to show whether the chemical is a hazard, corrosive, inflammable or toxic (*see* inside front cover) | state symbols the letters *g, l, s* or *aq* that indicate if the material is a gas, liquid, solid or dissolved in water

symmetrical a line can be drawn so that each part is a reflection or rotation of the other part

symmetry the number of lines that can be drawn through an object to give parts that are mirror images or rotated images of each other

symptoms signs, indicators of an illness | deficiency symptoms the changes that occur in the body when a specific nutrient is missing | relieve symptoms to reduce the signs of an illness | withdrawal symptoms the feelings that occur when an addictive drug is no longer being taken

syn- (*Greek* with) together, alike

synapse the gap between two nerve cells through which signals can cross

syncline a downfold in rock layers

syndrome a particular illness, a disease, the signs of a disease | severe acute respiratory syndrome (SARS) a lung infection that originated in the Far East at the start of the 21st century

synonym another word with the same meaning

synovial fluid the liquid that separates the ends of a joint | synovial membrane the material of the capsule at the end of a joint that forms a bag around the synovial fluid

synthesis the production, the making of a material using chemistry, the joining | photosynthesis the process that occurs in the palisade cells of green plants in which the light energy from the Sun is turned into chemical energy of sugars

synthesise (UK) / **synthesize** (USA) to make, to bring together, to produce | synthesise information to produce data without an experiment, to take the results of several experiments into one explanation

synthesised manufactured by people, made in a laboratory

synthesize (USA) / **synthesise** (UK) to make, to bring together, to produce | synthesize information to produce data without an experiment, to take the results of several experiments into one explanation

synthesized manufactured by people, made in a laboratory

synthetic not found in nature, made artificially | synthetic data information that has been produced using a theory in order to test a system | synthetic material threads and cloth made from substances that have been made in the laboratory

syphilis a sexually transmitted disease caused by a bacterium

syringe a cylinder surrounding a movable piston, equipment used with a needle to inject drugs | gas syringe a piston that fits gas-tight inside a cylinder and is used for collecting or moving gases

syrup a concentrated solution of sugar in water

system an arrangement, a logical grouping, an organisation for performing complex tasks in simple steps, the overall mechanism | biological systems could be large scale, such as all the organisms in an area, *ie* an ecosystem, or could refer to the organs within a living creature | blood system the method by which the body transports nutrients, waste products and chemical messengers | body system a group of organs and tissues that is arranged so as to complete complicated changes, *eg* digestion of food, exchange of gases | cardio–vascular system the heart, arteries, veins and capillaries that, together, ensure that blood is pumped to every cell in the body | cave system an underground set of caverns and vaults that are inter-connected by passages | central nervous system (CNS) the nerve cells in the spinal cord and the brain | circulation system / circulatory system the veins, arteries and heart that are responsible for ensuring that blood reaches every cell | classification system a method for putting objects into groups on the basis of observable features | control system the sensors, network of wires, the processing unit and the other components that allow automatic control of an event | defence system / defensive system the organs and tissues that are responsible for ensuring that any invasion by microbes is prevented, the damage is limited and the invader is killed | digestive system the organs that ensure that food entering the mouth is broken down in the gut and then absorbed in the intestine with unused and unwanted material being egested | double-circulation system having one set of vessels and a pump to move blood to and from the lungs and a second set of vessels and another pump to move the blood around the body | dynamic system the components of the system are moving and inter-acting with each other | electronic system solid-state sensors are linked to a computer that automatically controls the output to motors and valves | endocrine system the collection of glands that produce chemical messengers that are carried in the blood | exchange system method by which different goods or chemicals can be swapped | excretory system the organs and vessels of the body that are involved in removing chemicals that could be poisonous | exhaust system the series of tubes, heat-exchangers, silencers or mufflers and catalysts that allows gases produced by combustion to be released into the atmosphere | existing system the method that is used either today or at the stated time | food-production system the manufacturing chain from the intensive farmer through the packaging to the shopkeeper | global-positioning system (GPS) equipment using signals from satellites in orbit to show exactly where you are on the Earth | hazchem system agreed pictures that show the dangers associated with a particular substance | hormonal system / humoral system the collection of glands that produces chemical messengers and the way they interact with each other and with the nervous system | human body systems the sets of tissues and organs that perform particular functions, such as circulating blood or digesting food | humoral system / hormonal system the collection of glands that produces chemical messengers and the way they interact with each other and with the nervous system | hydraulic system machinery in which oil at high pressure is used to move and to control the movement of pistons in cylinders, the changes in the Earth's crust caused by movement of water | immune system the organs and tissues responsible for producing the white blood cells and antibodies that destroy an infecting microbe | imperial system the agreed standards of measurement that was used in those countries that did not adopt the metric system | labelling system equipment that is used to produce permanent markers, the plan that is used to identify components | life-support systems the machinery that ensures the temperature, concentrations of oxygen, carbon dioxide and moisture and air pressure are kept within the limits that are suitable for life | living systems the collection of producers and consumers that live in an area | metric system / SI system the agreed units for the measurement of mass, length and time that was developed by the French in 1805, and accepted world-wide in 1960 | muscle system the sets of long cells that can contract and relax, together with any tendons attached to the bones in order to make movement possible | nervous system the cells that respond to stimuli, pass messages to and from the brain and cause a response | organ systems the sets of organs that are each responsible for a major aspect of a complex task | organic system the small parts that make up the system may grow, divide and respond to local conditions so the system is able to survive | pneumatic system using air under pressure either to control a system or to provide the energy for opening and closing valves | reproductive system the organs that are responsible for ensuring the production and movement of gametes then the development and nurturing of offspring | respiratory system the several tissues and organs that are needed for exchange of gases to occur, including the lungs, the trachea and bronchi | root system the arrangement of plant tissues that is responsible for absorbing water and nutrients then moving the liquid to the stem | SI system [Système International d'Unités] a range of accepted measurements, based on standards that are kept in France, including length, mass and time | skeletal system the bones of the body, the arrangement of hard material that provides support and protection for the organs | Solar System the collection of planets, asteroids, moons, comets and dust that move around the Sun | transport system the fixed and moving parts that are used to carry materials around the organism | vascular system tubes for the transport of liquid | weather system areas of high pressure and low pressure in the atmosphere and their movement which are ultimately responsible for the weather

systematic pre-planned, methodical, a plan for collecting information was formed before the collection started | systematic investigation deciding near the start which experiments need to be carried out and what measurements should be taken | systematic measurements deciding which measurements should be made before the start of the experiment, so that no measurement is taken twice and none is missed out | systematic observations deciding the order that information should be collected | systematic study deciding which experiments, measurements and observations should be made and in what order

systematically methodically, keeping to a plan

Szent-Györgi (Albert von 1893–1986) started to study medicine at Budapest in 1911, but was called up into the Hungarian Army where he was both decorated for bravery and labelled a troublemaker! He finished his medical degree and went on to study natural chemicals. He isolated ascorbic acid in 1929, the year that Hopkins & Eijkman received the Nobel Prize for their work on vitamins. Szent-Györgi and was awarded the Nobel Prize in 1937 for showing that ascorbic acid was vitamin C. He moved on to explain the chemical changes that occur when muscles contract. He was in the resistance movement during World War II and, at the end, was offered the Presidency of Hungary, but decided to move to Woods Hole in the USA.

T... / tera ... (*Greek* monster) prefix for a million, million of a unit, 10^{12}

t [time] the duration, usually in seconds

t [tonne] a unit of mass equal to 1000 kilograms

tabla a drum

table a set of related results arranged in columns and rows, a flat surface, peice of furniture | table of results the measurements are arranged systematically in columns and rows | table salt a fine powder of sodium chloride [NaCl] | appropriate table the columns, titles, units and rows are all suitable for that experiment | periodic table the atoms in order of proton number in a suitable shape of table so that elements with similar properties are in the same column | results table a systematic arrangement of the measurements so as to show if your idea is correct | truth table method used in logic circuits for showing the output at different inputs | water table the upper level reached by underground water

tablet a pill containing a known dose of a drug, a solid medicine | broken tablet the pill has been split into smaller pieces | crushed tablet the pill has been mechanically ground to a powder | glucose tablet a pill made from sugar and eaten so as to give an immediate increase in blood-sugar level | indigestion tablet a pill that contains a neutralising agent | whole tablet a pill that has not been broken

tabulate to produce a table from available data

tabulating putting into a table, counting | tabulating data putting measurements in to columns with titles and units

tack a small nail with a wide head, a long stitch; to join together loosely

tackle equipment; to work at, to take on

tadpole the very young form of a frog that has a tail and gills and lives in water

tail (not tale which is a story) the slender extension of the spine of many animals

take to remove, to obtain | take account of to consider, to use details | take in to eat, to observe, to realise, to deceive | take off to remove a layer, to rise

taken removed, recorded, captured | time taken the duration from start to finish

talc a fine powder of magnesium silicates

tale (not tail which is the extension that a dog wags) a story

talk (not torque which is a turning force) a lecture, a speech; to speak, to communicate verbally

tall high

taller greater height, higher

tallest most tall, highest, having the greatest height

tallied counted, agreed in number

tally chart a table of results in which each positive item is given a tick or a tally

talons claws for gripping prey

tangle a muddle; to mix threads

tangy sharp taste

tank a large box, an army vehicle | aeration tank the large container used in a sewage plant in order to provide air for the microbes | ballast tank the cylinders on the side of a submarine that can be partially filled with water so the submarine remains at a particular depth | fuel tank the container in which the fuel is stored or carried | settlement tank a large box in a sewage plant that allows suspended material to sediment | storage tank a large container in which liquid can remain before being treated further | water tank a large container connected to pipes that allow water in or out, which is used for storing a volume of water that is adequate for the specific purpose

tap a control device for liquid flow, a small hit; to hit gently, to remove fluid | tap funnel an open cylinder that narrows at each end, but the bottom part has a device to control the loss of liquid | tap hole an opening at the bottom of a vessel that is usually kept closed with a removable bung | tap water the water that flows when the sink tap is opened | gas tap a valve used to control the flow of a gas, often refers to the tap that controls the flow of inflammable gas to a bunsen burner

tape a long strip; to seal, to record | tape cassette a plastic moulding that holds a magnetic tape for the recording and playing of music | tape measure a strip of material marked off in units of length | tapeworm a parasite in the gut that attaches by the head then has thousands of body sections | audio tape magnetic tape that is used for recording sound | magnetic recording tape / magnetic tape a very long strip of plastic that has been coated with a thin layer of very fine iron powder and can be used for recording information | sticky tape very long, thin material that has an adhesive on one side

taped recorded onto a magnetic tape

tar a thick dark liquid containing high-molecular-mass hydrocarbons | tar content the amount of nasty black tar that is produced when the cigarette is burned | tar sand sedimentary rock containing hydrocarbons with high melting points | tar spot a drop of tar, a stain produced by contact with tar | coal tar the dark liquid produced by heating coal then condensing the vapour

tare (not tear which is to rip) empty, a weed; to take to zero

target an objective, something to be aimed at | **target group** the set of people at which the work is aimed

tariff a list of taxes or charges

tarnish a darkening of a metal surface caused by a chemical reaction; to darken the surface of a metal

tarnished stained, dull, discoloured

tarnishing loss of the shine from the surface of a metal because of a chemical reaction

tarry to take your time, to move slowly, to delay

tarsals the bones in the ankle | **metatarsals** the long bones in the feet

tartaric acid [(CHOH COOH)$_2$] the acid found in many fruits, especially grapes

tasks jobs, challenges, chores

taste the sensation felt by putting food on the tongue; to eat a little, to find the sensation | **taste bud** a nerve ending on the surface of the tongue that responds to a particular set of chemicals | sharp taste tart, without any taste of sugar or salt

tasteless without taste, bland

taught (not taut which is stretched) instructed, passed on some knowledge or skill, gave lessons

taut (not taught which is instructed) stretched, tight

taxonomic concerned with classifying | **taxonomic features** the observable characteristics that are used to divide organisms into groups | **taxonomic groups** the many sets produced by dividing organisms

taxonomy classification of the millions of organisms on this planet, the divisions are: kingdom – phylum – class – order – family – *genus – species*

TB [tuberculosis] a disease caused by a bacterium *mycobacterium tuberculosis* that usually infects the lungs but may spread through the body

tea a drink, a late afternoon meal | **tea bag** a porous paper sac that retains the tea leaves but allows the hot water to pass in and out | **tea light** a small, wide candle that will burn for several hours, also called a night light | **tea-spoon** an implement with a long handle that is used for moving approximately 5 millilitres / 5 centimetre cube of liquid

teach to give information, to show, to educate, to instruct

tea light a small, wide candle that will burn for several hours, also called a night light

team a group of people with a common purpose

tear (not tare which is to zero) a rip, a crack, a drop of salty water from the eye; to rip, to pull apart | **tear glands** the group of cells at the side of the eye that produce a solution for rinsing and sterilising the surface of the eye | **tear resistance** the ability of the material to stop a cut or rip from spreading though the cloth

tears (not tiers which describes different levels) an excess of the liquid produced to clean the front of the eyes often in response to strong emotion

tea-spoon an implement with a long handle that is used for moving approximately 5 millilitres / 5 centimetre cube of liquid

teat a nipple, the tissue of a mammary gland where milk appears, a cylinder of plastic or rubber that is closed at one end | **teat pipette** a tube, closed at one end, with a cylinder that can be squeezed, used to transfer liquids

technique a method, a procedure | **alternative technique** a separate method | **appropriate technique** the procedure is the best for those circumstances | **aseptic technique** working in a way that ensures no microbes are present | **experimental technique** the practical method used | **insulation technique** the manner in which heat movement is prevented, the way of preventing a flow of electricity | **practical techniques** methods that are possible to carry out in practise, and give reliable results | **range of techniques** several different methods, using distinct and complementary types of equipment and analysis | **safe techniques** procedures that have little risk of hazard | **sampling techniques** methods that ensure the small amount taken is the representative of the major part | **separation techniques** processes for isolating the individual components from a mixture | **stroking technique** turning a rod of iron into a magnet by moving a permanent magnet in one direction along the rod | **suspension technique** a method for hanging an object, a procedure for getting particles to float in a fluid

technological the application of science, the development of new equipment, production of new materials | **technological development** advances in the equipment available | **technological solution** using science to produce machinery that will solve a problem | **technological support** developing new equipment to allow experiments to be carried out more precisely or economically

technology the equipment produced by applying science | **alternative technology** using renewable resources to use and to transform energy on a large scale | **biotechnology** using an understanding of the processes of life so as to make new materials, (the biggest user of biotechnology is biologically active washing powders) | **control technology** the hardware, from simple switches to complete computer systems, that allows you to decide the value of each important variable | low-level technology machinery that can be made using a few, simple tools, not complicated

tectonics structures, the study of the structure of the Earth's crust | tectonic movement the change in position and direction of the panels that make up the Earth's crust | tectonic plates the division of the Earth's crust into several thin, rigid panels, earthquakes and volcanoes occur where the plates meet | plate tectonics the study of the panels that make up the crust of the Earth

teeth (plural of tooth) the hard, white projections from the gums that are used to hold, tear, rip, bite into and to chew food | baby teeth (also known as 'milk teeth') the temporary teeth that start to become visible at a few weeks old and drop out about six years later | canine teeth long projecting teeth at the 'corners' of the jaw that are able to penetrate muscle and then lock together so preventing the escape of the prey | healthy teeth the teeth are strong, not chipped and without bacterial growth or plaque | incisor teeth the cutting teeth at the front of the mouth | milk teeth the 28 teeth produced by babies that drop out and are replaced by 32 permanent teeth | molar teeth the crunching teeth with flat surfaces near the back of the mouth | permanent teeth the teeth that replace the milk teeth and should remain in your jaw for the rest of your life | primary teeth the first teeth, milk teeth, baby teeth | sharp teeth able to cut into flesh or food | stained teeth the natural whiteness of the teeth has been lost due either to diet or to smoking | wisdom teeth the back set of molars that erupt from the gums during the mid-teens

Teflon™ (PTFE, poly-tetra-fluoro-ethene) a polymer made by joining millions of molecules of tetra-fluoro- ethene [CF_2:CF_2] forming a non-stick surface

tele– (*Greek* far off) at a distance

telecommunications spreading and obtaining data using electromagnetic waves

telephone electrical equipment that allows communication by speaking | string telephone two cylinders, each with a thin base closing one end, connected by a length of thread that is kept taut, used for transmitting speech

telescope equipment for making distant objects appear to be closer | Hubble telescope a telescope that was launched in 1990, orbiting the Earth, so there is no atmosphere to distort the image | radio telescope equipment for receiving and analysing long-wave electromagnetic radiation

television equipment for producing a visual image from a signal produced a long way away

tell to give information, to say

temp. temperature, temporary

temperature hotness, a measure of the speed of vibration or movement of particles, the figure shown on a calibrated thermometer | temperature affects changes that occur when the substance becomes hotter or colder | temperature change a variation in how hot or cold is the substance | temperature data information concerning variation in the hotness | temperature difference the change in hotness either over time or between two points | temperature gradient the average difference in temperature for every centimetre of thickness | temperature line an axis showing how hot is each item | temperature probe equipment for measuring how hot or cold is a substance, a thermometre | temperature range the difference between the hottest point and coldest point | temperature rise the increase in hotness | temperature scale the numbers that are attached to the two fixed points and the number of graduations between them, *eg* the celcius scale is fixed by the water freezing at 0°C and water boiling at 100°C | temperature sensor equipment that can be used to measure how hot is the material, a component that changes state at a specified temperature | temperature variation difference in hotness or coldness either through a period of time or between several points | absolute temperature the temperature measured on the absolute or kelvin scale, which is numerically the same as the temperature in °C plus 273.14 (*eg* the freezing point of water is 273.14 kelvin) | air temperature the temperature of the air in a shadow so the thermometer is not affected by radiant heat from the Sun | baseline temperature the stable temperature before the experiment started | body temperature the expected temperature of the healthy human body, usually taken to be 37.6°C | boiling temperature boiling point, the temperature above which the liquid form cannot exist | change of temperature to shift the temperature from one value to another, the value of the variation in temperature | characteristic temperature the temperature at which an obvious change occurs for that material, *eg* water freezes at 0°C | common temperatures the temperatures that would be expected to be found for that type of object or reaction | constant temperature the actions or the objects will remain at the same temperature | difference in temperature one object is hotter than the other by the amount stated | fixed temperature the temperature should not change | freezer temperature the temperature used in a food freezer, which should be –20°C for household freezers | freezing temperature freezing point, the temperature at which the liquid turns solid | freezing temperatures the weather is sufficiently cold that water will rapidly turn to ice | global temperature an average of the temperature at all points on Earth | high temperature the object is at, or needs to be at, a hotness that is difficult to achieve | higher temperature the hotness of the object needs to be increased, one object is hotter than the other | ignition temperature the temperature at which a substance will start to burn | increasing temperature the temperature is going up | low temperature the object feels very cold and is probably below 0°C | lower temperature one object is less hot than another, heat needs to be removed for the process to continue | measure temperature to use a calibrated instrument (thermometer) to give a numerical value for the hotness of an object | monitor temperature to measure the temperature in order to ensure that the values stay within defined limits | night temperature the temperature of the air after the Sun has set | outside temperature the temperature of the air outside the building | oven temperature the temperature that is used inside the oven for cooking, typically between 120°C and 240°C | range of temperatures the temperatures of several different objects | refrigerator temperature the temperature inside the refrigerator after the door has been closed, should be 4°C | rise in temperature the material becomes hotter | room temperature (rt) the temperature that is measured in the room, a comfortable working temperature of between 15°C and 25°C | skin temperature the temperature measured at the skin, this temperature is usually lower than the temperature of the body because heat is lost from the skin | starting temperature the temperature of the object at the start of the experiment | sub-zero temperatures below the freezing point of water, any temperature at which water will turn to ice | surface temperature the temperature at the surface of an object | typical temperature the expected temperature for that object | warm temperatures the conditions are pleasant for people

template a pattern, a mould, a guide

temporary not permanent, a limited period of time, a special occasion | temporary deafness loss of hearing that will be restored | temporary magnet a coil of wire that is magnetic only while an electrical current is flowing

tendon the tissue connecting muscle to bone, which is essential for movement

tennis ball a pressurised rubber sphere used in the game of tennis | tennis elbow a painful inflammation of the capsule or fluid at the elbow joint

tensile strength the force that is needed to pull the item into two

tension a pull, a stress, a strain | pre-menstrual tension (PMT) the changes in mood that occur in some women just before the start of her monthly menstrual bleeding | surface tension the pull between the molecules of a fluid that allows liquid bubbles to form and the meniscus to curve at the edge

tent a cloth shelter | oxygen tent covering the face with a plastic sheet so that the oxygen concentration of the air that is breathed can be made higher than the surrounding air

tentative possibly, not very certain

tepid warm, neither hot nor cold

tera... / T... (*Greek* monster) prefix for a million, million, 10^{12}

Terishkova (Valentina born 1937) was a Russian factory worked who qualified as a sports parachutist and became the first woman in space, in 1963, on the last flight of the *Vostok* series

term a technical word, an expression, a period of time | appropriate term the correct word, the specific expression | key terms the important words that are needed to understand the subject | long-term a long period of time | related terms words that have a similar meaning | scientific terms the expressions that have a special meaning to a scientist | short-term a short period, the immediate future

terminal final, end, a connector, the part of a component that connects to a wire | terminal bud the structure at the end of a twig that will become a leaf | terminal speed / terminal velocity maximum speed, the speed at which the pushing and resisting forces are equal | negative terminal the cathode, the part of the electrical cell that has an excess of electrons | positive terminal the anode, the end of a battery that has a positive charge

terminology jargon, the correct words that are used in any specialised area | appropriate terminology suitable words, use of words and equations that can be understood by the audience | scientific terminology the expressions that are specific to science, words with special meanings to scientists

terms of a viewpoint, providing a restriction on the analysis of information, conditions for an arrangement or an experiment

tern (not turn which is to rotate) a small seabird that is found worldwide

terra- (*Greek* the Earth)

terrestrial concerned with the Earth, consisting principally of land, living on the ground | terrestrial habitat the type of living area and conditions that are found on land | extra-terrestrial an object that originates, or is found, somewhere other than on this Earth

tertiary the third level | tertiary consumer the organism that eats the animal that has eaten a herbivore

Terylene™ a brand of polyester that is used in clothing

test a check, a measurement, an exam; to check, to measure | test for carbon dioxide clear lime water will turn milky if carbon dioxide is added | test for fat will turn paper permanently trans-lucent, will dissolve in alcohol and then give a milky solution when water is added | test for hydrogen a lighted splint will go *pop!* | test for oxygen relights a glowing splint | test for protein blue biuret solution will turn violet if protein is present | test for starch a yellow solution of iodine in potassium iodide will turn black if starch is present | test for sugar heating blue Benedict's solution with sugar will turn the liquid to green then yellow and, finally, to a dull red | test for water turns blue cobalt chloride paper to a pale pink, freezes at 0°C, boils at 100°C | test ideas to carry out experiments that will check the theory and the predictions that are possible | test predictions to state what should occur and then carry out experiments to see if the results match these predictions | test-tube a glass cylinder closed at one end, with a round bottom, which is used for mixing small quantities of chemicals | additional tests further checks, more measure-ments need to be carried out | alcohol emulsion test a solution is made by mixing food with alco-hol then water is added, the solution will turn milky if fat is present | biuret test is specific for proteins, blue biuret solution reacts with pro-teins to give a violet colour | breath test esti-mating the amount of alcohol in the blood by measuring the amount in a breath | chemical test a measurement that involves reaction with an-other chemical | fair test an experiment in which only one variable is changed | flame test spraying the material into a colourless flame and measuring the intensity and wavelength of the colour | food test any measurement that is carried out in order to find the composition of food | Heaf test a skin test to see if you are immune to tuberculosis | iodine test a yellow solution of iodine will turn black if starch is present | lighted splint test checking to see if a gas is hydrogen, which is shown by a lighted splint going a squeaky *pop!* | lime water test clear lime water turns milky if carbon dioxide is added | moisture test blue cobalt chloride paper turns pale pink if the air is damp | *pop!* test a lighted splint causes a mixture of air and hydrogen to go *pop!* | preliminary tests the first experiments that are carried out to check for safety and speed of reaction | safe test an investigation in which no hazard or danger is expected | squeaky pop test! the effect of hydrogen on a lighted splint is to go *squeak!* | starch test yellow iodine solution will turn black if starch is present

ter

↓

tex

tested checked, measured, analysed

testes (plural of testis) spherical organs that prod-uce the sperm in male mammals

testicles testes, spherical organs in which sperm are produced

testing measuring, checking, analysing, trying out | soil testing measuring the pH and minerals in the earth

testis (plural is testes) one of the small spherical organs in which sperm are produced

testosterone the male sex hormone produced in the testes and causing the secondary male characteristics

test tube a glass cylinder closed at one end with a round bottom that is used for mixing small quantities of chemicals | test-tube baby a child that has been born after the ovum was fertilised by sperm in a petri dish, and then the fertilised egg and implanted back into the womb of the mother | test-tube holder a peg for holding hot tubes safely | test-tube rack parallel strips of metal, plastic or wood, with holes that allow test-tubes or boiling-tubes to be held upright | test-tube reaction a chemical change that is carried out on a small scale

tetanus lockjaw, a disease caused by a microbe that causes all the muscles to contract

tetra- (*Greek* four)

text the writing, the words, the document | appraise text to scan through a section in order to obtain the main ideas | coherent text writing that uses full sentences and allows the arguments of the writer to be followed | continuous text writing in full sentences that flows and is complete

textiles concerned with the uses and production of cloths, materials for the manufacture of cloths |

textile industry the factories and people that are employed either to make cloth from wool or cotton or to make clothes from the material

texture the structure, the appearance, the arrangement, the composition by feel | rock texture the size and arrangement of the crystals within a rock | interlocking texture the grains or particles of a rock fit together so the rock is non-porous | non-interlocking textures the grains or particles of the rock do not fit closely together so the rock is porous | sugary texture small crystals that stick together

textured structured, made into new arrangements | textured vegetable protein (TVP) removing the protein from nuts or seeds, especially soya, and producing foods that look and taste different

thalassaemia (UK) / **thalassemia** (USA) an inherited disease in which the haemoglobin does not function adequately

Thales (of Miletos 625–550 BC) was a merchant who was born in the same town in Turkey as Anaximander and he would be familiar with all of the Mediterranean countries. Thales was considered to be one of the earliest scientists, he developed ideas in geometry and tried to offer natural explanations for all his observations, including the magnetism of some stones

thatch a roof made from bundles of plant material; to produce a roof from plant stems

thawed turned from ice to water

thawing turning from solid to liquid

thaws turns from solid to liquid because of an increase in the amount of heat energy

theater (USA) / **theatre** (UK) a large hall in which an audience can watch a live performance, a place where medical surgery takes place

their (not there which is position) possessed by more than one person

theme park an entertainment area with lots of exciting / thrilling rides

theories (plural of theory) ideas, hypotheses

theory (plural is theories) an idea, a hypothesis, a proposal | theory of matter an idea that all the properties of a substance can be explained by assuming that every substance is made from tiny particles | accepted theory an idea that has been proved, an established thought | cell theory the idea that all living organisms are made from tiny units called cells | collision theory kinetic theory, the idea that particles must collide with sufficient energy for a chemical reaction to occur | homunuclus theory the idea that the testes produced tiny replicas of people that then developed in the female | kinetic theory particle

theory, the speed of the particle depends on the temperature | particle theory the idea that all matter is made from tiny particles in constant motion | phlogiston theory the idea that 'burning stuff' is given off by any substance that is undergoing combustion | scientific theory an idea that is based on observations and can be used to predict how materials will react

therapy a course or a method of treatment

there (not their which is possession) a position, at a distance

therefore consequently, for that reason

therm- (*Greek* heat)

thermal anything to do with heat or temperature, an upwards movement of air | thermals under-clothes that are designed to prevent loss of body heat | thermal break a plastic barrier separating two metal structures | thermal capacity the amount of heat needed to change the tempera-ture of the substance by the stated temperature | thermal conductivity a measure of how quickly heat will flow through a rod | thermal conductor a solid material, usually metal, that will allow heat to move rapidly | thermal contraction the object becomes cooler and so becomes smaller | thermal current a convection current, the upward movement of a fluid caused by heating the lower regions | thermal decomposition the breakdown of a chemical caused by heating | thermal energy heat energy, vibrational energy | thermal expansion an increase in size caused by an increase in temperature | thermal insulation using material so as to prevent movement of heat | thermal insulator a material that prevents the movement of heat | thermal lining a thin layer of insulating material that will prevent the movement of heat | thermal radiation the heat or infra-red radiation given off by any surface that is at a temperature higher than the surroundings | geothermal to do with the hot rocks

thermal capacity the amount of heat needed to change the temperature of the substance by the stated temperature | specific thermal capacity the amount of heat energy that is needed to increase the temperature of one kilogram of the material by 1°C

thermals clothing (often underwear) intended to keep the wearer warm, upward currents of warm air

thermistor an electrical resistor in which the value of the resistance depends on the temperature

thermit process / thermite process the exo-thermic displacement reaction that occurs when aluminium is heated with iron oxide

thermo- (*Greek* heat) concerned with heat

thermocouple a type of thermometer made by wrapping each end of one type of metal wire around the ends of two other wires and measuring the potential difference

thermogram / thermograph a picture produced by using the infra-red or heat radiation

thermography using the heat loss from a surface to produce pictures

thermometer an instrument for measuring temperature | thermometer stem the thin hollow tube into which the liquid can expand | air thermometer / air-in-glass thermometer equipment that uses the change in volume or pressure of air to measure temperature, a flask with a large volume is attached to a hollow glass tube that is sealed with a drop of oil | alcohol thermometer / alcohol-in-glass thermometer a reservoir of alcohol and colouring is able to expand up a glass stem, invented by Fahrenheit in 1709 | appropriate thermometer choosing the thermometer with the correct range and accuracy | clinical thermometer an alcohol-in-glass thermometer with a kink in the stem that prevents the liquid from returning to the reservoir, a thermometer which retains the highest measurement until shaken | gas thermometer the volume (or pressure) of a reservoir of air is used to measure temperature | glass thermometer any method of measuring temperature that depends on a reservoir of liquid attached to a transparent glass capillary tube | immersion thermometer any thermometer where the reservoir has to be submerged below the liquid whose temperature is to be measured | liquid thermometer / liquid-in-glass thermometer the thermometer is a reservoir of the named liquid which expands into a thin tube | maximum-and-minimum thermometer an instrument that has markers to show the highest and lowest temperatures that were measured since the instrument was reset | mercury thermometer a reservoir of mercury is able to expand up a thin stem as the temperature increases, invented by Fahrenheit in 1714 | strip thermometer a tape, containing temperature-sensitive crystals, that shows the temperature of a surface

thermoplastic a plastic that can be repeatedly heated, reshaped then cooled

Thermos™ / Thermos™ flask a dewar vessel, a container with concentric walls made from silvered glass separated by a vacuum, and used to keep liquids at a constant temperature

thermoset a plastic that irreversibly turns hard after heating

thermosetting plastic synthetic material that starts off soft, but turns permanently hard after heating and cooling

thermostat a switch that is controlled by temperature

thiamine vitamin B1, a water-soluble vitamin found in yeast, deficiency leads to a disease called beri-beri

thick deep, wide, difficult to see through, flows slowly | thick clothing the outerwear that has several layers and prevents heat loss | thick glass a glass that is sufficiently deep for the effects of refraction to be obvious

thicken to make more viscous, to add more layers

thickening becoming more viscous, powder that is used in cooking to turn a liquid into a cream

thicker greater separation, increasingly difficult to flow, more viscous, more muddy

thickness distance, depth, width, muddy, difficult to make flow, viscosity

thigh the area of the body at the sides and front of the upper parts of the femur | thigh bone (femur), the bone joining the hip to the knee cap

thin not fat, slender, lean

things objects, gear, equipment, kit | living things organisms, microbes, plants

think to imagine, to contemplate, to analyse, to try to understand, to consider

thinking distance the length you travel while deciding what response to make to an incident in front of you

thinner less fat, lower diameter

thinnest least thick, most slim

thistle funnel equipment with a cylinder shaped like the flower of a thistle on the top of an open glass tube

Thomson (William, Baron Kelvin of Largs 1824–1907) was one member of an intellectual family – his father had started as a farm labourer and ended as professor of mathematics, and his brothers were each distinguished in science. William started studying at Glasgow, left to travel, then returned as Professor of Physics – a post he held for 53 years. Thomson showed that heat and electricity flowed in similar ways, and showed that electricity should be transmitted at high voltage, his house was amongst the first to be lit by electricity (1881). He made a fortune by directing the laying of the first successful transatlantic cable (1866) and he took up sailing with enthusiasm – which meant he had to develop new navigational instruments. His work on the expansion of gases led to methods for producing very cold liquid gases and the idea of an absolute temperature scale that is measured in kelvin

thorax the chest, the region of the body containing the lungs

thought an idea, a judgement, a conclusion | thought experiment using the imagination to think what could happen in the practical situation | creative thought taking known facts and providing new explanations

thousand ten hundred, 1000, 10³, kilo...

thread a filament, a thin string, a fine line, the thin column of liquid in a stem of a thermometer | plastic thread a filament made from a polymer | silken thread a soft, strong, glossy fibre

threat a menace, a promise to cause damage, a change that may cause loss of habitat

three the number between two and four | three-core flex the three insulated wires inside a plastic sleeve that connects the mains electricity plug to the equipment | three-dimensional model an example or form that has height, width and depth | three-pin plug the standard connector that is used to join electrical equipment to mains power in the United Kingdom

threw (not through which is finished or around) hurled, propelled an object into the air

thrive to be successful, to grow rapidly, to do well

thriving growing abundantly, doing well

throat the area at the back of the mouth, the larynx, the voice box | sore throat the area at the back of the mouth is painful, usually due to an infection

thrombosis (plural is thromboses) a clot forming inside a blood vessel that will block circulation

throne (not thrown which is hurled) a chair for the king or queen

through (not threw which is hurled) via, following a route, by means of, finished | break-through a method that helps solve many problems; to make a discovery, to develop theory that explains all available evidence, to reach the other side of a barrier | pass through to cause a gas to bubble through a liquid, to cause a fluid to flow between solid particles

throughout all the time, the duration of a project, all the object

throwing launching, hurling

thrown (not throne which is a special chair) hurled with force, flung away

thrush a type of bird, a fungal infection of the mouth, throat or vagina

thrust a directional and forceful push; to push | thrust force the push that causes an object to increase speed | up-thrust the force causing an object to float

thruster a rocket that produces push | forward thrusters rocket engines that eject hot gases at high speed so as to increase the forward speed of the rocket | reverse thrusters the tubes that eject hot gases in order to decrease the speed of a rocket

thumb the digit that is in opposition to the fingers of the hand

thumb tack (USA) a drawing pin, a short sharp needle with a wide surface at one end

thunder a continuing noise caused by the heating effect of lightning flash | thunderstorm noisy weather in which there is a massive amount of rainfall and frequent bolts of lightning

thyme (not time which is duration) a herb

thyroid gland a small organ in the neck that produces hormones for the control of growth

tibia the shin bone, the thicker of the long bones in the lower leg

tic (not tick which is an ectoparasite) a nervous twitch

tick (not tic which is a twitch) a tap, a beat, a mark, an ectoparasite in a group that includes lice and mites

ticker timer equipment that moves a small hammer 50 times each second

tidal concerned with the changing height of the sea | tidal barrage / tidal barrier the wall that is built across a bay so the changing height of tide forces water to pass through the dynamos | tidal energy / tidal power using the change in height of the sea to provide energy or power | tidal-power station a building that contains equipment for producing electricity from the rise and fall of tides | tidal range the difference in sea level at the time of the highest and lowest tides, varies from 30 centimetres in the Mediterranean to 16 metres off the Atlantic coast of Canada | tidal rivers the depth of the stream or river is dependent on the height of the sea

tide (not tied which is a knot) the regular change in the height of the sea | high tide the highest position reached by the sea before the height starts to decrease | low tide the height of the sea is at the lowest for that day | neap tide the smallest change in height that occurs each month | spring tide the highest that the sea reaches each month as the gravity from the Sun and the Moon pull in the same direction

tie a join, a link, a thin scarf; to fasten, to make a knot

tied (not tide which is movement of the seas) joined together in a knot

tiers (not tears which is water from the eye) the levels, the layers, the heights

tight strong, firm | tight-rope a rope that has been pulled tight between two supports so that a skilled person can walk along it | light-tight light can not get into, nor out of, the object | water-tight water is not able to penetrate either the material or any of the joins

tighten (not Titan which is a satellite of Saturn) to increase the compressing force

tighter more force is being applied, closer

tightly firmly, holding with a strong grip | tightly bound strongly joined | tightly packed squashed, pushed together, taking the least space

tight-rope a rope is held under tension high above the ground, so a skilled person can walk along the rope

tigon / tigron the sterile offspring of a male tiger and a female lion

tile a small, thin piece of solid material that will easily form a pattern with other tiles; to cover a surface with thin pieces of solid with regular shapes | dimple tile / spotting tile a surface marked with small pits or indentations | white tile a small flat block that is used for showing colours clearly

tilt to lean, to push to one side | tilt switch an on–off switch that is controlled by the angle of the component

tilted slanted, tipped, at an angle | tilted Earth the axis of rotation of the Earth is at an angle to the plane of the Earth's orbit

timber (not timbre which is frequency) wood that is ready for further use

timbre (not timber which is wood) pitch, frequency, quality of sound

time (not thyme which is a herb) (symbol t; the fundamental unit is a second) a period, a season, a sequence of events, the fourth dimension, the duration, an interval, a period defined by the position of the Sun and stars; to measure the duration of an event | time-exposure leaving the shutter of a camera open for sufficiently long that changes of position are easily seen | time interval the length of time between events | timekeeper a person who measures and records the time taken for an event | time-lapse photography taking a series of pictures at one rate then show-ing the images at a different speed | time line a stripe marked off in years on to which events will be written | timepiece / time piece a clock, a watch | time-scale the period of time taken, a line showing the sequence of events | time taken the duration from start to finish | time zones division of the Earth into 24 sections so that places in each section will show the same time | ancient times a period that was many centuries ago | cooking time the interval that the food must be at the set temperature in order to

become edible | daytime / day-time the period when the Sun is providing light | harvest time the time of year that a particular crop is to be picked | life-time the period from birth to death | orbital time the period taken for the satellite to complete one orbit | period of time a given interval | reaction time the number of seconds from the mixing of the reactants to the end-point of the reaction, the duration between an event happening and the person taking steps to avoid a collision | ripening time the interval taken for the object to turn from unripe into mature from | rotation time the period taken for the object to turn around once on its own axis | specific times regular intervals that are known in advance of the event

timed the period of time has been measured

timepiece a clock, a watch

timer a clock, a watch, a person who records the time, a sand glass | electronic timer a clock that can be started and stopped electrically and produces an output voltage | hand-held timer a clock that is small enough to be carried in one hand | ticker timer equipment that moves a pin up and down 50 times each second

time-scale the period of time, a line showing days or years | appropriate time-scale allowing sufficient time for the experiment to be com-pleted, to ensure that the time axis on a graph covers the same time interval as was measured in the experiment

timing deciding on a schedule of events, measuring the period of an event | electronic timing measuring the duration of an event by electrically linking the start and stop to a clock

tin (Sn, proton number 50, melting point 232°C) a dense metal (7.3 g/cm^3) that forms a thin coat of oxide and then resists corrosion, a container made of metal | tin can a cylindrical container made from steel coated with tin, used for storing food-stuffs | tin-plated a thin layer of tin [Sn] is used to cover and protect from corrosion an article that has been made from a cheap but strong metal such as iron [Fe] | tin plating using an electric current to lay down a layer of tin, or chromium, on to the surface of an iron article, so as to prevent corrosion

tincture a solution made by crushing organic material with alcohol

tinnitus a condition that involves ringing in the ears

tiny extremely small, too small to be seen | tiny droplets small spheres of water that are too small to be seen individually, but large numbers cause fog, mist or clouds | tiny grains fine granules of hard powder | tiny particles very small grains | tiny rocks small particles found on the Earth's surface

tip the end of a branch, a piece of advice; to turn out, to upend | fingertips the area of skin at the end of the fingers

tipped pushed over, a surface at the end of a point eg felt-tipped pens | diamond tipped having a single diamond at the end of a pointer, having many small diamonds firmly bonded to the end of a probe

tipping increasing the angle of a surface | tipping site an area reserved for the collection of waste matter

tiptoe to walk softly

TIR [total internal reflection] the reflection of all the light at a boundary between two transparent media, the behaviour of a beam of a light when moving from one material to a medium of lower density and meeting the surface at an angle above the critical angle

tire to become sleepy, to be weary

tire (USA) / **tyre** (UK) a band of steel or a tube of rubber that protects that rim of a wheel | tire tread the depth of the channels in the rubber of a car or bicycle tire | bald tire the raised treads of the tire have been worn smooth | bicycle tire a rubber covering that protects the inner tube | car tire the rubber tube on the wheels of cars that provides grip for the road and reduces vibration | pneumatic tire an air-filled tube that fits over the circumference of a wheel

tired ready for sleep, fatigued, feeling weary

tiredness the amount by which you are weary or ready to sleep

tissue a collection of cells, part of an organ, a thin cloth, a membrane | tissue fluid the liquid surrounding cells in animals, a liquid similar to blood plasma | tissue graft taking cells from an unaffected area, or from another person, in order to replace damaged cells | tissue grafting moving groups of cells from one site to another | tissue paper thin paper that is often translucent | erectile tissue the cells that allow the penis to become rigid | fatty tissue groups of fat cells within an organ | important tissues cells that are essential for life | muscle tissue the collection of muscle cells (but not the tendon) | nervous tissue a collection of nerve cells | organisation of tissues (UK) / organization of tissues (USA) the arrangement of the specialised cells within a tissue | plant tissue groups of cells that can be obtained from a plant | soft tissue parts of the body that are malleable so the tissue is easily torn and easily broken down by microbes after death

hence no fossils are formed from soft tissue | vascular tissue the tubes and canals that allow liquids to move through living organisms | xylem tissue a collection of cells that transport water in plants

Titan (not tighten which is to increase a force) the largest satellite of Saturn, discovered in 1655 by Huygens

titanium (Ti, proton number 22) a metal with a low density (4.5 g/cm^3) and a high melting point (1600°C) and so is widely used in aircraft | titanium dioxide [TiO$_2$] a powder that can be spread to give a brilliant white surface

TNT [tri-nitro-toluene] an explosive compound

to (not too which means as well, nor two which is a number between one and three) goes before a verb to give the infinitive, in future, towards | equal to the same as, identical | next to adjacent, standing as neighbours | reference to pointing towards a particular event | similar to emphasising the features that two objects have in common

toad an amphibian that reproduces in water but lives most of the time on land, similar to a frog, but with dry rough skin (a frog has damp, smooth skin)

toadstool a loose term for any mushroom that is shaped like an umbrella and is poisonous

toast a slice of bread that has been heated at each side so as to give a thin layer of caramel and burned starch; to heat strongly

toaster equipment for gently heating slices of bread

tobacco a dried leaf that produces nicotine gas when burned and this gas can be absorbed through the lungs (along with the carbon monoxide, carcinogens and tars)

together at the same time, joined | close together near to each other, separated by a small distance | hold together to push into close contact, to prevent from falling apart | group together / grouped together to put into sets with common characteristics

toilet equipment that allows faeces and urine to be removed from the area and sent to a collection area | toilet cleaner a chemical that removes the sludge and bacteria that grow on the inside of a toilet basin

toiletries chemicals that help a person remain clean and have a pleasant smell

toll a tax, a charge for using a road; to ring a bell | death toll the number of people who have died due to an event such as accident, a specified illness, or a natural disaster such as a tsunami

tomato (plural is tomatoes) a red fruit that is usually eaten as a vegetable or part of a salad, a bushy annual plant | tomato varieties different types of tomato that may prefer different environmental conditions or have different colours, size or flavour

tomatoes (plural of tomato) the red skinned fruit that is easily squashed | beefsteak tomatoes very large tomatoes | cherry tomatoes very small (and sweet) tomatoes | plum tomatoes have the shape of an egg or a plum

ton (not a tonne which is 1000 kilogram) an imperial unit equal to 2240 pounds weight

tongs equipment, usually metal, for holding other items in the flame of a bunsen burner

tongue the organ in the mouth that is muscular, and so can change shape, and has a top lined with cells that respond to different flavours (taste), a language | tongue rolling the ability to turn the tongue into a 'U' shape pointing out of the mouth, this ability is controlled by a single gene

tonne (t) (not ton which is an imperial measure) a metric unit equal to 1000 kilogram

too (not to which goes in front of a verb nor two which is a number between one and three) as well, also, in addition

tools equipment for making some jobs easier, and allowing other jobs to become achievable | power tool mechanical equipment, using electricity as the energy input, for carrying out a specific task

tooth (plural is teeth) long hard objects of enamel in the gums that are used for the mechanical breakdown of food | tooth ache a pain in the tooth | tooth decay breakdown of the structure of the tooth caused by bacteria growing in, or on, the tooth | tooth enamel the hard, white outer-coating of the tooth

toothpaste material that can be spread on to the teeth and used to remove bacteria and to neutralise any acid

top highest, best | top carnivore the predator that eats lower consumers, but is rarely eaten by anything else | top consumer the organism in a food chain that is not eaten by any predator | top-pan balance an electronic weighing machine in which the item to be weighed is placed on a single pan | top soil the layer of earth that has been turned over by worms and is suitable for the roots of plants | top speed the maximum rate of travelling, terminal velocity

topics units, problems, parts of a bigger plan, subjects for a conversation

topple to fall over because the centre of mass is outside the base

tor a hill of granite

torch (plural is torches) portable equipment for shining light; to set on fire deliberately | torch

bulb the lamp that is powered by a battery | torch circuit the switch, connectors and battery that are needed to make the bulb light in a torch | welding torch the hot flame at the end of the pipe at which oxygen and acetylene meet and burn

torque (not talk which is speech) turning force, moment, should be measured in newton-metres | torque wrench a spanner that is used to provide a measured amount of turning force

Torricelli (Evangelista 1608–1647) was an Italian orphan who was educated by the Jesuits then became assistant to Galileo. He invented the mercury barometer, and proposed the idea of atmospheric pressure, as a result of trying to raise water from a well that was 10 metres deep. He noticed that changes in atmospheric pressure were related to weather but Galton was the first to develop a weather map – in 1875.

tortoise a land-dwelling reptile that has a hard shell to protect its soft body and into which the tortoise can withdraw its feet and its head when threatened

toss a throw upwards; to throw

tossed thrown

tot a volume of 25 millilitres, a measure of alcohol, a small child; to add up

total all, everything, entire, the sum | total amount the entire quantity | total eclipse the Moon covers the whole face of the Sun, so there is darkness and the corona is visible | total energy the entire amount of energy from several sources | total internal reflection (TIR) the reflection of all the light at a boundary between two transparent media, the behaviour of a beam of a light when moving from one transparent material to a medium of lower density and meeting the surface at an angle above the critical angle | total mass the entire mass, including any material that has disappeared as a gas

touch a pat; to feel, to reach | touch receptor a sensory cell in the skin that sends a signal to the brain if it senses a pressure or tension

touched tapped, affected by, moved emotionally

tough strong, durable, difficult to change

tow a pull; to pull along behind, to drag using ropes

towards facing the direction of an object, moving to achieve a goal

tower a high, thin building; to stand much higher than others | cooling tower the massive structures at power stations that turn steam back into water | fractionating tower the large cylinder in which hot, crude oil is separated into fractions of differing boiling point

town a large collection of house, workplaces, shops and churches that is the focus for a large area of the surrounding countryside | town environment the combination of buildings, hard surfaces, lack of open space and pollution that is typical of a large number of people who are living and working close together | town gas any fuel that is distributed from a central point to the many houses in a town, originally this was coal gas, but is now usually natural gas (methane [CH_4])

toxic a chemical that will kill either specified calls or the organism, poisonous | toxic material the chemical that will kill the organism

toxin a chemical that is likely to kill an animal, often produced by microbes in the organism or by injection, *eg* from the fangs of a snake | persistent toxins poisonous chemicals that do not get broken down or changed into less poisonous material | anti-toxin a chemical that removes the destructive effect of a specific chemical

toy a plaything, a small object that reflects a real article | toy cars small, wheeled vehicles | wind-up toys playthings that are powered by a spring mechanism

trace a tiny amount; to find by following a trail, to follow an outline | trace amounts tiny quantities, very dilute | trace elements essential chemicals that are present in tiny amounts | oscilloscope trace the line that appears on the screen of a cathode ray oscilloscope when a signal is applied

trachea the strong and flexible windpipe that joins the mouth to the lungs

tracing paper translucent paper that is strong enough to be written on without tearing, used to transfer a pattern

track a trail, a path; to follow the signs | air-track a perforated bar which can be used with a pump to remove most of the frictional resistance of a moving object | caterpillar track a continuous loop of rectangular plates that are jointed together and this arrangement reduces the pressure of the vehicle on the land

tract a tube, an area, an essay

traffic vehicles | traffic noise the disturbing mixture of sounds produced by engines, tyres and mechanical movement of vehicles on the road

trail a track, a path; to follow, especially a long way behind | slime trail / snail trail the track of mucus that is left by a moving snail or slug

train transport that runs on rails; to improve the expertise, to become fitter for a job or as an athlete | magnetic train transport that runs on rails using electromagnetism to raise the train above the rails and to provide the force that changes the speed

trainee a person who is learning a skill

training providing lessons for a specific job, improving fitness, acquiring a skill

trampoline a strong cloth held under tension by springs attached to a metal frame that is used for people to bounce and exercise upon; to bounce on material that is held under tension

tranquilliser a chemical that causes the person to feel sleepy and relaxed

trans- (*Latin* across)

transducer equipment that changes any form of energy into electrical energy, often used for measuring changes in energy level

transect a line is drawn on the map and then a vertical profile of the landform and vegetation is prepared

transfer to move from one area to another | transfer heat to move heat from one item to another | transfer of energy moving the ability to do work from one location to another | transfer particles to move a chemical from one area to another, especially inside organisms | energy transfer moving the ability to do work from one item to another | heat transfer a measure of the amount of vibrational energy that changes places

transferred moved, changed places

transferring moving from one place or form to another | transferring energy moving the ability to do work

transform to change in a way that the end result is unrecognisable from the starting material | transform energy to change energy from one form to a very different form

transformation a change | energy transformation the change of energy from one form to another

transformer equipment that is used to change the size of potential difference (voltage) | energy transformer a transducer, an object that changes energy from one form to another, *eg* lamps change, or transform, electrical energy into light

transforming changing, converting | transforming energy changing energy from one form into another

transfusion transferring, moving liquids | blood transfusion using blood donated by one person to supplement the circulation of another

transistor an electronic component that uses one voltage to control another voltage

transition between | transition elements / transition metals the elements between Group 2 and Group 3 of the periodic table, these metals often produce coloured salts

transitional temporary, a transition metal

translate to change from one form into another, to interpret

translucent allows light through, but scatters the wave and so any image is fuzzy

transmission a broadcast, a movement, the drive-train of a car | transmission cables the very thick wires that are used for conducting high voltage electricity around the country | transmission of information moving data | heat transmission moving thermal energy, usually implying radiation | methods of transmission the means by which information is communicated, the processes by which a disease moves between people

transmit to send, to communicate | transmit force to apply a force at one part of a hydraulic or mechanical system which is then applied to a position that is at a distance and in a different direction

transmittance a measure of the amount of light that is absorbed by a material

transmitted sent, radiated | transmitted ray the line showing where the light beam has continued after passing through a transparent block

transmitter a source of radio signals

transparency a sheet containing a picture that can be projected on to a screen | overhead transparency a clear sheet onto which a picture is drawn that is projected on to a screen

transparent allows all the light through without scattering or absorption | transparent medium a material, *eg* clear glass, that will allow visible light to pass through

transpiration loss of water from the stomata in the underside of plant leaves | transpiration stream the movement of water through a plant caused by loss of moisture through the stomata

transplant to move an organ from one place to another, to move an organ from a donor to another organism | bone-marrow transplant the injection of a small amount of bone marrow from one person into the bones of another | organ transplant the movement of a working organ from a donor to replace the non-functional organ of a recipient

transplanted organs the organs, *eg* liver, heart, lungs, that are taken from one person (the donor) and used to replace the diseased organs in another person (the donor is usually dead but a living person can donate organs such as a kidney)

transport the method of moving; to move, to carry, to take from one place to another | transport minerals to move rocks | transport system the whole structure of moving and static parts that are used to move materials from one place to another, the blood and blood vessels of

mammals | public transport vehicles that should follow regular routes and timetables that may be used by anyone paying the fare | road transport using the lorries and cars that run on public highways in order to move goods and people

transportation a vehicle, banishment to a colony

transported moved, carried

transporting moving, carrying

transverse across the main direction | transverse section cutting in a direction at 90° to the longest axis | transverse wave the particles vibrate at right angles to the direction of travel

trap equipment for the capture of animals, a trick, a wheeled, horse-drawn vehicle; to capture an animal in a box | humane trap a method for capturing an animal without causing pain or damage

trapped unable to move | trapped air pockets of air that can not move and so provide heat insulation

trapping catching alive, capturing without killing

travel to move from one place to another | light travels the movement of light from a source | space travel making a journey beyond the atmosphere of the Earth

traveled (USA) **/ travelled** (UK) moved, journeyed

traveler (USA) **/ traveller** (UK) a person who moves

traveling (USA) **/ travelling** (UK) moving, changing position | light travelling the movement of light from a source

tray a shallow box | dimple tray a rectangle of plastic with an arrangement of many small depressions | seed tray a box that will be filled with earth and used for germinating seeds

tread the material used to reduce noise or wear, a step; to stand on | tire tread (USA) / tyre tread (UK) the depth of the grooves on the tyre of a car

treasure a collection of gold, silver or jewels that has been hidden, something of value

treat a special pleasure; to behave towards, to try to improve, to give medication

treatable able to be improved by correct handling and care

treating changing, improving, giving medicine | treating fields adding material to large areas of land in order to produce a better crop

treatment the care leading to a return to health, the handling | drug treatment the steps taken to reduce the dependency of an addict for a drug, the care taken to give the correct medicine | earlier treatment chemicals, such as drugs or fertiliser, had already been given, the medicines and care that were given in previous years | light treatment using the visible part of the electromagnetic spectrum to cause a change | medical treatment the techniques, tablets or instructions that will lead to improved health | sewage treatment / sewerage treatment the handling of human urine, vomit and faeces on a large scale so as to produce drinking water | slug treatment taking steps to get rid of all slugs | snail treatment taking steps that will reduce the number of snails | soil treatment improving earth by handling and adding material to the soil

treble three times, sound with a frquency between 200 and 600 hertz

tree a woody plant that grows every year, which has a single woody stem supporting a canopy of branches and leaves | tree beating gently hitting the branches of a tree so as to dislodge and collect any animal life | tree canopy the branches and leaves of a tree that form a layer above the ground | tree ferns plants, up to 30 metres tall, that have a single stem, but have leaves like a fern | tree trunk the strong stem that supports the branches and provides pathways for the movement of nutrients | ash tree the leaves are small and arranged in rows along a stem | deciduous trees woody plants that lose their leaves in autumn | family tree a diagram showing the relationship between the offspring at the bottom and the parents and grandparents further up the page | fir tree a tall plant that is an evergreen and produces cones | oak tree produces a strong wood and may live for a thousand years | silver tree the result of bending a copper wire to the shape of a tree and then placing into silver nitrate solution | willow tree grows near to water and produces a canopy that droops down to ground or water level

tremble to shake, to shiver

tremendous outstandingly large, gigantic, of great significance

trench a ditch, a narrow cut | ocean trench deep troughs in the ocean floor

trend a direction, a general tendency, a fashion | key trends the direction of the important variables

tri- (not try which means attempt) (*Latin* three)

triads groups of three elements with very similar properties

trial preliminary, starting, early, a first attempt | trial measurements the first set of data | trial run the initial experiment that leads some variables to be defined more precisely | clinical trials the final stages involved in developing a drug for human use | double-blind trials testing drugs by using two tablets that look identical but only one contains the drug, neither the experimenter nor

the patient know which pill has been given | time trial a race for cyclists

trialled carried out a test or procedure on a small sample

trialling trying a new procedure, initial investigation of an plan

triangle an outline with three connected sides, three porcelain rods that are joined by wires and used for holding small dishes | fire triangle the three legs that are essential for a fire – heat, oxygen and fuel | formula triangle placing the three variable of most simple equations into a triangle so that covering the unknown allows a decision as to the next mathematical operation, *eg* the speed equation can be written as

$$\text{speed} = \frac{\text{distance}}{\text{time}} \quad \text{or} \quad \frac{d}{s \mid t}$$

triangular a shape that appears to have three edges | triangular block a solid piece of Perspex or glass which has five faces, three are rectangles and two are triangles

triceps the muscles that straighten the arm

Triceratops a large herbivorous dinosaur that existed about 100 million years ago

trichloroethene [CCl_2CHCl] a toxic liquid (boiling point 87°C) that is used for dry-cleaning clothes

trickle to flow slowly, to seep

tricuspid valve tissue between the atrium and ventricle on the right hand side of the heart that ensures blood flows only in one direction

trigger a starting mechanism; to start, to initiate | electronically triggered the recording is started by an electrical signal

. . . trioxide a chemical containing three atoms of oxygen linked to one or more different atoms | sulphur trioxide (UK) / sulphur trioxide (USA) [SO_3] a pungent gas produced by burning sulphur or compounds containing sulphur, a major component of acid rain

trip a journey; to fall over because a small object impedes a foot | trip switch a circuit breaker, a re-settable switch that turns from on to off when an event occurs *eg* the current becomes too high

triple related to three, *eg* three times larger | triple vaccine an injection that causes the body to produce antibodies to measles, mumps and rubella, the MMR jab

tripod a structure with three legs and a triangular top used for supporting glassware

trolley a truck, a cart, a transport vehicle powered by electricity

troph- (*Greek* to nourish, to feed)

trophic responding to a stimulus, concerned with feeding | trophic level an indication of the position of the organism in the food web

tropical a general term for the rain and heat associated with the region between 23°N and 23°S, but tropical covers several different types of climate | **tropical disease** an illness that tends to be found in areas close to the equator, *eg* malaria, river blindness, sleeping sickness | **tropical forest / tropical rainforest** the extensive areas of large trees and diverse species caused by a climate in which every month is wet and daytime temperatures are high

tropics any area between 23°N and 23°S of the equator

tropism growing or moving towards | **geotropism** the response of plants to gravity so that shoots grow upwards and roots go downwards | **hydrotropism** the growth of roots towards water | **phototropism** the change of direction of leaves and the stem caused by the light from the Sun

troposphere the lowest part of the atmosphere

trough a bowl, a tub, an oblong container for water or animal food

trout a type of fish, some species are fresh-water and other species are found in the sea

truck a van, a lorry, a wheeled vehicle that is to be used for moving goods, the frame and wheels that is found at each end of a railway carriage

true correct, genuine, accurate, precise | **true north** an imaginary line that joins your position to the axis of rotation of the Earth

trumpet a brass, musical instrument; to tell everyone

trundle a truck; to roll along | **trundle wheel** a wheel that is connected by gears to a milometer and is used for measuring distance

trunk the major connection between the roots and the branches of a tree, the human body with limbs and head removed, a case, the extended nose-like part of an elephant | **tree trunk** the strong woody stem that supports the branches and provides pathways for the movement of nutrients

trustworthiness reliability, dependability

truth table the method used in logic circuits for showing the effects on the output of changing the input

try (not tri… which means three…) an attempt; to attempt, to experiment when the outcome is not easily predicted

trying attempting, checking, experimenting

trypanasoma / *trypanosome* single-cell organisms that live in animals, causing disease or death, and are transmitted by insect bites

trypsin an enzyme that breaks down proteins and is found in the stomach

tsunami a very high sea wave produced by an earthquake

Tswett (Michel 1872–1919) had a Russian father and an Italian mother; he studied in Switzerland, then worked in Russia. He developed chromatography, using columns containing sugar, in order to separate the coloured pigments from plant leaves

tuba (not tuber which is part of a plant) a brass musical instrument that produces a low pitched note when blown

tube a pipe, an open cylinder, a cylinder closed at one end | **tube worm** a creature with the shape of a cylinder that lives in the sand | **boiling tube** a glass cylinder that is closed at one end and used for mixing chemicals, a large test tube | **breathing tubes** the several tubes (trachea, bronchi and bronchioles) that connect the outside world to the air sacs of the lungs | **capillary tube** a small glass tube with a thin wall and a fine hollow centre | **cardboard tube** a cylinder made from thick paper | **combustion tube** a glass tube in which material can be burned safely | **delivery tube** a pipe that connects the source of a gas to the collection point | **digestive tube** the canal (intestinal tract) along which food moves so that breakdown, absorption and egestion can occur | **egg tube** the oviduct, the fallopian tube, the tube connecting the ovary to the uterus | **eustachian tube / eustacian tube** a pipe connecting the middle ear to the back of the throat that allows equalisation of the pressure on each side of the ear drum | **fallopian tube** the very fine pipe that connects the ovary to the womb and in which fertilisation occurs | **fine tube** a pipe with a very small internal diameter | **fluorescent tube** a light source in which an alternating current produces ultra-violet rays, which are turned to visible light by the glass envelope | **glass tube** a pipe made from glass | **ignition tube** a pipe in which burning can occur safely | **pollen tube** the pipe that grows from the pollen grain towards the ovary of the flower in order to allow transfer of the male nucleus | **rubber tube** flexible pipe made from rubber | **side-arm tube** a boiling tube with a hole, about 2 centimetres below the rim, that is extended to give a side pipe | **side tube** a small tube leading from the neck of a flask or the side of a boiling tube | **sorbent tube** an open glass tube packed with a powder that easily absorbs any gases | **specimen tube** a small cylinder with a screw cap that is used for collecting samples | **sperm tube** the canal joining the testis to the base of the penis | **test tube** a glass cylinder closed at one end with a round bottom that is used for mixing

353

small quantities of chemicals | TV tube the glass pyramid that has an electron source at the apex and produces a picture at the base | xylem tubes the cells in the plant stem through which water is transported from root to leaf

tuber (not tuba which is a musical instrument) a thickened root or underground stem that is used for storing food

tubercule bacillus / tuberculi bacillus the bacterium that causes tuberculosis (*Mycobacterium tuberculosis* causes tuberculosis [TB] in the lungs)

tuberculosis (TB) a disease caused by a bacterium that infects the lungs but may spread to other parts of the body and is often fatal

tubing cylindrical, flexible material | pressure tubing thick-walled rubber tube that will not change diameter, even if a high pressure is applied | rubber tubing a pipe or hose that is flexible because the walls are made from rubber | visking tubing a wide, open cylinder with walls that allow small molecules to pass through but will prevent movement of large molecules, tubing that is used to simulate the wall of the intestine

tug a short, sharp pull, a small boat for towing bigger ships; to pull, to jerk | tug-of-war a game in which two teams pull a rope in opposite directions

Tulgren funnel / Tullgren funnel a vertical cylinder closed at the bottom end by a gauze, then a lamp is inserted into the top end in order to cause the insects that are trying to escape the light to fall through the gauze

tumble a fall, a head-over-heels movement; to stumble, to fall over | tumble drier / tumble dryer a heated drum that separates clothing and evaporates the water

tummy belly, the stomach region

tumor (USA) / **tumour** (UK) a mass of cells caused by uncontrolled growth | benign tumor / benign tumour a growth of cells that will not cause any permanent problems | malignant tumor / malignant tumour an uncontrolled growth of cells that both invades neighbouring tissues and releases cells that grow elsewhere in the body

tungsten (W because called wolfram in Germany, proton number 53, melting point 3410°C) an unreactive metal that has a high density (20 g/cm^3) | tungsten filament thin strands of tungsten that are used in electric lamps because the metal has a high melting point

tuning changing an item, eg tension or length, so that the note produced sounds different | tuning fork an implement that has two prongs that vibrate at a known frequency

tunnel a passage, an underground route made by a digging animal; to dig a passage | wind tunnel

a room, large enough to take the object to be tested, that has a fan at one end that can produce air movement similar to a wind

turbid cloudy, muddy, murky

turbidity an estimate of how far light will penetrate a cloudy liquid

turbine a cylinder enclosing a series of vanes attached to the central spindle | steam turbine several sets of vanes enclosed by a cylinder and which are turned when hot water vapour is introduced at one end and moves rapidly to the other before condensing to liquid water | water turbine a series of vanes mounted inside a cylinder which are turned by flow of water through the cylinder | wind turbine a tower with vanes that are turned by the wind in order to generate electricity

turgid swollen, hard

turn (not tern which is a seabird) a rotation, a movement around a central point; to move an item around a central point

turning moving in a circular motion, pushing an item around a point | turning effect / turning force / turning moment torque, the product of the applied force and the distance to the pivot

TV [television] equipment for receiving pictures and sound from a distant transmitter | TV tube the glass pyramid that has an electron source at the apex and produces a picture at the base | satellite TV television information that was received from a satellite in geo-stationary orbit | Sky TV a provider of television programmes that distributes the signal using satellites

TVP [textured vegetable protein] material obtained from soya beans that can be flavoured and coloured to produce a variety of food products

tweezers forceps, small pincers

twelve 12, a dozen, the number between eleven and thirteen

twice two times, repeat, double

twig a small branch of a tree, a small branch that has fallen off a tree | dormant twigs small branches that are not growing, but will start to grow and develop when the conditions improve

twins similar pairs, two babies born at one time to the same mother | identical twins two babies born with identical genes because the daughter cells from the first division of the fertilised egg became separated the each developed into a baby | non-identical twins two babies born at the same time but each was formed separately by fertilisation of different eggs

twist a turn, a rotation; to wind, to form a thread

twisting rotating, moving because of a turning force

twitch a sudden jerk; to make a sudden jerking movement

twitcher a person who watches birds, an ornithologist

two (not to which is the start of a verb, nor too which means also) a number between one and three, a pair | two-second rule the recommendation of the Highway Code that you should be at least a two second gap between the car in front passing a point and your car reaching the same point NB it takes about two seconds to say "only a fool breaks the two-second rule" | two-way switch one of a pair of switches, each of which can control a single lamp

tying joining, knotting, sealing with string

Tyndall (John 1820–1893) left school to work as a surveyor in Ireland, became professor in Germany, then Director of the Royal Institution in London. He did many studies on heat, but is also remembered for his explanation of the colours we see in the sky. Every time that you see the beams of light in a cinema, visible because the light is scattered by dust, then you are seeing the Tyndall Effect!

type a general form, a common structure, a species, a pattern, an illustration, a representative; to place into a category | type of animal an organism showing the characteristics of that group | type of atom a fundamental particle with a particular set of properties | type of blood the classification of human blood depending on the presence, or absence, of three proteins called A, B and rhesus | type of cell the building block of life with particular characteristics | type of data information with common properties | type of particle grains with common characteristics | type of rock parts of the Earth's surface which have origins or properties in common | type of

water the origin, preparation or purity of the water | blood type the human blood has been analysed to see if any of the antigen markers A,B or rhesus are present as giving the wrong type of blood to a patient is often fatal | cell type the cells show some common features | food type the food contains similar nutrients | rock type the rock is similar to others of the same origin or place | soil type the variety of soil as shown by pH, sand or loam content or porosity

typhoid / typhus an infectious disease, caused by *Salmonella*, in which diarrhoea and drowsiness may lead to coma and death

typical showing the characteristics, exhibiting the features that are characteristic of a type of animal or plant | typical animal an organism that shows many of the features that are expected of most animals | typical cell a cell that shows all the important features | typical home the type of dwelling in which that set of people or animals would be expected | typical meal the combinations of food that could be expected on any day | typical plant the type of producer organism which is usually found in that environment | typical temperature how hot that type object usually is

Tyrannosaurus a dinosaur which was a carnivore, up to 13 metres long, and existed about 100 million years ago

tyre (UK) **/ tire** (USA) a band of steel or a tube of rubber that protects that rim of a wheel | tyre tread the depth of the channels in the rubber of a car or bicycle tyre | bald tyre the raised treads of the tyre have been worn smooth | bicycle tyre a rubber covering that protects the inner tube | car tyre the rubber tube on the wheels of cars that provides grip and reduce vibration | pneumatic tyre an air filled tube that fits over the circumference of a wheel

U uranium, proton number 92

u algebraic variable representing the speed of an object at the start of the experiment

UI [universal indicator] a solution that shows a colour dependent on the pH value, a mixture of three indicators

ulcer a defect in the surface, exposing tissue normally covered by epithilial cells

ulna the thinner of the two bones in the lower arm

ultimate final, end, last | ultimate source the origin where everything starts

ultimately eventually, as the last act

ultra- (*Latin* beyond)

ultra-low very, very low

ultrasonic using sound with frequency above 30 kilohertz, *eg* to detect submarines or to destroy gall stones, moving faster than the speed of sound | ultrasonic scan obtaining a picture of soft tissue, *eg* the embryo in the uterus, by analysing the reflection of high-frequency sound

ultrasound vibrations that have a frequency above the range of human hearing, sound with a frequency above 30 kilohertz | ultrasound scan obtaining a picture of the embryo by measuring the time that pulses of ultra-sound need to return from a surface

ultra-violet / ultra-violet light [UV] the part of the spectrum below blue, electromagnetic waves with a wavelength less than 400 nanometres | ultra-violet radiation the wavelength of the light is below that of visible light | ultra-violet rays a beam, that may not be visible to human eyes, containing wavelengths below 400 nano-metres

umbilical cord the tube, containing arteries and veins, that connects the mammalian foetus to the placenta

umbra the area that is dark because it is completely in the shadow, the area where an eclipse is total | pen-umbra a fringe region, a partial shadow, the area that is partially darkened by shadow because the light source is extended

unaffected not changed by the stated variable

unaided without help | unaided eye seeing without a lens or camera to improve the size of the image

unbalanced almost falling over, not steady, having more force in one direction | unbalanced diet the nutrients and energy in the food that is eaten do not match the needs of the body | unbalanced forces the force of push in one direction is different from the resistive force in the opposite direction

unborn / unborn baby a foetus, the offspring developing in the uterus of the mother

unchanged remaining the same

unclear vague, murky, not see through

uncombined not joined

unconsolidated not fixed, movable | unconsolidated material the grains of rock are able to be moved

uncontrolled without a plan, lacking direction, lacking order | uncontrolled growth the cells divide but do not produce functioning tissue or organs | uncontrolled variables items that can change in a random way

uncorroded clean, bright, showing no signs of changing from a metal to the oxide

uncover to remove a protective layer, to reveal, to find out

under below, beneath, less than | underground / under ground below the surface, hidden, within the soil | undernourished receiving insufficient food | under oil storing alkali metals in oil so they can not react with the air | under water beneath the surface of the water

underground below the surface, hidden | underground rivers streams of moving water that flow through caves and natural tunnels inside the rock | underground stem the structure containing the main vascular tubes is under the soil

underlay a sponge layer that is laid under a carpet for insulation

underneath below, beneath, lower

undernourished receiving insufficient food, not obtaining enough chemical energy

under oil storing alkali metals in oil so they can not react with the air

understand to realise, to perceive, to think, to make a connection between facts, to comprehend

understanding believing, learning, developing theories | scientific understanding to have a simple idea that explains many observations and is supported by experiment

undertake to agree, to promise, to carry out

under water beneath the surface of the water | underwater pressure the force per unit area caused by the weight of water above

undetected not discovered, not noticed, the item was not found although a search was made

undigested not broken down, intact | undigested food / undigested material substances that have been eaten, but have passed unchanged through the digestive tract and are egested in the faeces

undissolved material that will not disappear into the liquid, insoluble

undo to take apart, to open, to deconstruct

unfamiliar strange, unusual, obscure

unfertilised (UK) / **unfertilized** (USA) the nucleus of the egg has not fused with a male nucleus | unfertilised eggs (UK) / unfertilized eggs (USA) the ova have not fused with male gametes

unfit not healthy, the heart rate takes a long time to recover after exercise, not suitable for a particular purpose

unfortunately unluckily, unhappily

unhealthy the circumstances do not promote an organism to be in good condition | unhealthy diet the amounts of energy and nutrients in the food do not provide a balanced diet

unhelpful not very useful, not beneficial | unhelpful forces pushes and pulls that hinder progress

unhygienic / unhygienic conditions fat and bits of food waste are left lying around, allowing microbes to grow, and encouraging the presence of animals such as rats or mice

uni- (*Latin* one)

unicellular single cell | unicellular organism a living creature that comprises one cell

uniform the same throughout, lacking variation | uniform medium the substance is the same at all places | uniform speed constant speed, travelling at the same rate

uninhabitable conditions that do not support life

unique single, special, one off | unique features observable characteristics that are found only on that organism | unique individual one person or animal, emphasising the specific characteristics of that one organism | genetically unique the arrangement of instructions on the DNA of the chromosome is found only in that specified organism

unit an agreed measurement, a standardised quantity used for comparisons | units of alcohol a measure of the amount of ethanol in a drink so that the effects of different volumes can be compared | units of electricity the amount of electrical energy used, usually measured in kilowatt hours (kWh), a step in the calculation of cost for electricity | units of measurements the agreed quantities, *eg* length in metres, mass in kilograms, time in seconds | units of pressure should be the pascal (newtons per square metre) which is rarely used, the units often follow those of force and area, *eg* newtons per square centimetre, meteorologists use a millibar; blood pressure is measured in millimetres of mercury | appropriate units measurements that are suitable for that experiment and the measuring equipment available | astronomical unit the average distance from the Earth to the Sun, 150 million kilometres | atomic mass unit (amu) the mass of a proton or a neutron, 1.66×10^{-27} kg, one dalton | base units the arbitrary objects that form the basis of international measurement, *ie* the 1 kilogram mass and the 1 metre length that are kept in Paris and the 1 second measured by an atomic clock | basic unit the simple structures that are used to produce complicated forms | derived units agreed measurements that are obtained from the basic units *eg* a volume of 1 cm^3 | electrical units the measurements that are used in any electrical work | SI units (Système International d'Unités) a range of accepted measurements, based on standards that are kept in France, including length, mass and time

universal ubiquitous, found everywhere, everything, unlimited, at all times, overall | universal force something that causes a change of velocity and is found everywhere

universal indicator a mixture of three chemicals that gives a range of colours depending on the pH | universal indicator paper a filter paper has been soaked in universal indicator solution then dried | universal indicator solution a mixture of the three chemicals in alcohol | full-range universal indicator the liquid or paper that has many colours between pH 1 and pH 14

universe the whole, everything that exists from the smallest dust particle to the largest star

unknown not measured, not recognised, not identified, strange, undiscovered | unknown metal the material will conduct electricity but could be any of the metals | unknown solution the material dissolved in the water has not been identified

unlike opposite, not the same, different, dissimilar | unlike ends the parts at the extremes are not the same | unlike poles one part is a north pole and the other is a south pole

unmodified no changes have been made to the standard model

unpleasant upsetting, disagreeable, not desirable

unpolluted clean, unspoilt

unpredictable can not tell when an event will occur, random, irregular, not dependable | unpredictable eruption the volcano will erupt at some unknown date

unprotected bare, exposed, vulnerable | unprotected sex having intercourse without wearing a condom to prevent transmission of disease or to prevent pregnancy

unreacted / unreacted material excess, material that remains at the end of the reaction

unreactive inert, stable, not reacting | unreactive metal a metal that is low in the reactivity series, a metal that will not corrode

unripe not ready, not mature, picked too early | unripe apples apples that are not ready for eating because they are hard and sour

unsaturated not full, able to dissolve more, able to be absorbed | unsaturated fat the oil produced by plants or fish that has some double bonds | unsaturated solution a liquid containing a dissolved solid, which is capable of dissolving more of the same solid

unscrew to rotate one component so that the joint becomes slack or allows a fitting to be removed

unscrewing removing a screw by turning

unspecialised without any characteristic skill, not differentiated | unspecialised cells stem cells, cells that have no special function, but can develop into specialised cells

unspoiled / unspoilt keeping its natural beauty

untreated not given any medication, no chemicals have been added | untreated sewage the faeces are in the same state as when they left the body

untying removing a knot, releasing

unusual different, with different characteristics | unusual features characteristics or properties that are not usually found with that type of object

unwanted not needed, unused, excess, not required | unwanted pregnancy intercourse has taken place but the fertilisation was not intended

unwind to allow the tension is a spring to reduce, to lower by turning a winch

unzip to separate the two strands of DNA, to pull the controller so the zipper opens

up above, higher | uplift / upthrust the force causing an object to float | break up to disconnect, to separate white light into many colours, to disperse | dry up to remove moisture | fluff-up to change the direction of the feathers so that they are more upright and so trap more air and help the bird retain body heat | light up to set fire to a fuel, to increase the intensity of visible light | line up to place several members in a straight line | make-up to invent, to improve presentation | scale-up / scaling-up to make larger, to increase greatly the amount of reactant and product, to expand the area, the time, or the number of measurements for an experiment | set-up to establish, to put together | speed up to increase speed, to go faster | wind up to turn a key so as to increase the tension in a spring

upbringing the method by which the offspring learn the techniques needed for survival as an adult, usually done by parents

uplands the higher areas inland from the coastal plain | upland hills the hills that slope up from the uplands

uplift an upwards force in fluids caused by the lower layer being warmer, and so less dense, than the upper layer

upper higher, better, superior, above | upper arm the bone and muscles between the shoulder joint and the elbow | upper body the part of the human body above the waist | upper shore the land next to the sea that is covered with sea water only if the tide is very high | upper surface the outside of the top layer

upright a vertical pillar, a post providing vertical support

uptake the absorption

upthrust the force causing an object to float, the reduction in weight caused by floating in a liquid

uPVC unplasticised polyvinyl chloride, a plastic made from millions of molecules of vinyl chloride [CH_2:CHCl] | uPVC window / uPVC window frame the frame of the window is made from uPVC

upward vertical, above, away from the attraction of gravity | upward direction above, at greater height | upward force a force opposing the pull of gravity

uranium (U, proton number 92, melting point 1132°C) was used to give yellow colour to stained glass but is now used as a source of radio-activity

Uranus a gas giant planet that was discovered by Herschel in 1781 and named after the Greek and Roman god of the stars and the heavens, Uranus has rings and nine major moons

urban close to a town, an estate | urban environment the type of gardens and trees that would be expected on a housing estate | urban farm an area for rearing animals that is in the town | urban life living in an area that is close to a town

urea [$(NH_2)_2CO$] a white powder, the poisonous chemical produced by breakdown of protein that is removed by dissolving in water to produce urine

ureter the tube joining the kidney to the bladder

urethra the tube joining the bladder to the outside world, the urethra in the male allows sperm to leave the body

urinate to excrete urine from the bladder to the outside world

urine a solution of urea in water that is produced to maintain both the amount of water and the concentration of urea and salts in the blood

U R L [universal resource location / unified resource locator / unique resource locator] the identifier that makes every web address individual

usable (UK & USA) / **useable** (USA) available and suitable for a given purpose | usable products / useable products useful chemicals that have been produced as a result of either a chemical reaction or a separation procedure

usage employment, utilisation | land usage the purpose to which an area of ground is used

use the employment, the purpose, the method, the habit; to employ, to practice, to handle, to put into operation | use data to allow the information to support a claim | domestic use the purpose for which equipment is employed in the home | effective use the equipment carries out the work quickly and economically | efficient use the apparatus is used at minimum cost | energy use the amount and cost of the work done | everyday use the equipment is likely to be found in many houses, shops or buildings | medical use utilising a method or substance so as to prevent illness, to cure disease or to reduce pain | mis-use deliberately applying equipment or a method in a way that could cause harm | re-use to use the item again for the same purpose

useable (USA) / **usable** (UK & USA) available and suitable for a given purpose | re-usable / re-useable able to be used again and again

used employed, adapted for a purpose, worn out | used up finished, all the material has been utilised, none is left | widely used the item is found in many areas and as many applications

useful serving a purpose, making a valid contribution | useful bacteria microbes that can be grown in order to produce products that are needed, *eg* yoghurt or cheese from milk | useful change a difference that make the work easier | useful characteristics features that will help the organism to survive | useful compounds chemicals that are easily changed into other materials | useful devices equipment that can be utilised in many situations | useful energy the energy that is transformed into the required form of energy | useful facilities equipment or areas that can be used for many purposes | useful force a push or pull that causes a change in the required direction | useful gas the vapour or gas that is produced

may be used in another process | useful genes instructions in the DNA of the chromosomes that are thought to help survival | useful information data that can be used to bring about a better understanding | useful materials substances that make a task easier | useful products a reaction produces chemicals that can be used for other purposes | useful substance the material is valuable because it has a set of properties that matches a need

usefully practically, profitably. of value

usefulness appropriate for a particular purpose, the value, the advantages, utility

uses the purposes, the way a material is utilised | uses of metals the tasks that can be carried out using those materials

usual the standard practice, normal, a regular pattern

usually generally, most often

utensils equipment, tools | cooking utensils the equipment, especially pans and pots, that are important in heating and preparing food

uterine concerned with the uterus or womb | uterine wall the boundary of the uterus, especially the layer of cells on the inside of the uterus

uterus womb, the muscular compartment in which the fertilised egg will develop into a foetus | uterus lining the layers of cells on the inside of the uterus which is lost during menstruation and in which, after fertilisation, the egg will implant and continue to develop and grow | uterus wall the uterus lining, the tissue that comprises the uterus | pregnant uterus a fertilised egg has become implanted in the wall of the uterus and is developing into a foetus

utilisation (UK) / **utilization** (USA) the use of, applicability

utilise (UK) / **utilize** (USA) to use, to make use of, to employ

UV / uv [ultra-violet] radiation with a wavelength below that of visible light, *ie* less than 400 nanometres

V / volts the unit of potential difference between two points in a circuit

v [velocity] speed in a specified direction

vaccinate to inject with a weak or inactivated form of a virus in order to cause the body to produce defensive molecules that will protect against a live infection

vaccination injection of a weakened form of a virus so as to give protection against a full-scale attack by the same virus: introduced by Jenner using *vaccinia* to protect against smallpox

vaccine a chemical that is injected into people in order to protect against disease | MMR vaccine / mumps-measles-rubella vaccine / triple vaccine an injection that causes the body to produce antibodies to measles, mumps and rubella (German measles), the MMR jab | rubella vaccine the liquid that is injected in order to help the body to reject any infection by the rubella virus (that causes German measles) – should be given to all young women because this virus, though normally only mildly symptomatic, can cause defects in an unborn baby

vacuole a space within a plant cell that is filled with sugar solution, a packet of chemicals at the head of a sperm

vacuum a volume with less than one particle per cubic metre | vacuum cleaner household equipment in which a motor reduces the air pressure in a cylinder so allowing ingestion of dust and dirt | vacuum flask a sealed container with two walls of silver-coloured glass separated by a vacuum, which is used to keep fluids at a constant temperature, a dewar vessel | vacuum pump a machine that removes all the particles from a container so producing a vacuum

vagina the tube that connects the uterus to the outside world

vain (not vane which is a wing nor vein which is a blood vessel) worthless pride, conceited

valency the number of bonds, or arms, that an atom has in order to join to other atoms thus producing molecules

valid true, of current worth, follows from all known information, agrees with other ideas | valid conclusion the summary includes both the accuracy of the results and other knowledge | valid data a fair test was carried out and the measurements are accurate

validity the truth | validity of conclusions the agreement between the conclusion from your experiment and what is usually found or expected in similar experiments | validity of results the measurements are accurate and the instruments are precise

valley a hollow, a low point in a graph, an area of land that is lower than the surrounding area | Rift Valley a wide trough in the Earth's surface in the Highlands of Kenya

valuable important, significant, of great worth

value the amount, the number; to treat as important | current values the cost or number at this instant of time | energy values the number of joules of energy that are released when the chemical reacts with an excess of oxygen | known values the numbers or amounts that are known before the experiment begins | negative values numbers that have a minus in front, *ie* represent less than zero on the scale of measurement | nutritional value the importance of the named chemicals to your diet either for energy or because they are essential nutrients | pH value the amount of acid or alkali in a solution as indicated by the hydrogen ion concentration that is measured for the solution

valve equipment that allows liquids to flow in one direction only (there are valves in the heart and in the veins), large electronic components, devices for changing the flow of liquid | bicuspid valve / mitral valve the flaps between the atrium and ventricle on the left-hand side of the heart | heart valves flaps that ensure the heart pumps the blood only in one direction | mitral valve / bicuspid valve the flaps between the atrium and ventricle on the left-hand side of the heart | rectifier valve a diode, a glass valve for ensuring that a current can flow only in one direction | safety valve equipment that opens when the pressure exceeds a given value so that gases can escape and the pressure be reduced | semi-lunar valve the flaps of material between each ventricle and the respective artery that prevents the blood from flowing back into the heart | tricuspid valve the tissue between the atrium and ventricle on the right hand side of the heart

van de Graaff (Robert Jemison 1901–1967) an American who studied at Alabama, Sorbonne and Oxford before returning to Princeton. He built his first machine for producing and storing static electric charge in 1929, later models were bigger and could generate millions of volts. These machines have been important tools in analysing the structure of the atom.

van de Graaff generator equipment for producing a static high voltage, a machine that continuously separates charges using a moving belt, then stores the charge on a metal dome

vane (not vain which is worthless pride nor vein which is a blood vessel) the wing-like structure that is turned by the wind on a windmill or wind turbine | **wind vane** an instrument for giving the direction of a wind

vanish to disappear

van't Hoff (Jacobus Henrikus 1852–1911) graduated from Delft Polytechnic after two years, rather than three, he went on a tour of several European universities then returned to Holland, where his application to be a school teacher was turned down. He explained Pasteur's observation that some molecules can form crystals that are mirror images. His studies in chemistry led to him receiving the first Nobel Prize in chemistry in 1901.

vapor (USA) / **vapour** (UK) a substance that is present as a gas at a temperature below the boiling pint of that substance | condensing vapor cooling the vapor to a temperature at which the liquid is formed | water vapor the water that is present as a gas in the air

vaporisation (UK) / **vaporization** (USA) the turning of a liquid into a gas, usually suddenly or on a large scale

vaporise (UK) / **vaporize** (USA) to turn a liquid into a gas

vapour (UK) / **vapor** (USA) a substance that is present as a gas at a temperature below the boiling pint of that substance | condensing vapour cooling the vapour to a temperature at which the liquid is formed | water vapour the water that is present as a gas in air

variability the amount by which similar items differ from each other

variable an item that can change in value | variable composition a mixture in which the concentration of each component may differ, depending on the source of the mixture | variable power pack equipment that is usually connected to mains electricity, the potential difference of the output can be varied | variable resistor an electrical component with a resistance that is changed by sliding a contact, a rheostat | variable voltage source equipment in which the potential difference of the output can be changed | algebraic variable a letter that is used in an equation in order to represent a value that can change | appropriate variables choosing the items to be changed or measured experimentally in order to examine a particular question | compound variable an item whose value depends on two other variables, *eg* speed, which depends on distance and time or density, which is mass over volume | continuous variable a measure that can take any value, *eg* height,

weight | control (of) variables / control key variables ensure that the values of the important variables remain constant | control variable the experiment in which a crucial factor is omitted, *eg* a placebo given in clinical trials | dependent variable the item whose value depends on the values of other variables, the item that you expect to change and are going to measure, the output variable | environmental variables any measure that will change the conditions under which organisms live | identify variables to decide which items could affect the outcome of the experiment | independent variable the item whose value you can decide and which you are going to change during the experiment, the input variable | input variable the item whose value you are going to change during the experiment in order to measure the effect on the output variable | key variables items whose values are important to the experiment, so changing these values could change the output variables | outcome variable the result, the consequence of changing the value of the input variable | relevant variables any item or factor that changing would probably lead to different results | uncontrolled variables an item over which you have no control, *eg* room temperature

variation an alteration, a change, a modification, deviation, difference between measurements or individuals | considerable variation major differences, obvious changes | continuous variation the measurement may take any value | daily variation changes that occur regularly because of the apparent movement of the Sun | discontinuous variation the differences may take only specific values | environmental variation differences between individuals caused by the way they were raised and where they grew up | experimental variation error, small differences that occur whenever an experiment is repeated | genetic variation differences between individuals caused by different instructions in the DNA of their chromosomes | inherited variation differences caused by genes | magnetic variation the angle between magnetic north and true north | observable variation differences that are easily seen | seasonal variation changes that occur at particular times of each year because of changes in the environment | statistical variation random differences between measurements that should be identical | temperature variation changes in how hot an object feels

varied changed, assorted, composed of different items | varied diet many different types of food are eaten

variegated shows areas of different colour | variegated leaves the surface of the leaf has patches of different reds, yellows and greens caused by the distribution of the pigments such as chlorophyll

varies changes, differs, has more than one value

varieties (plural of variety) types, organisms that are closely related, but show important differences

variety (plural is varieties) particular type, variant, several different items | variety of forces different ways in which attempts are made to change speed or direction | variety of resources many different sources which supply the material or energy | variety of sources the material or energy may have started from several different places or stores | lettuce variety the particular type of lettuce, *eg* cos, iceberg | plant variety the particular type of that species of plant | tomato variety the particular type of tomato, *eg* plum, Tom Thumb, cherry

various different, several types

vary to change

varying changing, moving randomly, not remaining steady | varying composition the proportion of each component is not fixed

vascular concerned with tubes, the blood system, the system by which fluid is moved in plants | vascular bundles the structures for moving fluid in plants, groups of xylem and phloem | vascular plants organisms that have chlorophyll for photosynthesis, and also have tubes for the transport of water and sugar solutions | vascular system the collection of arteries, capillaries and veins through which blood is distributed in animals | vascular tissue any cell or group of cells through which flows fluid containing nutrients | non-vascular lacking tubes

vase a container made from pottery and which is often used for displaying flowers

Vaseline™ a yellow, greasy jelly that is used as a protective layer on skin

vaso- concerned with blood vessels | vaso-constrictor a chemical that causes some blood vessels to become narrower | vaso-dilator a chemical that causes some blood vessels to become wider

vast very large, enormous expanse

vat a large tub, a tank with an open top, a bath

Vauquelin (Louis Nicolas 1763–1829) the son of a farm-worker, he started as an apprentice pharmacist in Rouen at age 14, then, due to hard work and good luck over the next 18 years, he was appointed a Professor at the School of Mines. In 1798, he and Klaproth, in Germany, individually announced the discovery of chromium.

vector a measurement that has both size and direction (size alone is a scalar quantity) the direction in which a body is moving, a carrier of a disease, an insect that carries an infectious agent, *eg* a mosquito carries the malaria parasite

vegan a person who will not eat any product in which animals have been involved

vegetable a plant, but not a fruit, that is eaten by humans for its nutritional value | vegetable extract the fluid that is left when edible plants have been turned into juice then the solid parts removed

vegetarian a person who chooses not to eat any material produced from dead animals

vegetation plants, producers | vegetation cover the layer formed by plants growing together

vegetative reproduction asexual reproduction in plants, *eg* bulbs, rhizomes or runners

vehicle a car, a carriage, a lorry, a wheeled item used for transport | vehicle design the plan for an object with wheels | electric vehicle a car or transporter that uses a motor to turn the wheels

vein (not vain which is conceited nor vane which is the sail of a windmill) the blood vessels with thin walls and valves through which blood returns from the capillaries to the heart, a sheet of mineral in a rock | hepatic portal vein the blood vessel taking material that has been absorbed in the small intestine to the liver | hepatic vein the vessel (tube) that returns blood from the liver to the heart | leaf vein tubes that both provide support for the leaves and contain the phloem and xylem tubes | pulmonary vein the vessel (tube) that carries the oxygenated blood from the lungs to the heart | renal vein the blood vessel that carries blood from the kidney to the heart

velocity (plural is velocities) the speed and the direction of a moving object | velocity–time graph a diagram, showing time along the bottom axis and velocity up the vertical axis, in which the slope gives the acceleration and the area under the curve represents the distance moved | terminal velocity the maximum speed in a specified direction, pushing force and resistance force are identical

vena cava the major vein in the body through which all blood returns to the heart

Venn diagram a picture method for showing how sets with different properties will overlap and show common characteristics

vent a hole, a gap in the Earth's crust through which magma flows; to allow gas to escape

ventilate to change the air, to breathe

ventilation changing air | artificial ventilation using fans to extract and replace the air

Ventolin™ salbutamol, a bronchodilator, a drug that causes the bronchi to become wider, and thus facilitates breathing

ventricles the larger chambers of the heart, the parts of the heart that push the blood into the arteries

Venus the morning star, named after the Roman goddess of love, second planet from the Sun, surface temperature is extremely hot (480°C) because high concentrations of carbon dioxide lead to an extreme greenhouse effect, the atmosphere is so corrosive that the first probe (Venera 4 in 1967) dissolved before reaching the surface

verb a 'doing' word, *eg* to be, to act

verdigris the green material to which copper turns when exposed to the atmosphere

verge an edge, the side of a path; to be on the brink | grass verge the edge of the area, or the road, is covered with grass

version a statement, an account, a description, a story that gives one side | simplified version a description or diagram that shows the main features, but misses out the details and possible drawbacks

vertebra (plural is vertebrae) one of the bones of the backbone through which the spinal chord goes

vertebrae (plural of vertebra) the specially shaped bones that make up the spine | neck vertebrae the bones at the top of the spinal column that allow the head both to rotate and to nod

vertebrate an animal that has a backbone

vertical upwards, a direction pointing directly away from the centre of gravitational attraction or towards the sky, a line drawn directly away from you | vertical columns the sets of elements in the periodic table containing the elements that are arranged above and below each other

vertically moving along a line pointing to the sky

Vesalius (Andreas 1514–1564) was born in Belgium and initially studied there before moving to Paris and eventually settling at Padua in Italy. He demonstrated many dissections of human bodies and had published his masterwork *On the Structure of the Human Body* before he was 30. Diagrams in the book showed clearly many of the structures of the human body and disputed many of the claims of Galen. Vesalius became physician to the Kings of Spain, then died in Greece while on a pilgrimage to Jerusalem

vessel a cup, a bowl, a tube, a container | blood vessel any of the types of tube (artery, vein, capillary) through which blood flows | capillary vessel tiny blood tubes with walls that are a

single cell thick | Dewar vessel Thermos™ flask, vacuum flask, an insulated cylinder for storing liquids with minimum change of temperature | xylem vessels the long tubes in plant stems that transport water from roots to leaves

vet. a veterinary surgeon, a veteran

via by way of, using that route, by means of

viable able to live

vibrate to move quickly from side to side in a regular or rhythmic manner

vibrating moving regularly, rhythmic moving | vibrating source an item that is intended to move rhythmically

vibration rhythmic movement, sound | speed of vibration the frequency

vice versa the opposite way round

video a moving image, a machine for showing tape recordings of moving image | video camera equipment for making permanent records of moving images | video clip a short recording that highlights a specific item

view an appearance, that which you can see, an opinion, a belief; to look at | field of view the area that can be seen when an object is examined using a microscope or telescope

viewed seen, watched, regarded, observed

viewing seeing, watching

viewpoint the way that data are seen and interpreted, which will depend on your previous knowledge and experience | considered viewpoint providing an analysis that takes account of all the evidence and prejudices

vigorous with enthusiasm | vigorous exercise using muscles to move rapidly until respiration becomes anaerobic | vigorous reaction the chemical change produces large amounts of heat or bubbles in a short time

vigorously with force, shaken rapidly

village a group of houses, shops and at least one church, where a community resides

villi (plural of villus) the 'tiny fingers' that increase the internal surface area of the small intestine so increasing the rate of absorption of nutrients | microvilli (plural of microvillus) tiny folds (approximately 1 micrometre long) in the membrane of most cells, which increase the surface area

villus (plural is villi) one of millions of tiny fingers or folds of the inside surface of the small intestine

da Vinci (Leonardo1452–1519) painter, sculptor, engineer, scientist, architect – name a subject and Da Vinci was the master. His drawings of the difference in muscles when moving, show that he must have (illegally) cut bodies open, his ideas for flying machines and parachutes were still being studied five hundred years later. Leonardo was born and worked mainly in Italy, but was later employed, and given a pension, by the kings of France

vinegar ethanoic acid [CH₃COOH], the acid produced when wine or cider is infected with microbes

violence the threat and the use of force

violent furious, vicious, forceful | violent eruption powerful ejection of vast amounts of magma from a volcano | violent reaction an extreme response, a sudden and destructive change

violently extremely, viciously, forcefully

violet a colour with a wavelength shorter than blue, *ie* approximately 400 nanometres, a perennial plant | ultra-violet the part of the spectrum with wavelengths below blue or violet, *ie* less than 400 nanometres

violin a stringed musical instrument that is played with a bow

viral caused by a virus

Virchow (Rudolf Ludwig Carl 1821–1902) was a medical practitioner who made a breakthrough in the description of a disease (leukaemia) almost as soon as he graduated. His political views led him to change jobs several times and his arguments almost led to a duel with Bismark – but this was avoided. He developed the ideas of Schwann and Schleiden, that organisms are made from cells, by using improvements in methods for preparing and observing sections of organs.

virologist a person who studies viruses

virtual seems to exist but is an image | virtual image a series of pictures that fools your brain into believing that there is an actual event

virus (plural is viruses) a nucleic acid surrounded by a protein coat that can enter a cell and reproduce using the cell's own 'machinery' | virus coat the layer of protein molecules that is the outer part of a virus | cold virus the microbe that causes a person to feel ill with a cold | Ebola virus a virus that first appeared in 1976, causes internal bleeding then usually death | human immuno-deficiency virus (HIV) a virus that causes the immune or defensive system to stop working, producing a disease called AIDS (acquired immuno-deficiency syndrome)

viruses (plural of virus) strands of nucleic acid surrounded by proteins, viruses are capable of entering a cell and reproducing

viscosity (plural is viscosities) thickness of a fluid, the ability of a fluid to resist flow

visible able to be seen, obvious, conspicuous | visible change a difference that can be seen | visible light the part of the electromagnetic

spectrum, from about 700 nanometres to 400 nanometres, to which the human eye is sensitive | visible spectrum the pattern produced when white light is dispersed through a prism | visible stars the stars that you are able to see using either the eye alone (the naked eye) or a telescope

vision the sense of sight, a dream, that which is seen which may or may not be real | acute vision able to see tiny details | binocular vision using two eyes so as to allow distance to be estimated | blurred vision the image that is formed on the retina is not in sharp focus | color vision (USA) / colour vision (UK) the ability to see different parts of the spectrum, the human eye has cone cells that respond to red, blue or green light

visking tubing cellophane material in the form of a tube which has tiny pores that will allow water, sugar, salt and other small molecules to pass through the wall, but will stop the movement of large molecules

visor a protective screen that can be placed in front of the eyes

visual appearing to the sense of sight, able to be seen | visual demonstration an experiment where the changes can be seen | visual information data in the form of diagrams, pictures or graphs | visual signal a gesture that can be seen, using flags, showing a symbol

visualise (UK) / **visualize** (USA) to be able to see, to imagine

visually seeing, easily seen | visually impaired unable to see as well as is normal, partially blind

vital essential, important | vital air an early name for oxygen | vital capacity the maximum volume of air that can breathed out after taking a very deep breath, a measure of the size and condition of the lungs | vital organs the parts of the body that are essential for survival

vitamin any of approximately twenty chemicals that are essential for the human body to be healthy | vitamin A retinol, a chemical that is essential for good night-vision and adequate growth | vitamin C ascorbic acid, lack of vitamin C causes scurvy which was first cured by Lind in 1747, although vitamin C was not isolated until 1928 by Szent-Gyorgi | vitamin content the concentration of the particular vitamin | vitamin D a chemical found in milk and fish that can be made by the human body using sunlight, lack of vitamin D leads to rickets | fat-soluble vitamins the vitamins that are found in fat material, *eg* vitamins A, D, E

vocabulary words, text, meaning of words | appropriate vocabulary the use of words that are suitable for a particular level of knowledge | scientific vocabulary the words that are used in science to give a precise description

vocal concerned with the production of sound in animals, loud, noisy | vocal cords the larynx, the upper part of the windpipe where speech is produced in humans

voice a speech, a talk; to express an idea, to give an opinion | voicebox larynx, the top part of the windpipe that is used for producing sound

volatile a liquid that easily turns into a vapour close to room temperature

volcanic concerned with eruption of magma through the Earth's crust | volcanic activity any change caused by magma bursting through the crust | volcanic area a region where there are several volcanoes close together | volcanic ash the powder that falls after a volcano has pushed the magma high into the sky | volcanic cone the tall hill with a circular base that results from the emergence and cooling of the magma | volcanic eruption a surge of magma from the volcano | volcanic region an area where several volcanoes occur close together | volcanic rock igneous rock, the rocks produced by eruption of a volcano

volcano (plural can be either volcanos or volcanoes) a hill or mountain made by magma erupting through the Earth's crust | active volcano a hill of lava and magma that is continuing to produce more molten rock | dormant volcano a hill or mountain that was formed from magma, but has not erupted for some years | explosive volcano the molten rock is being thrown high into the air | extinct volcano the gaps in the Earth's crust through which the magma escaped, have become filled with solid material, leaving cold igneous rock | moderate volcano the molten rock is being pushed through the surface, but not thrown high

volcanoes / volcanos (plural of volcano) hills formed by molten rock being thrown out of the Earth's interior

vole / water vole an omnivorous, mouse-like mammal, with a large head and a short tail, that is found in Europe, Africa and North America

volt / V the unit used for comparing electrical potential differences

Volta (Count Allesanro Guiseppe 1745–1827) started work on electricity following the work of Priestley, but it took him 25 years to develop a reliable source of electricity. In 1798 he succeeded in producing the first battery, which proved that Galvani's idea of animal electricity could not be true. This steady source of electricity was important in the further work of Davy and Faraday

voltage potential difference (pd), the force that causes a current | voltage rating the size of the potential difference that is best suited for use with that component | voltage source equipment with terminals that have a potential difference | high voltage a potential difference that is high enough to cause injury or death to the user | low voltage a potential difference that will not cause any injury to someone touching the terminals | mains voltage the potential difference supplied to the domestic user, should be between 230 volts and 250 volts at 50 hertz alternating current in the United Kingdom or 110 volts at 60 hertz in the USA

voltage source equipment with terminals that have a potential difference | variable voltage source equipment in which the potential difference of the output can be changed

voltaic cell an electrical cell, two different metals separated by a salt solution that produces a voltage

voltameter / Hofmann voltameter glass tubing, of a crosspiece and two vertical tubes, with an electrode at the base of each upright tube, passing an electric current through water produces two volumes of hydrogen and one volume of oxygen

voltmeter an instrument for measuring the potential difference across a component in an electrical circuit

volts the size of the electrical potential difference (pd) between two points

volume the amount of a gas or liquid, the loudness of a sound | volume control the knob that is moved in order to change the loudness of the sound | blood volume the total amount of blood in the body | chest volume the capacity within the rib cage | fixed volume the amount of liquid remains constant | lung volume the largest amount of air that you are able to exhale

voluntary using your own free will, acting willingly | voluntary action a use of the muscles that you are able to control | voluntary control directing the use of muscles that you are able to control | voluntary response a movement that is under the conscious control of the brain

vomit the contents of the stomach that have been thrown out of the mouth; to throw the stomach contents out of the mouth, to be sick

vomiting throwing up the contents from the stomach, being sick

-vore (Latin to eat), eg herbivore (plant eater), omnivore (can eat anything), carnivore (meat eater)

Voyager 2 one of a pair of probes that were launched in 1977, Voyager has sent back data from each of the gas giant planets and continues to send back information about space

vulcanisation (UK) **/ vulcanization** (USA) the process of improving the properties of rubber by adding sulphur

vulcanise (UK) **/ vulcanize** (USA) to improve the properties of rubber by adding sulphur at a high temperature

vulnerable exposed, easily damaged, unprotected | vulnerable population the species is likely to become extinct in that area

vulva the external part of the female genitals

W / watts the unit of power, joules per second

waft to push along gently, to blow

wagon a railway truck, a vehicle made from a flat, horizontal storage area supported on four large wheels

waist (not waste which is rubbish) the part of the body between the top of the pelvis and the rib cage

wait (not weight which is a force) to stay, to remain

Wales (not whales which are marine mammals) one of the countries the comprise the United Kingdom

walk a route, a path; to pace, to travel on foot, to march

wall a narrow structure with height and width, an enclosure, a fence, a cliff | wall display artistic work that is put on the wall for decoration and education | wall insulation filling the cavity between double walls with a layer of foam or glass fibre | wall socket a connection that is mounted on a wall and into which an electrical plug will fit | capillary wall the very thin, single layer of cells that comprise the walls of a capillary, the smallest vessels in the blood circulatory system | cavity wall a house wall made of two solid layers with a gap between them | cell wall the rigid structure around the cells of plants and fungi | chest wall the membrane that keeps the chest air-tight | intestine wall the layers of cells and blood vessels that are between the muscles and the inside lumen of the intestine | outer wall the barrier nearer the outside | uterine wall / uterus wall the lining of the womb

wane to become smaller, to fade away

waning becoming less bright

war (not wore which is having clothes on) a fight, a dispute, a contest, a conflict | tug-of-war two teams pull the same rope in opposite directions

ware (not wear which is to put on, nor where which is a location) manufactured items that have a purpose | glassware any item made from glass that is used in the laboratory | hardware the equipment that is being used | software the programme that controls a system

warm a comfortable temperature, neither too hot nor too cold; to heat, to get hotter | warm–blooded animals with a constant body temperature | warm conditions the temperature is slightly too high to be comfortable | warm environment the area rarely gets below 10°C | warm front the mass of moving air is at a higher temperature than is the volume of static air | warm temperatures the conditions are pleasant for people | keeping warm retaining heat

energy | pre-warm to heat an item to a higher temperature before it is used

warmed heated, increased in temperature

warmer higher temperature | warmer climate a place that has a higher average temperature for every month | hand warmer equipment that uses a piece of glowing charcoal inside an insulated container to keep your hands warm

warmest highest temperature

warming heating, increasing in temperature, getting hotter | global warming the increase in average temperature of most areas of the Earth

warmth heat

warn (not worn which is dressed) to alert to danger, to awaken, to caution

warning a caution, a notice about possible danger | warning light a lamp that indicates a potential danger | warning sign a notice showing hazards, a diagram indicating possible risk | hazard warning a sign highlighting possible danger | health warning a notice indicating the likely effects on the body

warren a network of tunnels

washer a machine for washing clothes | washer / metal washer a flat ring of metal that provides a firm surface for a nut

washing getting clean, removing dirt | washing powder a fine solid that helps remove the dirt from clothes | washing soda [Na_2CO_3] sodium carbonate | washing up liquid a fluid that is added to the water to help remove grease from dishes | damp washing clothing that has been soaked in water and not all the water has evaporated

wasp any of several different types of flying insect | wasp sting the alkaline irritant that is injected by an attacking wasp

waste (not waist which is the stomach area) unwanted material, rubbish, refuse, garbage; to squander, to use without much gain | waste chemicals molecules that are formed in the cell, but need to be removed | waste energy the heat, sound and light energy that are produced whenever one form of energy is turned into another useful form of energy | waste gases the gases that are produced in an industrial process, such as the blast furnace, which can not be sold, but could contaminate the atmosphere | waste material a substance that is thrown away unused | waste products the unwanted chemicals that are formed as a by-product in reactions for producing useful chemicals | waste water the dirty water that has been used for washing | animal waste the faeces and urine that animals egest | bio-degradable waste unwanted material that can be broken down by weather, water or microbes | energy waste paying for input energy which is not turned into any useful product | household waste the bags, peelings, dust and packaging that are produced by most homes | industrial waste material that is produced on a large scale, but can not be sold, and is likely to cause pollution of the environment | nuclear waste the material from a nuclear power station that is not suitable as a source of energy, but is dangerously radio-active | persistent waste material for which no use can be found that will remain a hazard for many, many years | radio-active waste material that is produced as a by-product of making and using nuclear fuel, which is of no further use, but is dangerous because it is giving off radiation | solid waste faeces, discarded material that retains its shape

wasted not used | wasted energy the energy was available but not used

wasteland / waste land an area where life does not seem to exist, barren

watch (plural is watches) portable equipment for showing the time; to see, to view, to observe | watch glass a circle of glass that has the same cross-section as is used in watches | stop watch a clock that can be started and stopped to measure accurately a period of time

watching viewing, observing, examining

water [H_2O] a liquid that is essential for most of the reactions that sustain life, including photosynthesis and respiration | water absorption taking water into a material, porous rock taking in water | water availability the volume and purity of water that is present at different times of the year | water bath a tank containing water that can be held at a specified temperature | water-borne moved by rivers, carried in streams | water closet the wc, the room containing the toilet, the loo | water of crystallisation the definite amount of water that is found in a crystal, *eg* crystalline copper sulphate is always $CuSO_4.5H_2O$ | water current evaporation of water within an ocean | water cycle the movement of water particles from the oceans to the sky then condensation to fall as rain or snow and passing through the soil, plants and animals before eventually reaching the sea | water feature a garden ornament that involves flowing water | water flow the rate of movement of the liquid | water hyacinth a fast growing freshwater plant that could help to reduce chemical pollution of water, but may clog water channels | water inlet the position at which water enters the equipment | water jacket a flow of water around a pipe or

tank in order to keep the contents at constant temperature | water-jet a continuous stream of water leaving a hole at high speed, a boat that is pushed by a stream of high-speed water | water level the height of the water | water-logged filled with water, saturated | water loss the change in the amount of water during a period | water model the idea that the behaviour of electrons in electricity is similar to the movement of water through tubes | water outlet the position at which waste water leaves the equipment | water plant a green plant that is able to live in fresh water | water pollution changes to a river or lake caused by addition of chemicals to the water | water power using the kinetic energy of moving water in order to turn a wheel or dynamo | water pressure the force per unit area that is produced by the height of water above that point | water-proof material that prevents movement of water | water pump equipment that is used for moving water, equipment for removing air that is powered by the flow of water | water quality the suitability of that water source for a specified purpose | water regulation varying the volume of urine produced so that the concentration of solutes in the blood remains almost constant | water resistance the retarding force produced by an object moving through water | water-resistant not affected by water, not permeable to water | water resources the area from which suitable water can be removed and used | water rocket a missile made by pumping air into a bottle containing water, so causing the water to be pushed out of the back and the bottle to move forwards | water-soluble large amounts of the substance will dissolve in water | water supply the way in which suitable water is stored and distributed | water table the upper level reached by underground water | water tank a large container connected to pipes that allow water in or out, which is used for storing a volume of water that is adequate for a specific purpose | water-tight water is not able to penetrate either the material or any joints | water turbine a series of vanes mounted inside a cylinder which is turned by flow of water through the cylinder | water vapor (USA) / water vapour (UK) the molecules of water that have evaporated in to the air | water vole an omnivorous, mouse-like mammal, with a large head and a short tail, that is found in Europe, Africa and North America | waterway a river, a canal, a channel for the containment and movement of water | water weed plants that grow rapidly in rivers and lakes | water-wheel a series of buckets around the circumference of a wheel arranged so that water flowing into the buckets causes the wheel to turn | waterworks a collection of structures that make river water safe for drinking | boiled water the water has been boiled so as to get rid of all the dissolved air | boiling water water that has reached 100°C and so can no longer exist as a liquid, so changes into gas | bottled water drinking water that is bought in a sealed contained | cabbage water the solution that results when cabbage is cooked in hot water | carbonated water drinking water that contains carbon dioxide either as a natural solute or added under pressure | clean water water that is colourless and transparent, but may not be suitable for drinking | clear water water that has no colour and is transparent | cold water water at or below room temperature | colored water (USA) / coloured water (UK) water to which a dye has been added so as to make the liquid easier to see | contaminated water chemicals have been added to the water so the water is no longer suitable for a particular use | cooling water the liquid that is used to reduce the temperature of a tube or container | deionised water water which has been passed through a column that removes any charged particles | displacement of water a solid object will sink into a liquid such as water and increase the level of water | distilled water clean water produced by heating dirty or salty water, removing the water vapour and then cooling the vapour to produce a liquid | drinkable water / drinking water also known as potable water, water that will not produce any ill effects if drunk | electrolysis of water passing an electric current through water produces twice as much hydrogen as oxygen | fizzy water carbon dioxide is dissolved under pressure in water and forms bubbles when the pressure is reduced | freezing water water that has been cooled to 0°C so that ice is forming | fresh water water that does not contain salt, although there may be microbes capable of causing illness | hard water water containing dissolved magnesium carbonate, magnesium sulphate, calcium carbonate or calcium sulphate, so the water will not produce a permanent lather with soap | hot water water that is at high temperature, water that could burn if you put your hands in | irrigation water the water that is transported to be distributed over farmland | lime water a solution of calcium hydroxide in water | liquid water emphasising that the water is able to flow | loss of water the decrease in the amount of water from that item | mineral water contains chemicals that were

dissolved from the earth | moving water a stream, a river, tides, water that has energy of movement | open water an area of water that is sufficiently large to be affected by winds | pond water the static water that remains in a freshwater pond | pure water a liquid that contains water particles only, with no dissolved chemicals | rainwater / rain water the water that falls from the clouds and dissolves several other chemicals as the droplets fall through the air | river water the mixture of dissolved substances and suspended material that is in the water of a river | running water moving water, a river | salt water / salty water brine, a solution of sodium chloride dissolved in water | sea water the water the covers two thirds of the Earth and contains several per cent of sodium chloride, along with dozens of other dissolved chemicals | soft water water that very easily forms a permanent lather with soap | stagnant water a pool of static water containing very little dissolved oxygen, but lots of bacteria | sterile water water that has been treated so as to remove or kill all microbes | store water to keep a supply of water in conditions that allow the water to be used safely for a specific purpose | sugary water a solution of glucose or sucrose in water | surface water the rain that is not absorbed into the ground and flows off the surface into streams | tap water the water that is available in most homes and offices and is clean enough to drink because it has been treated with chlorine | test for water cobalt chloride paper is blue when dry, but turns pale pink if moisture is present, a liquid with a boiling point of 100°C and a freezing point of 0°C, a liquid that turns anhydrous copper sulphate from white powder to a blue solution | types of water a liquid that is mainly water, but may contain dissolved minerals or salt or gases or other chemicals | waste water the dirty water that has been used for washing

water-borne carried by rivers or streams | water-borne disease an illness caused by microbes that live and move through rivers and streams (11,000 children die each day from water-borne disease) | water-borne infections diseases caused by microbes that live in water

watered water has been provided (usually for growing plants)

water-logged filled with water, saturated | water-logged soil earth that is flooded

waterproof a material through which water is unable to penetrate, a coat for protection from rain | waterproof barrier a material that prevents entry or exit of water | waterproof cuticle a thin layer of cells that prevents loss of water from each surface of a leaf | **waterproof layer** a covering that prevents entry or exit of water

waterway a canal, a river

watery a thin solution, looking or behaving like water

Watt (James 1736–1819) was born near Glasgow and suffered poor health as a child, but was able to establish himself as an engineer. He realised that vast improvements could be made to the Newcomen engine, and set up a company which was both to produce much of the power that drove the Industrial Revolution and to turn Watt into a very rich man.

watt / W (not what which is a question) the unit of power, a rate of 1 joule per second | **kilowatt (kW)** a thousand watts

wave regular movement of the sea caused by wind, a disturbance that moves in a regular and repeated manner | **wave energy** the amount of energy in the wave, depends on both amplitude and frequency | **wave form** the shape of a wave which can be square, saw-tooth or sine | **wave front** the pattern produced as one looking down at the crests of a moving wave | **wavelength** the distance between two successive peaks | **wave movement** a rhythmical change that travels along a straight line | **wave power** a measure of the energy in the wave, obtaining energy from the vertical movement of sea waves | **electromagnetic wave** any part of the spectrum that includes light and radio waves | **infra-red waves** heat radiation, the part of the spectrum with a wavelength between 600 nanometres and 2000 nanometres | **longitudinal wave** the direction of vibration of the particles is in the same direction as the wave is moving | **primary wave / pusher wave** the longitudinal movement from an earthquake that is transmitted rapidly through the Earth and so arrives first | **radio waves** electromagnetic waves with wavelengths in the range of 1 millimetre to several kilometres that are used in communication | **sea wave** regular up and down movements of the sea surface caused by the blowing of wind | **secondary wave** the shaking movement of the Earth as a result of an earthquake | **seismic wave** a vibration throughout the Earth caused by an earthquake or volcano | **shaker wave** the slower moving wave produced by an earthquake, a transverse wave | **sound waves** regular vibrations of particles in the air | **transverse wave** the direction of vibration of the particles is at right angles to the direction of wave motion, *eg* a sea wave

wavelength the length of a repeating unit in a wave, the distance from one crest to the next crest

wax (plural is waxes) a plastic solid, a hydrocarbon with about a dozen carbon atoms, a water-proof chemical produced by animals and plants; to increase in brightness | **wax candle** a wick inside a column of wax | **wax-like** having some properties of a hydrocarbon that is solid at room temperature but melts below 400°C | **ear wax** the essential lubricant that keeps the ear canal and ear drum flexible, but can increase in amount and lead to temporary deafness | **molten wax** the temperature is sufficiently high that the wax will flow, but not high enough for combustion | **paraffin wax** a solid that is a mixture of alkanes with 18 to 36 carbons (melting point increases as the alkanes become larger)

waxing becoming brighter

waxy slippery, oily | **waxy cuticle** the lipid coating on the upper surface of some leaves that helps prevent evaporation of water | **waxy layer** a thin coating on the surface of many organisms that prevents loss of water | **waxy paper** the paper has been saturated with an oil, then dried | **waxy solid** material that is shiny, flakes easily and has low friction

way (not weigh which is to measure the weight, nor whey which is the liquid part of milk) the direction, the method, the procedure | **different ways** various methods | **efficient way** a method that achieves the desired result with the least amount of effort | **Milky Way** the collection of stars of which the Sun is one of many million members | **waterways** canals, rivers

wbc [white blood cells], leukocytes, the cells in the blood that are part of the immune system and are responsible for removing invading microbes

weak (not week which is 7 days) not strong, feeble, easily broken | **weak acid** a chemical that dissolves in water to give a pH that is below 7 but no lower than 4 | **weak alkali** a chemical that dissolves in water to give a pH that is above 7 but not greater than 10 | **weak forces** a push or a pull that has a very low effect | **weak joint** a place where two pieces meet, which is likely to break using very little force | **weak source** the number of radio-active counts is low

weakened (not weekend which is Friday night to Monday morning) strength has been removed, more easily broken | **weakened strain** a microbe that has been modified so it is easily destroyed

weaker less strong, more diluted

weakest least strong, most vulnerable

weakly (not weekly which is every seven days) not strongly, dilute, feeble | **weakly acidic** having a pH between 5 and 7 | weakly alkaline having a pH between 7 and 9

weakness (plural is weaknesses) a fault, a thin part

wean to change the diet of an offspring from milk to solid food

wear (not ware which is an object nor where which is a position) to dress in, to carry, to display on a person | wear down to rub away, to abrade, to make thinner | wear resistance the ability of a surface to withstand continual usage

weasel a small carnivorous mammal with short legs and a small head that is found throughout Africa, Europe and North America

weather (not whether which is an option) the conditions of temperature, wind speed and rainfall in an area | weather balloon a balloon that carries measuring instruments to a great height, then bursts! (The instruments are recovered by parachute) | weather conditions the amount of rain, wind speed and temperature in an area at a specified time | weather forecast a prediction of what the temperature, wind speeds and rainfall are likely to be in that area | weather forecaster the person who tells you what the temperature, rain and wind conditions are likely to be in the near future | weather front the line where a body of air at one temperature, humidity and pressure meets a body of air with different characteristics | weather machine a description of the air and water movements, pressure changes and temperature that are constantly changing over the world | weather map a diagram showing the pressure, temperature, wind strength and direction and amount of rainfall | weather patterns looking for regular changes in the weather so that predictions can be made | weather-resistant will not change despite changes in temperature, wind or light conditions | weather satellite a spacecraft that is orbiting the Earth in order to collect vast amounts of information concerning the weather at all places and all times | weather station a collection of instruments for measuring temperature, wind speed and direction and rainfall, that are monitored regularly | weather system the temperatures, wind speeds and rainfalls at different places and times that are all connected to the movement of one section of the atmosphere | calm weather there are few clouds, only a little wind and no waves | cold weather temperatures are sufficiently low that people must wear insulating clothing

weathered changed by movement of air, water, sand or animals, broken into pieces, fragmented, worn away | weathered rocks the results that are seen when a rock is left exposed for thousands of years

weathering changes in rock structure caused by changes in temperature, movement of air and water and by animals | weathering processes the methods by which rocks are changed in size and structure | biological weathering changes in rocks caused by living creatures | chemical weathering changes to rock caused by interaction with water and acid rain | freeze–thaw weathering breakdown of rock caused by water entering a crack then expanding slightly on freezing, causing the crack to become larger, then part of the rock falls off when the ice melts | onion-skin weathering the loss of thin layers of rock caused by alternating intense heat from the Sun with very cold nights | physical weathering breakdown of rocks caused by movement of air or water, or by changes in temperature

web a net, a grill | complex web a theoretical net which shows points being connected by many different paths | food web a diagram showing connections between the many producers and the several layers of consumers and predators | spider's web the net of silk produced by a spider as a means of trapping insects for food | worldwide web the communication between millions of computers and storage discs around the world

webbed feet the thickness of the foot is reduced and the bones connected by a flexible membrane, useful for swimming

wedge a prism-shape, a peice of wood, in the shape of a narrow 'V', that is used for stopping movement; to insert a piece of wood or metal so as to stop movement

weed a wild plant that grows in ground prepared for other specific plants; to remove unwanted plants | weed killers chemicals that prevent the growth of wild plants | weed plants any unwanted plant that is growing in a cultivated area | Canadian pond weed *Elodea*, a small perennial plant that grows just below the surface of fresh water | duckweed a small green plant that grows on the surface of fresh water | seaweed large plant-like structures, which are actually algae, and which grow in the oceans of the Earth | water-weed any plant that grows in an aquatic environment, may grow sufficiently fast and large that the waterway is blocked, a plant that has been used to remove poisonous chemicals from water

weeding removing plants that are growing in the places that you do not want them to grow

weedkillers / weed killers chemicals that kill wild plants | selective weed killers chemicals that kill certain types of wild plant, but allow others to grow

week (not weak which is opposite of strong) a period of seven days

weekend (not weakened which is made less strong) the two days of rest (Saturday, Sunday) at the end of the week

weekly (not weakly which is not strong) every seven days, regularly

Wegener (Alfred Lothar 1880–1930) was a German astronomer with research interests in meteorology. He proposed that many of the continents had been joined together in one land mass called Pangea, although the major part of the supporting evidence was not produced until the thirty years after his death. He died on an expedition to cross Greenland.

weigh (not way which is direction nor whey which is the liquid part of milk) to measure the weight

weighing measuring the weight | weighing pan the container in which material is held for weighing | weighing samples measuring the weight of small amounts of the material

weight (not wait which is to stay) the force of attraction between a mass and a planet

weight = mass x acceleration due to gravity (newtons) = (kilograms) (metres per sec per sec) weight is a force and so is measured in newtons (kilograms are the units of mass) | weight gain an increase in weight | height–weight chart a graph showing the desirable range of body weights for each height | birth-weight the weight of a baby when he / she is born | counter-weight a weight providing a similar force in the opposite direction to the weight that is being lifted | different weights comparing the weights of two or more objects | low birth-weight the baby has a mass below 3 kilogram at birth | lightweight smaller than expected, having a weight below a specified limit | variation in weight changes in weight, differences in weight | zero weight no force of attraction towards a planet

weighted more weight has been added, more important

weightless having no weight, seeming not to be falling

weld a joint in metal; to join two metals by heating

welding joining two pieces of metal by melting the area where they meet | welding torch the end of the pipe at which oxygen and acetylene meet and burn

welfare one's needs, the benefits, prosperity

well good, healthy, a vertical tunnel with drinking water at the bottom | well-nourished receiving

an adequate (or more than adequate) amount of food | artesian well a vertical tube connecting an underground lake of water to the surface | oil well the tube that is drilled in order to obtain the crude oil from underground

west occident, in the direction of the setting Sun

wet damp, rainy, moist, dripping; to cover with water | wet sand sand mixed with water and so is able to retain its shape | wet suit a covering of neoprene that traps layers of water and so helps keep swimmers warm

wetter more rain has fallen, the article has absorbed more water

wettest containing most water, has the greatest amount of rain

whales (not Wales which is a country) marine mammals, including the blue whale, which is largest animal that has ever lived

what (not watt which is a unit of power) part of a question, like 'which?' and 'how?'

wheat an annual grass that is important for production of flour | wheat growth the increase in size of the cereal plant over a year | winter wheat cereal that is often sown in autumn ready for a spring harvest, but may be sown in spring for a summer harvest

wheel a circular object that can rotate around a central pivot; to turn in a circle, to push a vehicle | wheelbarrow a container with one wheel and a pair of handles for transporting building materials or garden waste | wheel bearing the low-friction surface (ball-bearing, needle-bearing or white metal) between the axle and the wheel that rotates | wheel brace a spanner for removing the nuts that retain a car wheel | paddle wheel wood or iron boards are attached at right angles to the outside of a circle | trundle wheel a wheel that is connected by gears to a milometer and so can be used for measuring distance | water-wheel a series of buckets around the circumference of a wheel arranged so that water flowing into the buckets causes the wheel to turn

whelk a small marine mollusc | dog whelk looks like a snail, but lives in the sea

when time, period, while, part of a question

where (not ware which is an object, nor wear which is to put clothing on) a location, asking the geographical location of a place

whereabouts the geographical location, the position

whether (not weather which is climate) if, making clear the options, distinguishing alternatives

whey (not way which is a direction, nor weigh which is an amount) the liquid that is left after the removal of solids from sour milk |

whey powder the material produced when the solids from sour milk are dried completely

which (not witch who is a person who uses magic) what person, what items, the introduction of a descriptive clause

whine (not wine which is an alcoholic drink) a high-pitch sound; to produce an unpleasant noise that has a high frequency, to complain

whip a long, dense fibre that is held at one end and the other end is able to move rapidly

whiskers long hairs that grow close to the mouth of a cat, and are sensitive to touch

whisper a soft noise, a murmur; to talk very softly

whistle an instrument for producing a loud, note of high pitch; to produce a loud, high pitched note | dog whistle a tube that is blown so as to produce a sound that has a frequency above the range of human hearing but that dogs can hear

white contains all colours, a mixture of red, blue and green | white blood cells / white cells leukocytes, the cells in the blood that are part of the immune system and are responsible for removing invading microbes | white dwarf a star with a mass greater than that of the Sun in a volume that is smaller than the Earth | white hot at a temperature that is sufficiently high, over 1500°C, for the material to produce light that appears white | white light a ray containing all colours | white noise a sound containing a random mix of frequencies | white spirit a mixture of alcohols and other solvents | white surface an area that reflects all colours | white tile a small white plate that shows colours clearly | egg white albumen, the solution of nutrients that surrounds the yellow of an egg

whither (not wither which is to fade) to where

WHO [World Health Organisation] an agency involving nearly 200 countries, with the head office in Geneva, that was formed in 1948 that monitors medical conditions 'worldwide' and co-ordinates the fight against infectious diseases

whole (not hole which is a space) everything, in total, entire | whole tablet a pill that has not been broken

whooping cough (pertussis) a disease of the lung caused by infection with a microbe

whorl a characteristic of fingerprint where the ridges form a round shape, a ring of small leaves around a plant stem

why a question asked by every child and every scientist who is trying to find how things work

wick a twisted group of cotton threads that is used to transport the liquid fuel in a candle or a spirit lamp, porous material through which the solvent

moves in chromatography; to transport away using threads

wide broad, extensive | wide range covers many different types | wide ranging over a large number of different topics | wide-spectrum antibiotics chemicals that are safe for humans, but kill a large number of different bacteria

widely used in common usage, used by many people

wider broader, longer along that side

widespread found in lots of different places, over a wide area

width breadth, thickness

wild violent, native, natural wilderness | wild animals animals that are able to survive in the outdoors but are not easily domesticated | wild birds the species of birds that are native to that area | wildcat a well that is dug while exploring for oil | wild cat a cat which lives in the wild, surviving without any help from humans | wild life the organisms that are found in a specified area | wild plants the producers that are found in an area that has not been cultivated | wild rabbits the rabbits that live in the fields without human support

wildlife / wild life the organisms that are found in a specified area | wildlife sanctuary an area where animals live in the wild but are protected

willow / willow tree a type of tree that grows best near water

wilt to droop, to lose shape, to dry up

wilted slack, no longer upright

wilting drooping, becoming less turgid

winch a cylinder around which a rope is turned, that is rotated by a long handle, so causing the rope to move

wind (not wined which is providing wine) movement of air caused by differences in pressure, a draught, gases escaping from the gut; to twist, to turn | wind-blown spread to other areas by the movement of air | wind-dispersal scattered by being thrown into the air | wind energy using the kinetic energy of moving air in order to turn a turbine and produce electricity | wind farm a group of wind turbines scattered across the countryside | wind instrument musical equipment that produces sound when a mouthpiece is blown | windmill a building in which the grindstones are connected to the vanes that are turned by the wind | windpipe trachea, the flexible tube joining the mouth to the lungs | wind-pollinated flower / wind-pollinated plant a plant, eg grass, that scatters pollen onto the wind | wind pollination using the moving air to spread the pollen | wind power using the kinetic energy from wind to produce electricity | wind-proof material through which the moving air is unable to penetrate | wind speed the speed with which the air is moving | wind-swept the effects caused by having the wind blow over the surface for a long period | wind tunnel a large diameter tube with fans at one end that produce a continuous blast of high speed air | wind turbine a set of vanes attached to a generator so the kinetic energy of the moving air is converted to electrical energy | wind-up motor (not a true motor as electricity is not involved) using the stored energy in a tightened spring to rotate wheels | wind-up toy a plaything that is powered by tightening a spring | wind vane an instrument for measuring the direction of the wind | high winds movement of air that can cause damage – higher wind speed causes more damage | offshore-wind movement of air away from the shore towards the sea

winding rotating, moving in a circle

windmill a building in which the grindstones are connected to the vanes that are turned by the wind | giant windmills very large structures that have vanes turned by the wind

window an opening in a wall usually intended to let the light shine through, the glass that fits into the opening | window frame the wood or metal surround that holds the glass in the window | window pane the sheet of glass that is held by the frame of the window | window cill / window sill a decorative slab at the base of a window | oval window the small area where the anvil is connected to the cochlea | shop window a large pane of glass through which can be seen the goods that the shop sells, sometimes in a display | uPVC window the window frame is made from unplasticised poly-vinyl chloride and the glass is double glazed

windpipe trachea, the tube joining the nose and mouth to the lungs

winds movements of air, twists | high winds rapid movement of air that may cause damage to trees and buildings

wind turbine equipment made from a set of vanes attached to a electrical generator | giant wind turbine a tower at the top of which there is a set of vanes, each is over thirty metres long, attached to an electrical generator

wind up to increase the tension in a circular spring | wind-up radio a radio receiver that is powered by turning a key so as to increase the tension in a spring

windy blowing, stormy, breezy | windy environment an area where there is constant high speed movement of air

wine (not whine which is a high-pitched noise) an alcoholic drink made by fermentation of grapes or other fruits

wined (not wind which is to twist) being entertained by having alcohol provided

wings the flight organs of birds and insects

winter the season of the year when the Sun appears to be low on the horizon even at noon; to migrate to a better climate for the cold months | winter coat a fur that is deeper, warmer and lighter coloured than the summer coat | winter solstice the date, a few days before Christmas, when the mid-day Sun is at its lowest point in the sky | winter wheat cereal that is often sown in autumn ready for a spring harvest, but may be sown in spring for a summer harvest | midwinter a period of approximately one month each side of the winter solstice (December 21 in the Northern Hemisphere, June 21 in the Southern Hemisphere) when temperatures are low

wintering / over-wintering acts or responses that take place in order to allow an organism to survive the cold of winter

wipe to rub with a cloth in order to clean or to dry | wipe out to remove entirely, to cause to become extinct

wire a cable, a strand of metal covered with an insulating coat | wire mesh a net made from strands of wire | wire worm a click beetle, the larvae live on roots and can be a serious crop pest | blue wire the colour of the plastic coat that shows the wire goes to the neutral connection of a mains plug | brown wire the colour of the plastic coat that shows the wire goes to the live connection of a mains plug | colored wires (USA) / coloured wires (UK) the insulating sheath around the wire is coloured for identification | conducting wire / connecting wire a piece of metal is used to provide a conducting path between the two points | copper wire the thin conductor is made from copper [Cu], often covered with a plastic insulator | earth wire a cable, coloured green, that is used to connect the casing of the equipment to the water pipes of a building | fuse wire the filament of metal that melts if the current is too high so the circuit is open | heating wire the strand of metal that is intended to glow red hot safely | insulated wire a strand of metal covered with a layer of non-conducting material such as plastic | live wire the cable, usually coloured brown, that is above the neutral voltage | metal wire a filament made from a metal | neutral wire the wire in a socket that is coloured blue and is used to return the current to the generating station

wiring the cables that are used to join equipment, switches and electrical power sources

wisdom teeth the final molars that appear at the back of the mouth during the late teenage years

wispy cloudy, ghost-like, insubstantial

witch (not which which means what) a person who deals in magic, a supernatural being

withdrawal removal, taking out | withdrawal symptoms the shivers and headaches that occur when a person is trying to stop taking an addictive drug

wither (not whither which is to go) to fade, to shrivel

Withering (William 1741–1799) was a medic and a botanist who was in the same Lunar Society as Watt and Priestley. The twin strands of medicine and flowers were brought together in *An Account of the Foxglove* published in 1785, which is a superb account of a research project with all the supporting evidence

within inside, between limits

withstand to resist, to oppose

witness a person who sees an event; to be present at an event

wobble to make random movements

wolf (plural is wolves) a carnivorous dog-like mammal

wolfram (W, proton number 52, melting point 3410oC) tungsten, an unreactive metal that has a high density (20 g/cm^3)

wolves (plural of wolf) two or more of a carnivorous mammal that is similar to a dog

woman (plural is women) a lady, a female adult person

womb the uterus, the protected environment in which a developing foetus develops

women (plural of woman) female people | pregnant women females who are each carrying a developing foetus in the womb

wood the hard material that is obtained from the trunk and branches of trees | woodland an area in which trees are close together

wooden made from wood, stiff | wooden block a solid shape, usually cuboid, made from wood | wooden dowel a cylindrical length of wood | wooden ship a large boat in which most structural components are made from wood, usually powered by sails | wooden splint a thin piece of wood that is used to carry a flame for a short distance | wooden spoon a scoop made from wood

woodland an area in which trees are close together | woodland environment the conditions of light, wet, temperature and wind that are

associated with an area of trees | woodland life the types of animals and plants that are often found in an area of trees | evergreen woodland the area is covered with trees that retain some leaves throughout the year

wood-lice (plural of wood-louse) invertebrate animals that are found in damp places

wood-louse (plural is wood-lice) a terrestrial invertebrate animal that is found in damp patches under stones and trees

wood peckers birds that use their beaks to carve out holes in trees

woody having the appearance and physical properties of wood, hard, with a grain

wool a fibre or filament produced by spinning the hair from a sheep, goat or rabbit | cotton wool a fluffy material produced from fine threads of cotton | glass wool filaments of glass that have been loosely mixed together | mineral wool a mat made from inert threads | steel wool a loose ball of thin steel threads

woollen made from wool, made from springy fibres | woollen cloth material made from the fibres that have been combed or cut from the coat of animals such as sheep, goats or rabbits

woolly covered in a thick, long hair | woolly mammoth a large mammal, similar to the elephant that was found through most of the Northern Hemisphere, but became extinct about 12,000 years ago

words combinations of letters that provide specific meanings, speech, news, commands | word equation a shorthand form that shows the starting chemicals on the left hand side and all the products on the right hand side | word-search a rectangle of what appears to be random letters, but some straight lines will form important words that you have to find | associated words phrases that are related to the word you are given | crosswords word puzzles in which you have clues to discern each word and a pattern of boxes into which each letter must fit | key words the words that are important for that project

wore (not war which is a conflict) had on, covered

work the task, the experiment, the project; to carry out a task | work collaboratively to carry out experiments as a group and agreeing roles for each person | work done amount of energy transferred, energy used, measured in joules | workmen people who are skilled at manual tasks | work-place the area set aside for a particular task | work safely being aware of the hazards and taking steps to minimise risk | worktop a flat surface on which to carry out experiments | additional work further experiments that need to be carried out | display work exhibits and posters that are intended to be placed in public view | earlier work experiments that were carried out and the results used in the preparation of the current experiment or in the interpretation of the results | experimental work the method, results and measurements that are carried out in order to test an idea | fieldwork carrying out measurements and counting in the area where the animals are found in the wild | fireworks controlled explosions that are used to give visual pleasure | investigative work carrying out experiments in order to find more details about a subject | practical work an experiment involving equipment | preliminary work the initial investigation, the first set of experiments where conditions may not be optimal | previous work / prior work experiments that were carried out earlier and the results used to guide the experiments that you are doing | stonework the walls, foundations and decoration that are made by carving rocks | water works a collection of structures that make river water safe for drinking

workable possible, likely, practical

working operating, managing, toiling | working day the interval between starting work and finishing work | working days the amount of time that is spent completing the job | working environment the area and conditions in which a job is carried out | working model a small version of large equipment, an idea that can be used | working safely / safe working carrying out a task without causing any hazards so that accidents are unlikely to happen

workmen people who are skilled at manual tasks

world the Earth, the sphere on which life exists

World Health Organisation (WHO) an agency of nearly 200 countries, with the head office in Geneva, that was formed in 1948 and monitors medical conditions 'worldwide', and co-ordinates the fight against infectious diseases

worldwide found in most continents, affecting most people | worldwide web a network of information that can be accessed from any computer

worm an invertebrate animal that has a long body and no legs | annelid worm a phylum of invertebrates, a tubular animal with the body divided into distinct segments | earthworm the animal, that looks like a living tube, that helps the soil by providing holes and digesting leaf mould | flatworm an invertebrate animal that is very thin and so looks flat | nematode worm slender round worms, some are free-living in soils while others are parasites | ragworm a carnivorous

worm that swims close to the sea-bed | ringworm a fungal infection of the skin that starts at one point then spreads outwards as a red ring | roundworm an invertebrate animal that looks like a tube | seaworms invertebrate animals that have long, cylindrical bodies and live on the sea bed | segmented worm an invertebrate animal with a long body that is divided into distinct circles or segments | tapeworm a parasite found in the intestines of many animals, including people, that uses hooks to attach the head to the wall of the intestine and then absorbs much of the nutrients causing the host animal to suffer malnourishment | tube worm a creature with the shape of a cylinder that lives in the sand | wire worm a click beetle, the larvae live on roots and can be a serious crop pest

wormery layers of earth are held between two sheets of glass, separated by up to 10 centimetres, then worms are put in to live and to be observed

worn (not warn which is to alert) on a person, becoming thin or ragged, tattered | worn away becoming thin through use over a long period

wound a break in the skin, a cut; to damage an external part of the body, to have produced a coil

woven the fabric contains threads that run at right-angles and go under and over each other in a regular pattern

wrap (not rap which is to hit hard) a protective cover; to cover

wrapping a cloth or paper that is used to cover an object either for protection or to improve the appearance

wrench a tool for turning, a jerk, a sudden movement; to pull suddenly | torque wrench a spanner which has been calibrated to show the turning force that is applied

wriggling moving the body rapidly from side to side

wright (not right which is correct or not left, nor rite which is a ceremony, nor write which is putting pen to paper) a skilled workman, a craftsman

wrinkled small ridges or creases in a surface wrinkled skin one sign of ageing is that the skin is less flexible and forms many ridges

wrist the collection of several bones between the hand and the lower arm that allow free movement of the hand | wrist bones (carpals) the several small bones in the area between the arm and the hand | wrist joint the set of tendons, ligaments and small bones that allows the hand to move relative to the lower arm

write (not right which is correct, nor rite which is a ceremony, nor wright which is a craftsman) to make a permanent record on paper, to compose an essay | write-up to make a permanent record of the procedure used, the data obtained and the significance of the results

writing letters on a page, to put words onto paper, constructing a letter or a manuscript

written a permanent record on paper | written material any paper or magazine that has words or diagrams for information

wrong not right, mistaken, inaccurate

wrought iron an early form of steel, iron mixed with a small amount of carbon that is less brittle than cast iron

X chromosome the sex chromosome that is found in all human cells, females will have two X chromosomes and males have one X chromosome and one Y chromosome

X-ray part of the electromagnetic spectrum that is more energetic or higher frequency than ultra-violet light, a shadow photograph taken using X-rays | **X-ray crystallography** producing a pattern by reflecting a beam of X-rays from a crystal, then using the pattern of the atoms to explain the position

xeno- (*Greek* foreign)

xylem / xylem tubes / xylem tissue / xylem vessels the solid remains of pipe-shaped cells in the stem of a plant through which water moves from the root to the leaves

Y... / yotta... prefix for one million, million, million, million of a unit, 10^{24}

y... / yocto... prefix for one million, million, million, millionth of a unit, 10^{-24}

Y chromosome the chromosome in the nucleus that is found only in male people

yacht a small sailing boat that is used for pleasure

yard a unit of length of 36 inches or approximately 90 centimetres, an area of land, a garden (USA) | **scrap yard** an area of land that is used for storing and recycling unwanted metals especially cars | **steelyard** a type of balance used for measuring heavy weights by using movable weights, usually one arm is much longer than the other | **steel yard** a scrap yard, an area for collecting iron-containing materials

yarn thread, twisted fibres, an unlikely story

yarrow a perennial herb with a pungent smell

year the period of time from the Sun being at its highest point in the sky to when the Sun is next at its highest point, the period of time taken for a planet to orbit around the Sun, 365.25 days | **year length** the amount of time taken for a planet to orbit the Sun | **Earth year** the time period taken for the Earth to orbit once around the Sun (approximately 365 Earth days), often used to allow comparison between the year length of each planet | **leap year** a year, that occurs every four years, in which an extra day is inserted between 28 February and 1 March so as to ensure that the solstice continues to occur near mid-June | **length of year** the amount of time that a planet takes to orbit once around a star | **light-year** the distance that light travels in a vacuum in one year, 9.5×10^{12} kilometres

yearly annually, occurs each year, at the same time each year | **yearly adaption** the changes that take place in an organism each year in order to survive the different conditions that prevail in different seasons | **yearly changes** the cycle of differences that occur in growth, colour, size or activity each year

yeast *Saccharomyces*, a microbe with a nucleus, which is not animal nor plant, a protoctista | **yeast activity** the rate at which the yeast is producing carbon dioxide and alcohol | **yeast investigation** an experiment to find which factors encourage and allow yeast to grow | **activity of yeast** the rate at which the yeast is producing carbon dioxide or alcohol | **crushed yeast** intense pressure has been used to break open the cell wall of the yeast

yellow light with a wavelength of about 450 nanometre, the colour produced by mixing blue and green light | **yellow fever** an illness that Finlay discovered was caused by infection with a virus carried in mosquitoes | **yellow flame** a highly visible flame produced when there is not enough oxygen for complete combustion

yield the amount produced, the ratio of actual amount to predicted quantity | **crop yield** the mass of a specified crop produced in one acre of land | **high yield** a large amount is produced from a small area or from a low input

yocto... / y... prefix for one million, million, million, millionth of a unit, 10^{-24}

yoghurt / yogourt / yogurt a soft food made by adding certain microbes to milk and leaving to ferment

yoke (not yolk which is the yellow in an egg) a piece of wood for helping pull or lift, the object around which the wire is wound in a motor

yolk (not yoke which is a length of wood) the yellow part of a hen's egg

yotta... / Y... prefix for one million, million, million, million of a unit, 10^{24}

young immature, not old | **young people** teen-agers | **young plants** plants that have developed their first true leaves | **have young / produce young** to give birth | **live young** the offspring, when born, are capable of survival independent of the mother, although they may be immature

yo-yo two discs joined together then attached to a string so the discs can spin up and down

Z... / zetta... prefix for a thousand, million, million, million of a unit, 10^{21}

z... / zepto... prefix for one thousand, million, million, millionth of a unit, 10^{-21}

zenith the highest point, directly overhead

zepto... / z... prefix for one thousand, million, million, millionth of a unit, 10^{-21}

zero nought, nothing | **zero** a scale to move a pointer to the zero mark at the start of a measurement | **zero gravity** the measurement is taken sufficiently distant from a star or planet that any gravitational attraction is too small to be measured | **zero weight** material that has mass but is able to float | **absolute zero** the temperature at which there is no movement of any part of a atom, zero kelvin (0 K) or -273.1°C

zetta... / Z... prefix for a thousand, million, million, million of a unit, 10^{21}

zig-zag to move forward by alternately moving left diagonal and then right diagonal

zinc (Zn, proton number 30, melting point 420°C) a metal that is usually found as zinc sulphide [ZnS] that was described by Paracelsus in 1526 and isolated by Marggraf in 1746, zinc has been used for thousands of years as an alloy with copper, called brass. Zinc is layered over iron to prevent rust formation, zinc is the outer casing and one of the electrodes in disposable batteries | **zinc oxide** [ZnO] a white powder produced by zinc bonding to oxygen, that turns yellow when heated | **zinc sulfate** (USA) / **zinc sulphate** (UK) [$ZnSO_4$] a soluble, colourless salt produced by heating zinc in sulphuric acid

Zink the german spelling for zinc (Zn)

Zn zinc, proton number 30, melting point 420°c, a metal

zodiac the twelve constellations which early astronomers used to mark the course of the Sun and Moon around the Earth

zone an area, a section, part | **smokeless zone** an area of buildings in which any fuel should burn without producing carbon particles | **time zones** the artificial division of the Earth into 24 sections

so each section has noon at approximately the time when the Sun is overhead

zoo- (*Greek* animal)

zoo / zoological garden an area where many different animals are kept in order that they may be studied by experts and by the general public | **zoo keeper** a person who cares for and feeds the animals in a zoological park

zoology the study of animals

Zu (Chongzi 429–500) a Chinese mathematician who made a vast number of accurate observations leading to an estimate for the length of a year as 365.2429 days

zygote the fertilised egg

zymase a mixture of enzymes that can be extracted from yeast and will convert sugar into alcohol and carbon dioxide

α **radiation** alpha radiation, the helium nucleus, $^4_2He^{++}$ ejected from the breakdown of some radio-active nuclei

β **radiation** beta radiation, electrons ejected from the breakdown of atomic nuclei

γ **radiation** gamma radiation, the very high frequency electromagnetic radiation produced by the breakdown of some radio-active nuclei

δ (Greek letter delta) used to show a small change

μ (Greek letter mu) micro, a millionth part of a unit

π (Greek letter pi) the ratio of the circumference of a circle to the diameter, a constant equal to 3.14159 (approximated by 22/7)

Ω (Greek letter omega) ohm, the unit of electrical resistance

APPARATUS

APPARATUS is the equipment or hardware that is used either in carrying out an experiment or for measurement. Glass is almost the perfect material for scientific apparatus; high temperatures are used to melt the glass, which is then blown or moulded into complex shapes. The glass will keep its shape when cool, but will allow conduction of heat and is transparent to light; liquid thermometers (invented by Fahrenheit) would not be possible without these two properties. The late sixteenth century saw the development of lenses that were suitable for microscopes and telescopes. Leeuwenhoek described the first microscopic life, and Galileo observed the movement of the moons of Jupiter. Two scientific revolutions occurred near 1800. First, Volta invented the electrical cell in 1798; this invention allowed the development of the electrical motor, *eg* by Faraday, more reliable forms of lighting, *eg* by Edison, and safe methods of heating. The second scientific revolution was an attempt to develop common standards for measurements. leading to the Paris Convention of 1805. The scientific revolution of the twentieth century has been the introduction of equipment that allows data to be collected automatically and continually and the use of computers for analysing the data.

Selection of correct apparatus is important for a safe and successful experiment. Volumes of liquid should be measured using a measuring cylinder or a burette. Heating equipment is usually glassware, such as beakers, flasks (conical, round-bottom or flat-bottom, depending on usage) or boiling tubes and test tubes. The heating is carried out using a bunsen burner, or an electrical heater if the liquid is flammable; temperature is measured using an immersion thermometer. A distillation apparatus enables a liquid to be heated in a flask, the vapour removed and then condensed and the pure liquid collected. Electrical apparatus is often referred to as components.

Key People
Bunsen
Celsius
Dewar
Edison
Fahrenheit
Faraday
Galileo
Leeuwenhoek
Liebig
Lister
Petri
Torricelli

ASTRONOMY

ASTRONOMY is the study of everything that you can see in the sky that is outside the atmosphere. The subject probably started the first time our caveman ancestors looked up at the Sun, or the stars, and wondered what they were; many of the alignments at Stonehenge are related to the position of stars and the Sun at different times of the year, therefore allowing the structure to be used as a calendar. The Greeks were able to use observations and measurements in order to calculate the distances from the Earth to the Sun and to the Moon, and to estimate the diameter of the Earth. For more than twenty centuries, the accepted view was that the Earth was at the centre of the universe with the known planets (Mercury, Venus, Mars, Jupiter and Saturn) in orbit and all the stars at a fixed distance.

Two important events occurred before the invention of the telescope in the late sixteenth century: in 1543, Copernicus published his ideas of a heliocentric universe (but still with the stars at a fixed distance), then Brahe, without the aid of a telescope, produced an accurate catalogue of stars. Around 1600, Galileo used the newly invented telescope to observe the moons of Jupiter, therefore proving that not all objects were in orbit around the Earth. Several important events occurred towards the end of the seventeenth century: Roemer measured the speed of light, Newton not

Key People
Anaxamander
Aristarchus
Brahe
Copernicus
Einstein
Flamsteed
Foucault
Galileo
Halley
C. Herschel
W. Herschel
Hubble
Kepler
Lemaître
Newton
Ptolemy
Roemer

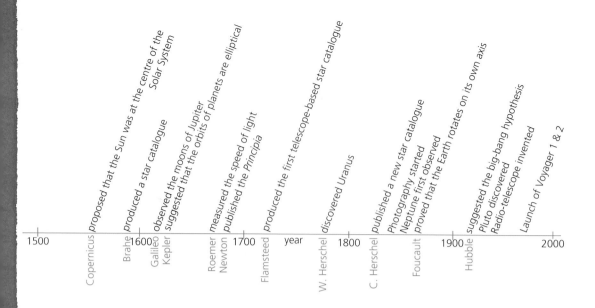

only proposed his ideas of force and gravity, but also produced a spectrum from sunlight and developed the reflecting telescope, and Flamsteed began precise measurements of the position of every star. Improvements in engineering, mathematics and the use of glass enabled the discovery of Uranus by Herschel in 1781 and of Neptune in 1846. Foucault in the mid-nineteenth century showed (by using a pendulum) that the Earth must be rotating, that the spectrum of sunlight gave information about the chemical composition of the Sun and developed glass mirrors which allowed very large reflecting telescopes to be constructed. During the same period, the invention of photography allowed very distant galaxies to be made visible. Exciting developments following World War II include radio astronomy, with dishes up to 300 metres diameter, computers and the launch of space probes. The Hubble telescope is one of many satellites that observe the stars without the distortions caused by the Earth's atmosphere, Voyager 2 has passed close to several planets and has sent back superb photographs, and NASA launched the New Horizons probe in 2006 in order to look at objects beyond the orbit of Neptune.

ATOMS & MOLECULES

ATOMS are the building blocks of the universe; MOLECULES, or compounds, are produced by atoms bonding together. More than two thousand years ago, Democritus proposed that all matter is made up of tiny particles, so small as to be invisible. This idea was lost until Boyle put forward a similar theory in the late seventeenth century. In 1808, Dalton published his measurements of atomic masses, then, a few years later, Berzelius produced more accurate measurements of mass and introduced the use of simple chemical shorthand for each type of atom. The discovery of radio-activity, by the Curies at the start of the twentieth century, provided the technology that allowed Rutherford to deduce that each atom comprises a tiny nucleus, with a positive charge and a large mass, surrounded by electrons, with a negative charge and zero mass. Moseley, in 1913, showed that the number of protons in the nucleus was unique for each element. The neutron was discovered by Chadwick in 1932.

Lavoisier
Moseley
Rutherford

The modern theory is that each type of atom has a unique number of protons; the number of electrons always equals the number of protons, although the number of neutrons can vary (forming isotopes). The electrons are arranged in shells or orbitals: the inner shell has a capacity of two electrons, the other shells can take up to eight electrons.

Millions of different compounds are produced by atoms forming bonds. Atoms with a full outer shell are most stable; molecules are produced by forming either ionic bonds or covalent bonds. An ionic bond is produced when an atom of one element loses one or more electrons to the atoms of another element, the particles now have opposite charges and so are attracted to each other. A covalent bond is formed if the outer shells of different atoms overlap so that each atom looks to have a full outer shell. The formula mass / molecular mass is calculated by adding together the relative atomic mass of every atom in the molecule.

BLOOD

BLOOD is the transport system of the body. Approximately 8% of the total body mass is blood so the average adult has 5.6 litres of blood (females have less, males will have more). The fluid is made from 3.0 litres of plasma (a liquid in which are dissolved: nutrients, waste chemicals, hormones, antibodies and chemicals that allow the blood to form clots), 2.4 litres of red blood cells (erythrocytes, small cells that are specialised to transport oxygen) and 0.2 litres of white blood cells (leucocytes, large cells that are part of the body's defence system). There is a constant turnover of red blood cells, each of the 48 million, million erythrocytes has a life-span of approximately 120 days so the bone marrow must be producing red blood cells at a rate of 5 million every second! Anaemia is a disease in which not enough iron is absorbed, less haemoglobin is produced and so there is a lowered ability to transport oxygen.

Key People
Ehrlich
Leeuwenhoek

The blood is pumped by the heart to the lungs where carbon dioxide [CO_2] is lost from the serum and oxygen [O_2] is absorbed and attaches to the haemoglobin in red blood cells. The blood returns to the heart and is pumped to the cells of the body; most cells will remove oxygen and nutrients and excrete carbon dioxide, urea and other waste products, some of the blood passes through the kidneys, where the urea [$CO(NH_2)_2$] is removed and the concentration of salts is adjusted, and some of the blood absorbs nutrients from the small intestine, then flows to the liver where poisons and toxins (such as paracetamol or alcohol [C_2H_5OH]) are removed. The blood then returns to the heart and the circulation through lungs, heart and body cells continues.

Blood is a defence system, containing antibodies and white blood cells, which prevent infection by viruses and bacteria. If a blood vessel is broken, *eg* by cutting the skin, then platelets help form a clot that prevents both the further loss of blood and the entry of microbes. Haemophilia is an inherited disease in which the blood will not clot and therefore bruises or cuts are potentially fatal.

CARBON CYCLE

The atmosphere when the Earth was formed (about 4600 million years ago) was probably 80% nitrogen (just like today) and 20% carbon dioxide. Evolution of life, first seen 2500 million years ago, led to vast amounts of algae, fungi and seaweed to start to exist approximately 400 million years ago; photosynthesis by the protoctista was essential for the growth of the organisms, but produced oxygen as a waste product.

$$\text{carbon dioxide} + \text{water} \longrightarrow \text{oxygen} + \text{glucose}$$

When an organism died, the remains were buried under sand and soil, and eventually turned into coal, thereby locking vast amounts of carbon underground.

At the same time, shellfish developed with shells composed of calcium carbonate ($[CaCO_3]$ is 10% carbon by weight), the shellfish died, sedimented and produced mountains of chalk, limestone and marble. The formation of coal and of carbonate rocks reduced the concentration of carbon dioxide in the atmosphere to 0.04%; this value has been constant for the past 100 million years because of the equilibrium between the removal of carbon dioxide by photosynthesis and the production of carbon dioxide by respiration and the burning of wood.

Use of the fossil fuels to produce power has led to a vast increase in the concentration of carbon dioxide in the atmosphere, and this has led to global warming.

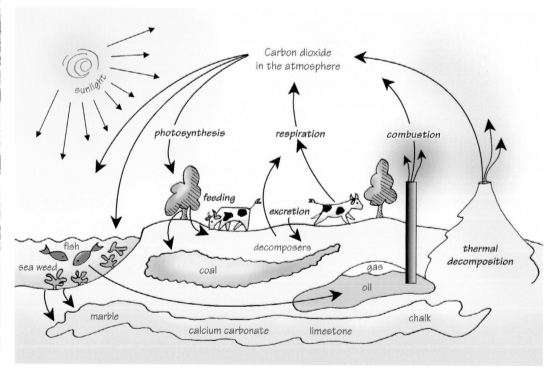

CELLS

The simple theory that every living creature (bacterium, fungus, protozoon, animal or plant) is made from cells, is the result of four centuries of developments. The Janssen family developed the lenses that allowed compound microscopes to be available from the start of the seventeenth century; this type of microscope was used by Hooke to examine the material that he drew superbly in Micrographia (1665), Hooke gave cells their name because the structures that he saw under a microscope looked like prison cells. Slightly unexpectedly, Leeuwenhoek produced hundreds of drawings of cells and creatures that he had examined using a simple lens. The next dozen decades saw the collection of evidence, interpretation of data and development of ideas, but the major steps forward occurred during the reign of Queen Victoria (1837 – 1901). Near the start of her reign, in 1838, Schleiden suggested that plants were made from cells; a year later, his colleague Schwann suggested that every living organism is made from cells, *eg* he highlighted the fact that fermentation will not occur without yeast. After Virchow had postulated that "cells could only arise from cells", there was an explosion of ideas, led by the two giants of microbiology: Pasteur in France, and Koch in Germany. Their understanding of how to grow cells provided proof of Virchow's hypothesis, and allowed a new understanding of the causes and transmission of disease.

Key People
Brown
Gram
Hooke
Janssens
Leeuwenhoek
Koch
Malpighi
Mendel
Pasteur
Petri
Schleiden
Schwann
Spallanzani
Virchow

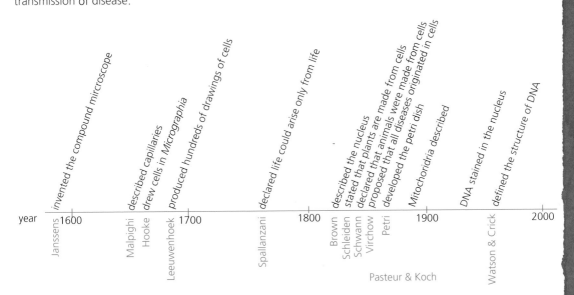

Every cell comprises a membrane surrounding the cytoplasm (*cell liquid*); the membrane controls which chemicals enter and leave the cell, and the cytoplasm is where the chemical reactions occur; the cytoplasm contains mitochondria, which are the organelles where respiration occurs. Every cell has at least one chromosome, the long, linear molecule that contains the genetic instructions. All cells, except bacteria, have the chromosomes in a nucleus.

Plant cells have rigid cell walls, made from cellulose, usually have a vacuole, and are capable of producing chloroplasts. Fungi are not capable of photosynthesis, but they do possess cell walls, which are made from chitin.

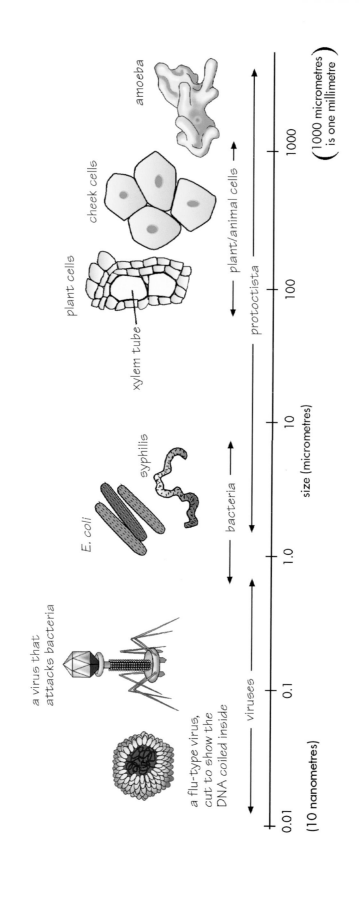

amoeba

cheek cells

plant cells

xylem tube

syphilis

E. coli

a virus that
attacks bacteria

a flu-type virus,
cut to show the
DNA coiled inside

viruses

bacteria

protoctista

plant/animal cells

size (micrometres)

0.01

0.1

1.0

10

100

1000

(10 nanometres)

(1000 micrometres
is one millimetre)

Asexual reproduction produces daughter cells that have genes identical to the parent cell and so show no genetic variation, these identical offspring are clones of the parents. Sexual reproduction uses gametes or sex cells, each of which contains half the usual number of chromosomes, so the fertilised egg cell will contain the full complement of chromosomes, and the offspring will differ from the parent.

Cells in multicellular organisms are usually specialised; the shape of the cell and the chemicals in the cell vary, so the cell is adapted to carry out its own special job, eg the human body has an estimated hundred million, million cells of over 220 different types, including ciliated cells in the trachea and oviduct, bone cells, blood cells and muscle cells. Plant cells, such as root hair cells, are also adapted to particular functions.

CIRCUITS

CIRCUITS is the study of the effect of components and connections on the behaviour of an electric current. A basic circuit requires a power source (cell, battery or power pack) connected to a component. The first reliable source of electricity was the battery, which was invented by Volta in 1798; previous work had been based either on static electricity or lightning (Franklin, the inventor of the lightning conductor wrote a book on electricity in 1751). Ampère and Oersted, in 1820, working independently, showed that a current always produces a magnetic field, Ampère went on to develop laws relating the size and direction of the magnetic field to the current, these ideas were published in 1827 – the same year that Ohm suggested that the current and potential difference are directly related.

Key People
Ampère
Edison
Franklin, B
Galvani
Joule
Kelvin
Oersted
Ohm
Volta

Ohm's law relates the potential difference (V for voltage), current (I for induced current, measured in amps) and resistance (R measured in ohms or Ω).

potential difference	=	current	x	resistance	Ohm's law
V	=	I	x	R	
volts		amps		ohms	units
V		A		Ω	

A simple method of showing the arrangement of components is to use symbols in a circuit diagram. The potential difference across a component is measured using a voltmeter in parallel with the component. The current through each component arranged in series is identical, so the ammeter is placed in series with the component.

Every current will produce heat; Joule, in 1840, suggested that more heat is produced at higher currents. A resistor is a component that obeys Ohm's law; the resistance of the resistor may be fixed or variable. A variable resistor is used to change the current, eg for a dimmer switch or volume control. The current in the resistor will produce heat, which can be used intentionally, as in a light bulb, where the filament glows white-hot, or in a fuse, where a component will melt and open the circuit if the current is too high for safety. Diodes are components, which behave like resistors when the current is flowing in one direction, but will not allow any current to flow if the direction is reversed; a light-emitting diode (LED) will produce light if the current is flowing.

CIRCULATION SYSTEM

Key People
Fabrizio
Galen
Harvey
Leeuwenhoek
Malpighi
Servetus
Vesalius

The circulation system is the transport system of the body: the system comprises all the vessels, pumps, liquids and chemicals that are involved in moving any material or heat around the body. Most of our understanding arises from work at the University of Padua in the sixteenth century: Vesalius published a textbook with clear diagrams of dissected parts; Fabrizio built an operating theatre and demonstrated the valves in the heart and in the veins; amongst his students was Harvey, who later produced an explanation for the valves in 1628. Malpighi was born that same year, and he went on to describe capillaries in the lungs of frogs.

The heart is two pumps joined together into one organ. The muscles of the heart relax so blood enters the right atrium (from the Latin for entrance hall), the contraction of the heart muscle forces blood into the right ventricle then the rhythmical relaxing and contracting of the heart muscles force blood through the pulmonary artery towards the lungs. The pulmonary artery divides in the lungs to give arteries that continue to divide so as to become smaller and more numerous until the blood vessels become the capillaries that surround the alveoli. Oxygen from the air diffuses into the blood at the same time as carbon dioxide is lost from the blood. The oxygenated blood (which appears bright red because the oxygen has attached to the haemoglobin) returns to the heart through the pulmonary vein, passes through the left atrium into the left ventricle of the heart and is pumped to the cells of the body *via* the aorta. This major artery divides, and becomes progressively smaller, until the blood passes along the capillaries that surround every cell. The majority of cells will extract nutrients and oxygen from the blood and excrete any waste products, *eg* urea and carbon dioxide, then blood is returned to the heart in the veins.

The blood that passes through the kidney has water, urea and some salts removed, so as to produce urine, which passes down the ureter and is stored in the bladder before excretion. A few cells, in the glands, will secrete hormones, which will affect many cells throughout the body. The blood that returns from the small intestine will have absorbed many chemicals, so the vein from the small intestine (the hepatic portal vein) goes first to the liver before continuing towards the heart; one function of the liver is the removal of poisonous chemicals such as paracetamol or alcohol from the blood. The blood helps to maintain the temperature of the body at 37°C by transferring heat form the muscles to the internal organs or skin.

CLASSIFICATION

Key People
Brown
Linnaeus

CLASSIFICATION (also called taxonomy) is the breaking down of a large number of objects into smaller groups; each member of the group has many features in common with all other members of the group. There are many reasons why taxonomy is valuable to science: one is to allow the observer to decide if a specimen is identical to a type of plant, animal, bacterium or protoctista that has been described previously or if the specimen is a totally new creature. A second use is to describe relationships between different organisms. A third reason is that scientists need to know that they are using exactly the same organism when carrying out experiments in different countries or at different times.

Classification

all life → kingdom → phylum → class → order → family → genus → species

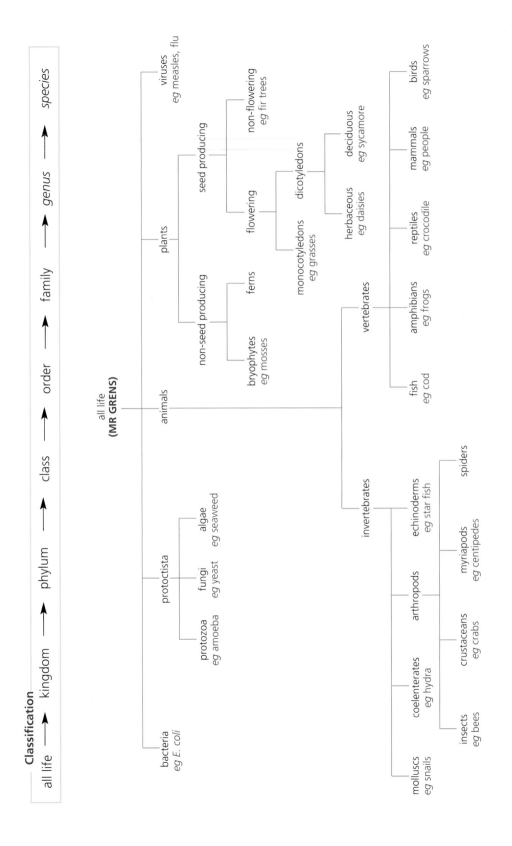

all life
(MR GRENS)

bacteria
eg E. coli

protoctista
- protozoa
  eg amoeba
- fungi
  eg yeast
- algae
  eg seaweed

animals

invertebrates
- molluscs
  eg snails
- coelenterates
  eg hydra
- arthropods
  - insects
    eg bees
  - crustaceans
    eg crabs
  - myriapods
    eg centipedes
  - spiders
- echinoderms
  eg star fish

vertebrates
- fish
  eg cod
- amphibians
  eg frogs
- reptiles
  eg crocodile
- mammals
  eg people
- birds
  eg sparrows

plants

non-seed producing
- bryophytes
  eg mosses
- ferns

seed producing
- flowering
  - monocotyledons
    eg grasses
  - dicotyledons
    - herbaceous
      eg daisies
    - deciduous
      eg sycamore
- non-flowering
  eg fir trees

viruses
eg measles, flu

There are several million organisms that fulfil most of the characteristics of Mr Grens (moving, respiring, growing, reproducing, excreting, nutrition and sensing the surroundings). There is no single method of classifying all the creatures of the Earth; one method divides all living organisms into five kingdoms (ie viruses, bacteria, protoctista, plants and animals), depending on the structure of the cell:

viruses (which are on the very borderline of living) have DNA inside a protein coat but do not have any cytoplasm;

bacteria have cytoplasm within a cell membrane, the DNA floats freely within the cytoplasm (there is no nucleus);

protoctista/protista are simple creatures that have some of the characteristic of animals or plants, eg a nucleus within the cytoplasm, but also show some unique features, eg fungi have cell walls that are not made from cellulose;

plant cells are always surrounded by a cell wall composed from cellulose; the majority of plant cells have a vacuole and a very few will possess chloroplasts; and

animal cells have a nucleus, containing the chromosomes, within a cytoplasm that is surrounded by a cell membrane

Further division of each of these kingdoms is possible, eg animals are classed as vertebrates (with a backbone) or invertebrates (no backbone); plants can be divided either into those that produce seeds and those that do not, or into plants with a vascular system and those that lack such a system.

DIGESTIVE SYSTEM

Key People
Schwann
Spallanzani

The digestive system (also called the gut, digestive tract or alimentary canal) is the series of organs that allows food to be ingested by the mouth, the nutrients to be removed, and any undigested material to be egested. Spallanzani studied the digestion by encasing food in a small cage tied to a length of string – he swallowed the cage, allowed digestion to occur then pulled the cage back out in order to study changes! A century later, Schwann isolated the first enzyme from an animal source.

The human digestive system starts with the mouth where the teeth mechanically break down the food into smaller pieces. Saliva is added, not only to moisten the food, so swallowing is easier, but also to start digestion of starch using amylase. The small ball of food moves from the mouth, through the oesophagus, or gullet, into the stomach. The food in the stomach undergoes chemical digestion, after the addition of hydrochloric acid and enzymes, and mechanical digestion, as the stomach squashes and squeezes the contents. After several hours, the semi-digested food is passed in small portions into the small intestine, where further enzymes and bile are added. During the next 16 hours, the mash of food is moved through the small intestine by peristalsis, and the nutrients are absorbed through the villi that line the inside wall of the small intestine.

The residue enters the large intestine, where water is removed (otherwise the faeces would appear like diarrhoea), and the remains are egested through the anus. Roughage, or fibre, appears to pass through the gut without visible change, but roughage is an essential part of a healthy diet.

DRUGS

DRUGS are chemicals that cause specific changes in living organisms. Drugs are classified as legal drugs or illegal drugs. Legal drugs are further divided into those used for medical purposes, which are given to treat an illness, and addictive drugs, such as alcohol or nicotine, that will cause chemical changes in the brain, but are not taken in order to cure an illness. Medical drugs may treat the symptoms, *eg* paracetamol or aspirin is used to reduce pain, or the drug may treat the cause, *eg* penicillin will kill bacteria. There are problems with most drugs, *eg* the painkiller can be addictive, and may cause damage to the liver or to the kidneys; the antibiotics will kill specific bacteria, but variation and mutation occur in the microbe, so drug resistance develops and the antibiotic becomes less effective, and ultimately ineffective.

There are three methods by which drugs are administered: many drugs are given through the mouth (oral administration) so they are absorbed in the intestine; some drugs, *eg* nicotine and Ventolin™ are inhaled and then absorbed through the alveoli in the lungs; and some drugs are injected into the blood in a vein or into a muscle.

Key People
Chain
Ehrlich
Fleming
Florey
Magendie
Paracelsus

EAR

The ear has two functions: to turn sound into nerve impulses that can be interpreted by the brain; and to provide the sense of balance. The part of the ear that you can see is the outer ear, which comprises the pinna, the ear canal and the ear drum. The ear drum prevents the entry of microbes, but allows the transmission of the

Key People
Bell
Edison
Helmholtz
Ohm

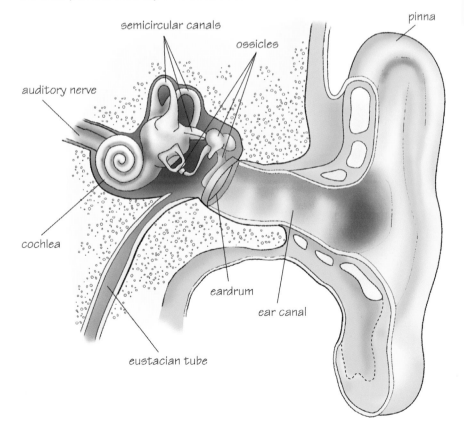

semicircular canals

ossicles

pinna

auditory nerve

cochlea

eardrum

ear canal

eustacian tube

vibrations that make up sound. A chain of three tiny bones, collectively called the ossicles (individually called the hammer, anvil and stirrup), connect the ear drum to the oval window of the cochlea; the cochlea is the organ that separates the different frequencies of sound and registers the intensity of each frequency, then turns the vibrations into nerve impulses that the brain can interpret.

The semi-circular canals, the organ of balance, are also in the inner ear, next to the cochlea. The eustachian tube connects the mouth to the middle ear, and ensures that the pressure on each side of the ear drum is almost the same; any large differences in pressure could lead to ear ache, and, in extreme cases, a burst ear drum.

EARTH

The planet Earth is the third rock from the Sun, the mass is 6×10^{24} kilogram and the diameter is 12,800 kilometres; two-thirds of the surface is covered with sea water, and Earth is the only planet on which life is known to exist. 2600 years ago, Anaximander suggested that the Earth is a cylinder floating in space; three centuries later, Aristarchus said the Earth moved around the Sun, and Eratosthenes measured the diameter of the Earth to be approximately 12,000 kilometres; he also introduced the idea of latitude and longitude. A further three centuries passed before Ptolemy declared that the Earth is a sphere. These seemingly modern ideas were lost from Western Europe and did not reappear until Copernicus published his book De *Revolutionibus Orbium Coelestium* in 1543.

Gilbert suggested that the Earth is a giant magnet, an observation that still can not be fully explained, but is related to the presence of a core of iron and nickel – an idea that was deduced by Cavendish after he had calculated the density of the Earth. The modern ideas that the effects of weathering and of rock cycle have been the same processes for millions of years began with Hutton about 1770. A few decades later, Smith produced a geological map, which showed the strata of Britain. A major argument erupted when Wegener, in 1912, put forward the idea of continental drift. Modern ideas are that the Earth was formed about 4600 million years ago; metals with high densities, such as iron and nickel, have formed a solid core, with a radius of 1250 kilometres at the centre of the Earth. This solid core is covered with a liquid core, to a radius of 3500 kilometres from the centre, then the outer 2900 kilometres is a mantle composed of magma or liquid

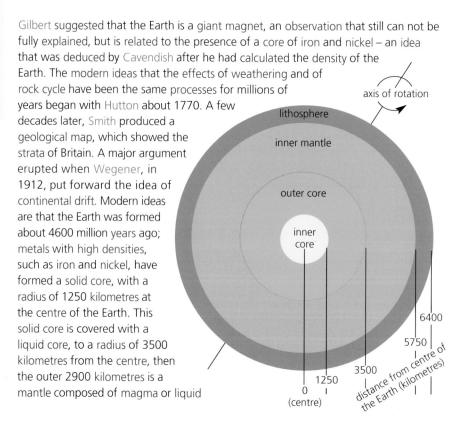

392

rock, with a very thin crust of solid rock. About 250 million years ago, this crust formed a single giant continent called Pangea, which broke into several parts or plates, these plates are floating on the magma (liquid rock) some plates are drifting apart (Europe and America are moving apart by about 20 millimetre per year), some plates are crashing together (the Himalayan mountain range was once under the sea, but has been pushed up by the Indian plate crashing into the Asian plate).

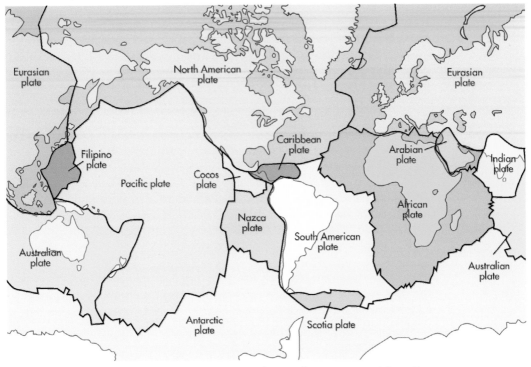

The idea that the Earth rotated on its own axis was known (but not proven) from the mid-seventeenth century, but it was not until 1850 that Foucault demonstrated, by using the movement of a simple pendulum, that the Earth must be rotating.

ECOLOGY

ECOLOGY is the study of the complex interactions between many species of animals, plants, fungi and microbes that live together in an area, together with the environmental conditions that are found in that habitat, and the seasonal variation. Often several ecosystems will interact, eg consider the ecosystem in and around a pond. The pond itself will be home to aquatic creatures, from microbes such as amoeba, through the plant life that produces oxygen and growth, to the consumers, such as the fish and frogs, that eat the plants and possibly each other, and, finally, there are the decomposers, which rid the pond of faeces and other debris such as dead bodies. Outside the pond, there will be animals and birds, which feed on the pond life and drink the water. There are also trees, which cast a shadow over part of the pond and so change the habitat. The number of each species will depend on the time of year, as many creatures start to produce offspring in spring, just as plants are starting to grow, so at one stage there will be lots of plants, producing lots of oxygen and providing shade and protection for the young animals, but

Key People
Darwin
Galton

these plants will be eaten by the offspring of herbivores, and the herbivores themselves will be eaten as there is a population increase of other animals, *eg* foxes or herons. The ecosystem is dynamic over the year, but should continue to exist unless pollution occurs – this will change the habitat, *eg* by introducing more heat or unfamiliar chemicals.

ELECTROLYSIS

Key People
Bunsen
Davy
Faraday
Volta

ELECTROLYSIS is a chemical reaction caused by an electric current. The discovery of a reliable source of electricity by Volta in 1798 was rapidly followed by the first experiments in electrolysis, *eg* Davy isolated sodium and potassium in 1807. Faraday developed the laws of electrolysis in 1832; Bunsen developed new electrical cells in the 1850s, and isolated at least six new elements.

An electrolysis experiment involves a potential difference being applied across two electrodes immersed in an electrolyte, thereby causing a current, *ie* a flow of charge. The electrodes are often made of graphite because the carbon will not react chemically with the electrolyte. The charge that moves between the electrodes is the flow of ions, so electrolysis needs a fluid – either gas or liquid – in order to allow the charged particle to move. Opposite charges attract; the cation, with a positive charge, is attracted to the electrode with a negative charge, *ie* the cathode. The ion reaches the electrode, gains electrons and forms a neutral molecule. Similarly, the anion is attracted to the anode, then loses electrons to form a neutral molecule.

Electrolysis of water produces two volumes of hydrogen for every volume of oxygen, therefore proving that not only is water not an element, but also that water must have the chemical formula of H_2O. Aluminium is a reactive metal that is extracted most easily by using electrolysis.

ENERGY

Key People
Helmholtz
Joule
Lavoisier
Thomson
   (Kelvin)
Tyndall

ENERGY is the ability to cause a change, also called work done, and is measured in joules (J) or kilojoules (kJ). Much of our understanding rests with three friends working in Glasgow (Thomson, who became Baron Kelvin of Largs), Manchester (Joule), and Heidelberg (Helmholtz), who worked on a variety of chemical, electrical and thermal methods that eventually resulted in the law of conservation of energy *ie* the idea that energy can be transformed but never destroyed.

Almost all of the energy that is used on Earth, starts with the Sun and will finish as heat energy. Nuclear reactions within the Sun produce energy that is radiated from the surface, and we are able to detect heat (by the effect on our skin) and sense light (by chemical changes in the eye).

Plants use light energy by a process called photosynthesis to produce sugars, which represent stored energy (chemical energy), that can be used for growth. Some plants, from ancient times, have been turned into coal, and some plants were eaten by sea creatures that died and were turned into oil. These two fossil fuels, together with growing plants, which can be considered as a renewable fuel, may be used as fuels to provide heat and light.

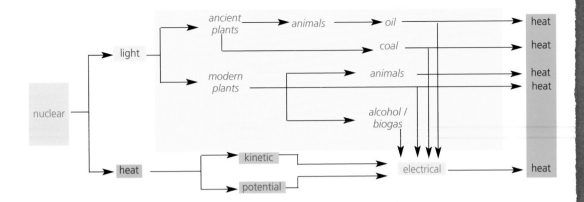

The heat energy not only causes the temperature of the soil and water to increase, so there is no permanent ice, but also changes the temperature of the air, leading to winds and waves that have kinetic energy, which can erode the land or be transformed into electrical energy. The heat energy evaporates the seas; the vapour rises and is blown by winds, eventually condensing as clouds and precipitating as rain, snow, sleet or hail, onto the land. The water then returns downhill to the sea, although the kinetic energy of the moving water will change the landscape, and can be used to drive machinery and to generate electricity. Electrical energy is important because it is simple to generate, using kinetic energy, then easily transferred over long distances through a pair of wires; electrical energy is also simple to transform into most other forms of energy

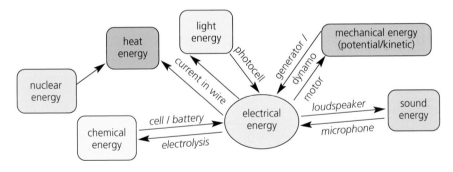

EYE

The eye is the organ that responds to light. The human eye is a light-tight sphere with a small region at the front (the cornea) that is transparent and allows light to enter the eye. Behind the cornea is the lens, a transparent structure that can change shape so the image on the light-sensitive part of the eye is always in focus. The iris, the coloured part of the eye will expand or contract so that the intensity of light passing through the pupil is always optimal. The light-sensitive part of the eye is the retina, a layer of cells that covers the back two-thirds of the inside surface of the eye ball. There are two shapes of light-sensitive cell in the retina; the rod cells are very sensitive to any wavelength of visible light but are not able to distinguish different

Key People
Fleming
Helmholtz
Maxwell

colours so you are able to see in black and white at low light intensities (that is why most stars appear as white dots on a black background). The second shape of light-sensitive cells are the cone cells; there are three types, each capable of responding to one of the three primary colours, *ie* red, blue, or green. The response of the light-sensitive cells is sent to the brain along the optic nerve.

The outside surface of the eye is kept moist by liquid produced in the tear glands, this liquid also contains lysozyme – the first antibiotic studied by Fleming.

FLOWERS

Key People
Linnaeus
Mendel

FLOWERS are the reproductive organs of plants that are insect pollinated. The flower is brightly coloured, to attract the insect, and the petals have veins pointing towards the nectary, which contains the sugar solution that the insect is seeking. The stigma, or female organ, will brush off any pollen from the hairs on the back of the insect; this pollen will form pollen tubes that will allow the male nucleus to reach the ova. The stamen will deposit fresh pollen onto the insect. Many flowers will carry both stamen and stigma, often at different times of the year, so as to encourage cross-pollination.

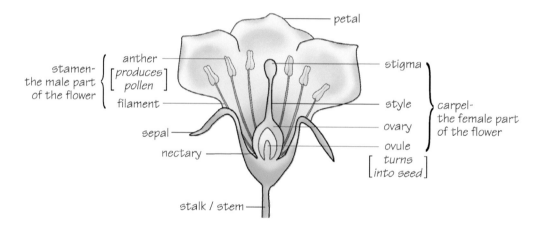

FOOD TESTS

Key People
Lind
Szent-Gyorgi

FOOD TESTS are simple, safe, specific methods for estimating the concentration of nutrients in food.

To test for starch, add a few drops of iodine solution to the solid food, the drops will turn very dark blue, almost black, if starch is present.

The test for glucose is slightly more complicated – the sugar must be released from any cells by grinding in a mortar with a pestle, mixing with water, then decanting into a test tube. A volume of Benedict's solution, equal to the volume of test solution, is added, and the test tube is put into a beaker of hot water. The presence of glucose is shown by the colour of the liquid changing from blue through green and yellow, to a brick red colour.

Fats are soluble in alcohol, but not in water, so the food is crushed with ethanol in a mortar using a pestle, the mixture is decanted into a test tube and water added to the clear liquid. If the mixture turns milky, then fats were present in the food. An alternative test for fat is to rub some paper with the food and if the paper turns permanently translucent then fat was present.

Proteins are detected by the biuret test. The food is dissolved in water, by using a mortar and pestle to break up the solid, then adding a few drops of sodium hydroxide solution followed by a few drops of dilute copper sulphate solution. A change of colour from blue to violet indicates that proteins are present in the food.

The amount of vitamin C (a chemical that Lind, in 1747, showed would cure scurvy but whose structure was not found for another two centuries) is estimated by using DCPIP [2,6 dichloro-phenol-indol-phenol].

FUELS

Fire has been used for cooking for at least a million years, but reliable methods for starting and controlling flames has existed for the past 10,000 years. Empedocles suggested that fire was one of the elements from which all substances are made (the others were air, earth and water). This idea remained until publication of *The Sceptical Chymist* by Boyle in 1661, which was rapidly followed by Stahl proposing that burning involved the loss of *phlogiston*, a material that had a negative weight. Scheele and Priestley independently made oxygen gas, in 1777, and showed that the gas supported combustion. Careful measurements by Lavoisier eventually led to the conclusion that burning involved reaction of a substance with oxygen.

Key People
Boyle
Bunsen
Diesel
Empedocles
Lavoisier
Priestley
Scheele
Stahl

The majority of fuels were originally living organisms; the fossil fuel called coal is the remains of plants that lived millions of years ago, and the oil that is underground is a complex mixture of hydrocarbons caused by the decaying sea creatures being exposed to high pressure and high temperatures over a very long time. These molecules can be separated by distillation to give useful products such as natural gas and petrol. The disadvantages of fossil fuels are that they will eventually run out, and their use increases the concentration of greenhouse gases. This not true of renewable fuels. Trees and plants will grow again and some crops, such as sugar, can be turned into alcohol by fermentation. Most fuels will burn to produce water and carbon dioxide; the water is not a problem, but the carbon dioxide is a gas that forms a layer in the upper atmosphere, reduces the loss of heat from the Earth and leads to global warming. Incomplete combustion, which means that there is not sufficient oxygen, will produce the poisonous gas carbon monoxide, and the black smoke of carbon. The carbon monoxide binds irreversibly to haemoglobin and so prevents the transport of oxygen in the blood. Hydrogen, is called a 'clean' fuel because it burns to produce water as the only product, and no harmful gases are released.

Cells use respiration to release energy; this is chemically identical to burning, but occurs at body temperature. Nuclear fuel is not strictly a fuel, but a method for providing heat energy from the breakdown of the nucleus of some types of atom.

INVESTIGATION

INVESTIGATION involves a cycle of activities. An idea, or theory, is used to think of a simple question with a predicted answer, then a method can be devised that will give sufficient data of adequate accuracy to answer the question, The results can then be compared with the prediction to see if they match the initial hypothesis.

The diagram represents the modern method of rigorous investigation where there are lots of ideas available on which to build. Up until the early fifteenth century, this strategy was not possible – few theories were available and the observations had to be qualitative (larger / heavier / hotter) or else different people would use different measurements for length and time. A technological leap was the availability of accurate clocks and the agreement of standards for length and mass.

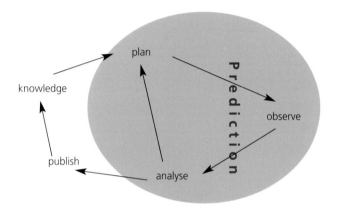

You need some knowledge in order to know which ideas have already been investigated, and you need to publish so that other people can try to repeat your plan and can use your results in their work Examples include Kepler, who analysed the astronomical observations of Brahe; Fleming took a well known observation on microbial growth and then used his own ideas to develop penicillin; Mendeleef integrated lots of ideas from many chemists in order to produce the periodic table.

JOINTS

JOINTS are where bones meet, usually forming levers that allow the body to move. The amount of movement allowed by a joint can range from immovable, eg the bones in the skull, through slightly movable, eg the vertebrae in the spine, to fully movable.

The fully movable types of joint can be either a hinge joint, (eg the jaw movement or the elbow), or a ball-and-socket joint, (eg the hip joint). In joints that allow movement, the two bones meet at a friction-free surface, this lack of friction is achieved by each bone ending in a layer of cartilage, and the two moving surfaces being separated by synovial fluid. The bones are prevented from moving too far from each other by ligaments. Muscles are the tissues that cause the bones to move about

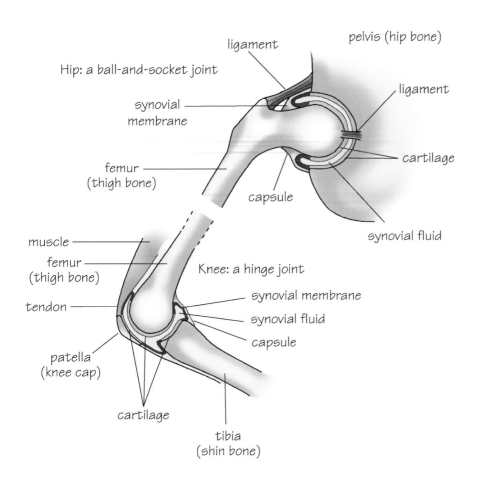

Hip: a ball-and-socket joint

ligament

pelvis (hip bone)

synovial membrane

ligament

femur (thigh bone)

cartilage

capsule

synovial fluid

muscle

femur (thigh bone)

Knee: a hinge joint

synovial membrane

synovial fluid

tendon

capsule

patella (knee cap)

cartilage

tibia (shin bone)

the joint. Muscles can only contract so antagonistic pairs of muscles are needed to allow control of the movement, the muscle on one side will contract at the same time as the muscle on the opposite side relaxes, causing the joint to bend. Straightening of the joint is achieved by the two muscles swapping function, the first muscle relaxes while the second contracts, *eg* the biceps cause the elbow to bend, and the triceps will the straighten the joint. The muscle is attached to a bone by a tendon.

KINETIC THEORY/PARTICLE THEORY

The KINETIC THEORY is the idea that everything in the world is made from tiny particles that are moving at high speed.

The particle theory was originally developed to explain the behaviour of air; Torricelli invented an instrument, the manometer, in 1648, which showed the atmosphere produced a pressure. Similar equipment was used by Pascal to show that air pressure goes down as the altitude increases. Charles, who had helped to build the first hot-air balloon, showed that the volume of gas depends on temperature; later (1848) Joule estimated the speed of gas particles and Maxwell extended the theory to give a general description of the behaviour of particles

Key People
Brown
Charles
Einstein
Joule
Kelvin
Maxwell
Pascal
Torricelli

The two assumptions of the kinetic theory are: (1) that the particles are moving, or vibrating, with a speed that increases as the temperature goes up; and (2) that a weak force causes the particles to be attracted to each other. These two ideas explain why the same molecules are able to form (for example) solid ice, liquid water and water vapour, and why each change of state occurs at a characteristic temperature. The material is solid at low temperatures because the attractive force holds the particles in a regular pattern. Increasing the temperature causes the outer electrons to vibrate more and more, until their movement causes the pattern to break down, and then the solid will melt to produce a liquid. The particles in a liquid are almost as close together as they are in the solid, but are able to move past each other. If the material is pure, then there will a single melting point, so that there will be a flat portion on the heating curve where the material is changing state at constant temperature. Mixtures contain several materials, each with their own melting point, so the heating curve has no distinct flat regions, although the temperature may remain constant as each substance melts separately. Continued heating will increase the speed of movement still further, so the temperature will be increasing, until eventually the liquid starts to boil and a gas is produced in bubbles. The boiling point is exactly the same temperature as the condensation point, and is characteristic of that substance. Cooling the gas will slow down the motion of the particles, until eventually condensation occurs; further cooling causes the liquid to freeze back to the solid. For any material, the melting point and freezing point are identical. Continued cooling of the solid will cause the temperature to drop and the vibrations to slow until all motion stops, this is absolute zero, a temperature of −273.14°C or 0 kelvin.

The particle theory also explains many other observations *eg*:

1. The several components of a mixture may be separated by distillation or chromatography because the particles retain their own properties. (We breathe in the mixture of gases called air, but extract only the oxygen because the particles keep their distinct properties).
2. Diffusion occurs in fluids (gases or liquids, the particles are moving) but not in solids (where the particles are not free to move)
3. Expansion occurs as material is heated because the particles are moving more rapidly and so push each other further apart.
4. Heat moves by conduction in solids (the temperature reflects the speed of vibration of the outer electrons) and by convection in a fluid (expansion causes the density to decrease).
5. The increase in the rate of a chemical reaction caused by increasing the temperature or concentration.

LIFE

Key People
Galen
Helmont
Linnaeus

LIFE belongs to any object that shows all of the seven characteristics listed below:

MOVEMENT: animals not only move around, but they also move jaws, and limbs, and the heart beats and food is moved through the gut. Plants also move, *eg* leaves will turn so as to face the Sun.

RESPIRATION: occurs in cells, where the chemical energy of glucose is turned into heat, movement and growth (chemical energy)

chemical energy ⟶ heat energy
movement energy
chemical energy

Aerobic respiration is used when there is lots of oxygen and turns the glucose into carbon dioxide and water

sugar + oxygen = carbon dioxide + water

Anaerobic respiration occurs when there is not much oxygen, the products usually include carbon dioxide and water, but other chemicals are also produced, such as lactic acid in muscles or alcohol in yeast (when anaerobic respiration is called fermentation). Anaerobic respiration is less effective than aerobic respiration, but is vital under conditions of reduced oxygen availability.

GROWTH: could produce larger cells, but a limit is reached when the oxygen and sugar can no longer diffuse fast enough and the cell has to divide to give two daughter cells.

REPRODUCTION: may be asexual, when a cell or even a complete organism, reproduces without the help of a partner – the offspring produced by asexual methods is identical to the parent. Two partners are needed in sexual reproduction; the male produces a gamete that moves, and the female produces an egg that contains a store of food. Fertilisation may be internal (as in mammals and birds) or external (used by amphibians and fish); development may continue externally (birds and lizards lay eggs) or can be internal (as in humans). Sexual reproduction introduces variation, with improved chances of survival.

EXCRETION: getting rid of chemicals that are not required, and are poisonous if they remain in the system, including the carbon dioxide produced by respiration and the urea produced by breakdown of proteins (to get rid of waste that was not absorbed is called egestion).

NUTRITION / FEEDING: producers need not only light, water and carbon dioxide, for photosynthesis, but also nitrogen and minerals from the soil in order to make proteins and chlorophyll. Every animal needs a balanced diet so as to get the right amount of energy, nitrogen, water and minerals.

SENSING: this is required by living organisms in order to find food, to escape predators and to find a mate. Plants need to sense gravity so the roots go down and the shoot goes up (geotropism), the roots need to grow towards water (hydrotropism) and many plants will turn their leaves to the Sun (phototropism). Animals need to detect plants and other animals, either visually or by smell; these same signals can be used to tell others of your presence for mating.

The seven characteristics can be remembered using a mnemonic, either MR GRENS or MRS GREF.

LUNGS

Key People
Malpighi

LUNGS are the essential organs for the exchange of gases – oxygen, from the air, is absorbed by the haemoglobin in the red blood cells, and carbon dioxide moves from the blood to the expired (breathed out) air. To allow this exchange to happen, the lungs start as a massive tube, the trachea, down which air is drawn, the trachea splits into the two bronchi, these tubes becomes more and more divided, eventually ending in tiny air sacs or alveoli. The alveoli are surrounded by blood capillaries, so the gases can easily diffuse between air and blood. Air is inhaled by increasing the volume of the chest, both by raising the ribs and by flattening the diaphragm, atmospheric pressure forces air into the lungs. Lowering the ribs and relaxing the diaphragm decreases the volume of the chest, so air is forced out.

Inhalers, such as Ventolin™, make breathing easier by causing dilation (opening up or widening) of the bronchi and smaller tubes that have become constricted. Exercise leads to cells respiring more rapidly so the concentration of carbon dioxide in the blood will increase, causing both the rate and depth of breathing to increase. The amount of oxygen available may not be sufficient for aerobic respiration, so vigorous exercise may lead to you feeling tired as the muscles produce lactic acid.

Smoking damages not only the delicate cells of the alveoli, so there is less surface area for gas exchange, but also the ciliated cells in the trachea, so the air is cleaned less effectively. In addition, smoking produces carbon monoxide, which binds permanently to the haemoglobin in place of oxygen. Infections such as TB (tuberculosis) or pneumonia can also cause difficulty in breathing, as the growth of bacteria blocks some air ways and causes others to be irritated.

MAGNETISM

Key People
Ampère
Coulomb
Faraday
Gilbert
Kelvin
Oersted
Volta

MAGNETISM is a force produced between two magnetic poles, either repulsion, if the poles are the same, or attraction if one pole is north and the other is south. A major discovery, almost a millennium ago, was that some rocks are naturally magnetic, so that when allowed to rotate, these rocks, or lodestones, would point along the north–south axis. Gilbert, in 1600, deduced that the Earth behaves as a giant magnet and introduced the terms 'magnetic pole' and 'geo-magnetism' in his book De Magnete. Extraction of pure metals showed that nickel, iron and cobalt were attracted to a magnet, and were capable of being turned into permanent magnets by stroking with a lodestone, but no other metal was affected by a magnetic field. These permanent magnets could be used to make the needles that are used in plotting compasses and for finding out the laws of magnetism. The development of simple batteries by Volta allowed Oersted to demonstrate that an electrical current will affect the needle of a compass, an observation that led Faraday to develop both the motor and the dynamo; it was Faraday who developed the idea that magnetism produced lines of force that can never cross. Another principle of magnetism is that the lines of force always try to take the shortest route. An agreed convention is that the lines of force point from north to south.

Imagine a world without magnetism – there would be no motors, no washing machines, no iPods, no street lights, no loudspeakers and no televisions.

MENSTRUAL CYCLE

The MENSTRUAL CYCLE is the sequence of events that occurs every month (*mensis* is Latin for monthly) in non-pregnant women of reproductive age, and is controlled by the female sex hormones. The only visible sign of this cycle is the period or loss of blood from the vagina, so this observation is taken as the start of the cycle. About two weeks after the start of bleeding, ovulation occurs as one of the ovaries releases an egg into the fallopian tube. At the same time, the uterus is preparing for pregnancy by increasing the blood supply, leading to the uterine wall becoming slightly spongy. The ovum is moved down the oviduct by ciliated cells and it is only during these 3–5 days of movement that the sperm can fertilise the egg. Chemical changes tell the body that the egg is not fertilised so the lining of the womb thins down both by resorption and by some loss of the lining, which is seen as the menstrual bleeding, beginning approximately 28 days after the start of the last menstruation, and lasting 2–5 days.

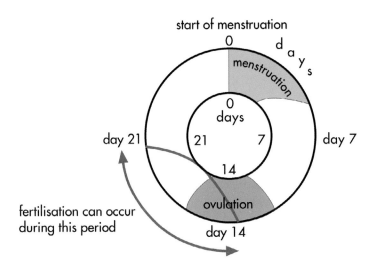

MOVING HEAT

MOVING HEAT is the flow of energy that occurs when there is a difference of temperature between two items. Temperature is a measure of how fast individual particles are moving, the amount of heat energy depends not only on the temperature, but also on the mass of material present and whether the material is changing state.

Conduction is movement of heat through a solid. The particles in a solid are in fixed position, *ie* they can not move around, so the temperature reflects the movement of the outer electrons of neighbouring atoms and conduction involves transfer of energy between these outer electrons.

Convection occurs in fluids, and is the movement of hot particles upwards and cooler particles downwards, leading to convection currents. Heating any material causes the particles to move apart, so the material expands and the density decreases so in a fluid (either liquid or gas) the particles that are hotter are also less dense and so will rise.

Key People
Black
Cavendish
Dewar
Joule
Kelvin
Newton

Radiation occurs from the surface; heat radiation behaves just like visible light, the only difference is that heat radiation, also called infra-red radiation, has a longer wavelength. The light and heat radiated from the Sun is able to pass through the vacuum of space and illuminate and warm the Earth. Heat radiation behaves just like light. A black surface will absorb both heat and light, whereas a white or shiny surface will reflect either type of energy.

Insulation is the prevention of heat movement, usually by trapping layers of air. The pockets of air can not move so there is no convection, air is not a good conductor, and radiation between layers of material is very small.

Heat can also be moved by evaporating a liquid and then condensing the vapour onto a cold surface. The evaporation requires heat energy, which is released by condensation. However, this method does transfer particles as well as heat.

NITROGEN CYCLE

The NITROGEN CYCLE is the movement of nitrogen atoms from the inert state of nitrogen gas in the atmosphere to the proteins, amino acids and DNA in living cells, and the return to the air. The atmosphere comprises approximately 79% nitrogen gas, but plants and animals are unable to use the nitrogen in this form – the nitrogen has to be converted to ammonium ions by lightning, and to nitrate ions by the nitrogen-fixing bacteria, especially those in the nodules that grow on the roots of legumes, *eg* clover. The nitrate ions are absorbed through the roots of plants and turned into amino acids and DNA in the cells, animals can then use these molecules to produce new proteins, excreting nitrogen as urea in the urine. Bacteria break down the bodies of dead organisms, releasing the nitrogen compounds back into the soil, where they are either absorbed by other plants or are converted back to nitrogen gas by denitrifying bacteria. The concentration of both ammonium ions and nitrate ions in the soil is increased by adding a NPK (nitrogen, phosphorus, potassium) fertiliser or spreading manure, this is used to improve the growth of crop plants. One problem is that adding too much fertiliser can lead to leeching and dissolving too much nitrogen in the local rivers. The excess nitrogen encourages growth of plants and algae, the plants die and provide nutrients for millions of bacteria that then remove all the oxygen from the water, so very little can live in that river.

NUTRITION / FEEDING

NUTRITION describes how an organism obtains the chemicals that are essential for the maintenance of life and for growth.

Plants use photosynthesis to convert the light energy from the Sun into the chemical energy of sugars. The plant needs nitrogen and phosphorus for making amino acids and proteins. Plants also need minerals such as magnesium, which is an essential atom in chlorophyll. These nutrients are obtained form the soil and absorbed through the root hairs. Photosynthesis is fundamental to all life on Earth, the green plants both release oxygen, so aerobic respiration can occur, and provide food for animals.

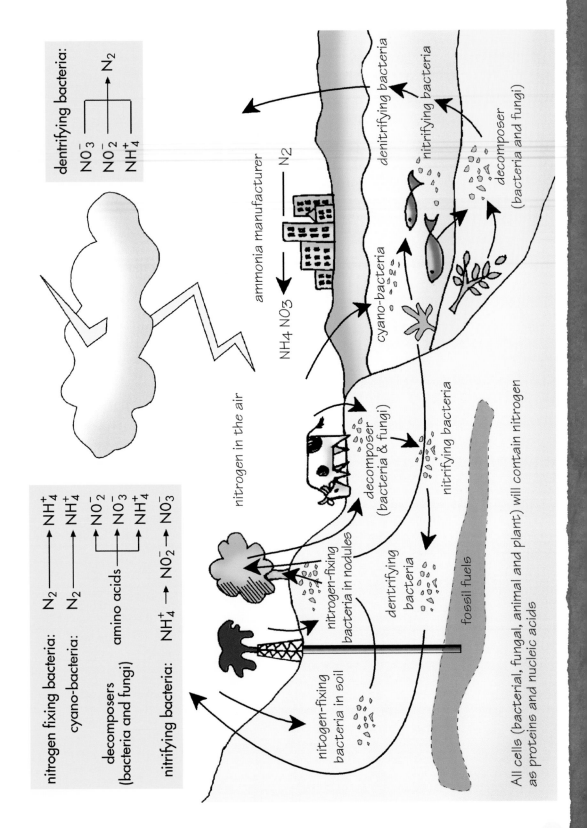

nitrogen fixing bacteria: $N_2 \longrightarrow NH_4^+$

cyano-bacteria: $N_2 \longrightarrow NH_4^+$

decomposers (bacteria and fungi) amino acids $\begin{array}{c} \longrightarrow NO_2^- \\ \longrightarrow NO_3^- \\ \longrightarrow NH_4^+ \end{array}$

nitrifying bacteria: $NH_4^+ \longrightarrow NO_2^- \longrightarrow NO_3^-$

dentrifying bacteria: $\begin{array}{c} NO_3^- \\ NO_2^- \\ NH_4^+ \end{array} \longrightarrow N_2$

nitrogen in the air

ammonia manufacturer

N_2

$NH_4 \ NO_3$

nitrogen-fixing bacteria in soil

nitrogen-fixing bacteria in nodules

dentrifying bacteria

decomposer (bacteria & fungi)

nitrifying bacteria

fossil fuels

cyano-bacteria

denitrifying bacteria

nitrifying bacteria

decomposer (bacteria and fungi)

All cells (bacterial, fungal, animal and plant) will contain nitrogen as proteins and nucleic acids

405

Animals obtain all their nutrients by ingestion of food. Sugars and fats are useful as a source of chemical energy; fats will often contain the fat-soluble vitamins. Proteins are ingested, but these macromolecules are too large to be absorbed, and so must be broken down by enzymes. The products of this breakdown are amino acids, which are sufficiently small to be absorbed and then transported to individual cells where they are reassembled to form new proteins. Plant materials, such as cereals and fruit, provide the roughage that is an essential part of any diet for moving the food through the gut, but the fibre is not digested and will be egested as part of the faeces. A balanced diet should provide adequate amounts of all the nutrients. If too much food is taken in, the excess is stored, often as fat; too little of a particular nutrient will lead to a deficiency disease or malnutrition.

Water is an essential part of the diet of any organism. Some organisms are adapted to a lack of water, *eg* cacti, camel, whereas others are able to live in the water, *eg* seaweed, fish.

ORGANS

Key People
Bichat
Erasistratus
Fabrizio
Fallopius
Galen
Vesalius
Virchow

ORGANS are easily identifiable structures within an organism, that will carry out tasks that are continual or long term, and are essential for life (MR GRENS *ie* movement, respiration, growth, reproduction, excretion, nutrition, sensing). The several organ systems in an organism will appear to be separate items, but they are inter-dependent, and each is functionally dependent on all the others. Every cell in the organism will contain identical genetic information in the DNA, but different cells will become specialised for the particular function that they have to perform.

Plants have four distinct organs: roots, stem, leaves and one or more flowers. The root system not only anchors the plant into the ground, but also ensures that the root hairs absorb water and nutrients. The stem has xylem, to carry water to the leaves, and phloem, to move soluble sugars to the rest of the plant. The leaves show very clearly that organs are made from tissues; the upper surface is covered by a cuticle, a thin layer that allows light through, but prevents the loss of water, photosynthesis occurs in the palisade cells which are above a spongy layer that allow diffusion of carbon dioxide and oxygen.

Animals have many needs if they are to survive. The organism must detect food and be aware of any predators and so needs the sense organs for hearing and sight. Sometimes the organ is obvious, as in the eyes and ears of mammals, but snakes also have a patch of cells near each eye that is sensitive to heat, so the animal can hunt at night. Birds have no external pinna, but do have an ear canal and the ossicles and cochlea that are essential for hearing the songs of other birds.

Many functions are sufficiently complex that several organs are required. The digestive system is needed so that food is ingested, digested, absorbed or egested, and waste products are excreted; the digestive tract is basically a long tube with the mouth at the start and the anus at the end. The mouth varies widely in shape and structure. Mammals and crocodiles have teeth that are able to grip, but the jaws of mammals allow the food to be ground and crushed, whereas the jaw of a crocodile

THE ORGANS OF THE BODY

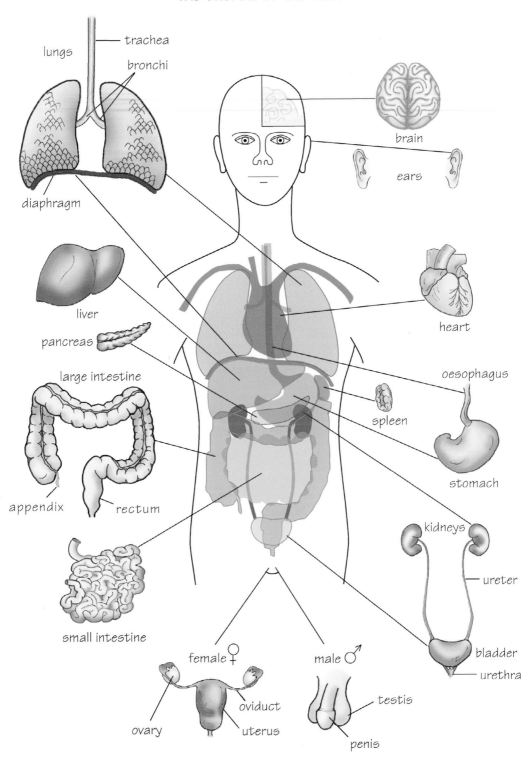

trachea

lungs

bronchi

brain

ears

diaphragm

liver

heart

pancreas

large intestine

oesophagus

spleen

stomach

appendix

rectum

kidneys

ureter

small intestine

bladder

urethra

female ♀

male ♂

oviduct

ovary

uterus

testis

penis

can not move sideways so the crocodile can not chew its food. The mouth-parts of insects and crabs may have six jaw pieces, although the mosquito and butterfly have in common that each uses a long tube for sucking blood and nectar, respectively. The mouth in humans is connected by the oesophagus to the stomach, then there is the small intestine, approximately 5 metres long, in which both digestion and absorption occur; this turns into the large intestine, an organ that is specialised for absorbing water.

The nutrients are absorbed into the blood, then filtered in the liver before passing into the circulatory system. The heart is specialised for pumping blood with continual, rhythmical contraction and relaxation. The blood vessels, arteries, veins and capillaries allow blood to circulate safely. The blood contains red blood cells (for carrying oxygen) and white blood cells (for defence) and platelets (to help form clots). The concentration of water in the blood is regulated by the kidney, which passes urea and water to the bladder for excretion. The blood also carries the chemical messengers from the several disparate organs that are the humoral system. The ovaries and testes are the primary reproductive organs that produce the sex hormones that affect the development of the rest of your body so, at puberty, the females will develop breasts, and males start to have hairy faces. The hormones affect the organs of movement, the bones and muscles of a male are larger and stronger than those of the female. The skeletal system will also need the specialised tissue at the joints that allow the bones to move, but it also keeps the different parts together. Movement of the rib cage causes air to flow in and out of the lungs, the trachea and bronchi are flexible tubes that are reinforced with cartilage so they will not collapse, and the alveoli allow exchange of oxygen and carbon dioxide. Movement of the jaw is essential for capturing food and starting the process of digestion.

The skin is the largest organ in the human body – with a mass of 4 kilograms and covering an area of 2 square metres.

PERIODIC TABLE

Key People
Balard
Berzelius
Bunsen
Dalton
Davy
Döbereiner
Klaproth
Mendeleef
Moissan
Moseley
Newlands
Ramsay
Scheele
Vauquelin

The PERIODIC TABLE is a schematic representation of atoms in order of proton number such that atoms in the vertical columns, or groups, have very similar properties. Dalton tried to find an arrangement for the 20 "elements" that were known at the start of the 19th century, but some of those "elements" were compounds (eg water), and there were many errors in the measurement of the atomic mass. Twenty years later, Döbereiner noted that many elements formed trios or triads with common properties, but his idea worked only for the first 16 elements. At the same time, Berzelius was making accurate measurements of the relative atomic masses of the 28 known elements. Two decades later, in the 1860s, many people were continuing the search for a simple pattern relating the properties of the 61 known elements. Most people, including Newlands in England, followed Dalton's idea of arranging atoms in order of atomic mass. In 1869, Mendeleef made two great leaps of imagination: first, he decided that not all elements were known, and so he left gaps in the arrangement; and second, he decided that some atomic masses could be wrong and so elements needed to be moved. These two ideas meant that the properties of the missing elements could be predicted and, within five years,

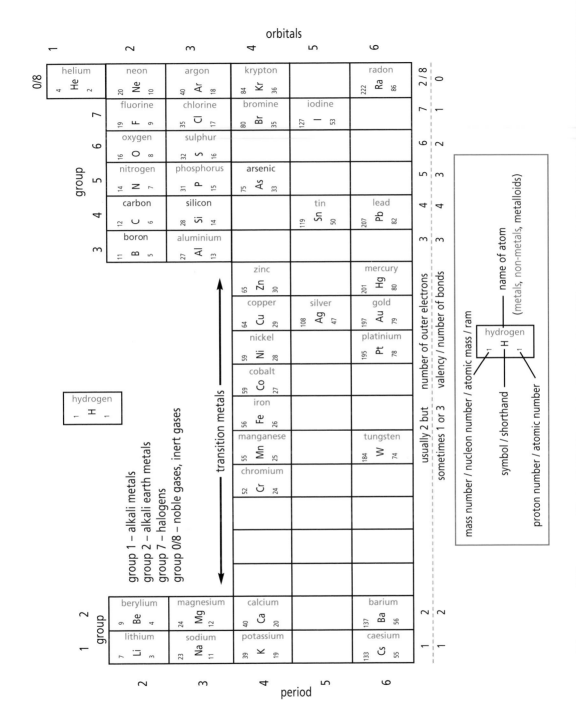

three of them had been isolated (gallium by a Frenchman, scandium by a Swede, and germanium in Germany). Newlands was loud in claiming credit for the idea! Bunsen used features within sunlight to show that there must be another element, called helium, but isolation of this inert gas depended on the development of refrigerators capable of reaching temperatures below −200°C; the new equipment was used by Ramsay, in the 1890s, to isolate all the noble gases. The last natural element was isolated in 1939 in France and so was named francium. The final ideas of the periodic table were added by two physicists studying phenomena that seemed to have no closely related application. Moseley showed, in 1913, that the elements are arranged in order of proton number or atomic number and, twenty years later, Chadwick, working in the same laboratory, was able to use the idea of neutrons to explain why there are differences in atomic mass or mass number.

There are over a hundred elements in the modern periodic table, of which two (bromine and mercury) are liquids and approximately 84 are metals (*ie* they will conduct electricity). The atoms are arranged in order of proton number on a pattern that has vertical groups and horizontal periods; the group number reflects the number of electrons in the outer shell, and the period is the number of orbitals. The group 1 elements are very reactive alkaline metals, the group 2 elements are the less reactive alkaline earth metals, which form salts that are often insoluble and so are found in the ground. The trend going down the group is that the reactivity increases because each period represents another orbital, which provides additional shielding of the outer electron from the influence of the nucleus. The group 7 elements are halogens, or salt formers, and the group on the far right of the periodic table is designated group 8 or group 0, and is called the noble gases or inert gases.

pH SCALE

Key People
Sörenson

The pH SCALE was invented in 1909 by Sörenson as a measure of the concentration of hydrogen ions in a solution, usually in water. The scale starts at pH 1, a very strong acid (*eg* hydrochloric acid [HCl]) and finishes at pH 14, which is a very strong alkali (*eg* sodium hydroxide [NaOH]). At the centre of the scale is pH 7, which is neutral, 3 pH units above pH 7 are the weak alkalis (*eg* lime water is calcium hydroxide [Ca(OH$_2$)] in water), and 3 pH units below pH 7 are the weak acids (*eg* methanoic acid or vinegar [CH$_3$COOH]). In the school laboratory, the value of the pH is measured using an coloured chemical such as universal indicator solution, which is a mixture of three chemicals, each of which changes colour at a different pH value. Professional laboratories will use a meter and a glass probe to give an accurate pH value.

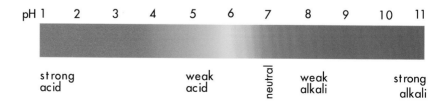

| pH 1 | 2 | 3 | 4 | 5 | 6 | 7 | 8 | 9 | 10 | 11 |

strong acid   weak acid   neutral   weak alkali   strong alkali

POLLINATION

POLLINATION is sexual reproduction in flowering plants. Pollen is the male gamete that is produced by the anthers of a flower on the end of long filaments and is transferred to the stigma of a different (or even the same) flower. Flowers that are wind-pollinating, such as grasses or cereals, will disperse a vast number of tiny pollen grains that are carried on the wind and should be captured by female flowers, but these tiny grains may also cause hay fever in some humans. Insect-pollinated flowers have to attract the correct type of insect by releasing a scent and by displaying a brightly coloured flower. The insect is guided to the sugar solution in the nectary and, as it passes the stamen, the insect is covered in pollen. The pollen grains must be sticky enough to attach to the back of the insect, and yet easily released when the insect visits another flower. The insect must have furry back to which the pollen can stick, but the grains can be easily dislodged to fall onto the stigma. The pollen that is deposited on the stigma develops a pollen tube that reaches down towards the ovary and the pollen nucleus will travel along this tube in order to reach an ovum and fuse with the female nucleus. Cross-pollination is important in producing variation, but many plants are also capable of self-pollination so that an identical plant is produced that can grow and possibly cross-pollinate in the following year.

PREGNANCY

PREGNANCY is the period between the fertilisation of the ovum by the sperm and the birth of the offspring. In women, ovulation occurs about 10 – 14 days after the start of the menstrual cycle, and fertilisation can occur only in the period of about 5 days between the ovum leaving the ovary and becoming implanted in the wall of the uterus. The fertilised egg may divide several times while completing its journey to the uterus; total division of the fertilised egg into two will lead to the development of identical twins. Non-identical twins result from the fertilisation of two eggs that had been released simultaneously. The ball of cells continues to divide, becoming an embryo, and then a foetus, as the head and limbs develop and the placenta starts to form. All the nutrients and oxygen that the foetus will need are exchanged from the mother's blood system into the foetal blood system *via* the placenta; the carbon dioxide, urea and other waste chemicals are passed back across the placenta to the mother. The foetus develops within the amniotic sac and is protected by the amniotic fluid. About 40 weeks after the last menstrual period, so after 38 weeks gestation, labour begins; the mucus plug in the cervix is released, the membrane containing the amniotic fluid breaks and powerful contractions of the muscles in the uterus cause the baby to be born through the birth canal. The umbilical cord can be cut once the baby starts breathing independently. A little while after the birth, the placenta (also known as the after-birth) detaches and is also expelled by the uterus.

Key People
Fabrizio

REPRODUCTION

REPRODUCTION is the ability to produce a new cell or offspring that is the same (or similar) to the parents. Asexual reproduction of cells occurs all the time within a complex organism, such as humans, in which the majority of cells live for a limited amount of time and need to be replaced: damaged cells need to be replaced and

Key People
Black
Fabrizio
Galton

new cells manufactured for growth. The growth that takes a single fertilised egg cell to the size of a teenager or young adult, is the result of asexual reproduction. The daughter cells formed by asexual reproduction will each have identical chromosomes, although not all the characteristics will be expressed in every cell because many cells in the body are specialised. Protoctista and bacteria almost always reproduce asexually.

Higher organisms reproduce sexually, which has the advantage of producing variation (by combining different chromosomes), but does require two parents. Each parent produces sex cells containing half the usual number of chromosomes. The female gamete (ovum) is always large and filled with food reserves; the male gamete (sperm in animals, pollen in plants) has to be able to move (or be moved) in order to fertilise the ovum.

Plants will often reproduce both sexually and asexually. Sexual reproduction involves the stamen of one flower, producing pollen, which is shifted to another flower either by insects or by the wind; self-pollination can also occur sometimes. Many plants will clone themselves (asexual reproduction) by growing new plants from roots, tips of branches or leaves.

Male animals produce sperm, which swim towards the ovum, this movement may result in fertilisation, either internally (as in mammals and birds) or externally (as in frogs and fish). The zygote then develops further either internally, *eg* in mammals, or externally as an egg, *eg* in birds.

Humans use internal fertilisation and internal development. Sperm are produced in the testes of the male, ejaculated from the penis into the vagina of the female then travel up the vagina, through the uterus and towards the fallopian tubes. An ovum is released from the ovary each month and may become fertilised while moving down the oviduct. The fertilised ovum (now known as the zygote) divides to form a ball of cells, which becomes embedded in the wall of the uterus and, by a process of asexual reproduction, a foetus develops that is born as a new child after a nine-month gestation.

RESPIRATION

RESPIRATION is one of the characteristics of life that is shown by all living cells; the energy released by respiration can be used for movement, growth or production of heat. The sugar molecule is broken down to produce smaller molecules and to release energy. Yeast uses fermentation, or anaerobic respiration, to produce alcohol, carbon dioxide and water.

$$glucose \longrightarrow alcohol + carbon\ dioxide + water$$

Yeast can also use aerobic respiration to turn the sugar into carbon dioxide and water only, this is the process used to make bread dough rise, and produces much more energy than anaerobic respiration.

$$glucose + oxygen \longrightarrow carbon\ dioxide + water$$

Humans, too, are able to use both aerobic and anaerobic respiration. The exchange of gases in the lungs is known as ventilation; there is normally a sufficient amount of oxygen transported in the blood for the sugar to be totally converted to carbon dioxide and water but during vigorous exercise, the amount of oxygen available can become inadequate, so some cells produce lactic acid.

$$glucose \longrightarrow lactic\ acid\ +\ carbon\ dioxide\ +\ water$$

Respiration is an important part of the carbon cycle, ensuring that the carbon dioxide, that was converted to glucose by photosynthesis, is returned to the atmosphere. Cells that possess chloroplasts are the only cells that can produce sugars using light energy by using photosynthesis, but all plant cells will use respiration at all times.

ROCK CYCLE

Almost since the dawn of time, people have realised that different types of rock are found in different areas, eg more than 4000 years ago, rocks had to be transported hundreds of kilometres from quarries in order to build structures such as Stonehenge or the Pyramids. In 1768, Lavoisier helped to produce a map that showed the distribution of different rocks in France; then, in 1815, Smith not only published a map that showed the surface rocks throughout Britain, but also used the ideas of strata (or layers) in order to explain the distribution of rocks. Between these two dates, in 1795, Hutton suggested that the processes causing rocks to change had remained the same for millions of years. The idea of a *restless Earth*, with the crust composed of plates that are moving in all directions and producing new rocks at the margins was proposed by Wegener between the two World Wars (ie between 1918 and 1939).

Key People
Hutton
Lavoisier
Smith
Wegener

The crust of the Earth is a series of plates covering a sphere of molten rock (magma) that reaches temperatures of 6000°C The magma reaches the surface, either by erupting as a volcano or creeping round the edges of the tectonic plates, then cools producing igneous rocks. A sudden cooling will freeze the structure of the liquid rock, so producing material that is glassy, eg obsidian, or material that is full of air holes, eg pumice. If the cooling takes place over a long period, then the rocks often contain crystals (usually mica or quartz) and the size of the crystals depends on the rate of cooling; the crystals in extrusive rocks are much smaller than the crystals found in intrusive rocks.

Weathering (the breakdown without transport) and erosion (where the fragments have been transported away) of the igneous rocks produce particles that sediment as strata (or layers) of sedimentary rocks. The cause of the breakdown may be biological weathering, chemical weathering or physical weathering. Examples of biological weathering include growth of plant roots, that split open rocks, the burrowing of small creatures and the movement of large animals. Chemical weathering is caused by the oxides of non-metals, such as sulphur dioxide or nitrogen oxides, dissolving in rain water to produce weak acids that are able to dissolve limestone, leading to the formation of caves. Physical weathering is caused either by changes of temperature or by movement of water. Sudden changes in temperatures, eg in a desert, may cause onion-skin weathering of rocks; repetitive

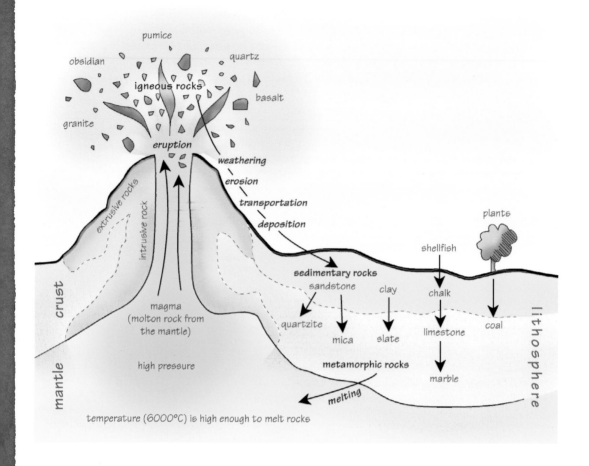

changes in weather conditions between warm temperatures, when rain falls, and freezing temperatures, when the water turns to ice and expands, lead to freeze–thaw cracking of rocks and the formation of scree. The kinetic energy of moving water or moving air can abrade individual rocks or wear down mountains. The continual wave movement of the seas erodes cliffs, so the coastline is forever changing shape. Water evaporates from the seas, precipitates as rain or snow to produce streams and rivers that flow and both wear the rocks away and carry the fragments down the slopes.

Some sedimentary rocks are formed as the result of living creatures dying and sinking to the ground, eg coal is the remains of dead trees, and chalk is the exoskeletons of millions of shellfish. The layer of chalk may be covered with other material; the weight of the additional layers of rock cause the pressure to increase, and chalk is pushed closer to the mantle so the temperature also increases, the soft rock slowly changes into a metamorphic rock (called limestone) and then into marble. Other examples of metamorphic rocks include slate, which has been produced from layers of shale, and quartzite, a rock that was originally sandstone.

The rock cycle is completed by the movement of one tectonic plate causing the edge of another plate to sink and the solid rocks are melted back into the mantle.

SATELLITES

A SATELLITE is any body that is in orbit around a much larger body. The natural satellites in the solar system include the nine planets, 5000 asteroids visible to telescopes, dozens of comets, and millions of tiny rocks that orbit the Sun, as well as the 61 moons that orbit different planets and the rings of dust that surround each of the four gas giants. Galileo's observation of the satellites of Jupiter was the final proof that the Earth was not the centre of the universe. Newton, born in the same year that Galileo died (1642), produced the mathematics that not only explained the motion of satellites, but also provided the theory that allowed artificial satellites to be developed three centuries later. The first artificial satellite, *Sputnik 1*, was put into orbit in October 1967. There are currently 3000 known satellites orbiting the Earth, mainly concerned with remote sensing or telecommunications. The remote sensing satellites need to be able to see details of crops, land usage, pollution or weather, and so are in low orbits that may be equatorial, polar or somewhere in between. The sensors will often be able to see through clouds and produce false-colour pictures of cereals, plant diseases, temperature or moisture levels. There are dozens of telecommunications satellites in geo-stationary orbit at 35,900 kilometres above the Earth's equator, but a minimum of three are sufficient to allow a satellite dish in fixed position and direction to communicate with another dish anywhere in the world; the disadvantage is the time taken for the signal to travel the vast distances. The Hubble telescope, launched in 1990, allows the use of a massive information-gathering system without the distortions caused by temperature gradients in the atmosphere. All of these artificial satellites are put into orbit using the chemical energy from rockets, then they use panels of solar cells to convert the energy from sunlight into electrical energy. The future use of satellites is to build a space station that not only will allow improved observation of the Earth, but also could act as a station for building craft that will explore the Solar System.

Key People
Galileo
Newton

SENSING

SENSING is the ability to detect and to respond to a stimulus.

The important sense in humans is sight; light causes a chemical change on the retina of the eye, so that a message is sent along the optic nerve to the brain. A pair of eyes at the front of the head allows a predator to judge distances and distinguish fine details, but prey often have a pair of eyes near the top or side of the head so they can look out for any attackers. Many nocturnal animals are sensitive to the heat radiation that is emitted by warm-blooded animals; many insects are sensitive to ultra-violet light, and can distinguish guide lines on the petals of flowers.

Sound is important both in carrying information and in making the animal aware of hidden dangers. The audible range of a human is from 20 hertz to 20 kilohertz, but this range decreases with age. Dogs can hear ultra-sound up to approximately 40 kilohertz, but animals that use echo-location, *eg* bats or dolphins, may emit and detect sound with a frequency up to 120 kilohertz

The tongue and the nose respond to chemicals. Tests carried out at the start of the twentieth century were interpreted as showing that the tongue has specific areas that

Key People
Bell
Halley

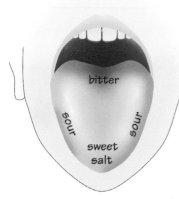

are sensitive to one of four tastes: bitter, salty, sour and sweet. Later work showed most areas of the tongue can respond to any of these four stimuli, but that certain areas are more sensitive than others. In addition, the tongue can detect some amino acids, including glutamic acid, and may be sensitive to fatty acids. The nose has many thousands of odour detectors. Dogs have a much more sensitive sense of smell than humans, and moths can detect the odour of potential mates over distances of more than a kilometre; insects are highly sensitive to the scent given off by flowers.

The skin contains hundreds of nerve endings, each of which will respond to a single stimulus, *eg* pain, pressure, touch or temperature.

The brain controls the voluntary actions in animals, but survival is improved by possessing reflex arcs.

Geotropism (the sensing of gravity) in plants ensures that the shoots grow upwards and roots grow downwards, then phototropism (sensing light) and hydrotropism (sensing water) ensure that the leaves receive most light, and that the roots have water to absorb.

SKELETON

The SKELETON is the collection of approximately 206 bones that gives shape to the human body, and forms many joints and levers. The bones are held together at the joints by ligaments; friction at the surface of the joint is reduced by lining the ends of the bone with cartilage, a material that is both tough and smooth, then separating the ends with synovial fluid. Tendons join the muscles to the bones and it is contraction of the muscles that causes the bones to move. Pairs of antagonistic muscles ensure that a joint can be both bent and straightened, *eg* biceps and triceps in the upper arm move the bones around the elbow joint.

The skeleton is essential for breathing; downward movement of the rib cage forces air out of the lungs, then raising of the rib cage causes air to enter the lungs. Movement of the lower jaw bone allows food to be chewed, and movement of the bones in the legs allows us to move around.

The skeleton provides protection to many organs, the rib cage protects the heart, the skull is a hard case around the brain and the delicate nerves of the body are routed through the canal that forms down the centre of the spine, made up of vertebrae.

The bone marrow produces both types of blood cell, the erythrocytes (red blood cells) and the leucocytes (white blood cells).

The skeleton is unable to function properly if there are major deficiencies in the diet, *eg* insufficient vitamin D in the diet leads to rickets.

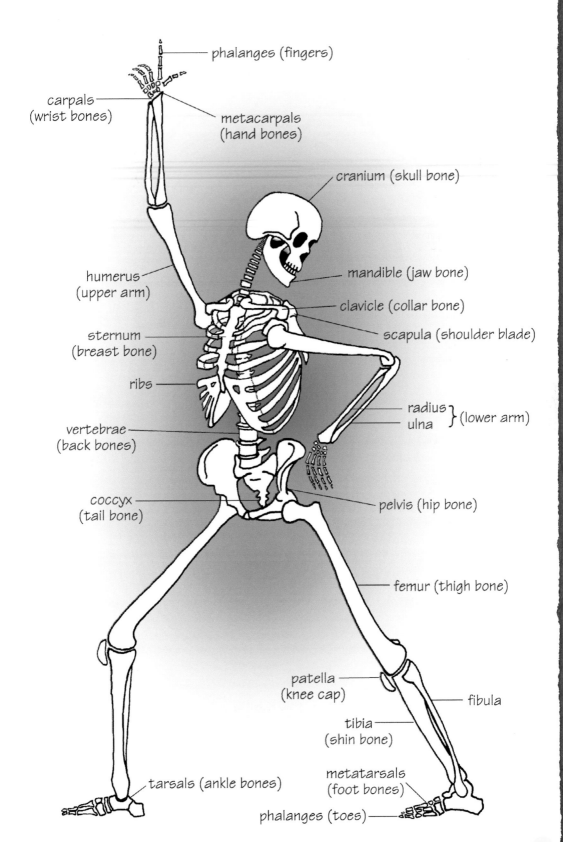

phalanges (fingers)

carpals
(wrist bones)

metacarpals
(hand bones)

cranium (skull bone)

humerus
(upper arm)

mandible (jaw bone)

clavicle (collar bone)

sternum
(breast bone)

scapula (shoulder blade)

ribs

radius
ulna } (lower arm)

vertebrae
(back bones)

coccyx
(tail bone)

pelvis (hip bone)

femur (thigh bone)

patella
(knee cap)

fibula

tibia
(shin bone)

tarsals (ankle bones)

metatarsals
(foot bones)

phalanges (toes)

SKIN

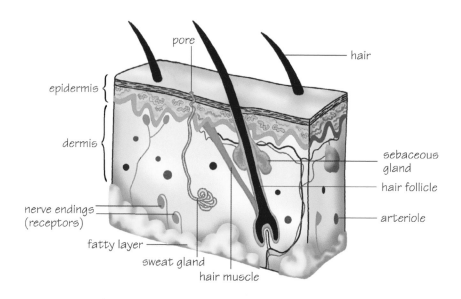

The SKIN is the largest organ in the human body, covering an area of 2 square metres to a average thickness of 0.6 millimetres. The 4 kilogram of skin is a waterproof barrier comprising many layers of cells; embedded in the layers are the receptors for temperature, and for touch or pain, and there are blood vessels to provide nutrients and remove waste chemicals. The skin is pitted with hair follicles, near the bottom of which are the sebaceous glands that produce sebum. Sweat glands open onto the surface and will produce sweat if the body needs to remove heat; another method of removing heat is for the blood capillaries near the surface to open wider and so allow more blood flow. The skin can insulate the body from loss of heat, both long-term (with layers of fat cells) and, more immediately, by reducing the flow of blood through the skin capillaries. The skin is sensitive to the different wavelengths of sunshine, the ultra-violet rays not only will cause the production of melanin and vitamin D, but also will increase the possibility of developing skin cancer. The infra-red waves in the sunshine can lead to sun burn. Physical damage to the skin is followed by loss of blood and could lead to invasion by microbes; the platelets in the blood will form a clot, so preventing further bleeding, and white blood cells will destroy the microbes, although an area of pus may be produced.

SOLAR SYSTEM

Key People
Aristarchus
Aristotle

The SOLAR SYSTEM is the collection of the many natural satellites that orbit the Sun and the Sun itself, the star that was called *sol* by the Romans. The idea of heliocentric model (a system centred on the Sun that was called Helios by the Greeks) was proposed by Aristarchus around 300 BC, but rejected because Aristotle thought that the Earth must be the centre of the universe. In 1514, Copernicus published an analysis of the literature that showed that the Earth must be in orbit around the Sun, but it was not until a hundred years later that Kepler showed that the orbits of the planets must be elliptical, and Galileo was able to show that moons existed that orbited another planet. In 1679, Newton used his ideas of gravity to explain all the observations.

The only source of light in the solar system is the Sun, other objects are seen by the light that they reflect. The inner planets and Jupiter reflect sufficient light that they can be seen with the unaided eye, but it was not until 1610, when Galileo examined the sky with his telescope, that Saturn was discovered. The planet Uranus was described by W. Herschel in 1781, and the first object in the asteroid belt was named in 1801 (Ceres, diameter of 1000 kilometres). The position of Neptune had been predicted and was seen in 1846, but it was not for another century, in 1930, that a photograph was obtained that showed Pluto. The discussion continues to this day as to whether Pluto has a companion called Charon. The planets and the asteroids all lie in the solar plane, but comets (the dirty snow balls of space) not only have very elongated orbits, but also may be at any angle to the plane of the planets.

Information has been obtained from space probes including the *Mariner 10* flypast of Mercury (1974), the *Venera* programme (1961–1983) to Venus and the landing of the *Viking* on Mars in 1976. The *Voyager 2* space probe was launched in 1977, and has sent back close up pictures of Jupiter (1979), Saturn (1980), Uranus (1986) and Neptune (1989). *Voyager 2* is continuing to send back important data.

A new model of the Solar System emerged at the start of the twenty-first century, when observations were taken which confirmed ideas that had been put forward fifty years earlier. In the 1950s, Oort had suggested that there is a vast cloud of dust and rocks outside the orbit of Neptune, then Kuiper suggested that many comets and meteors had their origins in the inner part of this cloud. These ideas were confirmed when Sedna was discovered in 2004, then several other major bodies were observed. The new model reduces the number of major planets in the solar plane to eight – the four inner planets and the four gas giants, but increases the diameter of the Solar System by a factor of a hundred, and the total number of objects by millions. The Solar System no longer has a sharp boundary – the region of space outside of the orbit of Neptune is composed of particles (ranging in size from dust to planets that are the size of the Earth) with orbits that are at random angles to the solar plane.

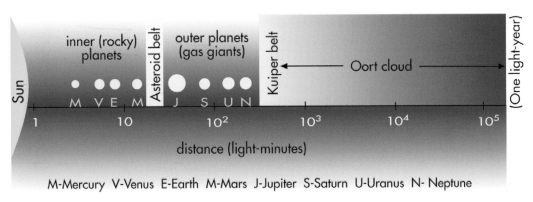

M-Mercury V-Venus E-Earth M-Mars J-Jupiter S-Saturn U-Uranus N- Neptune

SOUND

Key People
Bell
Edison
Helmholtz

SOUND is a longitudinal vibration of particles, so sound can not travel through a vacuum. We hear sounds because the wave is collected by the pinna, directed down into the ear canal and conducted across the ear drum. The ossicles transmit the sound to the fluid in the cochlea, which turns the vibrations into nerve signals, which are sent to the brain along the auditory nerve. The expected range of human hearing is 20 hertz to 20 kilohertz, but the range and sensitivity are permanently reduced as we get older. Temporary deafness can result from a sudden loud sound (eg with an intensity above 120 decibels), which may damage the ear drum, or by continuous exposure to noises above 100 decibels. Many animals, including dogs, are sensitive to ultra-sound: bats and dolphins can produce sound up to a frequency of 120 kilohertz, which is used for echo-location, sonar is a similar method that can be used to detect underwater objects.

TEETH

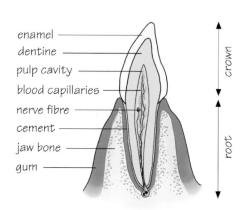

enamel
dentine
pulp cavity
blood capillaries
nerve fibre
cement
jaw bone
gum

crown

root

TEETH are responsible for the mechanical breakdown of food in the mouth. The food may be cut by the incisors, ripped by the canines or crunched by the pre-molars and molars. Each tooth is held firmly into the jawbone by the root, then grows through the gum, so you are able to see the crown. Inside each tooth is a pulp cavity, containing the blood vessels and nerve endings, which is surrounded by dentine. Outside, the enamel covers and protects the tooth. Teeth start to appear shortly after birth, but the crowns of these milk teeth break off after a few years, the roots are resorbed and the permanent teeth grow. The wisdom teeth (ie the molar teeth at the back of the mouth), do not fully form until a person is in their late teens. In each quarter of the jaw, the adult human should have two incisor teeth, a canine tooth, two pre-molar teeth and three molar teeth. This pattern is suitable for an omnivore, but other animals have different arrangements that are more suitable to their diet, eg carnivorous animals have large canine teeth. All teeth are covered with bacteria that may form hard layers of plaque (which your dentist is keen for you to remove). The bacteria in the plaque turn sugars into acid that dissolves the enamel leading to caries, tooth decay, toothache and possible loss of teeth. Brushing of teeth minimises this process and should be done twice a day.

THERMOMETERS

Key People
Celsius
Fahrenheit
Galileo
Kelvin
Sartorio

THERMOMETERS are instruments for measuring temperature. Galileo developed an air thermometer, in 1594, but the reliability of the measurements depended on the local air pressure; he may also have developed the thermometer in which hollow glass balls float or sink in water depending on the density, and hence on the temperature, of the water. Fahrenheit developed the liquid-in-glass thermometer in which a reservoir of liquid expands as a thread up a thin hollow stem, initially using alcohol (1709) and then using mercury (1714). He used a scale in which a mixture of equal parts of salt and ice is 0°F and the human body temperature was 96°F, later changed to 98.4°F. in 1742, Celsius suggested setting fixed points of 0°C for boiling water and 100°C for melting ice, but, within five years, he was using the more familiar 0°C for the freezing point of water and 100°C for the boiling point. The immersion thermometer was supplemented by the clinical thermometers in the 1860s and by maximum-and–minimum thermometers. The SI unit of temperature is the kelvin (K), which has a similar graduation to the celsius scale, but the lower fixed point is absolute zero (−273.14°C).

UNITS

Key People
Ampère
Coulomb
Dalton
Hertz
Laplace
Lavoisier
Newton
Ohm
Volta
Watt

UNITS are agreed standards for measurements. Four thousand years ago, the Egyptians must have had methods for measuring lengths and time in order to build the pyramids; two thousand years ago, the Romans introduced the mile as a length of a thousand strides, and the pound for measuring weights. These units have survived until the present day in the imperial system of measurements. The number of people and duration of time needed to build the massive Cathedrals of a thousand years past meant that agreement had to be reached on measurements, but each project developed its own units. 1789 saw both the start of the French Revolution and the setting up of a committee to reach agreement on a system of standards, this committee, which included Coulomb, Laplace and Lavoisier, decided that a metre should be defined as 1/10,000,000 or 0.000 000 1 the distance from the North Pole to the Equator. Accurate measurements were made to find this distance and, in 1798, a convention of all the French allies agreed to adopt the metric standard, England and America were not among the friends invited to the convention and so continued to use the imperial system.

A second convention in Paris, this time in 1960, called the General Conference on Weights and Measures, to which all countries were invited, agreed the Système International d'Unités or SI units. The SI base units include the kilogram, the second, the ampere and the metre; most other units can be expressed in terms of these measurements. The international standards include the platinum-iridium bar of exactly 1 metre length, and the platinum cylinder with a mass defined as 1 kilogram which are kept at Sèvres, near Paris. More recent definitions of the metre, second and kilogram are based on the behaviour of sub-atomic particles.

(l) distance	metres (m)	
(m) mass	kilograms (kg)	
(t) time	seconds (s, sec)	

Other units can be derived from the base units, *eg* the newton, a unit of force, and the pascal, which is used to measure pressure, can be calculated from distance, time and mass.

charge	coulombs (C)	potential difference	volts (V)
(I) current	amps (A)	power	watts (W)
energy	joules (J)	pressure	pascals (Pa)
force	newtons (N)	(R) resistance	ohms (Ω)
(f) frequency	hertz (Hz)	weight	newtons (N)

Many units that do not depend on the SI system, are still used for special purposes; astronomers measure distances in parsecs (approximately 3.3 light-years), food manufacturers provide energy values in calories and the height of horses is still measured in hands (4 inches).

WATER CYCLE

Key People
Galton

The WATER CYCLE is the continual movement of water from sea to sky, through plants, animals and land, then back to the sea. The heat from the Sun and the kinetic energy of the wind causes the evaporation of water from the surface of lakes, rivers and seas. Plants lose water from their leaves by transpiration, and animals release water into the air when breathing out. The water vapour rises and is blown by the wind and air streams. As the temperature drops, the air becomes saturated, and the water vapour forms tiny droplets, which are seen as clouds, fog or mist. These droplets will grow larger, then fall as rain, snow, hail or sleet, depending on the temperature. Some countries experience monsoons when vast volumes of water fall in a short period at specific times of the year followed by long periods of drought; other countries have a more regular supply of rain. Snow will remain where it has fallen, building up layers that may flow slowly as glaciers or move dramatically as avalanches, either of which may erode the rocks and soil. The snow will melt as the temperature increases, joining any water that has fallen as a liquid. Some of the water will percolate into the porous ground, to be absorbed by roots of plants or to form underground rivers; much of the water will run off the land by flowing as streams into lakes and rivers so that eventually the water returns to the sea.

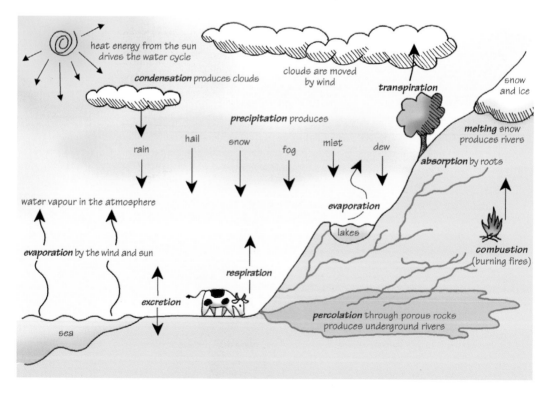

The kinetic energy of rapidly moving water will cause rocks to be broken and soil to be eroded. The fragments of rock are transported down the river, and eventually sediment when the flow of water slows down. Building dams across the rivers produces artificial reservoirs, which can be used to generate hydro-electric power, to prevent flooding, and to store water for drinking or for use by the local community. The prevention of flooding may lead to better management of water, with irrigation channels for the farmers, but the mud and nutrients that were carried by the river will start to fill the reservoir. The wildlife that starts to inhabit the water may be desirable, *eg* fish and birds for food, but some may not be so welcome in that they cause illnesses, *eg* bacteria or parasites.

WAVES

WAVES are the transmission of energy by the repetitive and regular movement of particles. In a longitudinal wave, such as sound, the particles are vibrating in the same direction as the energy is transmitted.

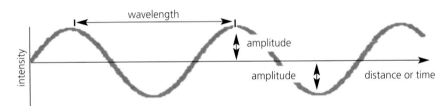

A sea wave is an example of a transverse wave because the particles of sea water are vibrating at right angles to the direction of travel. The waves produced by earthquakes are both longitudinal (the primary or pusher waves) and transverse (the secondary or shaker waves). Both longitudinal and transverse waves will travel in straight lines if the speed remains constant, but refraction results if the speed changes. All waves follow the law of reflection, the reflected sound wave being called an echo. Any wave will follow the law of refraction, bending towards the normal when the speed slows down.

THE LAST WORD

William's Words in Science is intended for any student trying to understand science, and so the meaning of the words and phrases are those that are used in science – the definitions are not exhaustive, and some words may have different meanings in other areas of use. Words have been selected by examining many of the textbooks that are used in Science at Key Stage 3, from exam papers, and from listening to the language used by staff and students – a total of over 13000 words and phrases! This statistic indicates that every pupil has to learn the specific meaning of at least 10 scientific words in every hour of Science learning from age 7 to 14 – truly a foreign language!

The following books have been used as guides for spelling and meanings:

A Brief History of Science	ISBN 1-84119-552-9
Cambridge International Dictionary of English	ISBN 0-521-48236-4
Chambers Concise Dictionary of Scientists	ISBN 1-85296-354-9
Chambers Handy Dictionary	ISBN 1-851-52528-9
Chambers School Science Dictionary	ISBN 0-550-10070-9
Collins Dictionary and Thesaurus	ISBN 0-00-433186-9
Collins Dictionary of Geology	ISBN 0-00-434148-1
Family Medical Encyclopedia	(Book Club Associates CN6795)
Dictionary of Science and Technology	ISBN 0-7475-6620-8
Henderson's Dictionary of Biological Terms	ISBN 0-582-46362-9
James Dyson's History of Inventions	ISBN 1-84119-617-7
Kingfisher Concise Science Encyclopaedia	ISBN 0-7534-0640-3
Oxford Dictionary of Physics	ISBN 0-19-280030-2
Oxford Dictionary of Plant Sciences	ISBN 0-19-680876-4
Oxford Dictionary of Scientists	ISBN 0-19-280086-8
Science Dictionary	ISBN 1-872686-22-2
The Cambridge Encyclopaedia	ISBN 0-521-44429-3
The Complete A – Z Biology Handbook	ISBN 0-340-66373-1
The New Elizabethan Reference Dictionary	(George Newnes Ltd)
Visual Factfinder Science	ISBN 1-84236-381-6
Webster's New World Dictionary	ISBN 0-7434-7069-9
Who's Who in Science and Technology	ISBN 0-340-75293-9

Answers to the questions in the *Introduction:*
1. Pressure is measured in bars;
2. Hard water will not easily form a foam with soap, whereas ice is the solid form of water that exists below 0°C;
3. Lime water looks just like drinking water, *ie* colourless and transparent;
4. Yes;
5. There are almost a hundred two-word phrases that contain 'plant' in the dictionary;
6. About 200 BC, by Erastothenes;
7. Berzelius was an educated Swede who proposed the use of two-letter abbreviations – sodium is natrium in Swedish, and silver is argent in Latin;
8. Einstein, in 1952;
9. Sir Isaac Newton;
10. krill (tiny marine crustaceans)

NOTES

NOTES

NOTES

NOTES

NOTES

NOTES

NOTES

NOTES